IMMUNITY
HYPERSENSITIVITY ❖ SEROLOGY

IMMUNITY
HYPERSENSITIVITY
SEROLOGY

SIDNEY RAFFEL, Sc.D., M.D.

Professor of Bacteriology, Department of
Bacteriology and Experimental Pathology,
Stanford University School of Medicine.

NEW YORK

APPLETON-CENTURY-CROFTS, INC.

WGE

To
Yvonne
Linda
Gail
Polly
Cynthia
Emily

Preface

The generally accepted implications of the word *immunity* have come to include more than the real meaning of the word itself. By definition this science is concerned with native and acquired resistance to disease-producing agents, processes in which many biologic, chemical and physical factors have a part. In actuality, however, antibody-reacting systems in general are often spoken of as immunologic, though in many cases these may have no real relationship to immunity. A brief sketch of the reasons for this overstretching of the term may serve to explain the intent of this book.

It happens that in the case of specifically acquired immunity the most spectacular occurrence in the body that we know about is the acquisition of humoral antibodies. These antibodies, however, need not necessarily be the major instruments of immunity; against a few diseases they undoubtedly are, but in most instances such a relationship has not been established. Nevertheless, antibodies appear regularly during the course of a disease simply as a physiologic response of the body to foreign substances, regardless of their eventual usefulness to the body. Now aside from their possible role in immunity, antibodies have been the object of a great deal of interest in their own right. For example, their high degree of specificity in reacting with the substances which have stimulated their formation makes them valuable tools for the recognition of proteins and polysaccharides, or for the classification of cells, such as human erythrocytes and bacteria. Such matters obviously have no direct connection with immunity; they merely derive from the study of a mechanism which *may* also play a role in immunity. Studies of antibody reactions are better described by the word *serology*. An immunologic response (i.e. resistance to an infectious agent) may be indefinable by any serologic method, and on the other hand a serologic system may, as in the examples just quoted, have no immunologic connotations whatever.

The dominating influence of antibody thought-patterns which has been responsible for this confusion of terms has made itself felt in another way also. Perhaps as a consequence of the long and intense preoccupation of immunologists with these remarkable substances of the serum, there developed a tendency to confine the perspective of the entire field of immunity within the bounds of the activities of antibodies. This distortion is at best a case of the tail wagging the dog, and at worst—in the many instances where a relationship of antibodies to immunity has not been established—a case of the dog being wagged purely by wishful thinking. A book about serology can be written with antibody as the stellar and practically the sole performer, but not a book concerned with immunity.

The author's intention here is to describe the phenomena of immunity in basic terms, especially with regard to resistance to bacteria, viruses and toxins. A good deal of space has been devoted to serologic considerations because most of our information lies in that realm, but in the long run the serologic reactions have been assessed as subsidiary to the general consideration of immunity, and as a subject separate from immunity in respect to such questions, for example, as the blood group reactions. Even so, it may be that overemphasis upon antibodies has been made in the earlier chapters, but this is perhaps remedied in the later discussions of individual infectious diseases where various other possibilities are considered in relation to acquired resistance.

Finally, it is customary in a preface to make acknowledgments for assistance received. This convention unfortunately makes it difficult for an author to do more than express himself in the stereotyped phrases reserved for such occasions. In the present case acknowledgments are few but sincere. I am most grateful to Mr. George A. McDermott and his assistants of the Appleton-Century-Crofts Company for the friendly and helpful relationship established during the long period of preparation of this book.

SIDNEY RAFFEL

Stanford
California

Contents

CONTENTS

Section Three: MECHANISMS OF RESISTANCE IN
VARIOUS INFECTIOUS DISEASES

Section Four: SEROLOGY AND ANTIGENIC SYSTEMS

IMMUNITY
HYPERSENSITIVITY ❖ SEROLOGY

1

PARASITISM

Since this book is mainly concerned with infection and resistance, a first step is to describe the characters involved and to localize the setting in which these phenomena take place. The central character is the animal body with differentiated systems of cells and fluids, some of which are concerned in resistance. The secondary characters are the microorganisms present in air, soil and water. The setting is their common environment, where the destinies of animals and microbes cross at many points. Some of these ecologic relationships include microbiologic activities of great importance for the welfare of man and beast. We will restrict attention to that one relationship in which the simpler forms attempt to parasitize higher animals, and the means available to the animal body to thwart this attempt.

Many microbes never come into a direct relationship with animals at all, presumably because their special nutritional and physical needs are not met by animal tissues, or because special mechanisms of the animal body inhibit or destroy them. These organisms are called **saprophytes.** The organisms which can establish the relationship are called **parasites,** and within the meaning of this word a great many things can happen. Thus, parasites may be entirely dependent upon host tissues for their own existence, as best exemplified by the filterable viruses. Most microbes, however, are **facultative** parasites; they can sustain themselves free in nature, at least for periods. But the organisms which we ordinarily consider saprophytic may also sometimes become parasitic, as when the host's defenses are impaired by other physiologic disturbances. Furthermore, the activities of a parasite in a host may be extremely variable; one may luxuriate so heedlessly that the resultant disease quickly leaves it without a home; another may make fewer demands so that the host's welfare is not too seriously interfered with and then the relationship may go on indefinitely during the lifetime of the host. Parasitism may be so mild as not to trouble the host at all; for example, an organism living in the intestinal tract may simply share the food supply (commensalism) or the microbe and host may mutually assist each other, the latter by supplying a pabulum, the former perhaps by synthesizing some essential metabolite for the host (symbiosis).

Parasitism does not necessarily imply a state of war between microbe and tissues, at least at the beginning of the relationship. A parasite may proliferate because a particular host has no normal means at its disposal to discourage

1

its growth, or it may fail to flourish simply for lack of some physical or chemical requirement in the tissues; in both cases aggressiveness has no part in the picture. But in other instances a battle ensues from the very beginning because the host possesses positive defense mechanisms and the parasite has aggressive properties of its own. If the parasite remains in the tissues for a long enough time a struggle is inevitable, for the host which lacks native defenses can acquire specific ones.

The main theme of this book is a description of the mechanisms of resistance to parasitism, first in the normal animal, then in the animal which has already been parasitized and as a consequence builds special defenses. In the course of this description certain features of the mechanisms of immunity which have a significance broader than that attaching to infection alone will be considered also.

2

MECHANISMS OF NATIVE IMMUNITY

Native immunity refers to the capacity enjoyed by a normal organism to remain unaffected by harmful agents in its environment. The term is restricted in this discussion to the normal **animal** and its resistance to microorganisms and their toxins. This resistance is for the most part a genetic endowment of an entire species with respect to a particular agent. Sometimes the immunity is absolute so that all individuals are entirely insusceptible to an agent; in other cases the resistance is relative, and here racial and individual differences become apparent within the species, one race or member being less susceptible than another. The latter differences, however, are not so marked as they may be between species. Whereas one of two species may be highly susceptible and the other entirely aloof to the same microorganism, within the species the difference is ordinarily one of degree, though an approach to the absolute may be brought about experimentally by inbreeding.

The reverse of this situation obtains in **specifically acquired immunity.** This is a highly individual property, not inherited, but dependent upon an individual's personal experience with a microbe or toxin. These points are more fully developed in Chapter 11.

The native defenses are of tremendous importance to the daily welfare of the body—much more so than the specifically acquired properties. This becomes apparent when we consider that though the tissues have all the makings of an excellent general culture medium, most of the microbes in the environment cannot grow on or in them, and even in the cases of those which can, actual invasion is infrequent compared with the ubiquity of microbes. This importance is not reflected in the proportionately small interest accorded by immunologists to problems of native resistance, for a reason which is quite obvious. The native defenses constitute an original grant, and whether or not we understand them they are there to provide a baseline of defense against foreign agents. Most scientific interest in immunity has been directed toward acquired resistance. This is not a grant; it must be won against microbes which have evaded the normal defenses and it must be built up while the attack is under way. It behooves us therefore to find out whether by artificial methods the potential host may be given a defense in advance of the attack. So immunologic investigations and writings have been largely channeled in this direction during the past 75 years.

Native resistance must depend upon one or a combination of these activi-

3

ties: (a) a barrier to the penetration of organisms beyond the integuments, (b) the inhibition or destruction of microorganisms upon and in tissues, and (c) the elimination of toxic substances liberated by living or dead microbes. These activities on the part of the potential host need not be of an aggressive nature; that is, the host does not necessarily have to have an inhibitory or neutralizing mechanism directed against a microbe and its toxins. Instead, it may simply fail to provide something which the microorganism requires, such as a sufficiently high oxygen tension in a particular organ or an enzyme system required by a particular virus. We might compare the two bases for native immunity—defensive mechanisms versus lack of pabulum—to the difference between gun emplacements along a nation's borders and the policy of scorched earth.

The mechanisms of defense will be discussed under these headings: first, the aggressive mechanisms and second, the passive mechanisms.

Aggressive Defense Mechanisms. 1. EPITHELIAL SURFACES. The skin and membrane coverings are physical barriers to penetration by most microbes solely on the basis of impermeability, but they seem to be more than mere mechanical barriers. The surface of the skin is bactericidal as may easily be demonstrated by placing drops of culture simultaneously on a glass surface and on the skin, and making subcultures at intervals. In one published experiment of this kind in which *Escherichia coli, Salmonella typhi* and *S. enteritidis* were used, viable bacteria had disappeared from the palmar surface of the hand after 10 minutes, but were almost quantitatively recovered from the glass plate. This bactericidal property apparently disappears shortly after death (1), and may be related to the presence of lactic and fatty acids in the sweat and sebaceous secretions (2).

The moist surfaces of the respiratory and urogenital passages catch many passing particles, and the epithelium in these areas is ciliated so that films of mucus with trapped particles are continuously swept outwards. Through this and other structural barriers such as the nasal turbinates the lungs are ordinarily kept almost free from objects floating in the air. In a study in which rabbits were made to inhale droplet nuclei containing *Serratia marcescens* it was found that when the atmosphere was charged with massive numbers of bacilli only 4 per cent of those inspired reached the lungs, while with more moderate concentrations only about 0.4 per cent of the inspired bacteria penetrated beyond the large bronchi (3, 4).

The moist mucous films of the respiratory and genital passages possess bactericidal and virucidal properties, as is true of other bathing fluids such as tears. The nature of these substances will be described below.

The gastrointestinal tract provides the usual epithelial protection and in addition bactericidal enzymes in the saliva and enzymes and high acidity in the stomach. The latter inhibits the multiplication of microorganisms completely so that the normal gastric content is sterile. The intestinal contents, and especially those of the large intestine, abound in various kinds of bacteria. The intestinal mucosa itself however contains effective bactericidal factors so that despite the profusion of bacterial numbers and types invasion of the body via the intestinal tract is not common.

2. BACTERICIDAL SUBSTANCES OF TISSUES AND BODY FLUIDS. It has been known for a long time that the body fluids, especially the blood, can suppress putrefaction (5). Of the voluminous early studies on this point most were concerned with the apparent involvement of natural antibody, requiring complement, in this process. There is some question about the origin of such antibodies, whether they are truly natural to the body or are **acquired** through subtle exposures to microorganisms and other antigens in the environment (see Chapter 6). It is a fact that the wide distribution and peculiar serologic properties of certain of these antibodies makes it seem likely that they may indeed be native to the body. In any case, the mechanism involved is the one which we see operative in acquired resistance, and for the sake of clarity of discussion this mechanism will be reserved for the sections dealing with acquired antibodies.

Evidences of the ability of deeper tissues to discourage colonization by microbes are everywhere obvious—for example, in the failure of most wounds to become infected. In part at least this must be due to certain native anti-bacterial substances which are known to exist in normal tissues and body fluids. These factors are often only vaguely characterized, but some can be recognized by their activities, and at least two such substances can now be described in chemical terms.

(a) Lysozyme. This bactericidal enzyme was first recognized by Fleming in 1922 (6). It occurs in various animals, in the tissues as well as in all the body fluids except cerebrospinal fluid, aqueous humor, sweat and urine. Its concentration varies with locale in different animal species; in the human being tears happen to contain it in high amount. Egg white is a rich source of this enzyme.

Lysozyme is a basic protein which functions as a **mucolytic enzyme**, splitting sugars from aminopolysaccharides of the bacterial membrane so that the cellular contents leak out (7). It may also destroy the Gram-staining property of staphylococcus and of *Clostridium welchii* by the removal of ribonucleic acid and a simultaneous hydrolysis of surface polysaccharides (8).

The bactericidal activity of lysozyme was first described in relation to a bacterium isolated from the air, *Micrococcus lysodeikticus*. It is active, however, against sarcinas, certain enterococci and other microbes. The enzyme usually dissolves bacteria though it may kill certain species without dissolution. Bacteria may become adapted to it as to other deleterious biologic and chemical agents through the process of discontinuous mutation. Since lysozyme occurs in intestinal mucus, nasal secretions and saliva, its probable relationship to the bactericidal effects of epithelial surfaces is obvious. This enzyme has aroused interest also in connections unrelated to native immunity. Thus its presence in intestinal mucus is possibly related to the genesis of ulcerative colitis, and its presence in semen may be responsible for dissolving the mucus plug in the canal of the cervix (9).

(b) Antianthrax polypeptide. A second tissue bactericidal substance has been isolated and characterized more recently. Bloom and his co-workers (10) have shown that the anthracidal property of the tissues and fluids of animals insusceptible to anthrax is a basic polypeptide containing a large amount of lysine. In vitro this substance kills *Bacillus anthracis,* and when injected into mice it acts as an antibiotic agent. The substance is also effective in vitro against other organisms (11) including *B. megatherium* and *E. coli* (see page 292).

(c) Antinvasin. In the plasma of normal animals Haas (12) has reported the presence of enzymes which inactivate hyaluronidase. The latter is itself an enzyme which is produced by certain bacteria and may be related to their ability to spread through the tissues (see Chapter 3). The hyaluronidase-inactivating substance is termed antinvasin, implying that hyaluronidase accounts for the invasive activity of the bacteria which produce it. This premise is not clearly justifiable, and the activities of the supposedly defensive enzymes have not been supported by other studies (13).

Other humoral bactericides are recognized grossly by their source and activities (14a). In serum, von Behring many years ago described a substance which he called **beta lysin,** active against aerobic spore-forming bacilli. Beta lysin appears to be a multiple enzymic system; the sera of different animals affect different groups of bacteria. Most sera act upon the same organisms attacked by lysozyme, but in addition other microbes including pneumococci, streptococci and staphylococci may be attacked.

Metchnikoff described a substance in blood derived from leukocytes and called **leukin** or **endolysin.** This may kill typhoid and anthrax bacilli and the staphylococci. Substances of different specificities have been found in other locales. Human tears, for example, possess a staphylococcus-destroying substance other than lysozyme (14b). Saliva contains antibacterial agents, also distinct from lysozyme, acting most markedly upon the diphtheria bacillus. The normal nasal secretion is especially noteworthy in this respect, for in addition to inhibiting a variety of gram-positive bacteria it may also neutralize the infectivity of a number of viruses, including influenza, louping ill, herpes and the related virus B. For the latter there appears also to be a neutralizing factor in normal human plasma (15). Certain lipoidal factors from various normal sera may also inactivate encephalitis and psittacosis viruses (16). Antiviral substances will later be discussed at greater length.

An interesting possibility for the role of enzymes in native resistance has been suggested in studies concerned with the relative insusceptibility of mice to tuberculosis. The tubercle bacillus contains an unusually large proportion of lipids. Mouse tissues were found to be rich in phosphatase and lecithinase active upon the phosphatides of the bacillus; in contrast, the tissues of the susceptible rabbit and guinea pig showed little enzyme activity (17). Several factors complicate a too-ready acceptance of this explanation, not the least of which is the involved susceptibility relationships in tuberculosis. Thus, the rabbit was studied in this regard as a susceptible animal; it is, to the bovine variety of bacillus, but it is relatively insusceptible to the human variety. Nevertheless, the findings described may apply to the special instance of murine insusceptibility studied, and in any case serves very well to illustrate the kind of chemicobiologic study which may be fruitful in unraveling the nature of host-parasite relationships.

A peculiarly inverted kind of mechanism has been described by Braun (18) with regard to suspectibility and resistance to *Brucella abortus*. Cultures of this organism show a certain proportion of rough colonial mutants composed of avirulent bacilli. The serum of **susceptible** species contains a globulin factor which suppresses this mutation tendency or inhibits the growth of the avirulent bacilli, so that in these animals proliferating bacilli are all virulent. Insusceptible species on the other hand do not interfere with the development of avirulent bacilli, and presumably this may account for the failure of infections to progress in such animals. In other words, native resistance (insusceptibility) is apparently the result of a laissez-faire policy on the part of the potential host; nature takes its course, and this course is the appearance and the proliferation of nonvirulent organisms. The potential hosts which interfere with this process do so to their own detriment, and constitute a susceptible species. Braun states that the correlation is complete: man and the cow, rabbit, guinea pig, hog and cat suppress rough (R) variants and are all susceptible; the hamster, rat, mouse, chicken, quail, duck and pheasant do not suppress these variants and are natively resistant. This work is provocative and interesting, but certain important questions still need answers; e.g. in the insusceptible species where R variants are being produced, what meanwhile are the simultaneously developing virulent smooth (S) forms up to? Why do they not produce disease?

A similar effect has been reported to occur with staphylococcus (19).

3. ANTIVIRAL SUBSTANCES OF TISSUES AND BODY FLUIDS. Virus-neutralizing properties have been found in nasal secretions and the plasma of normal human beings. A currently developing line of investigation which may give insight into a mechanism of native antiviral resistance is worth description even though the evidence is conflicting and the question still at issue.

Some years ago Hirst (20) found that influenza virus causes agglutination of chicken red blood cells. The virus is first adsorbed to these cells, then spontaneously frees itself. After elution the virus remains intact, but the red cells are no longer susceptible to agglutination. Excised lung tissue similarly shows adsorption and elution of this virus (21), and Hirst interprets the reaction as comparable to the action of an enzyme (virus) upon its substrate (erythrocyte receptors). There is evidence, contested however, that the infectivity of the virus for susceptible cells rests to some extent upon the same property of attacking cellular receptors as is indicated by its effect upon erythrocytes. In favor of this is the demonstration that destruction of these receptors in the lungs of mice decreases the susceptibility of these animals to influenza infection (22). Other workers on the other hand have demonstrated the existence of viral particles which are hemagglutinative but not infective (23).

Several years ago Francis (24) showed that normal human serum can inhibit the hemagglutinative activity of virus. The inhibitor is apparently a mucopolysaccharide, obtainable also from other sources than serum, including human erythrocytes (25). Another normal viral inhibitor, possibly a protein, has also been described (26).

If we assume that the viral hemagglutinating property is concerned in the infectivity of the virus, it is suggestive that the serum inhibitor is a normally occurring substrate in human plasma which may divert the activity of the virus from susceptible cells.

The value of all these antibacterial and antiviral factors to the animals which possess them is not always specifically clear. Certainly infections occur despite the normal inhibitory substances. But this, of course, is not the point at issue; the point is how much wider would be the range of organisms pathogenic for animals, and how much more frequently would infection be caused by those which are pathogenic, if these inhibitory influences were not at work. The situation which we regard as normal in the relationship of potential hosts with microorganisms of the environment is one in which parasitism is infrequent in contrast to the abundance of microbes surrounding us. This situation would undoubtedly be far different in the absence of such mechanisms as have been described.

4. PHAGOCYTES. Phagocytes are "eating cells" which occur in the blood and other tissues of the body. Ordinarily certain of them engage in devouring worn-out constituents of the body itself, but if foreign objects get beyond the skin and covering membranes the cells attempt to engulf these too, often very successfully. The ability to phagocytize was undoubtedly one of the earliest accomplishments of living cells since the incorporation of food particles by engulfment could be successfully accomplished by any blob of undifferentiated protoplasm. Metchnikoff (27) first appreciated the continuity of this function through evolutionary development, carried on by specialized cells even in the most highly organized of animals, and he first realized also the importance of this activity in resistance to infectious agents.

The phagocytes are classified into two cellular systems. The first consists of the more highly differentiated granular leukocytes of the blood, the cells which derive from the bone marrow (myeloid cells). The second is made up of mesenchymal elements, the cells which line lymph and blood sinuses and which form part of the supporting framework of lymphoid and other tissues comprising the so-called reticulo-endothelial system. The smaller cells of the first system are the microphages described by Metchnikoff, while the reticulo-endothelial cells are the macrophages.

(a) Blood Leukocytes. The phagocytic elements among the leukocytes are the polymorphonuclear cells and the monocytes. The first comprise about 70 per cent of the total white cells of the blood (3,500 to 7,000 cells per cubic millimeter in the normal human being) and the monocytes add an additional 3 to 5 per cent of the total leukocytes. The origin of the monocytes is disputed; they may be mesenchymal cells which migrate in and out of the blood stream, or they may originate from lymphoid tissue. About three fourths of the leukocytes of the blood then are phagocytic cells, destined to become pus cells whenever a foreign object arouses an inflammatory reaction in the tissues. The number of leukocytes may increase (leukocytosis) or decrease (leukopenia) during infections and under other circumstances as well. Both variations may occur during the course of one infectious disease.

(b) Reticulo-Endothelial System. The modern conception of the system of macrophages or tissue phagocytes was formulated chiefly by the pathologist Aschoff (28). Metchnikoff had conceived of the middle embryonic layer, the mesenchyme, as an organ with a primary duty of defending the body against microbial invasion. Aschoff and Kiyono by the use of vital stains succeeded in differentiating the cells of the mesenchyme which have a marked phagocytic ability from others which may, under forced circumstances, take up particles into their cytoplasm, but are relatively passive in this regard.

The cells of the reticulo-endothelial system, as shown in the diagram, fall into two main classes.

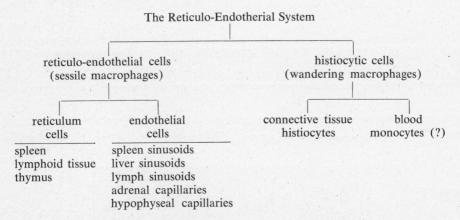

The Reticulo-Endotherial System

reticulo-endothelial cells
(sessile macrophages)

histiocytic cells
(wandering macrophages)

reticulum
cells

endothelial
cells

connective tissue
histiocytes

blood
monocytes (?)

spleen	spleen sinusoids
lymphoid tissue	liver sinusoids
thymus	lymph sinusoids
	adrenal capillaries
	hypophyseal capillaries

The **wandering** macrophages (histiocytes or clasmatocytes) are found in connective tissue throughout the body. With their generalized distribution and their ability to undergo mitosis, these cells are of great importance to the welfare of the body. In certain locations they may occur in concentrated collections, as in the milky spots of the omentum (Fig. 1). These cells contribute to the reputation of the omentum as the "abdominal policeman."

The **sessile** macrophages are cells of the reticular (supporting network) and the endothelial or littoral (channel-lining) tissues of various organs and tissues, especially the spleen, liver, lymphoid tissue and bone marrow (Figs. 2-5). These cells are fixed in their locations but their positions are strategic, along finer channels of blood and lymph flow, so that they may pick up particles carried to them.

The macrophages, particularly of the spleen and bone marrow, under

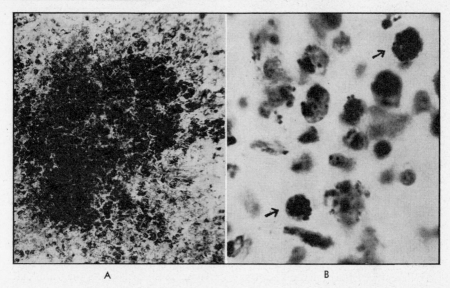

A   B

Fig. I. A, low power view of milky spot on the surface of the omentum after ingestion of India ink by histiocytes. B, higher magnification of peripheral histiocytes with ingested particles.

normal conditions take up senile erythrocytes, digest them, and pass the hemoglobin constituents in part as bile pigment to hepatic epithelial cells. The iron is conserved for new red blood cell formation by the bone marrow.

The largest single collection of macrophages in mammals occurs in the spleen; in birds, in the liver.

(c) Function of the Phagocytes in Resistance. The role of the phagocytic cells in native resistance is the engulfment of particulate or soluble matter,

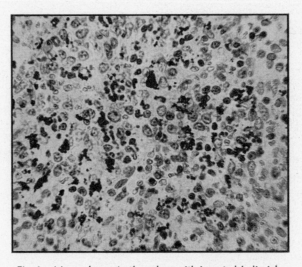

Fig. 2. Macrophages in the spleen with ingested India ink.

quick or dead, which enters the tissues. Such objects are either digested or, if indigestible, are simply stored safely away so that they no longer serve as irritants to the tissues at large. The latter situation is commonly seen in the lungs of individuals who have lived for a time in a soot-polluted atmosphere.

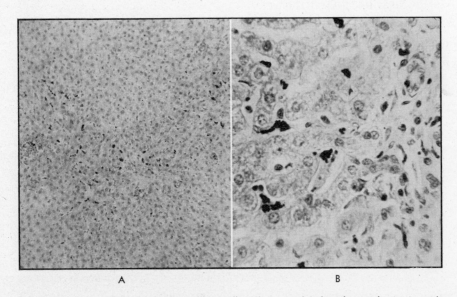

A   B

Fig. 3. A, low power view of Kupffer stellate cells with ingested India ink particles in sinusoids of the liver. B, the higher magnification illustrates the way in which these cells straddle sinusoids between strands of hepatic epithelium.

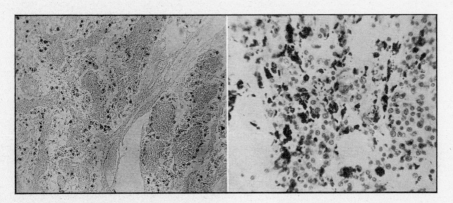

Fig. 4. Reticulo-endothelial cells of lymph node sinusoids laden with ingested particles.

Fig. 5. Macrophages in the bone marrow with ingested India ink particles.

Carbon accumulations may be seen in the lungs grossly, and microscopically are found deposited in macrophages in the lymphoid nodules of the lungs. These cells with their indigestible content may remain viable for long periods. When the cells die, the particles are taken up by fresh cells.

There are numerous examples available of the ability of the phagocytes of normal animals to ingest and dispose of a variety of microorganisms (29) and of the importance of this activity to native immunity. Rabbits deprived of their leukocytes through treatment with chemicals can no longer resist an otherwise avirulent form of pneumococcus (30), and guinea pigs made leukopenic and infected with staphylococci in a local wound develop diffuse cellulitis instead of the usual localized abscess (31). A similar situation is seen in man during the course of agranulocytic angina, a disease of the myeloid tissue in which a marked reduction of circulating leukocytes occurs. Secondary infections made this a frequently fatal disease until the advent of antibiotics; now bacterial invasions can be kept in check until the bone marrow resumes its normal function (see Chapter 12). There are of course many microbes which cannot be phagocytized effectively by the cells of the normal animal, and others which are not destroyed after being engulfed.

The relative activities of blood leukocytes and tissue phagocytes in dealing with invaders is clear in general outline, though some differences occur with different parasites. The white blood cells are the first to appear in an area of bacterial invasion after migrating through the walls of adjacent capillaries. Blood leukocytes may phagocytize avidly, but they are relatively fragile cells and the local accumulation of acids in an area of inflammation eventually kills them (32). The macrophages gather more slowly, but these are hardier elements and proceed to ingest not only the foreign irritant but also leukocytic and other cellular debris. The macrophages possess another advantage in their ability to undergo division *in situ*. As a result, the number of these cells can increase locally, and in addition giant cells may form by the fusion of single cells, or by nuclear division. Such **giant foreign-body cells** are able to wrap themselves around very large objects.

A small number of microorganisms in a localized area may undoubtedly be dealt with by the rapidly mobilized polymorphonuclear neutrophils themselves, but if a wider dissemination of a large number of microorganisms occurs the macrophages bear the brunt of the clearing process. The latter cells may be more effective phagocytizers than the former (33) though this too may vary with the microorganism concerned. (For general reviews of this subject see Taliaferro [29c] and Robertson [34].)

(d) Mechanics of Phagocytosis. A consideration of the process of phagocytosis brings up three separate points. One must account for: one, the attraction of cells to an area of microbial invasion; two, the act of phagocytosis itself; and three, the eventual disposition of the microorganism inside the phagocyte.

One. Attraction of cells to the site (Chemotaxis). Injury to tissue excites an inflammatory response. A main event in inflammation is the dilatation of local capillaries with slowing of the blood stream, and exudation from the distended vessels of plasma, leukocytes and sometimes of erythrocytes. The inflammatory response varies widely in its character according to the nature of the stimulus, so that the exudate may be serous, highly cellular (purulent) or bloody (sanguinous). The basic point of chief interest to us now, however, is the fact that leukocytes and plasma proteins leak into the tissues.

Once outside the capillaries the leukocytes begin an extraordinary migration toward the source of irritation. This is apparently guided by diffusible factors from the irritant itself. Most microorganisms attract polymorphonuclear cells (35), as do products of tissue injury (36) and indeed all amino acids to some degree (37). The attraction of polymorphonuclear cells is readily demonstrated. However, tissue culture studies have given only a suggestion of the same effect in the case of macrophages (38). Possibly macrophages are provided at the source of irritation simply by the division of local elements, or their attraction may occur slowly, over a period of days (39).

Attraction of leukocytes is termed positive chemotaxis. Negative chemotaxis or repulsion by microorganisms seems to occur rarely, but various chemical substances may have this effect (40). In some cases, however, microbes may fail to attract without actually repelling cells (41).

The mechanism of guidance of cells is not presently understood, though various suggestions have been made, including the lowering of surface tension of the leukocyte on the side facing the diffusing substance, so that pseudopods form, or the existence of a difference in electric potential between injured and normal tissues (42). An entirely satisfying explanation would be welcome.

Two. The act of ingestion (Phagocytosis). Now that the phagocyte has arrived within striking distance of the agent to be dealt with, the next question concerns the mechanism of engulfment. Fenn (43b) and Mudd and coworkers (43a) have ascribed this to a decrease in the surface energy of the phagocyte. This surface change is brought about by substances diffusing from the microbe. Since detergents also decrease the surface energy of cells, Berry and others recently used these to test the hypothesis and found that in vivo as well as in vitro all of the detergents employed increased phagocytosis (44). It has been observed by Knisely (45) that inert particles such as India ink or kaolin must acquire a fibrin-like coating of blood proteins before they can be ingested by macrophages of the liver. Possibly this is true to some extent of living agents as well, although it is obvious from in vitro studies that many bacteria can be phagocytized in a saline medium.

Certain microbes are not effectively phagocytized in the normal animal; these are the pathogenic agents which, uninhibited by any of the native mechanisms described in this chapter, proceed to set up infection. The chemical properties of these bacteria which apparently determine the failure of phagocytosis will be described in the next chapter but we might consider here the insight into the mechanics of this failure recently provided by Wood and others (46) from studies with virulent pneumococci and *Klebsiella pneumoniae.* Neither of these bacteria is engulfed in a fluid medium or upon a smooth surface, but if they become trapped against a rough surface (such as alveolar lining) or between two phagocytes they can be ingested. Thus, some phagocytosis of these virulent organisms occurs even in the normal animal, but under the special circumstances described the process is not sufficiently extensive to stop the progression of the disease. The advent of acquired antibody permits the phagocyte to function against virulent bacteria even in fluid or upon a smooth surface (see page 119).

Three. The intracellular destruction of microorganisms. Exactly how microbes are destroyed after ingestion is not clear. Proteolytic enzymes are present in phagocytes; a trypsin-like ferment active at about neutrality occurs in polymorphonuclear cells, and a pepsin-like enzyme active in weak acid is present in macrophages (47). The pH of the cytoplasms of both types of cells appears to be about 3.0 (48). Whether or not this acidity kills microorganisms so that they may then be digested is not known. There are indications that different parasites may be better destroyed by one or the other type of phagocyte; thus, macrophages are much more effective in destroying streptococci and pneumococci than are polymorphonuclear cells, although the latter are just as active in phagocytosis (33, 49).

Although many virulent bacteria cannot be phagocytized effectively in the normal animal, certain ones may be very easily engulfed but then continue to live and multiply within the cytoplasm. Indeed the phagocyte itself in such cases may serve as a vehicle of dissemination through the body. There are certain notorious examples of this kind; among the bacteria, the gonococcus and meningococcus are always associated with the intrapolymorphonuclear locale, and influenza bacilli, staphylococci, lepra and tubercle bacilli may all remain viable and in some cases multiply within cells (50). Among the viruses, vaccinia forms colonies within leukocytes (51), and the rickettsias of Q fever in the mouse proliferate predominantly in the histiocytes of the spleen and liver (52). Certain protozoal parasites, among them *Leishmania donovani* and *Trypanosoma cruzi,* also survive and multiply in the macrophages which take them up (53). In these cases obviously the phagocytic cells have no more significance in native resistance than in the instances where phagocytosis does not take place at all.

Three examples have been chosen to illustrate how the normal body makes efficient use of its phagocytic cells by whatever route microorganisms may enter the tissues.

One. Intravenous route. Figure 6 represents diagrammatically the fate of particles which enter the venous stream. These encounter the first capillary bed with a slowing of the blood flow in the lung. Lagging particles may here be taken up by the blood leukocytes. This can be a rapid and fairly effective process. Larger particles, especially inert substances, may be engulfed by the alveolar phagocytes. Usually, however, relatively few particles are taken up in this location in the normal animal; most pass through the lung to the arterial circulation and are more effectively phagocytized when they reach the terminal channels in the liver and spleen, where macrophages are abundant. Bull (54) demonstrated practically complete clearing by the rabbit of *Salmonella typhi* (not a pathogen for this species) within 20 minutes after the intravenous injection of millions of bacilli; this took place chiefly in the liver and spleen, though the lungs and lymph nodes also took part. With other bacteria it has been found that 80 per cent removal is effected by the splanchnic vascular bed alone (55).

Two. Intraperitoneal route. The response to bacteria in the peritoneal cavity is at first a local accumulation of leukocytes from the blood, as would occur in any inflammatory reaction, within perhaps an hour. More slowly, histiocytes from the omentum approach the particles; after a sufficient interval the entire omentum may move to localize an infectious process.

Many bacteria rapidly leave the cavity by way of lymphatic channels. On the diaphragmatic surface especially there are terminal lymphatics or lacunae separated from the cavity only by the peritoneal epithelium and a loosely woven basement membrane. Respiratory movements of the diaphragm help pump particles into these channels through the alternately separated cells of the epithelium (56). Particles which enter the lymph stream are subjected to very effective filtration by the adjacent lymph nodes. Drinker and others (57) have found that 99 per cent of the streptococci entering a lymph node fail to appear in the efferent lymph. Any particles which come through the node eventually flow into the thoracic duct and thence into the subclavian vein. The gauntlet of the vascular and splanchnic phagocytes must then be run (58). These various paths are diagrammed in Figure 7.

Three. Cutaneous or subcutaneous route. The most common exposure of the tissues to infection is by way of the skin and subcutaneous tissues (Fig. 8). Most often of course the process is terminated locally by blood leukocytes and, when necessary, by the histiocytes of the connective tissues. But McMaster (59) points out that the plexus of lymphatics in the skin is so abundant that any minor wound cannot fail to result in the injection of organisms directly into the lymph stream. This is especially the case because severed lymphatics, unlike blood vessels, remain open for long periods and drain fluids away from the wound. Within minutes bacteria may be transported to the regional lymph node. Bacteria may also enter local capillaries; in both cases subsequent events follow the descriptions already given.

Although the routes described all lead eventually to the same end, there are certain differences in the efficacy of the phagocytic systems in suppressing infectious agents introduced by different portals. This sometimes becomes evident when a highly virulent organism is employed in a susceptible host. Thus, Ørskov (60) found that a single pneumococcus injected into the peritoneal cavity of a mouse can be fatal, while 50,000 bacteria injected into the blood stream are effectively removed by the tissue phagocytes and destroyed, so that the animal survives.

In summary, it is evident that phagocytosis is the greatest single activity contributing to native resistance. The phagocytes are ubiquitous, readily mobilized, and rapidly active in maintaining the homeostasis of the body in the face of potential parasites. As has been pointed out, however, certain microbes cannot normally be handled by these cells, and in these cases progressive infections may be set up. The failure may be either in the capacity

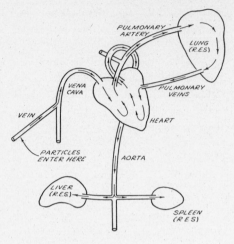

Fig. 6. Vascular route.

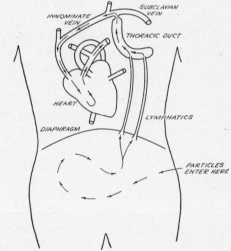

Fig. 7. Peritoneal cavity route.

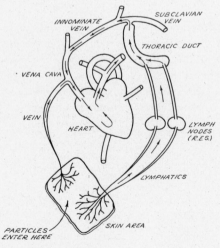

Fig. 8. Skin or subcutaneous tissue route.

to engulf the offending agents, or in the ability to destroy them after phago-cytosis has occurred. For these relatively exceptional agents, the pathogenic microorganisms, additional defenses must be acquired by the host.

5. INFLAMMATION. The inflammatory reaction is considered separately for the sake of emphasis. It represents a summation of most of the effects already discussed and introduces in addition other features which may be helpful to the normal body. The essence of this response to injury is dilata-tion and increased permeability of capillaries with emigration of cells and plasma constituents into the tissues. As a result of plasma leakage a fibrinous network forms in the tissue spaces, and this coagulum mechanically adsorbs particles. In addition, fibrin serves as a pathway for more effective leukocytic migration, and the surface phagocytosis described by Wood (46) is more apt to occur in such a network. The total possible benefits which the host may derive from the inflammatory reaction may then be summarized as follows:

(a) Blood leukocytes are supplied in large numbers.

(b) The formation of fibrin in the tissues may mechanically localize bac-teria and assist the functioning of phagocytes.

(c) Exudation of plasma may bring humoral antibacterial factors to the site of invasion in greater than usual concentration.

(d) The increased blood and lymph flow may dilute and flush away toxic bacterial products.

(e) The local rise in temperature may discourage the proliferation of some microbes. At least one very definite example of this kind is known (61, 62).

Inflammation then is a reaction of much value to the native defense of the body. In common with the other native defense mechanisms its greatest usefulness is in providing a normal baseline of protection from parasitism by any vagrant microbe in the neighborhood. As for the benefits of such mech-anisms in dealing with pathogenic agents—agents which by definition are relatively insensitive to the normal host defenses—the answer must obviously be that these mechanisms per se are of very limited use. At best, a small number of potentially pathogenic microbes may be overcome in the normal animal; this will depend of course upon the relative virulence of the organ-isms as well as their number, for in some instances a single bacterium can cause fatal infection. It is even possible in certain circumstances for these mechanisms to serve the host to disadvantage, as when the phagocyte acts as a vehicle for dissemination, or when the sweep of fluids through the tissues becomes so accelerated in an intense inflammation as to broadcast microbes which in a calmer environment might have remained localized.

Passive Defense Mechanisms. It was suggested early in the chapter that microbial invasion may be thwarted by a passivity on the part of the normal tissues, a failure to provide a suitable environment for growth. Instances of such processes of native immunity are discussed under the headings which follow.

1. BODY TEMPERATURE. It is reasonable to suppose that the body temperatures of various animals may inhibit organisms which would in other respects find the tissues a suitable medium. A classic example was provided by Pasteur's demonstration that chickens, normally resistant to anthrax, become susceptible when immersed in cold water. A reversed example is seen in the behavior of the same bacterium in lizards, animals whose body temperature depends on that of the environment. Ordinarily they are resistant to *Bacillus anthracis,* but if their temperature is raised to the mammalian range they become susceptible. In neither of these cases is it known what mechanisms may be affected by the temperature change.

A clearer example has emerged from the work of Rich and McKee (61) and Enders and Shaffer (62) with the type III pneumococcus in the rabbit. Encapsulated pneumococci of other types produce progressive fatal infections in the normal rabbit. In contrast the encapsulated type III diplococcus after intradermal injection proliferates for 12 to 24 hours and produces a local hemorrhagic lesion, but this then begins to regress and eventually heals completely. An analysis of this situation revealed that as the body temperature of the rabbit rises from the normal of about 102° F. to 104° or above (40° to 41° C.) in response to the incipient infection, the pneumococci begin to lose their capsules and to die off in the tissues, later being taken up by phagocytes. It was found then that most strains of the type III organism, unlike other pneumococci, are inhibited by the fever level of temperature in vitro as well as in vivo. Three factors were distinguished as contributing to the native resistance of this animal: (*a*) the more sluggish growth of type III organisms even at normal rabbit temperatures as compared with other pneumococci; (*b*) the fever temperature which inhibits growth and leads to loss of capsules, and (*c*) terminal phagocytosis. Of these the fever was most important, for despite the relative sluggishness of growth a large number of organisms appeared in the tissues some hours after inoculation, and phagocytosis could not occur unless the bacteria were first rendered amenable to engulfment by the loss of their capsules. The effect of temperature here is analogous to the influence of acquired antibodies in rendering virulent pneumococci susceptible to phagocytosis. The importance of temperature is further indicated by the fact that type III strains adapted to growth at 41° C. are virulent for the rabbit.

2. TISSUE METABOLITES. For some microbes the tissues may fail to provide certain essential metabolites so that progressive multiplication fails to take place. This effect is suggested by studies of the filterable viruses described later. In other cases perhaps too much of one or another element may interfere with the pathogenic potentialities of the microbe. A fairly good illustration of this is seen in the host-parasite relationship established by the diphtheria bacillus in the human being. Mueller (63) has shown that a very small concentration of iron in the medium is optimal for the production of toxin by certain strains of *Corynebacterium diphtheriae,* and that the iron content of diphtheritic membranes from human beings may be many times

this optimal. Consequently it appears probable that only a limited number of strains may produce severe disease in the potential host which contains large amounts of this mineral in its tissues (64).

The hypothesis that a lack of necessary nutriments may explain some instances of native resistance to viruses and rickettsias seems especially reasonable because of the intimate dependence of these parasites upon the metabolic activities of the cells which they inhabit. There is no concrete evidence for this as yet; only the suggestion provided by experiments in which cells have been modified in their metabolic activities as the result of vitamin deficiencies, for example, and have changed in their susceptibility to certain viruses (see page 178).

3. OXYGEN TENSION IN TISSUES. The degree of availability of oxygen in various tissues may deter microorganisms which would otherwise be parasitic. Limited examples can be described for both possibilities, i.e. that the oxygen tension of normal tissue is too high or too low for optimal growth of a particular microorganism.

The anaerobic spore-bearing bacilli (genus *Clostridium*) are not able to parasitize normal tissues. However, if an area becomes devitalized by injury so that it no longer has access to vascular or atmospheric oxygen, a pathway for infection is established. In such a locale the tetanus bacillus can proliferate and produce as a metabolic by-product a neurotoxin which diffuses into surrounding healthy tissue and is eventually carried to the central nervous system. The bacilli of gas gangrene (*Cl. perfringens* and other species, see Chapters 3 and 26) also depend upon injury for their start, but once under way these more resourceful parasites pave the way for their own extension through the tissues by the production of necrotizing toxins. In both cases the oxygen level of uninjured tissues is protective for the potential host.

A reversed example is provided by the tubercle bacillus. This organism requires a good deal of oxygen for its metabolic activities, a requirement which may at least partially influence the host-parasite relationship. In the rabbit the bovine variant of the bacillus produces a progressive disease marked by early involvement of the lungs. At first tubercles also form in the liver, but later these regress so that by the time the animal dies no gross evidence of tuberculous changes can be seen in this organ at all. The progressively severe involvement of lung parenchyma interferes with aeration of the blood and as a consequence the oxygen tension in the liver falls below that compatible with active multiplication of bacilli. If infected animals are maintained in an atmosphere with low oxygen content the general progress of the disease can be inhibited. (65).

A similar illustration may be afforded by the host-parasite relationship in pulmonary tuberculosis of the human being. It has been known for many years that secondary or recurrent tuberculosis shows a marked predilection for the apices of the lungs, especially the right apex. Dock (66a) has supplied a rational explanation for this and related observations. He points out that in a person who is standing or sitting the weight of the column of blood in the pulmonary artery exceeds the systolic pressure exerted by the right ventricle. Consequently the upper portions of the lungs will receive little or no blood from the right heart, i.e. venous blood for oxygenation. The alveoli in this part of the lungs will then retain air richer in oxygen than other areas, hence more favorable for the multiplication of tubercle bacilli; and, further, less of the defensive factors (phagocytes, antibodies) will be brought to the area and less bacteria removed. The fact that the right apex is more frequently involved than the left Dock attributes to the anatomic configuration of the right pulmonary artery; it is longer than the left one and angles sharply twice in making its way around the aorta to the lung. The supply of venous blood to the right apex is thus smaller than to the left.

On this basis it is understandable that long-chested individuals should be most prone to apical tuberculosis, that people with mitral stenosis rarely develop tuberculosis because of their increased pulmonary arterial pressures, and that persons with pulmonic stenosis are especially liable to apical tuberculosis since the pulmonary arterial pressure is low. The effectiveness of rest in the horizontal position as a therapeutic measure is also understandable, for obviously in recumbency the weight of the blood column in the arteries no longer opposes the pressure of the heart.

In support of these deductions the recent experimental results of Olson and his co-workers (66b) are of great interest. Surgical interference with the pulmonary arterial circulation in experimentally infected monkeys results in the development of strikingly more extensive caseous disease in the lung on the manipulated side.

4. PHYSIOLOGIC AND ANATOMIC BARRIERS TO PROGRESS OF INVASIVE ORGANISMS. Sabin and Olitsky and King (67) have described the development of resistance with increasing age to the viruses of vesicular stomatitis and eastern and western equine encephalomyelitis in mice and guinea pigs. In the case of the neurotropic stomatitis virus the resistance becomes apparent between 30 days and about one year of age provided that the virus is injected peripherally rather than into the brain itself. In young nonresistant mice a peripheral injection is followed by the progression of virus to the central nervous system via appropriate nerve routes. In the older resistant animals the virus is halted at barriers which vary according to the injection site. Thus, after nasal installation the agent traverses the olfactory nerves to spread through the brain in young animals, while in older ones it stops at the anterior rhinencephalon and eventually disappears. Injected into the hind leg muscles of older mice it fails even to invade the local nerve, whereas in younger animals it progresses to the central nervous system by way of the sciatic nerve. After intra-ocular inoculation the virus in older mice is halted at the retina; in young animals it follows the decussating pathway of the optic nerves into the brain. If, however, the virus is inoculated inside the barriers in older mice, into the brain itself, it proceeds to cause encephalitis just as in young animals. There is thus no age immunity of the brain per se, but rather the development of some kind of impediment to viral progression

at points peripheral to the brain. In the case of eastern encephalomyelitis virus an analogous change in the blood vessel walls in older animals has the effect of preventing invasion of the brain by blood-borne virus.

5. INDIFFERENCE OF TISSUES TO BACTERIAL TOXINS. The native resistance shown by certain species of animals to generally injurious bacterial toxins appears to depend upon an indifference of cells rather than the possession of specific neutralizing substances. In the case of diphtheria toxin for example, the rat can resist perhaps 1,000 times the minimal lethal dose for the guinea pig (68). Samples of blood or urine assayed for free toxin several hours after injection reveal that much of it fails to be taken up by the tissues. In contrast, after the same interval, only small amounts remain free in the guinea pig (69). Cold blooded animals, such as the toad and frog, appear to be entirely insusceptible to this toxin as well as to tetanus toxin.

SUMMARY

The range of defenses of the normal animal against microbes and their toxins is considerable and varied. Some appear to be purposeful, directly attacking organisms so that these are inhibited in their multiplication or destroyed. Other defenses are more passive, interposing barriers which by one means or another discourage entrance to the tissues, or failing to provide the proper menstruum for the proliferation of microorganisms.

The pattern of native defense is a very flexible one. Most organisms of the environment are entirely prevented from establishing themselves as parasites. Others may live on in certain localities to become the characteristic flora— for example, the staphylococci, streptococci and diphtheroid bacilli on human skin—without ordinarily penetrating more deeply. Still other microbes may surmount all these barriers and proceed to multiply and disseminate in the tissues, in some cases releasing toxins also, and to produce disease. Such organisms are called pathogenic, and the next chapter will deal with the characteristics which account for their infectious abilities. In turn, most of the remainder of the book will be taken up with the means by which the body may **acquire** specific immunities against such pathogenic organisms and their toxins.

BIBLIOGRAPHY

1. Arnold, L., Gustafson, C. J., Montgomery, B. E., Hall, T. G., and Singer, C.   Am. J. Hyg., 11:345, 1930.
2. Bergeim, O., and Cornbleet, T.   Am. J. M. Sc., 205:785, 1943.
3. Cralley, L. J.   Am. J. Hyg., 36:303, 1942.
4a. Wells, W. F., Ratcliffe, H. L., and Crumb, C.   Am. J. Hyg., 47:11, 1948.
  b. Robertson, O. H.   Physiol. Rev., 21:112, 1941.
5. Nuttall, G. H. F.   Blood Immunity and Relationships, London, Cambridge University Press, 1904.
6. Fleming, A.   Proc. Roy. Soc., London, s.B., 93:306, 1922.
7a. Meyer, K., Thompson, R., Palmer, J., and Khorazo, D.   J. Biol Chem., 113:303, 1936.
  b. ——— and Hahnel, E.   Federation Proc., 5:147, 1946.
  c. Dubos, R.   The Bacterial Cell, Cambridge, Mass., Harvard University Press, 1945.

8a. Webb, M.   J. Gen. Microbiol., 2:260, 1948.
 b. Kern, R. A., Kingkade, M. J., Kern, S. F., and Behrens, O. K.   J. Bact., 61:171, 1951.
 9. Kurzrok, R., and Miller, G.   Am. J. Obst. & Gynec., 56:15, 1928.
10a. Bloom, W. L., Watson, D. W., Cromartie, W. J., and Freed, N.   J. Infect. Dis.. 80:41, 1947.
 b. Weissman, N., and Graf, L. H.   J. Infect. Dis., 80:145, 1947.
11. Bloom, W. L., and Blake, F. G.   J. Infect. Dis., 83:116, 1948.
12. Haas, E.   J. Biol. Chem., 163:63, 89, 101, 1946.
13a. Hechter, O., and Scully, E. L.   J. Exper. Med., 86:19, 1947.
 b. Meyer, K.   Physiol. Rev., 27:335, 1947.
14a. Myrvik, Q., and Weiser, R. S.   Am. Rev. Tuberc., 64:669, 1951.
 b. Thompson, R.   Am. J. Ophth., 24:635, 1941.
15a. Burnet, F. M., Lush, D., and Jackson, A. V.   Brit. J. Exper. Path., 20:377, 1939.
 b. Strong, P. S.   J. Immunol., 30:403, 1936.
16a. Casal, J., and Olitsky, P. K.   Science, 106:267, 1947.
 b. Utz, J. P.   Proc. Soc. Exper. Biol. & Med., 69:186, 1948.
17a. Thomas, R. M., and Bessau, I.   Yale J. Biol. & Med., 12:185, 1939.
 b. Gerstl, B., and Thomas, R. M.   Yale J. Biol. & Med., 13:679, 1941.
 c. ——— and Tennant, R.   Am. Rev. Tuberc., 46:600, 1942.
18a. Braun, W.   J. Bact., 51:327, 1946; 52:243, 1946; 58:291, 299, 1949.
 b. ——— Bact. Rev., 11:75, 1947.
 c. ——— and Hange, S.   J. Immunol., 60:443, 1948.
 d. Cole, L. J., and Braun, W.   J. Immunol., 64:111, 1950.
19. Hoerlein, B. F.   J. Bact., 56:139, 1948.
20. Hirst, G. K.   J. Exper. Med., 76:195, 1942.
21. ——— J. Exper. Med., 78:99, 1943.
22. Stone, J. D.   Australian J. Exper. Biol. & M. Sc., 26:49, 287, 1948.
23a. Friedewald, W. F., and Pickles, E. G.   J. Exper. Med., 79:301, 1944.
 b. Gard, S., von Magnus, P., and Svedmyr, A.   Proceedings IV International Congress of Microbiology, Copenhagen, 1947, pp. 301-302.
24. Francis, T. J., Jr.   J. Exper. Med., 85:1, 1947.
25a. Burnet, F. M.   Australian J. Sc., 10:21, 1947.
 b. Lanni, F., and Beard, J. M.   Proc. Soc. Exper. Biol. & Med., 68:312, 1948.
 c. deBurgh, P. M., Yu, P. C., Howe C., and Bovarnick, M.   J. Exper. Med., 87:1, 1948.
 d. Hirst, G. K.   J. Exper. Med., 89:223, 233, 1949.
 e. Gottschalk, A., and Lind, P. E.   Brit. J. Exper. Path., 30:85, 1949.
26. McCrea, J. F.   Australian J. Exper. Biol. & Med. Sc., 24:283, 1946.
27. Metchnikoff, E.   Resistance to Infective Diseases, Cambridge, England, Cambridge University Press, 1905.
28. Aschoff, L.   Lectures on Pathology, New York, Paul B. Hoeber, Inc., 1924.
29a. Kyes, P.   J. Infect. Dis., 18:277, 1916.
 b. Jaffé, R. H.   Physiol. Rev., 11:277, 1931.
 c. Taliaferro, W. H.   Ann. Rev. Microbiol., 3:159, 1949.
30. Rich, A. R., and McKee, C. M.   Bull. Johns Hopkins Hosp., 64:434, 1939.
31. Lawrence, J. S., Pearse, H. E., and Mider, G. D.   Arch. Path., 28:36, 1939.
32. Menkin, V.   Am. J. Path., 10:193, 1934.
33. Robertson, O. H., and Van Sant, H.   J. Immunol., 37:571, 1939.
34. ——— Physiol. Rev., 21:112, 1941.
35a. McCutcheon, M., and Dixon, H. M.   Arch. Path., 21:749, 1936.
 b. Dixon, H. M., and McCutcheon, M.   Proc. Soc. Exper. Biol. & Med., 38:378, 1938.
36. Silverman, D.   Arch. Path., 25:40, 1938.
37. Wells, H. G.   The Chemical Aspects of Immunity, New York, The Chemical Catalog Co., 1929.
38. Coman, D. R.   Arch. Path., 30:896, 1940.
39. Lasfargues, E., and Delauney, A.   Ann. Inst. Pasteur, 73:14, 1947.
40. McCutcheon, M., Coman, D. R., and Dixon, H. M.   Arch. Path., 27:61, 1939.
41. Allgöwer, M., and Bloch, H.   Am. Rev. Tuberc., 59:562, 1949.
42. Abramson, H. A.   J. Exper. Med., 46:987, 1927.

43a. Mudd, S., McCutcheon, M., and Lucké, B. Physiol. Rev., 14:210, 1934.
  b. Fenn, W. O. J. Gen. Physiol., 4:373, 1921.
44. Berry, L. J., Starr, R. W., III, and Haller, E. C. J. Bact., 57:603, 1949.
45. Knisely, M. H., Bloch, E. H., and Warner, L. Det Kongelige Danske Videnska-
    bernes Selskab, Biologiske Skrifter, 4:1, 1948.
46a. Wood, W. B., Jr., Smith, M. R., and Watson, B. J. Exper. Med., 84:387, 1946.
  b. Sale, L., Jr., and Wood, W. B., Jr. J. Exper. Med., 86:239, 1947.
  c. —— Smith, M. R., and Wood, W. B., Jr. J. Exper. Med., 86:249, 1947.
  d. Smith, M. R., and Wood, W. B., Jr. J. Exper. Med., 86:257, 1947.
  e. Wood, W. B., Jr., and Smith, M. R. Science, 106:86, 1947.
  f. Smith, M. R., Perry, W. D., Berry, J. W., and Wood, W. B., Jr. J. Exper. Med.,
    67:71, 1951.
47a. Opie, E. L. Physiol. Rev., 2:552, 1922.
  b. Jobling, J. W., and Petersen, W. F. Bull. Johns Hopkins Hosp., 26:356, 1915.
  c. Weiss, C., and Czarnetzky, E. J. Arch. Path., 20:233, 1935.
48. Rous, P. J. Exper. Med., 41:379, 399, 1925.
49. Gay, F. P., and Clark, A. R. Arch. Path., 1:847, 1926.
50a. Rous, P., and Jones, F. S. J. Exper. Med., 23:601, 1916.
  b. Lyons, C. Brit. J. Exper. Path., 18:411, 1937.
  c. Oliver, J. J. Exper. Med., 43:233, 1926.
  d. Fell, H. B., and Brieger, E. N. J. Hyg., 45:359, 1947.
51. Merling, K. B. E. J. Path. & Bact., 57:21, 1945.
52. Burnet, F. M., and Freeman, M. M. J. Australia, 2:299, 1937.
53a. Meleney, H. E. Am. J. Path., 1:147, 1925.
  b. Taliaferro, W. H. Rev. Kuba, 3:150, 1947.
  c. Huff, C. G., and Coulston, F. J. Infect. Dis., 75:231, 1944.
  d. Goodpasture, E. W., and Anderson, K. Am. J. Path., 13:149, 1937.
54. Bull, C. J. Exper. Med., 22:475, 1915.
55. Martin, S. P., Kerby, G. P., and Holland, B. C. Proc. Soc. Exper. Biol. & Med.,
    72:63, 1949.
56. MacCallum, W. G. Bull. Johns Hopkins Hosp., 14:105, 1903.
57. Drinker, C. K., Field, M. E., and Ward, H. K. J. Exper. Med., 59:393, 1934.
58. Kruse, H., and McMaster, P. D. J. Exper. Med., 90:425, 1949.
59. McMaster, P. D. Ann. New York Acad. Sc., 46:743, 1946.
60. Ørskov, J. Compt. rend. Soc. de biol., 93:959, 1925. Ztschr. f. Immunitätsforsch.
    u. exper. Therap., 98:174, 1940.
61. Rich, A. R., and McKee, C. M. Bull. Johns Hopkins Hosp., 59:171, 1936.
62. Enders, J. F., and Shaffer, M. F. J. Exper. Med., 64:7, 1936.
63. Mueller, J. H. J. Immunol., 42:353, 1941.
64. Zinnemann, K. J. Path. & Bact., 55:275, 1943.
65. Rich, A. R., and Follis, R. H., Jr. Bull. Johns Hopkins Hosp., 71:345, 1942.
66a. Dock, W. Am. Rev. Tuberc., 53:297, 1946.
  b. Olson, B. J., Scott, H. W., Jr., Hanlon, C. R., and Mattern, C. F. T. Am. Rev.
    Tuberc., 65:48, 1952.
67a. Olitsky, P. K., Sabin, A. B., and Cox, H. R. J. Exper. Med., 64:723, 1936.
  b. Sabin, A. B., and Olitsky, P. K. J. Exper. Med., 66:15, 1937; 67:201, 229, 1938.
    Proc. Soc. Exper. Biol. & Med., 38:597, 1938.
  c. King, L. S. J. Exper. Med., 71:95, 1940.
68. Cobbett, L. Brit. M. J., 1:902, 1899.
69a. Coca, A. F., Russell, E. F., and Baughman, W. H. J. Immunol., 6:387, 1921.
  b. Pettit, A. Ann. Inst. Pasteur, 28:663, 1914.

3

MECHANISMS OF PATHOGENICITY AND VIRULENCE

The preceding chapter described the existence, in normal men and animals, of an array of mechanisms for thwarting the aims of potential parasites. If these mechanisms entirely fulfilled their promise there would be no such thing as infectious disease. But we know that certain microbes can establish themselves in the tissues in spite of the provisions for defense; there they proceed to multiply, and once having gained this foothold, they may produce disease of varying severity, by the liberation of toxic substances which may injure or destroy cells, by interfering with normal physiologic patterns such as pulmonary reflexes or electrolyte balance, and by other activities varying with the particular infectious agent concerned. Organisms with such capabilities are called **pathogenic**, i.e. productive of disease. Another word—**virulence**—has come to be associated with the **degree** of pathogenicity, so that a pathogenic microbe is classed as one of low, high or intermediate virulence according to its ability to subvert the host.

There is some confusion about the propriety of considering pathogenicity a property of a parasite per se. The alternative viewpoint would delineate pathogenicity as the flexible result of a balance between the parasite and its host. According to this view a parasite in a host with a high level of resistance would be restricted or entirely suppressed in its activities, while in a host with depressed native resistance even an ordinarily innocuous organism could give rise to infection. The defect in this viewpoint is its attempt to define one element of an equation in terms of fluctuations in the other. Obviously, manipulating the balance on the side of the host will give the effect either of increasing or minimizing the weight of the parasite as a pathogenic agent. A more logical approach would judge pathogenicity when the host factor is kept constant. This is of course impossible to do literally, but a generally satisfactory approach to this ideal can be attained by testing the pathogenicity of a microbe in **normal members only** of a particular species of animal. Normality of host includes general well-being and especially excludes previous experience with the microbe in question. Such a restriction still leaves as a variable the well-known variations in native resistance regularly displayed by individuals of a species to any infectious or other injurious agent, but this disparity can be brought to an average level by testing a sufficient number of individuals. Simple statistical methods are available for experimentally

24

establishing the pathogenic activities of microbes so that results may be satisfactorily duplicated (1).

If the condition of testing for pathogenicity in a group of normal animals is met, the validity of considering pathogenicity as a microbial property can be established. This is evidenced by the common observation that different strains of a single species of organism differ in their powers to produce disease in the same host, a result which could hardly reflect anything other than variations in specific properties inherent in the microbe itself. These properties however are not necessarily rigidly fixed nor permanent in any particular case. Quantitative as well as qualitative factors enter into the comparison of strains of an organism for relative virulence, for it is often found that a large number of a less virulent strain may accomplish the same final effect as a very small number of a highly virulent strain. Avirulent strains, however, will have no pathogenic action in any dose; the absence of virulence reflects a qualitative difference between microbes.

Specificity of Pathogenicity. No single microorganism is pathogenic for all species of animals, nor is the level of pathogenicity usually the same in two susceptible species. Disregarding for the present the factors which may determine such differences (and very little is known about these), it is often found, for example, that an organism isolated from a serious human infection may progress very reluctantly or not at all in a guinea pig or mouse. On the other hand, the fact that an organism cultured from a patient quickly dispatches the animal employed as a diagnostic aid does not allow the inference that it may be of similar consequence, or of any consequence, to the individual from whom it was originally isolated. Obviously it is incorrect to describe the virulence of an agent without the qualification of a specific host. Interesting examples of the specificity of pathogenicity are provided by the activities of various tubercle bacilli in different hosts, as shown in Table 1.

Table I. Pathogenicity of varieties of tubercle bacilli for different host species

Host	BACILLUS		
	Human	Bovine	Avian
Human being	3+ *	3+	0
Cattle	0	2+	1+
Guinea pig	4+	4+	0
Rabbit	0	4+	2+
Fowl	0	0	4+

* 4+ = maximum pathogenicity.

The organisms included in the table are those forms pathogenic for one or more hosts. In addition, there are strains of these bacilli which are entirely avirulent for all species of animals; for example, the H37R$_a$ strain of the human tubercle bacillus. In this case the bacillus has lost all trace of those properties essential for its establishment in the tissues even of susceptible hosts.

General Requisites for Pathogenicity. Pathogenic organisms may produce disease in many ways. Some, such as the diphtheria bacillus, multiply in a restricted area and produce toxins which diffuse through the body to poison various tissues; others may grow in more intimate association with the tissues themselves and may also enter the blood and lymph streams, affecting the host eventually through intoxication, derangement of cellular metabolism or destructive changes incident to hypersensitivity. From the immunologic point of view, however, the primary consideration is the ability of the microorganism **to establish itself** and **to multiply** in the tissues. These facts, common to all forms of pathogenicity, are the basic steps from which a variety of consequences may ensue.

In a few instances, well exemplified by the cholera vibrio, the infectious agent is so superficially located in relation to tissues, in the lumen of the intestine, that no particular explanation seems necessary to account for its multiplication in that area once it has been ingested. But in the great majority of cases we must account for the fact of progressive multiplication of microbes in intimate relationship to tissues which we know are endowed with certain defensive abilities.

A second requisite for pathogenicity is the ability of an organism spontaneously to communicate from host to host. In nature it would avail a microbe little, whatever its capacity to proliferate in the tissues, if it could not successfully transfer to fresh potential hosts. Though one might expect this ability, called **infectivity** or **communicability,** more or less to parallel the microbe's proliferative powers in the body, this is not always the case. Topley and his co-workers (2) have found strains of mouse typhoid bacilli in which these two potentialities diverge, one strain with moderately high virulence following injection possessing little ability to produce severe epidemics by natural spread through mouse communities. Communicability may depend partly upon the ability of the organism to maintain in the environment those properties upon which it depends for its survival when it finds host tissues (3). In part also it may depend upon its ability to penetrate to underlying tissues. Thus, it has been found that colonial variants of the anthrax bacillus which produce equivalent disease after subcutaneous injection differ widely in their abilities to invade the body through the lung after inhalation (4).

Well known examples of the divergence of communicability from capacity to establish progressive disease once in the tissues are easy to find. The human tubercle bacillus is almost universally lethal for guinea pigs into which it has been injected even in small numbers, yet animals kept in a tuberculous environment do not often acquire the disease spontaneously. In contrast, human beings can easily contract an initial infection from environmental exposure, but can handle the subsequent progression of the infection much better than can guinea pigs. Again, although multitudes of mice have succumbed to injections of pneumococci in the laboratory, these animals never acquire pneumococcus infection in nature. In contrast many mild parasites, such as the relatively nonpathogenic colon bacillus, so readily communicate from host to host that no one remains free of them for more than a few hours postnatally.

Mechanisms of Pathogenicity. The question of pathogenic mechanisms can be studied by determining what properties disease-producing organisms may have which are lacking in nonpathogenic species. Even more pointed information may be gained by contrasting pathogenic forms with nonpathogenic variants of the same species.

Of the requisites for pathogenicity previously discussed, we shall be concerned here with the mechanisms by which organisms may establish themselves in the tissues. The first essential requirement of a pathogenic agent is obviously an ability to utilize the host as a medium. In addition, the fact that the normal animal body possesses various instruments of defense suggests that the properties determining the pathogenicity of microorganisms should be aggressive ones—abilities directed toward the neutralization or destruction of the host's defensive powers. Although most of the factors discussed later in detail are of this kind (because these are the ones about which we have most information), it appears reasonable to suppose that in some of the many instances where we remain ignorant of pathogenic mechanisms no special ability of the agent exists at all; the ability to establish infection may be entirely independent of aggressiveness on the part of the parasite. This could be the case if the potential host possessed no defense mechanism effective against the particular parasite. For example, certain organisms live quite contentedly within phagocytes, and they may also remain unaffected by any of the humoral bactericidal enzymes. In such a case the organism would require no property except the ability to utilize the nutrients and the gaseous environment supplied by the tissues. It is well known that a variety of saprophytic organisms can flourish in the tissues of the body depleted of phagocytes simply on the basis of utilizing the tissues as a medium. It seems entirely possible that an analogous situation may exist in those cases where the phagocytes of the normal body are intact but leave the parasite unharmed, and apparently themselves remain unharmed by the parasite (5). To account for avirulent strains of such organisms one might suggest that these are simply altered somewhat in their metabolic requirements, perhaps in a relatively minor respect (6), and the loss of virulence occurring after variable periods of time in organisms cultivated outside the body may in such cases reflect the loss of metabolic abilities which are not required for multiplication in artificial media, but are necessary for growth in the tissues.

We know little as yet about such passive mechanisms of virulence. More information is available concerning positive properties of bacteria which have been referred to as aggressive mechanisms. In the sections which follow some of these aggressive mechanisms will be discussed from the standpoint of their possible roles in helping microbes to establish themselves in the host and to cause disease in their various ways.

1. SOMATIC ANTIGEN. The bacterial body is made up of a variety of chemical substances. Some of these substances are antigens and consequently they provoke the manufacture of specific antibodies. In certain of the pathogenic bacteria it has been found that characteristic antigens are present in the virulent forms and that when the organisms lose these components they also lose their virulence. Such cells become entirely nonpathogenic derivatives of pathogenic bacteria, a change which may be reversible. This is the case in the pneumococci, hemolytic streptococci, salmonellas, *Klebsiella pneumoniae, Hemophilus influenzae* and *Bacillus anthracis*.

In these species the superficial antigens seem to occur in strata. The outermost layer may take the morphologic form of a microscopically visible capsule, as in the case of the pneumococcus. But even in those instances where visible capsules do not ordinarily occur, a corresponding outer layer of antigen exists in the potentially virulent organism. In most of the bacteria which are known in this respect, this outer stratum is polysaccharide, alone or existing as a complex with other substances. In the pneumococcus and in some of the hemolytic streptococci the sugar apparently makes up the capsule, while among the gram-negative enteric bacilli complexes of carbohydrate with lipid and protein occur. In these cases however the antigenic specificity of the complexes derived from different species and types resides largely in the configuration of the polysaccharide portion of the complex. Since these outermost antigens impart to colonies of bacteria a smooth appearance such organisms are referred to as smooth or S forms.

Sometimes spontaneously in culture or in vivo some of the descendants of S forms lose their outer antigens and the daughter colonies composed of such cells are of different appearance from the original, since now a deeper-lying and chemically different substance becomes the surface component of the bacterium. The colony loses its smooth topography, becomes dull or granular, and it is now called the rough, or R, colonial form. This separation of R from S forms is called **dissociation** (7). Single S cells may give rise to S and R progeny, and the process may be pushed along by culturing S forms in medium containing antibodies directed against the outer antigen. The change may be reversible; R forms may give rise to S, but this is a relatively infrequent occurrence.

The loss of outermost antigen entails, in addition to the chemical, antigenic and morphologic alterations described, a loss of virulence. The obvious inference to be drawn from this is that the activities of these external antigens in the animal body may explain the virulence of the organism, and this expectation is not disappointed. It has been found that these antigens may interfere with several of the mechanisms of native resistance.

First, the normal bactericidal activities of tissue fluids are neutralized or otherwise evaded. This has been demonstrated with the somatic antigens of a variety of enteric pathogenic bacilli (8), and perhaps more clearly with the polypeptide capsular substance of the anthrax bacillus which neutralizes an anthracidal substance present in normal tissues ([9], see also page 290).

Second, these antigens may induce a significant degree of leukopenia. The somatic antigen of *Salmonella typhosa* is especially active in this respect, a fact of interest in relation to the low leukocyte level characteristic of typhoid fever (10).

Third, such antigens may interfere with phagocytosis (11). This effect is readily demonstrated by sampling exudates from animals injected with S and R forms of the same bacterium. Figure 9 illustrates such an experiment

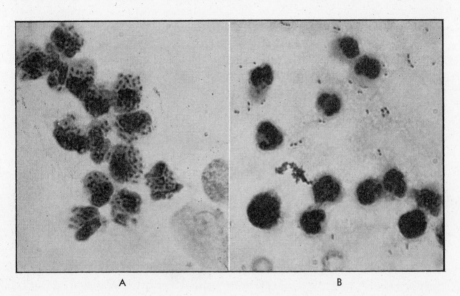

A   B

Fig. 9. A, phagocytosis of R pneumococci in the peritoneal cavity of a mouse. B, failure of S pneumococci to be phagocytized under the same conditions.

carried out with capsulated and unencapsulated strains of a type I pneumo-coccus injected into the peritoneal cavities of mice. The exudate illustrated in Figure 9A was sampled two hours after the inoculation of avirulent (R) cells, and the extent of phagocytosis is striking. Figure 9B portrays the situation two hours after the injection of virulent and capsulated cocci. Leuko-cytes are seen in the vicinity of the microbes but no phagocytosis has occurred. The importance of capsular polysaccharide in determining this difference, and as a consequence the eventual fates of the injected mice, was revealed some years ago by Felton and Bailey (12) who injected the capsular substance of the type II organism along with attenuated pneumococci of the same type, and produced fatal infections.

The existence of a degree of flexibility in the relationship between capsu-lar antigens and phagocytosis has been shown by the recent work of Wood with hemolytic streptococci, pneumococci, staphylococci, and *Klebsiella* (13). It was seen that even the virulent members of these encapsulated species may be phagocytized in normal animals on the surfaces of tissues, where organisms can be trapped by phagocytes. But phagocytosis does not occur in a fluid medium such as an inflammatory exudate. Since however, the difference between the success or failure of an organism to establish itself in the body undoubtedly depends upon subtle differences in the capacity of the host to defend itself, the inability of phagocytes to function effectively in fluid exudates may well determine this outcome. It is of interest in this connection that in the case of the type III pneumococcus, its generally higher virulence for human beings may be due to a slime layer coating the polysaccharide capsule, which makes these organisms resistant to phagocytosis even upon tissue surfaces (13b).

There is evidence then that at least two elements of defense in the normal animal, one humoral, the other cellular, may be thwarted by the presence in several species of pathogenic bacteria of a smooth phase surface antigen. In one case the external antiphagocytic substance is not antigenic; this appears to be true of the hyaluronic acid capsule frequently found on group A hemolytic streptococci, and probably related to their virulence (14).

Unfortunately for our peace of mind, certain other evidence makes it clear that these paragraphs do not tell the entire story. Although spontaneous loss of virulence among the bacterial species considered here is most often associated with loss of external antigen, there are exceptions to this correlation. S forms are not always virulent as indicated by the following two examples.

Pike and Mackenzie (15) have worked with two strains of *S. enteritidis,* both colonially smooth and with qualitatively and quantitatively identical outer antigens. In one case however, the injection of 7 organisms into a group of mice killed 84 per cent; in the other case 10^6 organisms were necessary to effect the same result. The reason for this wide difference in virulence could not be determined. Possibly the less virulent strain lacked some metabolic ability essential for its utilization of the host as a pabulum (16). This may correspond with the observation that encapsulated organisms of other species after isolation from one host may be avirulent for a second until adaptation has occurred. This is the case for example with encapsulated hemolytic streptococci isolated from human beings and injected into mice. At first they are harmless for the new host, but with continued passages these organisms become virulent for the mouse. Obviously this rests upon some other basis than the content of capsular material.

Working with a related bacterial species, *S. typhimurium,* Maaløe (17) has also found wide differences in virulence for mice, a highly virulent strain killing them regularly, an avirulent practically never, though both strains were identical in colonial morphology and antigenic properties. Both organisms could **establish** themselves initially in regional lymph glands after penetrating the intestinal wall, but the avirulent failed to persist.

The conclusion to be drawn from such exceptions is that an intact antigenic structure is necessary to the virulence of the species under discussion, but does not assure it (18). Other factors in addition to the outermost antigens must therefore be necessary for virulence. In this same connection we have also to consider the disturbing fact that ordinarily nonpathogenic species of microbes, for example, *Escherichia coli,* possess antigenic complexes of the same nature as those found in pathogenic species, yet do not frequently cause disease. It seems probable that such organisms may lack other factors essential for maintenance in the tissues.

It has been reported that rough variants of *Shigella sonnei* and of *S. typhimurium* may be related to human and murine infections (19). The evidence for this is not clear cut (20).

We may summarize the crux of this discussion as follows: In some bacterial species the presence of an externally located antigen is well correlated with their pathogenic potentialities, but some may be avirulent in spite of having such antigen because the bacteria lack other requisites for proliferation in the animal body. Pathogenicity undoubtedly reflects the additive effects of perhaps several properties, some of which we can roughly estimate, while of others we are probably still entirely ignorant.

2. LEUKOCIDIN. Antigenic toxins are excreted or secreted by certain bacteria, chief among them the beta hemolytic streptococci and staphylococci, which destroy polymorphonuclear leukocytes. This differs from the leukocidal property of somatic antigens just discussed. The effect of this soluble toxin may sometimes be appreciable; in a deep-seated staphylococcus infection for example many immature leukocytes are found in the circulating blood, the reflection of an attempt by bone marrow to replace destroyed cells. Not many investigations have been made of the point, but several studies have indicated a correlation between leukocidin production and the virulence of staphylococci. The majority of pathogenic staphylococci produce this substance, while nonpathogenic strains usually do not (21). There is some evidence also that the virulence of streptococci may be in part determined by their ability to produce leukocidin (22). However, nonpathogenic strains of both organisms may elaborate this substance in large amounts. Obviously then the issue is not entirely clear cut, and here again we may be dealing with one of a number of factors contributing to rather than determining virulence.

3. NECROTIZING TOXINS. In some cases organisms may be entirely lacking in the ability to establish themselves in viable tissues because the gaseous environment is unfavorable for their metabolic activities. The anaerobic clostridia are outstanding examples of this, and require as a condition preliminary to parasitism that an area of tissue be devitalized, usually by trauma. The tetanus bacillus takes advantage of this circumstance only to the extent of local growth; it never invades contiguous undamaged tissues and were it not for its powerful neurotoxin which diffuses to neighboring capillaries and lymphatics and is so carried to the central nervous system, this organism would be entirely without pathogenic activity. Gas gangrene bacilli on the other hand elaborate substances which appear to pave the

way for their extension. *Cl. perfringens,* a representative member of this group, produces several soluble enzymes. One is a lecithinase, referred to as alpha toxin, which causes general cellular necrosis (23); a second is a proteolytic enzyme which attacks collagen (24). The correlation between lecithinase production and virulence is high, though by no means absolute, but the suggestion is evident that the ability of gas gangrene organisms to extend their activities from the original traumatized focus depends in large measure upon the progressive devitalization of contiguous tissues by this enzyme, aided perhaps by collagenase (25). The readiness with which a small number of washed spores or bacilli, ordinarily not injurious for animals into which they are injected, can be made lethal by the addition of whole toxin to the inoculum, indicates that these enzymic constituents must be of considerable import to virulence (26). But other factors must be of importance also, since some strains producing large amounts of lecithinase are nevertheless avirulent.

In an analogous sense, the characteristic toxin produced by the diphtheria bacillus may be closely related to the proliferation of this organism in the local area which it infects, in addition to being responsible for much of the subsequent disease picture itself. The toxin destroys polymorphonuclear cells, among others, and it has been shown that simple neutralization of the toxin by antitoxin in animals results in much improved phagocytosis of even the most virulent bacilli (27). Other possibilities exist in this case also to account for virulence, as discussed in the chapter dealing with diphtheria.

4. SPREADING FACTOR—HYALURONIDASE. In 1928 Duran-Reynals observed a remarkable extension of dermal vaccinial lesions in rabbit skin in the presence of extracts of normal testicle and other tissues (28). This spreading effect is easily demonstrated with India ink. A small amount of ink injected into rabbit skin may spread through six or seven square centimeters within a few hours, while the addition to the inoculum of spreading factor increases the area as much as twenty-fold during the same period. The activity is not confined to skin; subcutaneous tissue and muscle are similarly affected.

The spreading factor was subsequently found to be produced by various bacteria, notably streptococci, staphylococci, some strains of *Corynebacterium diphtheriae* as well as other organisms (29). Meanwhile, the nature of this substance was also clarified; it is, or is closely related to, the enzyme hyaluronidase; this is active upon hyaluronic acid which serves in the tissues as a gelatinous cellular binder (30).

In the case of the streptococci especially it seems a rational possibility that a substance with this property might help to explain the general tendency of the organism to cause diffuse infections. Such an expectation is considerably dampened however by the fact that many strains of virulent hemolytic streptococci possess hyaluronic acid capsules themselves, and hence do not produce the enzyme which acts on this substrate (31). Such organisms however appear often to produce a spreading factor of nonhyaluronidase nature (32). Apparently only a poor correlation exists between spreading factor and virulence for man as judged by its production by streptococci isolated from human infections (31b, 33).

More pointed evidence of a relationship between hyaluronidase and virulence has come from studies of the staphylococccus and clostridia. In the first instance Duran-Reynals (29a) investigated 53 strains for their ability to produce the factor and found a high correlation between this and the invasiveness of the strain as judged by the source of isolation (see also 29b). In the second case, McClean (29c) concluded as the result of attempts to correlate invasiveness with the production of spreading factor by the clostridia that "broadly speaking, it is those organisms which are characterized by their capacity for dramatic local invasion that elaborate a diffusing factor." But within a species studied in detail it was not possible to carry the correlation to its ultimate conclusion. McClean therefore suggested that hyaluronidase production alone cannot be responsible for determining invasive power but may be instead an accessory "in promoting local penetration of the tissues and dissemination of the infection throughout the body of the host."

Autolysates of the pneumococcus have been described as making ordinarily subfatal doses of this organism lethal for rabbits, apparently on the basis of a substance similar to hyaluronidase in its activity. Rough strains of pneumococci mixed with such material were not rendered pathogenic however, fulfilling the expectation that the possession of a capsule is an essential prerequisite to virulence, while other factors may be additive (34).

The sum of evidence permits us to conclude then that the elaboration of spreading factor may be related to the **invasiveness** of some pathogenic organisms (35). Invasiveness itself however is not synonymous with virulence, first because some organisms may produce serious disease unmarked by invasion, and secondly because a too rapid spread though the tissues may actually defeat the objective of establishment in the tissues. The latter possibility has been emphasized by Duran-Reynals. If a bacterium is of such a grade of virulence that a certain minimal number is necessary to establish infection in an area of tissue, the rapid dissemination of these organisms through 5 or 10 times this area may result in their destruction by the native defenses which can cope with scattered organisms, but can not operate effec-- tively against the same number in a restricted region (36).

The final assessment permitted by available evidence with respect to spreading factor and virulence is this: That the factor may perhaps augment virulence by increasing invasiveness, but since dissemination through the tissues is not in itself sufficient in an organism which lacks other abilities essential for its proliferation in the body, this factor is at most an accessory rather than a pivotal mechanism of pathogenicity.

5. FIBRINOLYSIN (STREPTOKINASE). In 1933 Tillett and Garner (37) discovered an interesting property of the group A hemolytic streptococci which again may contribute to our understanding of the mechanisms of virulence. In young culture filtrates of streptococci isolated from human infections they

found a soluble factor with a marked ability to lyse human fibrin. Later, a similar substance was found to be produced by strains of beta hemolytic staphylococci, and by other bacteria as well, though less frequently (38). It has since been shown that the substance is not itself an enzyme but rather an activator (kinase) of a prelytic factor of normal blood which may be activated by certain chemicals also. Recently suggested terms refer to the streptococcal activator as streptokinase, to the inactive serum precursor of the proteolytic enzyme as plasminogen, and to the activated enzyme as plasmin (39).

Here again, as in the case of hyaluronidase, an activity of the streptococcus would seem to facilitate our understanding of the invasiveness and virulence of this organism. As was described in Chapter 2, the fibrin laid down in the tissues during an inflammatory process provides certain benefits to the host, including a pathway for the migration of leukocytes and a localizing barrier to bacteria. The dissolution of fibrin should mean that both these protective provisions are lost to the host and that the organism might not only establish itself more readily in its initial locus, but might also invade surrounding tissues unhampered by adsorption to fibrin strands.

Such a conclusion seemed indicated in retrospect by the clinical and pathologic studies of streptococcal bronchopneumonia carried out during World War I. It was observed that early pleural and alveolar exudates were remarkably thin, and the rapid spread of infection was referred to this fact (40). About 20 years later Tillett (41) reviewed the question of fibrinolysin and streptococcal virulence and concluded that strains obtained from serious human infections were more frequent and more potent producers of the factor, though recognizing that streptococci isolated from normal individuals and belonging to groups infrequently involved in human infections could also produce it.

World War II provided opportunities for more elaborate studies of this point, and the results were less conclusive. However, of the organisms cultivated from human sources those belonging to group A, the most frequent human pathogens, were again found to produce streptokinase more often and in greater average amount than those of other groups (42).

The answer to the question of the relationship of streptokinase to virulence is thus not clear, but the trend of observations indicates that in the sum of factors contributing to the status of an organism as an infectious agent, this probably plays a part. A precise determination of this point involves many complexities (43).

Another proteolytic mechanism is also elaborated by some strains of hemolytic streptococci; this digests fibrin as well as other proteins among which, paradoxically, is the M capsular antigen of the streptococcus itself (42b). Little is known as yet about the possible relationship of this factor to virulence.

6. HEMOLYSINS. The production of erythrocyte-destroying toxins is characteristic of a variety of pathogenic bacteria, especially the streptococci,

staphylococci, *Cl. perfringens* and other anaerobic bacilli, and *H. pertussis*. So far as we know, the destruction of red blood cells would have little influence upon the initial step essential to a pathogenic agent, the ability to establish itself in the tissues. In a more remote sense however this property might serve the parasite to advantage later, since it would be dealing with a host at a subnormal physiologic level. It could be speculated, for example, that anemia might result in an impairment of the functional activities of many cells, among them the phagocytes.

Despite the marked activity of this bacterial substance upon erythrocytes in vitro however, it is very questionable whether in any but one of the instances mentioned hemolysis also occurs in vivo. The single exception is clostridial infection, in which bronzing of the skin and pigmentation of the serum make intravascular hemolysis a very evident occurrence. It seems unlikely that this fact per se would add anything to the progression of the infectious agent, for the same toxin which effects this change—the lecithinase —simultaneously causes other profound changes which are directly concerned with the extension of the bacilli.

As regards the other hemolytic microbes, there is little valid evidence that the lysins are active in vivo, yet anemia is a commonly observed sequel to many infectious processes. Evidence however indicates that such anemias develop as the result of defective hemoglobin formation rather than erythrocyte destruction, a phenomenon probably related to some fault in protein metabolism as well as a diminution of plasma iron due to impaired absorption from the gastrointestinal tract (44). It seems doubtful therefore that bacterial hemolysins play a role as such in determining the degree of virulence of the microbes which produce them. In other guises however they may be concerned; thus, Todd (45) has shown that an hemolysin of the streptococcus (streptolysin O) has a powerful lytic action on leukocytes, and is apparently the leukocidin of this organism.

7. COAGULASE. The aureus variety of staphylococcus produces a coagulase which is a prothrombin-like substance which, when activated by a constituent of blood, causes clotting (46). It is difficult to see how such an activity could further the pathogenic ends of a bacterium, yet among the factors discussed this is one that is best correlated with the potential virulence of the organisms which produce it, as judged by their sources of isolation. Over 96 per cent of staphylococci obtained from human infections produce this enzyme, whereas few staphylococci cultured from the surface of the skin, for example, are positive in this respect (21). This fact provides a simple test for the probable pathogenic significance of a staphylococcus isolated from a lesion, but there is as yet no reasonable suggestion as to its possible significance with respect to pathogenicity. It is possible that coagulase may exert some yet unknown influence upon tissues or fluids aside from its clotting activity.

Virulence of Bacteria. RÉSUMÉ. The few properties of bacteria discussed here are mostly of the kind which may explain the basic aspect of pathogenicity—the ability of an organism to proliferate in the tissues. The rest of the disease process, acute or chronic, will follow upon this in accordance with the subsequent activities of parasite and host. Of these primary factors, it is apparent that no one factor represents the sole source of virulence, for organisms with any one of these attributes may yet lack the capacity to cause disease. In most cases also, with the possible exception of the capsular or somatic antigens, one or more factors may be lacking in an organism which retains its virulence. But in sum these properties probably help to determine virulence, and when one is lacking another may be highly developed. At the present time there can be no serious attempt to formulate precise pictures of virulence for individual strains or even species of bacteria in a specific host, but we can learn from such information as has been discussed something of the features which mark such a picture.

Little mention has been made of those instances in which bacteria cause disease primarily upon the basis of their diffusible toxins, as happens for example in tetanus, in staphylococcal, streptococcal and salmonella food poisoning, and to some extent in scarlet fever. These are special instances in which the eventual **disease** processes result largely from bacterial poisons, while the basic question of **establishment of the parasite in the tissues** enters to a limited extent only. The role of bacterial toxins in the causation of disease will be taken up in later discussions of individual infectious diseases. Nothing has been said either of the eventual effect on the disease picture of the development of hypersensitivity of the host to an infectious agent. This has much to do with the pathogenesis of the disease but not, strictly speaking, with the pathogenicity of the etiologic agent. The hypersensitivity of infection is discussed in Chapter 15.

Virulence of Viruses and Rickettsias. There is scant information to guide an appraisal of the properties which may determine the virulence of a virus for a susceptible host. As in the case of the bacteria, the conception of virulence properties inherent in the viral agent itself is validated by differences in the abilities of strains of the same virus to cause disease in a particular species of host. An example is the 17D strain of yellow fever virus used for human vaccination. It lacks the ability of the parent strain to cause progressive disease though it probably survives and multiplies for a time in host cells.

With regard to the first consideration in dealing with virulence—the ability of an agent to establish itself in the host—suggestive evidence has been provided by studies of influenza virus. Hirst (47) found this virus to have the property of agglutinating erythrocytes. It seems probable that receptors present on the red cells serve as substrate for an enzyme elaborated by the virus. Recent work has revealed that a mucopolysaccharide present in normal human serum can interfere with this enzymatic activity of the virus by itself serving as substrate for the reaction (48). If now we infer that this viral activity, i.e. attaching to cellular receptors, is concerned in its infectiousness for host cells (evidence for this viewpoint is presented in Chapter

2), then we may look upon the viral enzyme as a property of virulence. A virus with greater ability to neutralize the plasma substrate should be better able to attach to host cells, and thus to establish itself soon after entrance into the body (49). The important question in this line of reasoning is the validity of the viewpoint that cellular receptors involved in hemagglutination are also concerned in the first stage of infection by virus. Very suggestive evidence of such a relationship is the fact that a similar receptor system for virus has been demonstrated in the cells of ferret lungs (50), and that treatment of mice with receptor-destroying enzyme decreases their susceptibility to influence virus infection (51). On the other hand, there is evidence that the hemagglutinative and infectious capacities of a virus need not run parallel in that hemagglutination may occur in the absence of infectivity (52). It seems possible that a virus could attach to receptors, however, and still lack other properties essential for its propagation, so that perhaps these findings do not rule out the importance of the hemaglutinative enzyme to pathogenicity (53).

The interesting work of Pearson and co-workers with a neurotropic virus (Theiler's) has shown that two amino acids, lysine and histadine, inhibit its reproduction. The virus, on the other hand, inhibits the incorporation of glucose into the building up of these amino acids in the cell. This constitutes beginning evidence of a metabolic influence as a possible virulence factor (54).

The secondary expressions of virulence, that is, the relative abilities of organisms to provoke more or less serious disease after they have become established in the host, may depend partly upon toxic activities recently described for viruses and rickettsiae (55). Suspensions of typhus fever rickettsias injected intravenously into mice cause a marked decrease in blood volume because of loss of plasma through altered lining cells of the vascular bed (56). Presumably there may be differences in the intoxicating abilities of various strains of the same agent, and these may determine in part the eventual pathogenicities of the organisms.

Synergistic Infections. A discussion of virulence would be incomplete without mention of combined infections wherein two infectious agents exert a pathogenic effect of which either agent acting alone would be completely incapable. There are several clear cut illustrations of this. A virus and a salmonella (*choleraesuis*) often occur together to cause hog cholera; distemper in dogs has been found to be primarily caused by a virus with *Brucella bronchiseptica* as a frequent secondary invader, and influenza virus, while itself causing a mild respiratory disease, may permit invasion by streptococci, staphylococci, pneumococci or *Hemophilus* with the production of bronchopneumonia. The last combination of circumstances is generally considered to account for the highly lethal pandemic of influenza and pneumonia which occurred in 1918. Although there has been no good opportunity since that time to study this situation in human beings, Shope (57) has established clear evidence for such an occurrence in influenza of swine, and Wilson and others (58) have shown that the granulocytopenia induced by the relatively harmless influenza virus in monkeys permits group C streptococci, also ordinarily inactive in this host, to cause serious disease in these animals.

It seems probable that in most, or perhaps all, of the cases described these effects depend upon a modification in the host by one agent which puts it at a disadvantage with respect to the second. The effect thus is not upon the virulence of the secondary agent. Analogously, the reverse effect may occur, i.e. one agent may so alter the host that for a time it becomes less susceptible to a second. This occurs with certain viruses and is called the interference phenomenon. A more detailed discussion of this effect is given in Chapter 10.

BIBLIOGRAPHY

1. Reed, L. J., and Muench, H. Am. J. Hyg., 27:493, 1938.
2. Topley, W. W. C., Greenwood, M., and Wilson, J. J. Path. & Bact., 24:523, 1931.
3. Coburn, A. F., and Pauli, R. H. J. Exper. Med., 73:551, 1941.
4a. Young, G. A., Zelle, M. R., and Lincoln, R. E. J. Infect. Dis., 79:233, 1946.
  b. Zelle, M. R., Lincoln, R. E., and Young, G. A. J. Infect. Dis., 79:247, 1946.
5. Goodpasture, E. W., and Anderson, K. Am. J. Path., 13:149, 1937.
6. Downs, C. M., Coriell, L. L., Eigelsbach, H. P., Plitt, K. F., Pinchot, G. B., and Owen, B. J. J. Immunol., 56:229, 1947.
7. Arkwright, J. A. J. Path. & Bact., 24:36, 1921.
8a. Thibault, P. Ann. Inst. Pasteur, 63:462, 1939.
  b. Cundiff, R. G., and Morgan, H. R. J. Immunol., 42:361, 1941.
9. Bloom, W. L., Watson, D. W., Cromartie, W. J., and Freed, M. J. Infect. Dis., 80:41, 1947.
10a. Morgan, H. R. J. Immunol., 41:161, 1941.
  b. Olitzki, L., Avinery, S., and Bendersky, J. J. Immunol., 41:361, 1941.
11a. Ward, H. K., and Enders, J. F. J. Exper. Med., 57:527, 1933.
  b. Robertson, O. H., and Van Sant, H. J. Immunol., 37:571, 1939.
12. Felton, L. D., and Bailey, G. H. J. Infect. Dis., 38:131, 1926.
13a. Wood, W. B., Jr., Smith, M. R., and Watson, B. J. Exper. Med., 84:387, 1946.
  b. ——— and Smith, M. R. J. Lab. & Clin. Med., 32:1406, 1947; J. Exper. Med., 90:85, 1949.
14. Kass, E. H., and Seastone, C. V. J. Exper. Med., 79:319, 1944.
15. Pike, R. M., and Mackenzie, G. M. J. Bact., 40:171, 1940.
16. Mackenzie, G. M., and Brewster, K. C. Federation Proc., Part 2, 6:429, 1947.
17. Maaløe, O. Acta path. et microbiol. Scandinav., 25:237, 414, 1948.
18a. Boivin, A. Ann. Inst. Pasteur, 67:377, 1941.
  b. Kauffmann, F. Ztschr. f. Hyg. u. Infektionskr., 117:778, 791, 1936.
  c. Batson, H. C., Landy, M., and Brown, M. J. Exper. Med., 91:231, 1950.
19. Webster, L. T., and Burn, C. J. Exper. Med., 46:887, 1927.
20. Schneider, H. A. J. Exper. Med., 84:305, 1946.
21. Blair, J. E. Bact. Rev., 3:97, 1939.
22. Gay, F. P., and Oram, F. J. Immunol., 25:501, 1933.
23. Macfarlane, M. G., and Knight, B. C. J. G. Biochem. J., 35:882, 1941.
24. ——— and MacLennan, J. D. Lancet, 2:328, 1945.
25a. Kass, E. H., Lichstein, H. C., and Waisbren, B. A. Proc. Soc. Exper. Biol. & Med., 58:172, 1945.
  b. Evans, D. G. J. Path. & Bact., 57:75, 1945.
26. DeKruif, P. H., and Bollman, J. L. J. Infect. Dis., 21:588, 1917.
27. Ørskov, J., Andersen, E. K., and Poulsen, J. V. Acta path. et microbiol. Scandinav., 21:181, 1944.
28. Duran-Reynals, F. J. Exper. Med., 50:327, 1929.

29a. ——— J. Exper. Med., 58:161, 1933.
  b. Schwabacher, H., Cunliffe, A. C., Williams, R. E. O., and Harper, G. J.   Brit. J.
       Exper. Path., 26:124, 1945.
  c. McClean, D.   J. Path. & Bact., 42:477, 1936.
30a. Chain, E., and Duthie, E. S.   Brit. J. Exper. Path., 21:324, 1940.
  b. Rogers, H. J.   Biochem. J., 42:633, 1948.
31a. Seastone, C. V.   J. Exper. Med., 77:21, 1943.
  b. McClean, D.   J. Path. & Bact., 53:13, 1941.
32a. Duran-Reynals, F.   Bact. Rev., 6:197, 1942.
  b. Blundell, G. P.   Yale J. Biol. & Med., 14:373, 1942.
33. Crowley, N.   J. Path. & Bact., 56:27, 1944.
34. Goodner, K.   J. Exper. Med., 58:153, 1933.
35. Meyer, K.   Physiol. Rev., 27:335, 1947.
36. Duran-Reynals, F.   Ann. Inst. Pasteur, 57:597, 1936.
37. Tillett, W. S., and Garner, R. L.   J. Exper. Med., 58:485, 1933.
38a. Neter, E., and Witebsky, E.   Proc. Soc. Exper. Biol. & Med., 34:549, 1936.
  b. Zinsser, H. H., and Williams, W. G.   J. Bact., 58:501, 1949.
39a. Milstone, H.   J. Immunol., 42:109, 1941.
  b. Christensen, L. R., and MacLeod, C. M.   J. Gen. Physiol., 28:559, 1945.
40a. MacCallum, W. G.   Monograph No. 10, Rockefeller Institute for Medical Research,
       1919.
  b. Goodpasture, E. W.   J.A.M.A., 72:724, 1919.
41. Tillett, W. S.   Bact. Rev., 2:161, 1938.
42a. Commission on Acute Respiratory Diseases.   J. Exper. Med., 85:441, 1947.
  b. Rammelkamp, C. H., and Dingle, J. H.   Ann. Rev. Microbiol., 2:279, 1948.
43. Todd, E. W.   J. Exper. Med., 89:309, 1949.
44a. Cartwright, G. E., Lauritsen, M. A., Jones, P. J., Merrill, I. M., and Wintrobe,
       M. M.   J. Clin. Investigation, 25:65, 81, 1946.
  b. Hemmeler, G.   L'Anémie Infectieuse, Basel, B. Schwabe A. G., 1946.
  c. Hahn, P. F., Bale, W. F., and Whipple, G. H.   Proc. Soc. Exper. Biol. & Med.,
       61:405, 1946.
45. Todd, E. W.   Brit. J. Exper. Path., 23:136, 1942.
46. Smith, W., and Hale, J. H.   Brit. J. Exper. Path., 25:101, 1944.
47. Hirst, G. K.   J. Exper. Med., 76:195, 1942.
48a. Francis, T. J., Jr.   J. Exper. Med., 85:1, 1947.
  b. Gottschalk, A., and Lind, P. E.   Brit. J. Exper. Path., 30:85, 1949.
49. Hanson, R. P., Upton, E., Brandly, C. A., and Winslow, N. S.   Proc. Soc. Exper.
       Biol. & Med., 70:283, 1949.
50. Hirst, G. K.   J. Exper. Med., 78:99, 1943.
51a. Stone, J. D.   Australian J. Exper. Biol. & Med. Sc., 26:287, 1948.
  b. Burnet, F. M.   Bull. Johns Hopkins Hosp., 88:119, 1951.
52a. Gard, S., von Magnus, P., and Svedmyr, A.   Proceedings IV International Congress
       of Microbiology, Copenhagen, 1947, p. 301.
  b. Friedewald, W. F., and Pickles, E. G.   J. Exper. Med., 79:301, 1944.
  c. Tamm, I., and Fluke, D. J.   J. Bact., 59:449, 1950.
53. Jawetz, E.   California Med., 69:435, 1948.
54a. Rafelson, M. E., Jr., Pearson, H. E., and Winzler, R. S.   Arch. Biochem., 29:69,
       1950.
  b. ——— Winzler, R. J., and Pearson, H. E.   J. Biol. Chem., 193:205, 1951.
55. Watson, D. W., and Brandly, C. A.   Ann. Rev. Microbiol., 3:195, 1949.
56. Clarke, D. H., and Fox, J. P.   J. Exper. Med., 88:25, 1948.
57. Shope, R. E.   J. Exper. Med., 74:41, 49, 1941.
58. Wilson, H. E., Saslaw, S., Doan, C. A., Woolpert, O. C., and Schwab, J. L.   J.
       Exper. Med., 85:199, 1947.

4

MECHANISMS OF ACQUIRED IMMUNITY

ANTIBODY AS A SPECIFIC IMMUNE MECHANISM

In Chapter 2 the mechanisms by which the normal body may protect itself against infection were described. Chapter 3 described the kinds of properties possessed by pathogenic agents, i.e. agents which are able by one or another means to circumvent these powers of native resistance. Our discussion now returns to the host, and the ultimate effort which it can make in attempting to rid itself of such pathogenic organisms and their products. This effort involves the acquisition of a resistance surpassing that of its native endowment and directed **specifically** against the particular organism which afflicts the host.

The most obvious alteration, and the one most studied, in the individual who has had an opportunity to develop specific immunity is the advent of **antibody**, readily found in the blood, but occurring also in the tissue fluids, sometimes in the cerebrospinal fluid, and in certain cells. As will later be discussed fully, antibody is composed of plasma globulin and has the property of combining specifically with the substance, **antigen**, which stimulated its production. As a result of this combination various spectacular things may occur. For example, the antigen molecules or particles may be clumped, or formed cells containing the antigen may undergo lysis, or such cells may be more readily ingested by phagocytes, or, if the antigen molecule is toxic, this toxicity may be neutralized. In short a number of things may happen to the antigen—or to an infectious agent of which the antigen is a component— which by their nature should redound to the advantage of the body endeavoring to overcome an infection or intoxication.

In some instances antibody has been adequately proved to be the essential agency through which resistance is effected. In many other cases its importance has so far been difficult either to prove or to disprove, and in at least one case, that of anthrax, it seems doubtful that conventionally defined antibody does take part in acquired immunity (see page 292). These latter two situations are not so unreasonable as they might seem. The formation of antibody is a general physiologic response of the body to any antigenic substance, whether this is entirely bland or extremely harmful to the tissues. The fact that antibodies are produced against the various antigens of a bacterial cell is in itself simply an expression of the same general response; it cannot be considered a priori evidence of resistance because we must know the answers to such questions as these: (a) Are there surface antigens with which any of these antibodies may unite so that they may promote clumping or phagocytosis? Many of the antibodies will have been produced against deeper lying antigens released from deteriorating bacteria in vivo, but these can have little if any effect upon intact viable microbes in which these antigens are not oriented to the outside world. (b) If we suppose that antibodies against properly situated bacterial components are present, we have still to contend with these facts: that antibody lysis is restricted to only a few species of bacteria, that agglutination in itself does not injure microorganisms, and that some agents are entirely indifferent to phagocytosis, persisting or even multiplying inside phagocytic cells. (c) Suppose the infectious agent, for example a virus, takes up an intracellular residence before there has been opportunity for ample exposure to antibodies. Would the presence of antibodies then be of actual importance to resistance?

These and other questions make it impossible to generalize the interpretation of the influence of antibodies upon immunity; evidence must be separately obtained for each etiologically different infection. It is a truism that nature is sparing with her designs and there are a few well-known instances in which antibody is of primary importance to resistance, but there exist many cases where such a relationship is not clear and in some in fact the evidence is against there being a relationship. Certain of these examples are discussed in the individual analyses of infections in Section Three.

This preliminary warning that antibody may not always be crucial to resistance does not deprecate its general importance in immunology since we must appreciate its nature and activities in order to assess its role in resistance in individual cases. Furthermore, the antibody response may be useful for diagnosis of infectious diseases regardless of its relationship to resistance. There are other important aspects of antibody activity entirely apart from infectious disease; for example, in relation to the hypersensitive states and in studies of human blood groups and transfusion reactions. Consequently this and several succeeding chapters will be concerned with various aspects of our present information concerning the origin, nature and activities of antibody.

With one outstanding exception for which there is clear evidence, the occurrence of antibody depends upon the prior application of a stimulus to the body in the form of an **antigen**. The clear exception is that of the blood group antibodies of human beings and some of the higher apes. In this case the occurrence of antibody is genetically determined without relationship to any process of immunization. There may be other similar exceptions in the existence of normal antibacterial antibodies as will be discussed in Chapter 6, but for these the evidence is not so defined, and other factors than genes may account for their existence.

Since antibody is especially marked by the specificity of its reactivity, and since this specificity complements the structure of the antigen which stimulates its production, a proper beginning to the understanding of antibody must begin with a description of antigenicity.

ANTIGENS AND ANTIGENIC SPECIFICITY

An antigen is a substance which upon introduction into the animal body causes a response, after a suitable interval, which is revealed by the ability of the body fluids (and sometimes the cells) to react with the provoking substance. This reactivity is most easily demonstrated in the serum of the animal and is of course dependent upon the presence of antibodies. These modified serum proteins combine with the antigen to produce any of a variety of visible reactions, depending upon the state of the antigen (i.e. whether in solution or part of a bacterial cell) and the technical procedure used. In certain circumstances the cells of the animal may become reactive with antigen independently of humoral antibody so that they are injured or killed by exposure to the antigen (see Delayed Hypersensitivity, page 251). In either case the antigen has induced a highly specific physiologic response in the body.

Although the immunologist often deals with antigens in relation to infectious organisms, they can be described much more clearly in the fundamental terms of isolated chemical substances of known composition.

Kinds of Chemical Substances Which Are Antigenic. It was believed for many years after the discovery of antigenic activity that only proteins could function as stimulants of antibody in the animal body. Indeed there came to be a traditional allusion to an exception proving this rule, the finding in 1907 by Ford and Abel (1) of the production of antibodies against a toxic glucoside isolated from the toadstool *Amanita phalloides*. Since then it has come to be appreciated that nonproteinaceous substances, particularly polysaccharides, may also act as inducers of antibody production, though certainly by far the greatest number of antigens are proteins.

General Properties of Molecules Which Cause Them to Be Antigenic. It is still difficult to say precisely what properties determine the ability of a molecule to act as an antigen. At one time, when only proteins were considered to be antigens, it was believed that **molecular weight** and the possession of an **aromatic radical** were the deciding factors (e.g. gelatine without tyrosine or phenylalanine in the molecule is not antigenic). The first of these properties still cannot be disregarded, for antigenicity generally begins at about the molecular weight level of 10,000. But smaller molecules may be antigenic and prophecy is difficult. In addition to size, it seems to be essential that there be a repetition on the surface of the molecule of certain immunologically critical groupings, described later as determinant groups. The antigenicity of smaller molecules which do not fulfill these criteria may depend upon their combination, following parenteral injection, with the proteins of the body (2); in this case they would not be truly antigenic but haptenic (see page 45), yet it is often nearly impossible to draw a sharp line at this technical difference. French workers (3) have reported that very small molecular substances may also function as antigens, e.g. ethyl alcohol and phloridzine, and that the subsequent reactions between these substances with antibodies are revealed by an increase in viscosity and a decrease in refractive index of the mixture, changes not seen with normal serum. These interesting findings require confirmation.

Molecular Properties Responsible for Antigenic Specificity. The concept of antigenic specificity received first precise direction in the work of Obermayer and Pick, who found that the antigenic properties of a protein molecule could be altered if certain simple chemical radicals, such as —NO, were introduced into it. The subsequent work of Landsteiner and his associates and others (4) brought the subject into sharp focus, and provides a brilliant example of the perspective and detail characterizing first rate scientific work. The specificity of antigens was investigated from the standpoint of the antibody response as well as cellular sensitization which is not always associated with demonstrable humoral antibody but which depends upon antigenic stimulation and shows analogous specificity (see Chapter 14). This work demonstrated systematically that simple chemical groupings may determine the antigenic properties of molecules, and provided the concept of the determinant group, i.e. the chemical group which endows the molecule with antigenic specificity. A summary of the more crucial experiments and conclusions follows.

1. DETERMINANT GROUPS. The importance of single chemical groupings to the antigenic properties of a molecule was demonstrated by diazotizing the arsenic-containing substance atoxyl, and coupling it with proteins. The atoxyl, which itself is not antigenic, becomes a determinant of antigenicity

$$ASO_3H_2 \qquad ASO_3H_2$$

$$\text{(ring, NH}_2\text{)} \qquad \text{(ring, N=N—Cl)} \qquad + \quad \text{protein} \longrightarrow \text{atoxyl-azo-protein}$$

ATOXYL   DIAZOTIZED
                ATOXYL

(p-amino-benzene-arsonic acid)

when inserted into the protein molecule, and the antibody produced by an animal injected with atoxyl-azo-protein is directed in combining-activity chiefly against the atoxyl itself. The new antigenic specificity which the protein has acquired by the insertion of atoxyl is revealed in the following ways.

(a) Antibodies against atoxyl-azo-protein A combine also with atoxyl-azo-proteins B and C. This constitutes proof that the atoxyl, and not the protein with which it has been combined, is chiefly responsible for the immunologic specificity of the antibody.

(b) Antibodies against atoxyl-azo-protein A will not react with protein A which has been diazotized with another acid group, such as sulfonilic acid.

(c) The antibodies against atoxyl-azo-protein may in the test tube be neutralized or inhibited by **atoxyl itself,** so that no free antibody remains to react with the atoxyl-azo-protein.

2. IMPORTANCE OF ACID RADICALS IN THE DETERMINANT GROUP. It was learned further from the antigenic system described that an even simpler portion of the atoxyl group is of central importance to immunologic specificity. Arsenic acid ($H_3As O_4$), which represents only a portion of the atoxyl group, can also neutralize the antibody against atoxyl-azo-protein. Thus, the antigenic specificity of atoxyl resides largely in this acid radical.

As the result of many studies of this kind, using a variety of diazotized aromatic acids and, later, peptides composed of two or three amino acids (4a), it was learned that the specificity of antigens is determined in large part by the **acid radical.** In naturally occurring protein antigens it is probable that the **amino acids** are the chief determinants of specificity.

3. POSITION OF SUBSTITUENTS IN THE DETERMINANT GROUP. An aromatic determinant group which lacks an acid radical is less sharply specific than one with such a constituent group. In determinant groups not containing acid radicals the **position** of substituents in the ring becomes more important than their **nature.** An instance is the following:

An antibody directed against

Cl

NH$_2$

(*p*-chloro-aniline)

reacts equally well with any of the following groups:

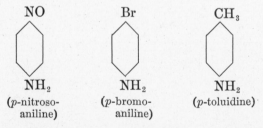

NO   Br   CH$_3$

NH$_2$ NH$_2$ NH$_2$

(*p*-nitroso-   (*p*-bromo-   (*p*-toluidine)
aniline)   aniline)

A glance reveals that these molecules differ in the para substituent. However, because the different radicals have identical **positions** in the ring, the antibody directed against any one determinant is equally active in reacting with the others. The **nature** of the group is thus of minor importance to specificity. On the other hand, if any of these radicals were changed to the ortho or meta **position** the specificity of the group would become altered.

The **position** of a double bond in such a determinant group may also affect specificity.

4. SPATIAL CONFIGURATION IN THE DETERMINANT GROUP. Dextro and levo isomers of a determinant group have different antigenic specificities. Landsteiner and van der Scheer (4a) converted tartaric acid isomers to tartranilic acids; antibodies against these revealed the sharp specificity of the dextro and levo forms, but antibody against either reacted fairly well with the meso form. Antibody against the meso acid reacted only homologously however. Similar specificities have been found with the *cis* and *trans* forms of various substances. In all these cases the difference determining specificity is a difference in position of two groups with respect to a carbon atom, such as:

$$H - C - OH \text{ and } OH - C - H.$$

It is apparent then that the antigenic specificities of proteins may be altered by introducing simple groups into the molecule, by diazotization, as well as by halogenation, by direct reaction, and by other means. In these determinant groups, acid radicals have the greatest influence upon specificity, while the position of radicals in the group, the position of double bond, and spatial configuration are of subsidiary but demonstrable importance also. When this information is applied to the explanation of antigenic specificity in natural proteins, which do not possess groups of the kind introduced experimentally, it may be deduced that the variety and arrangement of amino acids on the surface of the molecule act as the determinant groups. The serum proteins of such closely related species of animals as the horse and ox are serologically distinguishable.

The question arises as to how many different determinants a single protein molecule may possess, and consequently how many antibodies of different specificity it can engender. Actually, one chemically homogeneous antigen may induce several antibodies of somewhat differing specificities. Thus, in the case of an antiserum to arsanil-azo-sheep serum globulin, all of the antibody is precipitated by the complete antigen, but a portion of the total antibodies may be precipitated separately by the arsanil group joined to a foreign protein and another portion by the sheep globulin alone. Obviously then any complex antigenic molecule, though it is a single chemical substance, may be inhomogeneous antigenically because it possesses more than one kind of determinant group. The major or **dominant** determinant group characterizes the molecule—in the instance just given this is the arsanil group itself. But the attached sheep globulin also possesses subdeterminants as does the region of combination between the two components (5).

Haptens. The determinant groups are not in themselves capable of acting as antigens in the animal body. Landsteiner introduced the term hapten to denote a substance which, itself incapable of stimulating antibody formation, would, when combined with a suitable carrier molecule, act as a determinant of antigenic specificity. The carrier substance is thus responsible for the fact of antibody production, while the hapten imparts specificity to the antibody. The resultant antibody will now combine with the hapten alone, so that this substance which fails to induce antibody formation is able to react with the antibody already formed in response to the complete antigen. In the case of some haptens the combination with antibody may result in visible precipitation; other simpler substances may merely unite with antibody without showing any visible evidence of the combination. The evidence for reaction in this case is the fact that no antibody remains to precipitate with the complete antigen in which the hapten is a determinant. This type of test is called an inhibition reaction, i.e. the simple hapten by combining with the antibody inhibits its subsequent reaction with complete antigen. Such a union of simple haptens with antibody may occur in vivo as well as in the test tube, thus giving rise to hypersensitive reactions in allergic animals (6).

It should be pointed out that the distinction between complete antigens and haptens is not always sharp. Certain very simple chemical substances, for example picryl chloride, may act as antigens when injected alone into the tissues. It has been shown (2) that this and other substances attain antigenicity in vivo through their ready ability to combine spontaneously with proteins. The inoculated subject provides the carrier molecule for such simple chemical groups. It may thus be difficult, if not impossible, to be certain in some cases whether a substance is antigenic per se, or only as the result of its combination with proteins in vivo.

In some instances it appears to be necessary only that the hapten be adsorbed to a protein carrier; this seems to be the case with certain polysaccharides when mixed with a protein obtained from the Shiga dysentery bacillus (7), and perhaps also with lipids when mixed with normal serum (see page 47). The carrier proteins in this case are called schleppers, i.e. substances which serve solely to pull the hapten along to the antibody-producing cells (8).

Carbohydrates as Antigens. Although the large majority of antigenic substances are proteins, carbohydrates and lipids have been studied extensively in this connection also. The former are of especial interest as constituents of many bacterial cells. Dochez and Avery (9) in 1917 discovered the presence of a polysaccharide in the capsule of virulent pneumococci which precipitated with anti-pneumococcal serum, and Zinsser and Parker (10) at about the same time found evidence of similar nonproteinaceous residue antigens in staphylococci, pneumococci, and in influenza, typhoid and tubercle bacilli. Precise information concerning the antigenic properties of such polysaccharides began with their isolation by Avery and Heidelberger (11) from pneumococcal capsules. Some of these specific soluble substances (SSS), which determine antigenic types among the pneumococci, may be so highly purified as to react with antisera when diluted several million times. The constituent units of certain of these polysaccharides (types I, II, III and VIII) are now known.

For some years it was believed that these substances were haptens capable only of reacting with antibody induced by the capsule of the intact bacterial cell. Later, however, some were obtained without drastic chemical manipulation (12) and it has been amply demonstrated that when these are injected by certain routes (intracutaneously or subcutaneously) into human beings or mice they may markedly stimulate the production of antibody (13). This does not occur in the rabbit however, possibly because antigenicity of the polysaccharide may depend upon its adsorption to tissue protein, and this does not take place in the rabbit. This possibility is suggested by Morgan's (7c) observations of the adsorption, with resultant antigenicity, of various polysaccharides to a protein obtained from the Shiga dysentery bacillus. An alternative possibility to explain the failure of antigenicity in the rabbit is the presence of tissue enzyme which inactivates pneumococcal polysaccharide (13c, 13d).

As for the chemical structure of antigenic polysaccharides certain of the pneumococcal capsular substances are best known. The type III substance is made up of units of aldobionic acid united by glucoside linkages. (Aldobionic or cellobiuronic acid consists of a molecule of glucose and one of glucuronic acid, the latter derived from glucose by oxidation of the terminal —CH_2OH to —COOH. The glucoside link (—O—) uniting the aldobionic acid units leaves the acid radical free.) It has been suggested (14) that there are perhaps 180 aldobionic acid molecules so linked to make up a polysaccharide of minimum molecular weight 62,000. The type VIII polysaccharide is composed of similar structural units; its molecular weight is estimated as 140,000. Goebel (15a) has been able to synthesize a substance containing glucuronic acid which has the antigenic properties of type II pneumococcal polysaccharide; antibodies to it protect mice against large doses of virulent type II organisms.

In view of what is known concerning the importance of acid radicals to antigenic specificity, it is interesting to note the presence of free acid groups in these pneumococcal carbohydrates. Other, but not all, polysaccharides of bacterial and plant origin also contain uronic acids of which the carboxyl groups are free. It is easy to see that serologic cross reactivity should occur among polysaccharides composed of similar units. In each case however there is a higher degree of reactivity of antibody with its homologous substance and this is probably based on differences in the spacing of the groups (15b).

Lipids as Antigens. The antigenic activity of lipoidal substances per se is very questionable. It seems apparent that even the lipids of higher molecular weight, such as lecithin and cholesterol, will not function as antigens in vivo when injected alone. It is possible, though the evidence is still controversial, that if these substances are mixed with normal serum they may then function as determinant groups (16).

Haptens of lipoidal character may occur in a variety of animal and plant cells. The best known example is the Forssman antigen (see page 445), a substance which is distributed in biologic strata ranging from bacteria to man. This hapten is extractable from tissues with alcohol or ether, and for some time it was regarded as a straightforward lipid. Later chemical studies however indicated that a polysaccharide is present in the lipoidal extract, and this may have a good deal to do with its haptenic endowment (4a, p. 446).

In certain gram-negative bacteria, including many of the salmonellas, Boivin (17) found antigenic complexes extractable by trichloracetic acid. These were subsequently revealed to be composed of polysaccharide, protein and lipid. The first two of these components are antigenic, but the lipid is not; if this is chemically removed from the complex the residuum continues to function antigenically as did the original complex.

Some years ago Rivers and his co-workers (18) made the interesting observation that monkeys repeatedly injected with rabbit brain eventually developed a demyelinating encephalomyelitis, presumably upon the immunologic basis that the inoculated animal eventually forms antibodies directed against nervous tissue, and that these then react with its own brain substance (19). This experiment has since been confirmed repeatedly in other species of animals, and with homologous brain tissue (20). The antigen involved appears to reside in the myelin sheath, which is made up largely of cerebroside, but attempts to isolate the antigen have so far not been conclusive, since a protein fraction as well as extracts rich in lipids have induced paralysis and identical pathologic alterations in inoculated animals (21).

It is thus difficult to arrive now at a final assessment of the antigenic properties of lipids. It may be safely assumed that they are not complete antigens in any case, but it is possible that they can act as haptens, and the information presently available suggests this. Heidelberger believes that the vague status of lipids as antigens may be explained by the lack of repetition of structural units in lipoidal molecules (22); the importance of this characteristic to antigenicity has been mentioned before (see Doerr [4d], pp. 61-62, and Landsteiner [4a]).

General Discussion. The foregoing discussion has pointed out those properties which determine whether a substance will function as an antigen and, more definitely, the chemical features of a molecule which are of importance in determining its specificity as an antigen.

It is apparent that antigenic specificity, influenced as it is by minor structural differences between molecules, is of a high order. Paradoxically however a wide range of cross reactivity is possible between diverse antigens and antibodies because of similarities in chemical groups, or simply in the positions of groups within molecules. An antibody will react to the fullest with the antigen which has incited its formation (the **homologous** antigen) and as we have seen this specificity may depend only upon a particular feature of spatial configuration. But the same antibody will cross react with other antigens (**heterologous** antigens) which have a similar, but not identical, arrangement of reactive groups. Such cross reactions are less extensive than the homologous reaction, to a degree depending upon the identity of the two antigens. The combination of high specificity along with cross reactivity imparts to serologic reactions a good deal of flexibility, as will be pointed out in appropriate connotations later in the book, especially in connection with the specific antigenic properties associated with animal organs, and with the conception of autoantibody formation. An inkling of the latter may be inferred from the description already given of the investigations dealing with antibodies to brain tissue. The inoculation into an animal of brain substance from another species provides an antigen sufficiently distinct chemically from the recipient's own nervous tissue to provoke the formation of antibodies; but once formed the latter may cross react with the animal's own nerve substance because of the **similarities** in antigenic properties. This possibility is not a proved one, but available evidence is strongly suggestive.

It is important to gain a clear notion of the fact that the term "antigen" denotes a single chemical substance. All of the preceding discussion has been concerned with molecular rather than biologic species. There is an unfortunate tendency however, in dealing with bacterial and other vaccines, to refer to these also as antigens in the sense of being single chemical substances. Bacterial and other cells, and even many viruses, are composed of a variety of substances, some of which are antigenic. Of the antigens in a microorganism, certain ones may be pertinent to the responses of acquired resistance in an infected host; the remainder may be entirely unrelated to immunity. It is obviously important then to look upon a microbe as a bag of distinct antigens, for only with this viewpoint can immunologic host-parasite relations be analyzed and understood.

ANTIBODIES

Antibody is defined as a humoral globulin produced by the body in response to an antigen, and capable of reacting with the antigen in some observable way. This definition is amplified considerably in succeeding paragraphs.

Nature of Antibody. Antibody is found in the blood and lymph, and under some conditions in the cerebrospinal fluid. Ordinarily its presence signifies a previous antigenic stimulus but, as mentioned before, there is at least one instance where this sequence is lacking. This is in the case of the iso-antibodies of the major human blood groups; their occurrence is governed wholly by genetic factors. There may be other examples also (see page 81). Whatever the reason for the occurrence of antibodies, whether stimulated by specific antigens or determined by genes, they have the common feature of appearing in the **globulin** portion of plasma and lymph. Indeed, they are themselves globulin molecules, as has been proved by evidence gathered during just the past few years.

1. The composition of plasma and serum. When blood is withdrawn from the body it clots, and the fluid which exudes is called **serum**. This con-

tains, among other solutes, about 7 per cent of proteins. If clotting is prevented by the addition of an anticoagulant the fluid portion after removal of cells is called **plasma,** and it contains all the proteins of the serum plus those proteins (thrombin and fibrinogen) which take part in the mechanics of clot formation. In terms of protein concentration there is actually little difference between plasma and serum, because the clot-forming substances represent a minor portion of the total blood proteins. So far as the presence of antibody is concerned there is no difference between the two; clot formation does not involve the protein which functions as antibody.

For about a century it has been known that when plasma is subjected to various chemical and physical manipulations, including precipitation by salts or dialysis against distilled water, the protein readily separates into two major fractions, **albumin and globulin.** Albumin is homogeneous in its behavior toward such procedures, but globulin divides further into a euglobulin and a pseudoglobulin portion, the latter more closely approaching albumin in its properties of solubility in salt-free medium and its precipitability by salts. The ratio of albumin to total globulins in the serum is about 1.5, or 2 to 1. Albumin molecules are smaller than globulin, having a molecular weight of 69,000. In most animal species the normal globulins range in molecular weight between 150,000 and 200,000.

A great deal of practical knowledge about plasma proteins has been gained during the past few years (23). The several lines of development which have permitted more precise chemical studies of proteins have been applied also to investigations of antibody, and it may be of some interest to sketch briefly the methods which have been responsible for these advances.

2. Analysis of proteins in the ultracentrifuge. Centrifuges which attain extremely high speeds (rotational speeds of 60,000 revolutions per minute and better) carry the sedimentation of particles far beyond the ordinary conception gained from the commonly used centrifuges. Ultracentrifuges throw down larger molecules from solution. The speed of sedimentation of molecules depends chiefly upon their shape and weight, though other factors also influence this. If therefore a solution containing a mixture of molecules is centrifuged, the molecules of one kind will sediment at a characteristic velocity. This will result in the separation of the different kinds of molecules, each sedimenting in a homogeneous front, or boundary. By the use of an ingenious container which permits light to traverse the centrifuging fluid, photographs may be made of these molecular boundaries at intervals during the process of sedimentation. Such investigations have permitted antibodies to be characterized precisely on the basis of their sedimentation characteristics, and to be compared with normal serum proteins (24).

3. Analysis of proteins in the Tiselius electrophoresis cell. The electrophoresis cell consists of a U tube with a positive electrode on one side and a negative electrode on the other. A solution of electrolyte fills the tube between. Charge-bearing particles placed in such a tube may be observed for direction of movement under the influence of an electric current. Upon

this simple basis has evolved one of the most useful procedures currently available for the study of proteins and other molecules in single or mixed solutions. Some years ago Tiselius in Sweden (25) developed this kind of apparatus to a high degree of usefulness. The U tube was divided into four sections which open one into the other while the apparatus is in use, but which may be sealed off by sliding the segments upon each other, as illustrated in Figure 10. This permits the isolation of individual components from a mixed solution of molecules after appropriate separation has been effected by the following procedure.

If a solution of proteins is placed in the bottom section, and buffer is layered over it, then the passage of current will cause the migration of each constituent at a characteristic velocity dependent upon the charge and the molecular volume of the protein at the particular pH, temperature and salt concentration employed. The direction of migration will depend upon the pH at which the solution has been buffered; toward the anode on the alkaline side of the iso-electric point and toward the cathode on the acid side. Eventually the various proteins will form individual boundaries, the fastest moving molecules progressing into the buffer, the next fastest into the protein ahead of it, and so on, each protein forming a moving front whose position is determined by the speed with which that protein moves.

Now, with colorless proteins these boundaries cannot of course be seen directly. In order that they may be visualized the U tube is constructed of optical glass, and either of two optical systems is commonly employed. Both depend upon the fact that light passed through the cell will be differently refracted by the protein than by the buffer. The degree of refraction will depend upon the concentration of the protein through which the light passes. One optical system, the Lamm scale method, makes use of a millimeter scale placed behind the cell, and photographed through it. The refraction of light caused by the protein at its boundary produces a distortion in the scale markings, and this is translated to show relative boundary positions as well as protein concentrations. In the Toepler schlieren method a sharp-edged scanning plate is moved through the beam emerging from the cell. This obliterates the refracted light from each boundary successively, leaving a blank space on the photographic plate. By synchronously moving the film horizontally as the schlieren plate scans the cell vertically, one obtains a peak, the height and extent of which depends upon the degree of refraction, i.e. the concentration of the particular protein. With both methods one can get photographic records of the relative positions of boundaries as well as the relative concentrations of each protein in a mixed solution. Or a single homogeneous protein may be characterized by its migration rate under specified conditions.

Since the migration of individual constituents in a mixture can be visualized at will it is possible to isolate single components by manipulating the cell segments pictured in Figure 10 (see Kabat and Mayer [26] for details).

The electrophoresis apparatus then permits the study of solutions of proteins in these ways:

(*a*) Characterization on the basis of mobility.

(*b*) Determination of relative concentrations on the basis of the degree of refraction of light.

(*c*) Isolation of individual components by manipulation of the cell sections.

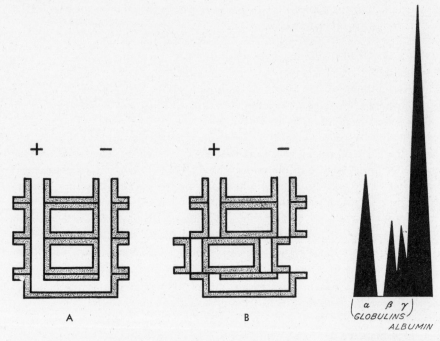

Fig. 10. A, segments of Tiselius cell aligned. B, a segment pushed to one side, closing off the individual compartments.

Fig. 11. Diagrammatic representation of the electrophoretic pattern of normal rabbit serum.

An illustration of the application of this method to normal serum is shown in Figure 11. The record was obtained by the schlieren plate method, each boundary appearing here as a peak, and the area under each peak indicating the concentration of that component. As is true of normal sera generally four protein components are seen at the pH and ionic concentration employed. The fastest moving of these is albumin. Trailing this are three types of globulin molecules; the alpha is the fastest of these, then the beta, and last the gamma.

Physicochemical Characterization of Purified Antibody. It is possible to isolate antibodies from other plasma constituents for study by the methods just described. If antibody is permitted to react with antigen and the resultant aggregate is washed free of residual serum, one may then by appropriate means cause a shift in the reaction equilibrium so that free antibody appears in solution. High concentrations of sodium chloride may effect this result, and barium hydroxide, barium chloride, and hydrochloric acid have also been used (27). By treating toxin-antitoxin floccules with trypsin, and following this with ammonium sulfate precipitations, Northrop (28) succeeded in obtaining crystalline diphtheria antitoxin.

Employing the concentrated salt method Heidelberger and co-workers (29) have obtained solutions of serum protein consisting entirely of antibody. When such preparations are submitted to ultracentrifugal and electrophoretic analysis they are found to be globulin. This is most frequently of gamma type, but the specific globulin nature may vary according to the species of animal vaccinated, the antigen employed, the route of administration of antigen, and the duration of the vaccination period, as detailed more fully in Chapter 5.

These lines of evidence, as well as earlier information derived from fractional precipitation methods, point to the conclusion that antibody is plasma globulin, so altered as to react specifically with antigen. As said before, it is most often the case that this is gamma globulin, and in all respects except for its specific reactive ability it appears to be the same as normal gamma globulin.*

* There is some recent evidence (Jones, W. G., Pollard, A. L., and Holtman, D. F. J. Bact., 58:307, 1949) that rabbit antibrucellae sera may contain two amino acids with phenolic groups not found in normal serum.

BIBLIOGRAPHY

1a. Abel, J., and Ford, W. W.   J. Biol. Chem., 2:273, 1907.
  b. Ford, W. W.   J. Infect. Dis., 4:541, 1907.
2a. Landsteiner, K., and Jacobs, J.   J. Exper. Med., 61:643, 1935.
  b. Rosenthal, S. R.   J. Immunol., 34:251, 1938.
  c. Gell, P. G. H., Harington, C. R., and Rivers, R. P.   Brit. J. Exper. Path., 27:267, 1946.
  d. ——— Harington, C. R., and Michel, R.   Brit. J. Exper. Path., 29:578, 1948.
3. Loiseleur, J., and Levy, M.   Ann. Inst. Pasteur, 73:116, 1947.
4a. Landsteiner, K.   The Specificity of Serological Reactions, 2nd ed., Cambridge, Mass., Harvard University Press, 1945.
  b. Marrack, J. R.   The Chemistry of Antigens and Antibodies, London, His Majesty's Stationery Office, 1938.
  c. Wells, H. G.   The Chemical Aspects of Immunity, New York, The Chemical Catalog Co., 1929.
  d. Doerr, R.   Die Immunitätsforschung, Vienna, Springer Verlag, 1948, Band III and IV.
5a. Hooker, S. B.   J. Allergy, 8:113, 1937.
  b. Haurowitz, F.   J. Immunol., 43:331, 1942.
6. Tomcsik, J., and Kurotchkin, T.   J. Exper. Med., 47:379, 1928.
7a. Boivin, A., and Mesrobeanu, L.   Compt. rend. Soc. de biol., 112:76, 1933.
  b. Raistick, H., and Topley, W. W. C.   Brit. J. Exper. Path., 15:113, 1934.
  c. Morgan, W. T. J., and Partridge, S. M.   Biochem. J., 35:1140, 1941.
8a. Sachs, H.   Zentralbl. f. Bakt., 104:128, 1927.
  b. Lewis, J. H.   J. Infect. Dis., 57:94, 1935.
9. Dochez, A. R., and Avery, O. T.   J. Exper. Med., 26:477, 1917.
10. Zinsser, H., and Parker, J. T.   J. Exper. Med., 37:275, 1923
11. Avery, O. T., and Heidelberger, M.   J. Exper. Med., 38:81, 1923; 42:367, 1925.

12. Pappenheimer, A. M., Jr., and Enders, J. F. Proc. Soc. Exper. Biol. & Med., 31:37, 1933-34.
13a. Francis, T., Jr., and Tillett, W. S. J. Exper. Med., 52:573, 1930.
  b. Mac Leod, C. M., Hodges, R. G., Heidelberger, M., and Bernhard, W. G. J. Exper. Med., 82:445, 1945.
  c. Harley, D. J. Path. & Bact., 41:491, 1935.
  d. Dubos, R. J., and MacLeod, C. M. J. Exper. Med., 67:791, 1938.
14. Heidelberger, M., Kabat, E. A., and Mayer, M. J. Exper. Med., 75:35, 1942.
15a. Goebel, W. F. Science, 91:20, 1940.
  b. Burger, M. Bacterial Polysaccharides, Springfield, Ill., Charles C Thomas, 1950.
16. Sachs, H., and Klopstock, A. Biochem. Ztschr., 159:491, 1925.
17. Boivin, A., and Mesrobeanu, L. Compt. rend. Soc. de biol., 113:490, 1933; 114:302, 307, 1933.
18a. Rivers, T. M., Sprunt, D. H., and Berry, G. P. J. Exper. Med., 58:39, 1933.
  b. ———— and Schwentker, F. F. J. Exper. Med., 61:689, 1935.
19. Witebsky, E., and Steinfeld, J. Ztschr. f. Immunitätsforsch. u. exper. Therap., 58:271, 1928.
20. Kabat, E. A., Wolf, A., and Bezer, A. E. J. Exper. Med., 89:395, 1949.
21. Koprowski, H., and Jervis, G. A. Proc. Soc. Exper. Biol. & Med., 69:472, 1948.
22. Heidelberger, M. J. Mt. Sinai Hosp., 9:893, 1943.
23. Cohn, E. J. Am. Scientist, 33:61, 1945.
24a. Pedersen, K. O. Ultracentrifugal Studies on Serum and Serum Fractions, Uppsala, Sweden, Almqvist and Wiksells Boktryckeri AB., 1945 (in English).
  b. Svedberg, T., and Pedersen, K. O. The Ultracentrifuge, Oxford, Clarendon Press, 1940.
25. Tiselius, A. Tr. Faraday, Soc., 33:524, 1937.
26. Kabat, E. A., and Mayer, M. M. Experimental Immunochemistry, Springfield, Ill., Charles C Thomas, 1948, Chapter 25.
27a. Felton, L. D., and Bailey, G. H. J. Infect. Dis., 38:131, 1926.
  b. Haurowitz, F., and Tekman, S. Nature, London, 157:335, 1946.
  c. Lee, K-H., and Wu, H. Proc. Soc. Exper. Biol. & Med., 43:65, 1940.
  d. Chow, B. F., and Wu, H. Science, 84:316, 1936.
28. Northrop, J. H. J. Gen. Physiol., 25:465, 1942.
29a. Heidelberger, M., and Kendall, F. E. J. Exper. Med., 64:161, 1936.
  b. ———— and Kabat, E. A. J. Exper. Med., 67:181, 1938.

5

MECHANISMS OF ACQUIRED IMMUNITY

THE ORIGIN AND NATURE OF ANTIBODY GLOBULIN

The question of antibody origin might logically be expected to be related to that of the origin of the normal plasma globulins. The subject of the plasma proteins in relation to metabolism, to shock and to burns has been a very live one for some years, and especially during the recent war years. But one finds in the literature of physiology that so far as site and mode of manufacture of proteins are concerned, discussions are largely concerned with the albumin. This no doubt is because the plasma albumin shows considerably more variation under pathologic circumstances than does globulin, in addition to being quantitatively the largest protein constituent of plasma. It has thus remained largely for investigators interested in immunity to try to trace the derivation of globulin. This is a difficult matter at best and some of the efforts have been marked more by zeal than precision. The large literature on this question has not yet provided final answers, but some highly suggestive ones have sifted out of the accumulation of many years of study. The cells implicated by current evidence as possibly taking part in the synthesis of globulin and antibody are: (1) cells of the reticulo-endothelial system, (2) lymphocytes, and (3) plasma cells. These possibilities are not necessarily mutually exclusive, as will be seen.

1. Reticulo-endothelial system (RES) as producer of antibody. The bulk of investigations has been concerned with reticulo-endothelial cells. They came very naturally to the minds of immunologists because of the well-known propensity of these cells for taking up foreign substances introduced into the body. Furthermore, the reticulo-endothelial cells may retain some antigenic materials for months during a process of slow breakdown (1).

There have been various approaches to the question of the relationship of reticulo-endothelial cells to antibody formation. During the early years in the development of methods of tissue culture Carrel and Ingebrigsten (2) attempted to demonstrate the production of antibody to goat erythrocytes in cultures of guinea pig bone marrow and lymph node. Their results were positive, but later attempts to confirm them have been equivocal (3). Other workers however have had more regular success by injecting antigens into animals in advance and subsequently removing appropriate tissues for culture (4). It has been suggested that reticulo-endothelial cells may lose their ability to take up antigens under the conditions of growth in vitro (5), or perhaps some preliminary process must occur in the body before cells can produce antibodies in vitro. Not long ago Landsteiner and Parker (6) reported observations also made with tissue cultures, but with a different experimental rationale. They serially cultured chick embryo muscle in rabbit plasma 35 times so that any of the plasma proteins originally present with the explanted cells were diluted beyond recognition. They then found by serologic methods that chick globulin continued to appear in the culture as a product of the metabolism of the growing fibroblasts, and related this to the activity of the reticulo-endothelial system through the observation (7) that fibroblasts and macrophages may each change to the other. It should be noted that this work deals with the formation of normal globulin rather than antibody, but as mentioned before these probably have a common origin.

Sabin (8) has considered the question by cytologic methods and describes the shedding of surface cytoplasmic layers by macrophages; she suggests that this substance may be globulin or antibody. However, lymphocytes and plasma cells also go through this process (9) and it is quite possible that these also shed antibodies.

A great deal of the attention devoted to RES cells has been concerned with organs rather than with individual cell types; the results consequently are often open to more than one interpretation. Many workers have been preoccupied with the spleen as an organ rich in reticulo-endothelial elements. This has been either extirpated or blockaded with colloidal substances in an effort to demonstrate the effect of its elimination upon antibody formation, and on the other hand more positive information has been sought by extracting it and evaluating the antibody content of its juices. The consensus of conclusions from many such experiments points to this organ, in the mammal at least, as an important depot for the formation of antibody. Obviously however the presence in the spleen of cellular types in addition to those comprising the RES—for example, large aggregations of lymphocytes and, under certain circumstances, of plasma cells—complicates an exact appraisal from the cellular standpoint.

Methods of study based on the destruction of reticulo-endothelium generally have also been employed. These procedures have included the use of x-rays, radium, toluene, mustard gas and other agents. These have for the most part effectively interfered with antibody production but it seems unlikely that the toxic activities of these agents are limited to the cells of the RES (10).

Despite these difficulties the sum of the evidence available indicates that the cells of the reticulo-endothelium are involved in the manufacture of antibodies.

2. Lymphocytes as producers of antibody. It has long been known that during the course of acute infections and intoxications there occurs an enlargement of the spleen referred to as acute splenic tumor. This organic alteration occurs simultaneously with immunologic responses to the infectious agent or its products, and Rich (11) has questioned by experiment whether

the splenic alteration is not in fact entirely a reflection of the antigenic rather than the pathogenic properties of the etiologic agent. This was found to be the case; acute splenic tumor can be induced with noninfectious antigenic substances. The cells responsible for the hypertrophy were found in the malpighian corpuscles and pulp, the hypertrophy arising from the enlargement as well as the mitosis of nonphagocytic cells which were judged, from their appearance and type of locomotion, to be lymphocytes. The coincidence of this anatomic reaction with the formation of antibodies suggested that the two events might possibly be related.

Other evidence also has implicated lymphoid tissues in antibody formation. McMaster (12a, 12b) and Burnet (12c) have presented evidence that lymph nodes draining the area of antigen injections may be concerned in the formation of agglutinins and of antiviral antibodies, and similar indications have been obtained for antitoxins (13). Earlier work (14) in which lymphoid tissue was damaged by x-irradiation revealed a marked interference with antibody formation. But other cells, notably those of the reticulo-endothelial system, cannot be excluded as participants in the results observed in all such experiments.

More recently the question has been approached in a more direct way through a study of the components of the efferent lymph flowing from nodes which drain the site of injection of antigens. Ehrich and Harris (15) investigated the popliteal lymph nodes of rabbits subsequent to the injection of antigens into the foot-pad. It was found that the efferent lymph collected by cannulation contains antibody before this appears in the blood. Furthermore, when the lymphocytes were separated from the lymph itself, the cells were found to contain antibody in concentrations five to seven times higher than the fluid, early after the injection of antigen. Later the concentrations became equalized as the cells gave up more to the fluid.

As an independent supplement to these observations there has developed simultaneously a series of studies of the function of certain endocrine secretions in the formation of normal plasma globulin, and of antibody. Fox and Whitehead (16) first reported increased antibody formation in animals receiving extracts of the adrenal cortex. Somewhat later evidence was submitted that gamma globulin is a constituent of normal lymphocytes, as indicated by electrophoretic studies (17). As a next step, Dougherty and White (18) observed that adrenocortical hormone, or pituitary adrenotrophic hormone, causes dissolution of lymphocytes with the release of gamma globulin. The final obvious step, the demonstration that **altered** gamma globulin, i.e. antibody, is also released in greater quantities under the influence of secretions of the adrenal cortex (*cf.* Fox and Whitehead [16]) was subsequently reported by these same workers (19).

We have here then a chain of circumstantial evidence which seems airtight: that lymphocytes contain gamma globulin, that this is released through the dissolution of the cells under the influence of adrenocortical hormones, and that animals undergoing vaccination produce more than usual amounts of antibody when treated with such hormones. Supplementing this chain of evidence is the well-known description of the alarm reaction and adaptation syndrome of Selye (20). Many kinds of injury result in a characteristic type of bodily response consisting of first, the release of epinephrine from the adrenal medulla; this influences the pituitary to release adrenotrophic hormone, which in turn causes the adrenal cortex to secrete its hormones. Subsequent to this there occurs shedding of cytoplasm and necrosis of lymphocytes and plasma cells in the thymus, lymph nodes, spleen and gastrointestinal tract. Other tissue changes take place also. The possible relationship of this syndrome to what has just been described when a foreign **antigenic substance** is the insulting agent to the tissues is highly suggestive indeed. It must be noted however that other cells aside from lymphocytes undergo dissolution as part of the alarm reaction, e.g. plasma cells, and Selye's syndrome need not necessarily be interpreted in relation to the lymphocytes as antibody producers.

It would seem that this extensive front of evidence including histologic, physiologic and serologic studies, should leave nothing to be desired in the final appraisal of the role of lymphocytes in antibody production. This does not seem to be the case however, for the more important observations have recently been questioned, including the relationship of lymphocytes to either normal globulin or antibody (21) as well as the role of adrenal cortical hormone in releasing globulin and antibody into the circulation (22). In the latter case in fact there is now strong evidence that antibody formation may be inhibited rather than increased in quantity, as will be described in more detail later in this chapter. Some of this reversal of opinion seems especially cogent because it comes from investigators who originally supplied experimental conclusions supporting the lymphocyte's activities in producing antibody.

At present therefore there is not much basis for taking the antibody-forming function of lymphocytes too seriously, though the possibility cannot yet be excluded. Some of the studies which have indicated its importance in this regard have simultaneously brought to the fore another cell, the plasma cell, as a strong contender for this role. This is the last of the definitive cell types to be seriously considered as antibody producer.

3. Plasma cells in antibody production. In recent years observations in patients and animals have indicated that plasma cells may be concerned in the production of normal globulin and antibody. Bing (23) and others since have observed in patients with hyperglobulinemia due to various causes the presence of increased numbers of plasma cells in the tissues. In rabbits, Kolouch (24) reported an increase of plasma cells in the bone marrow paralleling the curve of antibody responses to a streptococcus, and other investigators have found that hyperimmunization causes a marked proliferation of plasma cells in the spleen, the renal fat and other tissues, a result which is not seen following the injection of nonantigenic substances (25).

They believe that these cells take part only in the formation of antibody, not of normal globulin, since few plasma cells are present in the nonimmunized animal. Fagraeus (26) has demonstrated the formation of antibody by splenic explants of rabbits which had previously been injected with antigen, and showed that the red pulp, containing many plasma cells, produced large amounts of antibody while the lymph follicles, separately explanted, produced little or none.

More recently, Ehrich and others (21c) have again studied by histologic and histochemical methods the popliteal lymph nodes of rabbits, after the injection of antigen into the foot-pads. The chemical test employed to reveal the presence of ribose nucleic acid indicates concomitantly the production of cytoplasmic protein, since this nucleic acid is concerned in the synthesis of cytoplasmic material. They found that the highest concentrations of extractable antibody coincide with the peaks of cytoplasmic protein and of maturation of the plasma cells, between the fourth and sixth days after antigen injection, at a time when the lymphocytes were still in an early stage of proliferation. This conclusion is obscured however by simultaneously published experiments by Harris (27) in which the same methods were employed with different results; in this case nucleic acid, antibodies and lymphocytes seemed to develop coincidentally, while plasma cells did not increase beyond the limits normally seen. It is obviously difficult in these circumstances to arrive at a final interpretation of the antibody-forming activities of plasma cells, but the evidence in favor seems good. The Scandinavian workers (Gormsen, Bjørneboe, Fagraeus) believe that plasma cells develop from reticulo-endothelium, as did certain earlier investigators also, and that the splenic lymphoblasts described by Rich and others (11) may be transitional cells or immature plasma cells. In this view then, the RES and plasma cell sources of antibody are not mutually exclusive, the latter developing from reticulum and taking part in the process of antibody synthesis when the immunizing stimulus has been intense, either because of repeated injections of an antigen or as the result of the simultaneous administration of a mixture of antigens (25). Whether the lymphocyte also may be considered a source of antibodies is more in question. It is of interest in this connection that some cytologists have thought lymphocytes and plasma cells to be related cellular types (26, 28).

EVIDENCE OF ORIGIN DERIVED FROM INTERFERENCE WITH ANTIBODY FORMATION. A promising pathway to further information about the site or sites of antibody formation is the study of agents which inhibit this and related immunologic responses. This has already been mentioned in regard to the use of colloidal dyes, x-rays and other agents employed to influence the activities of reticulo-endothelial cells. Other substances are also thought to affect antibody formation; for example, nitrogen mustard (bis beta-chlorethyl amine) is toxic for lymphocytes and apparently suppresses antibody production (29) and may thus undermine acquired resistance (30). Sodium salicylate may also interfere with antibody manufacture, a possibility which suggests an explanation for its therapeutic usefulness in rheumatic fever (31). The mechanisms of activity of these substances are not clear however.

Great interest has been stimulated by the recent findings that other substances, normal endocrine secretions of the anterior hypophysis and the adrenal cortex, have some kind of intimate relationship to the production of antibodies and the development of the hypersensitive states (see Chapter 13), among a host of other effects upon normal and abnormal physiologic processes. Hench and his colleagues (32) recently found that one of the adrenal cortical secretions—compound E or cortisone—as well as the adrenocorticotrophic hormone of the anterior pituitary (ACTH) has a dramatic alleviatory action in rheumatoid arthritis. This disease is probably one of hypersensitive origin. Other diseases of presumptive and known hypersensitive etiologies including rheumatic fever, lupus erythematosus, asthma and hay fever have since been found to yield to treatment with these hormones (33). There is evidence furthermore that antibody formation in rabbits is inhibited by them (plasma cells disintegrate in cortisone-treated animals [34]), though this has not been established for human beings (35). At the time of this writing numerous investigations are under way dealing with the multiple facets of the activities of these substances; it is too early to know yet what specific alterations may account for their immunologic effect, but it seems obvious that a new path has been opened for the exploration of bodily responses to antigenic substances, and that these will bear fruit before long (36).

POSSIBILITY OF MULTIPLE CELLULAR SOURCES OF ANTIBODY. It is tempting to believe that actually various cells may take part in antibody formation depending upon the nature of the antigen, the route by which it gains entrance to the tissues, the intensity and length of exposure to the antigen, and probably also upon the species of animal under consideration. This possibility is suggested by several considerations. First, Bjørneboe (37) has shown that immunization with a mixture of antigens—for example, of pneumococcal vaccines of different types—results in an amount of total antibody much greater than that obtained by vaccination with an equal concentration of a single pneumococcal vaccine. This suggests the possibility that under a restricted antigenic stimulus certain cells produce antibody globulin to their capacity, while if the stimulus is made multiple other cells may take up the responsibility of manufacturing antibody also. Second, globulin is not so homogeneous a component of plasma as is albumin; it precipitates fractionally on salting out or dialysis, and in the electrophoresis cell it splits into several components. We demonstrated some years ago that in the serum of vaccinated rabbits the poorer combining antibody occurs chiefly in the fraction which precipitates on dialysis (the euglobulin), while the antibody of better combining ability is found in the water-soluble (pseudoglobulin) fraction. Thus, in sera obtained early in the course of immunization most antibody is found in the euglobulin, and later most occurs in the pseudoglobulin, paralleling the general increase in multivalent antibody as vaccination proceeds (38). Electrophoresis studies have shown that while most antibodies in the commoner laboratory animals and in man occur in the gamma portion, this is not always the case. It will be described more fully in the next chapter that in the horse, cow and pig, immunization with bacteria results in antibody globulin molecules of large size, migrating probably with the alpha component, and that when the horse is immunized with diphtheria toxin, as well as with certain other proteins, the antibody appears as a new electrophoretic component (T) between the beta and gamma globulins. This is of ordinary globulin molecular weight, but its serologic properties are different from those seen when other proteins or bacterial antigens are employed for immunization of this animal, and the response depends not only upon the chemical nature of the antigen and the species of animal immunized, but also upon the route of administration (39). Another instance of the heterogeneity of antibody response as related to the circumstances of immunization is provided by the observation of Paic (40) that the rabbit, which ordinarily produces gamma globulin antibody of normal molecular weight, responds differently to the administration of sheep erythrocytes; the hemolysin has a considerably greater size (about 1,000,000 molecular weight) than other antibodies produced by this animal.

It is apparent then that in physical and chemical properties and in serologic behavior, the antibodies even in one species of animal are not homogeneous when they are produced against different antigens, or against the same antigen at different times after exposure to it, or following different routes of introduction of antigen into the body. It appears suggestive that different cells may take part in producing molecules with these various characteristics. Madden and Whipple (41) as a result of their studies of normal plasma protein production have stated that under certain circumstances various globulin fractions may be formed by almost any tissue. A correlated serologic and cytologic study in a species of animal, such as the horse, which produces antibodies of defined differences in electrophoretic and serologic properties under different circumstances might be revealing in this respect, although the difficulties in such a study would of course be considerable.

THE SPECIFIC ALTERATION IN THE GLOBULIN MOLECULE WHICH RESULTS IN ANTIBODY. The influence of antigen upon whatever cell types produce globulin is sufficiently subtle that the globulin molecules thereafter produced gain a specific combining power without, in most cases, changing in any other observable way. By this is meant that usually antibody globulin shows the same physical and chemical behavior as normal globulin, and furthermore it is serologically indistinguishable from normal globulin if both are employed as antigen, i.e. antiantibody reacts equally well with the normal globulin of the same species. (Exceptions will be discussed later.) Despite this deft touch in modifying globulin formation the impress of antigen upon the synthesizing mechanism is nevertheless a profound one, since antibody may be produced for years following one antigenic stimulus, and Schoenheimer and others (42) have demonstrated that the half-life of the globulin molecule in plasma is only two weeks, making a continuously fresh supply necessary. The globulin-producing cells once stimulated to alter their product do not easily forget the lesson; more surprising, the descendants of these cells carry on the specific ability, in some cases throughout the lifetime of the individual, (e.g. yellow fever antibody [43]).

Just how this modifying influence of antigen takes place is still a matter for speculation. A currently acceptable hypothesis is that proposed at about the same time by Breinl and Haurowitz (44) and Mudd (45). These views suppose in essence a modification of polar forces or stereochemical arrangement of the globulin molecule as it is formed under the influence of complementary radicals on the antigen molecule. Pauling (46) refined this conception by speculating in detail upon the possibility that a reconfiguration of the coiled arrangement of the protein chain, again in the presence of the antigenic molecule, may account for the specifically reactive antibody globulin. Alexander (47) and Burnet (48a) both look upon the process as involving changes by the antigen of self-replicating cellular catalysts or enzymes involved in the production of globulin, a change analogous to the development of adaptive enzymes by bacteria in the presence of a proper substrate. This view better accounts for the long continuation of antibody formation than the conceptions previously given which seem to make necessary the continuous presence of antigen in the body in order that it modify developing globulin molecules over a period of time. There is a variable evidence concerning the persistence of antigen in cells (48a); work with antibodies labelled with fluorescent dye or radioactive iodine indicates that protein antigens disappear from the blood and tissues before the major part of the antibodies have been formed against them (48b, 48c). Bacterial polysaccharides, on the other hand, may remain in cells for considerable periods (48d).

These views are still hypothetic, and for the purpose of explaining observed facts concerning the activities of antibodies diagrammatically it is convenient to choose the view of Breinl and Haurowitz, picturing electrical forces or polar groupings of the globulin molecule in the form of a pattern. With such imaginary models we can illustrate many of the combining properties and activities of antibodies. In this scheme, we assign to the normal globulin molecule a certain ordained arrangement of polar groups which give it its characteristic electric properties. The fields of force of the globulin molecules which develop under the influence of antigen may become rearranged so as to mirror the arrangement of forces of the antigenic determinant. As a result the altered globulin gains the ability to react specifically with the antigen at the sites where the polar forces of the two are matched.

Now, in the course of formation of such altered globulin molecules, all are not equally impressed with the fields of force of the determinant antigenic group, so that variations on the central theme occur. If we take as an example a simple determinant group, metanilic acid:

SO_3H

attached to protein

NH_2

we may diagrammatically depict the major or dominant pattern of polar group forces as shown in Figure 12. This of course has no resemblance to reality; it is an entirely imaginary diagram. Now a new globulin molecule synthesized in the presence of this pattern might, if completely arranged to match with it, have the mirror form shown in Figure 13. These two molecules would react in straightforward fashion.

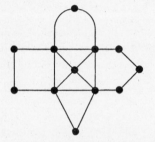

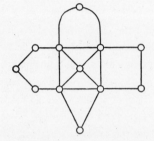

Fig. 12. Diagrammatic pattern of polar forces on an antigen molecule.

Fig. 13. Diagrammatic pattern of polar forces on an antibody molecule.

Actually not all and possibly none of the molecules of developing globulin bear this complete imprint. Some may have only the partial patterns seen in Figure 14. But such partial patterns are sufficient to permit these antibodies still to react with the matching portion of the original determinant group, metanilic acid, and the more complete the reciprocal antibody pattern the better the reaction.

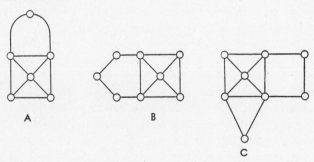

Fig. 14. A, B and C represent partial patterns of polar forces on antibody molecules.

Now let us see what happens when a heterologous but chemically related antigenic determinant group is brought into the picture. As an example we will take one which is structurally closely related to metanilic acid but has a different acid radical, *m*-amino benzoic acid:

$$\text{COOH}$$
$$\text{NH}_2$$

The portion of the pattern of polar groupings in this antigenic group which is the same as that in the metanilic acid may be depicted as in Figure 15. If we mix this antigen with the serum produced against metanilic acid, only the antibodies B and C of Figure 14 can cross react with it, because only these antibodies match the portion of the antigenic pattern shared by the two antigens. The antibody A will not cross react because it fails to mirror this common portion of the antigenic pattern. Whatever the factual validity of these illustrations, they do provide a picture of a commonly observed result, i.e. the lack of reactive uniformity of antibodies produced against a single chemical determinant, and the varied abilities of such antibodies to react with another, but chemically related, antigenic molecule.

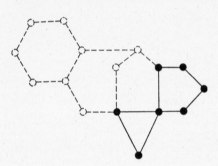

Fig. 15. Diagrammatic pattern of polar forces on an antigen molecule structurally related to that shown in Figure 12.

To be emphasized then is the fact that antibody molecules elaborated in response to a single chemical determinant group are not serologically homogeneous, but are built around a central pattern. The serologic equivalence of two chemically different antigens therefore depends upon the similarity in pattern of their polar forces, hence the similarity in the antibody patterns which they impress. This may explain why the **position** rather than the **kind** of an atom in a molecule may often influence serologic specificity, since position determines the pattern of electric forces. On this basis even the dextro and levo forms of an antigen would line up correctly with a portion of their respective heterologous antibodies, that portion which possesses the mirror pattern common to both stereoisomers.

This concept may be carried further to interpret other observed facts concerning the reactive properties of antibodies. It is commonly found that as immunization of an animal progresses the antibody shows three characteristic changes in serologic properties: (1) it increases in amount, (2) it decreases in specificity of reactivity, and (3) it increases qualitatively in its ability to react with antigen.

1. The increase in quantity is an expected consequence of time and

progressive treatment. After the first immunizing injection, subsequent injections result in an increase of altered globulin to a point beyond which further treatment is of no avail.

2. The decrease in specificity of reactivity of the antibody later in the period of vaccination reflects a broadening of the pattern of the rearranged polar grouping, so that now more of the antibody molecules being produced possess complete or more nearly complete mirror patterns, as illustrated in Figure 13. Such antibodies are able to combine with a greater variety of heterologous antigens which possess one or another fragment of the antigenic pattern in common with the homologous antigen (49). In addition, a related effect has been demonstrated: that the antibody initially formed against a complex antigen is directed against a dominant determinant group of the antigen, but with progressive immunization other antibody molecules are formed with mirror patterns especially directed against minor determinants of the antigen. These then might cross react with another antigen possessing a group similar to the minor group of the homologous antigen (50). Thus, one serum may contain antibodies of differing degrees of complementariness to one determinant group on the antigen molecule, as well as antibodies directed against a second minor antigenic group—quite a diversity of antibodies against a single chemical substance. Absorption of the serum with a chemically different antigen possessing part of the dominant group will thus remove some of the antibody, that which has the appropriate fragment of pattern, and will leave the others behind. Similarly, absorption with a chemically different antigen which possesses a configuration like the minor determinant will absorb the antibodies directed against this, leaving the others behind. These effects are shown with sera obtained after successive vaccinations with the homologous antigen, at a time when the various patterns have had an opportunity to develop.

3. Finally, it is found on continued immunization that the individual antibody molecule gains a decidedly increased ability to react with its antigen. This reflects the broadening alteration of pattern as described, and in addition an increase in the number of sites of such alteration of pattern upon the globulin molecule, so that instead of a modification involving a single area of polar forces, two or possibly more sites are now changed. Each antibody molecule now becomes able to react with two or more antigenic determinants. If we make use of the analogous chemical terms, the first antibody produced is univalent, and as immunization proceeds more and more of the antibodies produced become multivalent * (51). Since antigen is also multivalent in

* An apparent exception to this occurs in the case of anti-Rh antibodies in human beings, where late-produced antibody is more apt to be nonagglutinating for appropriate erythrocytes than is the earlier-formed antibody. The later-occurring antibodies have, however, a greater affinity for antigen because of more completely developed reactive sites, for the nonagglutinating are preferentially absorbed from a mixture of both types of antibodies. Actually there are good reasons for believing that these are not examples of univalent antibodies; their inability to agglutinate seems to depend rather upon the erythrocytes. The reasons are discussed in detail in relation to the Rh system, page 491.

that the determinant group is repeated a number of times on the whole antigenic molecule, we have a mutually multivalent reactive system. This concept is of importance to the understanding of the mechanism of antigen-antibody reaction which will be described in the next chapter. The concept of increased reactivity and multivalence of antibody is an old one, often expressed as avidity of antibody for its antigen, especially in relation to diphtheria antitoxin (52).

DIFFERENT COMBINING SITES UPON ONE ANTIBODY MOLECULE. In view of the fact that one antibody molecule may bear more than one combining site for an antigen, an interesting question concerns the ability of a single molecule to function as antibody for two different antigenic determinants. Can two antigens administered simultaneously to an animal cause characteristic changes at different points on the same globulin molecule? Ordinarily this does not occur; injection of a mixture of antigens results in the production of distinct antibodies (48, 53). A suggestion that this may happen, however, is embodied in the study of the antibodies formed against the antigenically related polysaccharides of types III and VIII pneumococci. About one third of the antibody produced by the horse against type VIII SSS is precipitable by type III SSS, and in this fraction are found antibodies of two degrees of reactivity. One of these appears to be univalent with respect to the heterologous antigen, but multivalent for the homologous SSS. It is difficult to imagine how this could be so unless the individual combining sites upon this antibody molecule are differently oriented in their reactive abilities, only one of them being able to combine with the heterologous antigen (54).

In summary then, the antibody molecules formed in response to a single chemical antigen may show the following variations, simultaneously present in the serum:

1. Antibody with a single **partial** pattern complementing the pattern of forces on the major determinant group of the antigen (univalent antibody).

2. Antibody with a single **complete** pattern against the major determinant (univalent antibody but with firmer reacting ability).

3. Antibody with two (possibly more) patterns against the major determinant group (multivalent antibody).

4. Antibodies with one or more patterns conforming to a minor determinant group of the same antigen molecule (univalent and multivalent antibodies).

The first and second antibodies are univalent, the third is multivalent, and the fourth similarly may be univalent or multivalent against the second determinant group. In a general way the numbers also indicate the sequence of their formation as vaccination is prolonged. Early formed antibody is chiefly univalent and highly specific; later antibodies are mainly multivalent and more cross-reactive. Such sera have greater avidity for antigen, a given amount of antibody combining with more antigen more firmly than does the earlier-formed immune body, because of the more complete patterns, the addition of patterns against minor antigenic determinants, and the repetition of patterns upon each molecule of antibody.

BIBLIOGRAPHY

1a. Rous, P., and Beard, J. W.   J. Exper. Med., 59:577, 1934.
   b. Kruse, H., and McMaster, P. D.   J. Exper. Med., 90:425, 1949.
   c. Kaplan, M. H., Coons, A. H., and Deane, H. W.   J. Exper. Med., 91:15, 1950.
2. Carrel, A., and Ingebrigsten, R.   J. Exper. Med., 15:287, 1912.
3. Salle, A. J., and McOmie, W. A.   J. Immunol., 32:157, 1937.
4. Parker, R. C.   Science, 85:292, 1937.
5. Beard, J. W., and Rous, P.   J. Exper. Med., 67:883, 1938.
6. Landsteiner, K., and Parker, R. C.   J. Exper. Med., 71:231, 1940.
7. Parker, R. C.   Methods of Tissue Culture, New York, Paul B. Hoeber, 1938.
8. Sabin, F. R.   J. Exper. Med., 70:67, 1939.
9. Downey, H., and Weidenrich, F.   Arch. f. mikr. Anat., 80:306, 1912.
10. Jaffe, R. H.   Physiol. Rev., 11:277, 1931.
11a. Rich, A. R.   Proc. Soc. Exper. Biol. & Med., 32:1349, 1935.
   b. ――― Lewis, M. R., and Wintrobe, M. M.   Arch. Path., 22:228, 1936.
12a. McMaster, P. D., and Hudack, S. S.   J. Exper. Med., 61:783, 1935.
   b. ――― and Kidd, J. G.   J. Exper. Med., 66:73, 1937.
   c. Burnet, F. M., and Lush, D.   Brit. J. Exper. Path., 19:17, 1938.
13. Oakley, C. L., Warrack, G. H., and Batty, I.   J. Path. Bact., 61:179, 1949.
14a. Hektoen, L.   J. Infect. Dis., 17:415, 1915; 22:28, 1918.
   b. Murphy, J. B., and Sturm, E.   J. Exper. Med., 61:245, 1925.
15. Ehrich, W. E., and Harris, T. N.   J. Exper. Med., 76:335, 1942; 81:73, 1945; 84:157, 1946; Fed. Proc. Am. Physiol. Soc., 5:220, 1946.
16. Fox, C. A., and Whitehead, R. W.   J. Immunol., 30:51, 1936.
17a. White, A., and Dougherty, T. F.   Absts. Proc. Meetings Am. Chem. Soc., New York, 1944, 37B; Endocrinology, 36:207, 1945.
   b. Kass, E. H.   Science, 101:337, 1945.
18. Dougherty, T. F., and White, A.   Proc. Soc. Exper. Biol. & Med., 56:26, 1944.
19a. ――― and Chase, J. H.   Proc. Soc. Exper. Biol. & Med., 56:28, 1944; 57:295, 1944.
   b. Chase, J. H., White, A., and Dougherty, T. F.   J. Immunol., 52:101, 1946.
   c. Dougherty, T. F., and White, A.   J. Lab. & Clin. Med., 32:584, 1947.
20. Selye, H.   Endocrinology, 21:169, 1937; Clin. Endocrinology, 6:117, 1946.
21a. Andreasen, E., Bing, J., Gottlieb, O., and Harboe, N.   Acta physiol. Scandinav., 15:254, 1948.
   b. Harris, T. N., Rhoades, J., and Stokes, J., Jr.   J. Immunol., 58:27, 1948.
   c. Ehrich, W. E., Drabkin, D. L., and Forman, C.   J. Exper. Med., 90:157, 1949.
22a. Eisen, H. N., Mayer, M. M., Moore, D. H., Tarr, R. R., and Stoerck, H. C.   Proc. Soc. Exper. Biol. & Med., 65:301, 1947.
   b. Murphy, J. B., and Sturm, E.   Proc. Soc. Exper. Biol. & Med., 66:303, 1947.
   c. Abrams, A., and Cohen, P. P.   J. Biol. Chem., 177:439, 1949.
   d. Milne, J., and White, A.   Proc. Soc. Exper. Biol. & Med., 72:424, 1949.
23. Bing, J., and Plum, P.   Acta med. Scandinav., 92:415, 1937.
24. Kolouch, F.   Proc. Soc. Exper. Biol. & Med., 39:147, 1938.
25a. Bjørneboe, M., and Gormsen, H.   Acta path. et microbiol. Scandinav., 20:649, 1943.
   b. ――― Gormsen, H., and Lindquist, F.   J. Immunol., 55:121, 1947.
26. Fagraeus, A.   Antibody Production in Relation to the Development of Plasma Cells, Stockholm, Esselte A.B., 1948.
27. Harris, T. N., and Harris, S.   J. Exper. Med., 90:169, 1949.
28. Dougherty, T. F., and Gormsen, H.   Anat. Rec., 97:14, 1947.
29a. Phillips, F. S., Hopkins, F. H., and Freeman, M. L. H.   J. Immunol., 55:289, 1947.
   b. Spurr, C. L.   Proc. Soc. Exper. Biol. & Med., 64:259, 1947.
   c. Bukantz, S. C., Dammin, G. J., Wilson, K. S., Johnson, M. C., and Alexander, H. L.   Proc. Soc. Exper. Biol. & Med., 72:21, 1949.
30. Taliaferro, W. H., and Taliaferro, L. G.   J. Infect. Dis., 82:5, 1948.

31a. Coburn, A. F., and Kapp., E. M. J. Exper. Med., 77:173, 1943
  b. Derick, C. L., Hitchcock, C. H., and Swift, H. F. J. Clin. Investigation, 5:427, 1928.
  c. Homburger, F. Proc. Soc. Exper. Biol. & Med., 61:101, 1946.
  d. Sullivan, C. J., Parker, T. W., and Hibbert, R. W. Proc. Soc. Exper. Biol. & Med., 67:508, 1948.
  e. Good, R. A., Campbell, B., and Good, T. A. Proc. Soc. Exper. Biol. & Med., 72:341, 1949.
32. Hench, P. S., Kendall, E. C., Slocumb, C. H., and Polley, H. F. Proc. Staff Meet., Mayo Clin., 24:181, 1949.
33. Carlisle, J. M. Brit. M. J., September 9, p. 590, 1950.
34a. Germuth, F. G., Jr., and Ottinger, B. Proc. Soc. Exper. Biol. & Med., 74:815, 1950.
  b. Teilum, G., Engbaek, H. C., and Simonsen, M. Acta Endocrinol., 5:181, 1950.
35. Mirick, G. S. J. Clin. Investigation, 29:836, 1950.
36. Fischel, E. E. Bull. New York Acad. Med., 26:255, 1950.
37. Bjørneboe, M. Acta path. et microbiol. Scandidav., 20:221, 1943.
38a. Raffel, S., Pait, C. E., and Terry, M. C. J. Immunol., 39:317, 1940.
  b. ———— and Terry, M. C. J. Immunol., 39:337, 349, 1940.
  c. Witebsky, E., Mohn, J. F., Howles, D. J., and Ward, H. M. Proc. Soc. Exper. Biol. & Med., 61:1, 1946.
39a. Pappenheimer, A. M., Jr. J. Exper. Med., 71:263, 1940.
  b. Heidelberger, M., Treffers, H. P., and Mayer, M. J. Exper. Med., 71:271, 1940.
  c. Boyd, W. C., and Hooker, S. B. Ann. New York Acad. Sc., 43:107, 1941.
  d. Heidelberger, M. J. Exper. Med., 86:77, 1947.
  e. Treffers, H. P., Heidelberger, M., and Freund, J. J. Exper. Med., 86:83, 95, 1947.
40. Paic, M. Bull. Soc. chim. biol., 21:412, 1939.
41. Madden, S., and Whipple, G. H. Physiol. Rev., 20:194, 1940.
42. Schoenheimer, R., Rattner, S., Rittenburg, D., and Heidelberger, M. J. Biol. Chem., 144:541, 545, 555, 1942.
43. Sawyer, W. A. J. Prev. Med., 5:413, 1931.
44. Breinl, F., and Haurowitz, F. Ztschr. f. physiol. Chem., 192:45, 1930.
45. Mudd, S. J. Immunol., 23:423, 1932.
46. Pauling, L. J. Am. Chem. Soc., 62:2643, 1940.
47. Alexander, J. Protoplasma, 23:423, 1931-32.
48a. Burnet, F. M., and Fenner, F. The Production of Antibodies, 2nd ed., Melbourne, Macmillan and Co., 1949.
  b. Coons, A. H., Leduc, E. H., and Kaplan, M. H. J. Exper. Med., 93:173, 1951.
  c. Dixon, F. J., Bukantz, S. C., Dammin, G. J., and Talmage, D. W. Federation Proc., 10:553, 1951.
  d. Coons, A. H. Federation Proc., 10:558, 1951.
49a. Magnus, P. Ber. d. deutsch. bot. Gesellsch., 26a:532, 1908.
  b. Hooker, S. B., and Boyd, W. C. J. Immunol., 26:469, 1934; 30:41, 1936.
  c. Landsteiner, K., and van der Scheer, J. J. Exper. Med., 71:445, 1940.
50a. Hooker, S. B., and Boyd, W. C. J. Immunol., 25:61, 1933.
  b. Haurowitz, F., and Schwerin, P. J. Immunol., 47:111, 1943.
51a. Locke, A., and Hirsch, E. F. The Newer Knowledge of Bacteriology and Immunology, ed. by Jordan, E. O., and Falk, I. S., Chicago, University of Chicago Press, 1928, Chapter 78, p. 1049.
  b. Malkiel, S., and Boyd, W. C. J. Exper. Med., 66:383, 1937.
  c. Heidelberger, M., and Kendall, F. P. J. Exper. Med., 62:467, 1935.
  d. ———— Treffers, H. P., and Mayer, M. J. Exper. Med., 71:271, 1940.
52a. Roux, E. Compt. rend. Xième Congrès Internat. Hyg. et Demog., Paris, 1900, p. 21.
  b. Barr, M., and Glenny, A. T. J. Path. & Bact., 34:539, 1931.
  c. Jerne, N. K. A Study of Avidity, Acta path. et microbiol. Scandinav., Suppl. 87, Copenhagen, E. Munksgaard, 1951.
53a. Landsteiner, K., and van der Scheer, J. J. Exper. Med., 67:709, 1938.
  b. Heidelberger, M., and Kabat, E. A. J. Exper. Med., 67:181, 1938.
  c. Haurowitz, F., and Schwerin, P. J. Immunol., 47:111, 1943.
  d. Liu, S-C., and Wu, H. Chinese J. Physiol., 14:81, 1939.
54a. Heidelberger, M., Kabat, E. A., and Shrivastava, D. L. J. Exper. Med. 65:487, 1937.
  b. ———— Kabat, E. A., and Mayer, M. J. Exper. Med., 75:35, 1942.

6

MECHANISMS OF ACQUIRED IMMUNITY

GENERAL CHARACTERISTICS OF ANTIBODIES AND ANTIBODY PRODUCTION

Antibody Responses. 1. General Curve of Response. A general kind of antibody response curve to an initial injection of antigen is that shown in Figure 16.

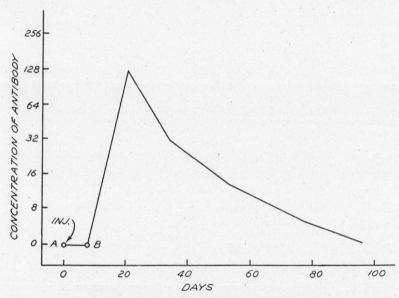

Fig. 16. Antibody response to primary vaccination.

In Figure 16, the **induction phase** A to B is followed by a rapid rise in titer reaching a peak between the tenth and fourteenth days, usually. The subsequent decline is at first sharp, then levels off until, after two to three months, antibody can no longer be detected.

This curve shows wide variations with different circumstances, including the animal species, antigen and route of injection. For example, the rabbit generally produces maximum antibody much more quickly than the horse. The route of injection of antigen and other factors may also influence this. Some of these factors will be discussed later.

2. Secondary Response and Anamnesis. If antigen is injected at intervals the antibody reaches a peak of effectiveness and concentration, varying individually with the animal, beyond which it cannot go. It may be pointed out in this connection again that forcing the issue of antibody production by repeated injections of antigen will generally result in more efficient, i.e. multivalent, antibody globulin molecules.

Now, if the spacing of injections is sufficiently **short** so that antigen is reintroduced into the body while antibody resulting from the previous injection is still present, there may result a **negative phase** in which the level of humoral antibodies is depressed (1). This is illustrated in Figure 17, and

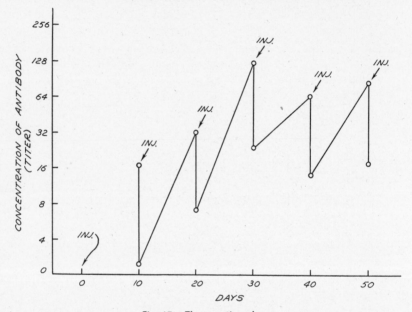

Fig. 17. The negative phase.

results from the combination of injected antigen with circulating antibody in vivo. That this is a specific effect has been shown by experiments in which a variety of antibodies were stimulated by the simultaneous administration of a mixture of antigens to rabbits. The subsequent reinjection of one of the antigens in large amount caused the disappearance of the corresponding antibody from the circulation while the others remained intact (2). The effect is not always demonstrable; for example, it does not occur in patients with atopic antibodies following injections of the homologous antigens (see page 222).

If on the other hand injections of antigen are spaced widely so that during the intervals circulating antibody wanes, then the negative phase is no longer seen. The reinjection of antigen in this case reveals another important characteristic of antibody production, the influence of the **secondary antigenic stimulus** (3). The reappearance of antibodies in the blood under these circumstances shows the following differences from the initial response: (*a*) there is a more rapid appearance, (*b*) the antibody often attains a greater concentration, (*c*) the antibody is frequently of better combining quality, and (*d*) it is apt to persist longer in the blood. A comparison of the two types of response is shown in Figure 18.

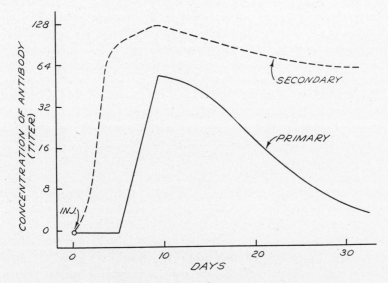

Fig. 18. A comparison of secondary and primary antibody responses.

These differences in responses in the restimulated subject broaden the basis upon which we may consider the protective effects conferred by vaccination. In those cases where antibody is concerned in immunity, protection should depend not alone upon the level of antibody present at any particular time, but largely also upon the training of the antibody-forming cells and their consequent ability to respond quickly and effectively to a challenging infection or intoxication (4). As a matter of fact, however, these advantages of the secondary stimulus are not always apparent. Toxoids are more likely than bacteria to cause a clear-cut secondary response. This difference may be due to the necessity for cells to disintegrate before the component antigens are liberated; this factor retards to some extent the rapidity with which the antibody-forming cells may react (5).

The response to the secondary antigenic stimulus is related to the **anamnestic** or remembering reaction of the antibody-producing cells (6). These may be stimulated to produce higher concentrations of antibody even by unrelated antigens, or sometimes by the injection of nonantigenic substances. Hektoen and Welker (7) produced antibodies against a variety of antigens in single animals and waited until precipitins had disappeared from the blood. When one antigen was then reinjected all the precipitins reappeared. This kind of activation is seen to occur occasionally in febrile diseases; it is especially characteristic of infectious mononucleosis, a dyscrasia of the lymphatic system of unknown etiology. In addition to the frequently high levels of an antibody (against sheep and ox erythrocytes) which is characteristically associated with this disease there may occur appreciable concentrations of antibodies acting upon various bacteria such as *Salmonella typhosa* and *Brucella abortus*. Whether these represent antibodies which the tissues once produced and which this stimulus has caused to be produced again, or whether this disease causes variously distorted globulin molecules to appear *de novo,* some by chance reactive with these bacteria, is a matter for speculation.

3. Influence of Heredity and Age. As might be expected, the ability to produce antibodies is controlled by genetic factors, and consequently it is possible by inbreeding to produce strains of animals which form antibodies against particular antigens more readily than do their unspecialized brethren (8). There is evidence that this ability varies for different antigens in the same subject (9). Such differences may explain the inability of some individuals to produce antitoxins after repeated injections of diphtheria toxoid or even as a result of the disease itself. The ability to produce antibodies is lacking in newborn babies and animals. In infants this is true as well for the blood group iso-agglutinins, antibodies which depend entirely upon hereditary rather than antigenic factors for their appearance. Until rather recently it was generally believed that the antibody-forming capacity might be lacking during the first six months of life, but experiences with alum precipitated pertussis vaccines suggest that responses may occur between the first and second month (10). The early deficiency in antibody-producing capacity is coincident with a poorly functioning globulin synthesis. Various studies have revealed that the sera of newborn animals are low in globulin content, and that increases in beta and gamma globulins occur after birth at intervals varying with the animal species (11). Gormsen (12) has observed that infants first show the presence of plasma cells in the bone marrow at three months of age. This observation may be significant from the viewpoint of the plasma cell as a possible producer of antibody.

Old age is also a period of poor antibody production. Studies in old people have shown that the level of the isoagglutinins falls sharply (13). This decrease in a normally occurring antibody suggests a slackening in the general ability to form antibodies, and such a probability is borne out by observations in experimental animals (14).

Physicochemical and Serologic Variations of Antibodies. The serum globulin usually increases after vaccination to a variable extent. This change requires no particular explanation other than that vaccination not only causes a specific alteration in some of the globulin molecules being produced, but also stimulates the formation of more than normal amounts of globulin. Often all of the additional globulin may be antibody, but this is not always the case (15). Increases in plasma globulin may follow the injection of nonantigenic substances also (16). If injections are carried out gently, small doses of antigen being given with long intervals between, this increment of globulin may not occur at all, antibody molecules apparently simply replacing normal globulin.

Antibodies formed under various circumstances are found to be quite different in their physicochemical properties as well as in their serologic behaviors. These differences are interesting not only in themselves, but also because they suggest several related possibilities: that different types of cells may produce antibodies of differing chemical and serologic behaviors, and that the various kinds of hypersensitive responses may be determined by such properties of antibodies, hence by the kind of cells most actively involved in responding to antigens under such circumstances as are to be discussed later. These broader possibilities will be considered in more detail in their proper place (see Chapter 13); our concern here is with the conditions determining differences in antibodies, and the nature of these differences.

A diversity of the antibody response to a single antigenic substance has been known for some years to occur, both with regard to its chemical properties as globulin (17) as well as its activity in combining with antigen in vitro and in vivo. For example, Goodner and Horsfall (18) have shown differences in the precipitative as compared with mouse protective activities of antipneumococcal antibody in individual horse sera.

Various factors are now known to influence the chemical and serologic differences in antibody responses to single antigenic substances. These factors are often interrelated, but for the sake of clarity they are discussed here under four separate headings:

1. The species of animal producing the antibody.
2. The antigen employed.
3. The route of administration of the antigen.
4. The intensity of the vaccinating procedure, including individual dosage, number of doses given, and the duration of the vaccination period.

1. Variations in antibody dependent upon the species of animal producing it. In many animals including the rabbit, the monkey, and man most antibodies are gamma globulin molecules (with certain exceptions to be discussed under differences dependent upon antigens). Thus, antibodies to pneumococcal SSS produced by these three species all have the physicochemical properties of normal gamma globulin. In contrast, the horse, cow and pig produce anticapsular antibodies of high molecular weight, in the neighborhood of 900,000 rather than the usual (gamma) weight of 150,000, and migrating in the electrophoresis cell between the beta and gamma components (19). This large type of antibody may be induced in the horse with certain other antigens also, e.g. the globulin of rabbit serum (20).

Despite these physicochemical differences the antipneumococcal antibodies produced by all six of these species behave similarly in their reactions with SSS. Flocculation occurs over a wide range of mixtures, varying more or less with the quality of the particular antibody sample in accordance with the description of precipitative reactions provided earlier. The important diversity of antibody formation exemplified here then has to do only with the physicochemical properties of antibody molecules.

2. Variations in antibody dependent upon the antigen employed. Granted these differences in type of antibody globulin produced by different species of animals, it might be supposed that any single species would respond to different antigens in essentially the same way, particularly if the different antigens belong to the same chemical category. But this is not the case. In man, an exception is seen in the case of the Wassermann antibody, which has a molecular weight of about 1,000,000 (although a portion of the antibody is of normal globulin molecular weight) and which migrates electrophoretically between the beta and gamma globulins (21a). Other examples are the blood group isoagglutinins and typhoid O antibody (21b). In the rabbit, antibodies to sheep erythrocytes provide an analogous exception. Their sedimentation in the ultracentrifuge suggests a molecular weight also in the neighborhood of 1,000,000 (22). Data obtained from antiviral sera indicate the occurrence of neutralizing substances in different electrophoretic fractions, varying with the viruses employed (23).

A very interesting divergence of responses in relation to antigens has been studied in the horse. As was said before, pneumococcal SSS and rabbit serum globulin induce antibodies of large molecular weight in this animal. In contrast, injections of diphtheria toxoid result in antibody of normal globulin molecular weight (184,000) but migrating as a new component (termed T) in the electrophoresis cell, between the beta and gamma globulins (24). Certain other antigens including egg albumin, the albumin of rabbit serum, and hemocyanin have been shown to stimulate antibodies with similar physicochemical properties (25). Such antibodies are further distinguishable by the fact that if they are employed as antigens in the rabbit, the antiglobulins thus induced clearly differentiate the antibacterial from the antitoxic type of antibody globulin (26).

In this case it is not only in physicochemical characteristics that the antibodies against these two groups of antigens differ. They differ also in depending upon certain routes of administration of antigen for their formation, and they differ in their serologic behaviors with antigen. Antibodies of the antipneumococcal type show the ordinary broad range of precipitation with varying quantities of antigen, forming floccules even in zones of large antibody excess. The antitoxic type of antibodies in contrast precipitate antigen over the very narrow range of concentration limited to the equivalence zone.

3. Effect of route of administration of antigen upon antibody responses. Although in many instances the route by which antigen gains access to the body is probably of minor importance in determining the eventual amount and characteristics of the antibody produced, there are cases in which this factor is of prime significance. For example, in rabbits the intravenous injection of pneumococci or streptococci results in the production mainly of anticapsular antibodies. On the other hand, intracutaneous or subcutaneous injections of these same organisms lead to the production of antinucleoprotein antibodies

almost exclusively, and simultaneously results in the development of the delayed type of hypersensitivity to the bacteria ([27], see also page 246). An analogous example is provided by the work just described on the antibodies produced by the horse. The antitoxin type of response, consisting of antibody of restricted flocculative ability and with special electrophoretic characteristics, is induced by **subcutaneous** or **intramuscular** administration of the appropriate antigens, but **not by intravenous** injection (25c). The other kind of response by this animal, of the antipneumococcal type, results from the **intravenous** injection of this group of antigens. The subcutaneous inoculation of such antigens results only in a meagre formation of univalent antibodies of the same general class as the precipitative type, but so poorly developed in their ability to react with antigen as to be entirely nonflocculative (20, 28).

Such differences might imply an importance of mechanical factors, such as length of persistence of the antigen in the body, in determining whether an antigen injected by a certain route will stimulate antibody formation. Thus, soluble proteins such as egg albumin or diphtheria toxoid injected intravenously may be ineffective because they are too rapidly excreted, and pneumococci injected subcutaneously might on the other hand be subject to rapid deterioration. Dubos and MacLeod (29) have indeed found that pneumococci injected intradermally into rabbits soon lose their Gram-staining characteristics and their type-specific antigenicity. But such factors as these do not in general seem to be the important ones, for pneumococcal nucleoproteins and rabbit serum globulin **are effective** antigens when injected intravenously (but not subcutaneously), whereas diphtheria toxoid precipitated on alum and thus made particulate still remains a poor antigen when injected intravenously (30). It would seem that factors other than (or in addition to) the mechanical ones of excretion or destruction of antigens may be concerned in the effect of route of access of antigens upon the antibody response. There may be for example a differential ability of cells to respond to different antigens, so that the route of access to the tissues may determine whether adequate concentrations of a particular antigen will reach **those cells best able to respond to it.** Perhaps an analogous possibility may be exemplified by the various antibodies found in human beings with atopic hypersensitivity. It has been shown (31) that the antibodies formed by the hypersensitive subject as the result of spontaneous exposure of mucous membranes to pollens and other air-borne substances are **heat labile.** If the patient is given **injections** of the pollen for therapeutic reasons, antibody of **heat-stable** character develops. This differs from the spontaneous antibody also in its reactivity with antigen; it blocks the transfer of hypersensitivity to normal recipients by the heat-labile antibody. Again we see a difference in physicochemical and immunologic properties of antibodies to the same antigen in the same subject, the difference depending upon the route by which the antigenic stimulus has been delivered. Curiously enough, and again compatible with the importance of route of administration of antigen, it is not possible regularly to induce the production of the atopic heat-labile type of antibody by the **injection** of antigen even in a subject who has shown his capacity to produce antibodies of this general type through spontaneous exposure. Occasionally small amounts of antibodies with these properties are found after ordinary antigenic stimulation, and extracts of the roundworm *Ascaris* seem to be especially prone to elicit them. But for the occurrence of these antibodies as the total serologic response antigens must apparently be absorbed via the respiratory mucosa, and it may be that in this location occur the cells which produce antibody of this general nature (see page 218).

4. Effect of dosage and duration of vaccination period upon the antibody response. The ordinary effect of increasing dosage, number of injections, and the total period of vaccination upon the antibody response is what might be expected—an increase in quantity and quality of antibody in the serum to a point, more or less rapidly reached, where further injections have no effect upon this level. The relationship between the response and the total dosage of antigen is a very crude one, once the latter goes above the minimal effective amount. The great disparity possible between amounts of antigen injected and of antibody produced is unusually well illustrated by the vaccination of human beings with the specific polysaccharide of the pneumococcus. Here the use of a very small dose of antigen appears actually to favor a larger formation of antibody. After one injection of 0.05 mg. of this antigen one subject produced a total of about 17 gm. of circulating antibody protein (32).

When we analyze the relationship between dosage, duration of the vaccination period and antibody production more closely, certain very interesting points turn up with regard to the chemical and serologic properties of the antibody from one animal examined at different points in the course of vaccination. So far as chemical properties are concerned, it is often found that a shift in globulin association may occur as the course of vaccination progresses. Several investigators (17, 33) pointed this out years ago with respect to antipneumococcal horse sera fractionated by means of dialysis or salt precipitation. The author has provided evidence based on dialysis that the early formed univalent antibody may be associated with one globulin fraction, and later multivalent antibody with another portion of the globulin in rabbits (34). Differences in the globulin associations of antibodies with progressive vaccination have been found to occur in the sera of other species also, as revealed by electrophoretic and other types of examinations (35).

Along with such changes in physicochemical properties, antibody shows alterations also in its serologic characteristics as vaccination progresses. If very small quantities of antigen are injected repeatedly, the antibody produced may remain predominantly univalent. With larger doses the antibody resulting from the first injection will often prove to be univalent also, but after subsequent injections and the passage of time, more of it takes on the property of multivalence. Circulating antibody is probably at no time all of one or the other type; it is rather a heterogeneous mixture in which one or the other kind predominates to give the serum an over-all activity reflecting the major component.

The author and his co-workers have made the observation that in the rabbit univalent antibody may be largely associated with one fraction of the globulin, multivalent with another. Possibly this may suggest a frequent relationship between the chemical and the serologic characteristics of the antibodies produced at the various times during the process of vaccination.

Observations have been described which do not strictly coincide with the channels used for the foregoing discussion. Many variations may occur; for example, large molecules of globulin such as are produced by the horse in response to the pneumococcus are also found occasionally and in small amounts in normal horse serum as a blood protein without antibody properties (36). On the other hand, after prolonged vaccination horse antipneumococcal antibody may be made up partly or entirely of gamma globulin (37). Again, equine diphtheria antitoxin has been obtained with the electrophoretic characteristics of beta or gamma globulin instead of the T component described before, and with variable flocculative abilities broader than that ordinarily seen (38).

Many other details of information which could be used to characterize variations in antibodies have been omitted here; for example, the differentiation of antibodies formed by a single individual against a single antigenic substance on the basis of their relative abilities to cross the placental membranes to the fetal circulation. Instead, the central theme of these accumulated studies has been stressed. This emphasizes a considerable elasticity in the physicochemical and serologic characteristics of antibodies varying chiefly with the four factors, frequently interrelated, in terms of which the subject has been discussed (39).

It was suggested before that this information may throw light on the possibility of a multicellular origin for antibody. It may be worth considering that different cells may be potential producers of antibody, some acting more effectively in response to antigens with one particular set of chemical properties, some against other antigens, and the resultant antibodies may show dissimilarities such as are seen for example between horse antibodies against pneumococcal polysaccharides and against diphtheria toxin. Another factor determining which cells may best respond could be the route by which the antigen gains entrance to the body. One route may bypass the cells most capable of dealing with the antigen in question; another route may result in optimal interaction with these cells. It seems possible also that the initial exposure of the tissues to an antigen may bring into play cells which are not well equipped to produce antibodies, and later, after longer and repeated exposures, better qualified cells take up the task. Some such viewpoint is suggested also by evidence derived from the specific reactivity of various cells in the delayed hypersensitive states (see Chapter 14). In this kind of reactivity antibody of the humoral type seems to have no part, but instead various cells of the body become responsive to exposure to antigen and the cells themselves can transfer this sensitivity to normal recipient individuals. Presumably an antibody-like substance is possessed by these cells. Since it has never been demonstrated that antibodies are brought to the cells by the blood or lymph streams, it seems reasonable to suppose that the specific reactivity for antigens may be elaborated within the various tissue cells themselves.

This concept of a multicellular origin of antibodies encompasses then a variety of suggestive experimental observations and it is supported by the opinion of expert investigators of protein manufacture with such statements as, "it may be that under certain circumstances almost any tissue can contribute to a globulin fraction" (40). In the same vein, recent evidence from studies with labelled amino acids has indicated that protein synthesis may occur in the intestinal wall and perhaps in the pancreas (41).

These data may also suggest an explanation for the well defined differences among the hypersensitive states, as, for example, the different circumstances in which Arthus and human atopic reactivities come about and subsequently manifest themselves. This question is considered more fully in Chapter 13 where the details of the hypersensitive states are described.

Local Formation of Antibodies. A question related to the preceding discussion concerns the possibility that antibodies may be formed locally at a site of antigen deposition in the tissues. If, as previously suggested, the formation of antibodies by different cells may account for their peculiarities, then evidence is needed that local antibody formation can take place. There are practical implications in such a possibility also, for example, the local vaccination of the nasal or intestinal or other membranes.

Certain observations would make it seem likely that antibodies may be formed at a site of antigen localization in the tissues. Thus, patients with neurosyphilis may have demonstrable Wassermann antibodies in the spinal fluid when these are absent from the serum. Kabat and his co-workers (42) have shown that the spinal fluid of such patients may contain percentages of gamma globulin higher than the serum and they conclude, as have others before (43), that these antibodies must be formed in the central nervous system. A similar possibility has been suggested by Morgan (44) from studies of immunity in poliomyelitis (see page 390).

The experimental evidence on this point, however, has been conflicting. Antibodies to bacteria (45), toxin (46), and vaccinia and variola viruses (47) have been demonstrated in local areas of inoculation—including nasal membranes, skin, and the abdominal cavity—by several investigators. Burnet (48) was unsuccessful in his efforts to show this effect with toxin, but succeeded with vaccinia virus. Oakley (46) believes that the conditions under which such experiments are carried out may be of great importance to their outcome; if an opportunity is provided for the accumulation of the proper cells at the site of antigen injection, antibody formation may subsequently occur upon reexposure to the antigen. If this viewpoint is correct it gives no support to the concept of a multicellular origin of antibody, since it makes the local production dependent upon the migration of a certain type of cell (presumably the macrophage) into a particular area of the body.

Vaccination by the oral route is a matter of some theoretic as well as practical interest and the possibility has some relationship to the question of the local formation of antibodies. The latter aspect however has not been seriously looked into because it has been found that intact antigens may be absorbed to some extent from the gastrointestinal tract. As a consequence, investigators have occupied themselves with the problem of the generalized antibody response. Small amounts of protein may enter the blood stream from the gut intact (49) and with certain bacteria at least there appears to be sufficient absorption of antigen to result in a humoral antibody response. This has been demonstrated to occur with pneumococcal vaccines (50). Large doses of antigen are required since only a fraction escapes digestion, and the consensus of opinion is that this is not an optimal route for the administration of antigenic substances.

Following infections with certain of the enteric pathogens, or even as a result of parenteral vaccination with these organisms, antibodies have been reported to occur in the intestinal content. These appear to be independent of those in the blood and may presumably arise from cellular elements of the intestinal wall itself. This evidence is discussed in relation to cholera and dysentery on pages 307 and 316.

Antibody Responses to Multiple Antigens. The tissues are well able to respond to more than one antigenic substance simultaneously, as attested by the variety of antibodies which may be elaborated to a single bacterial vaccine. In addition, the body sorts the mixture of antigens to which it is exposed, so that distinct globulin molecules are produced for each antigenic substance. There is undoubtedly some limit to the number of diverse antigens to which the cells can respond in this way, but Hektoen and Boor (51) found that the injection of a mixture of 35 purified antigens into rabbits resulted in the formation of antibodies against all but one, and these in good titer. A crowding out effect becomes apparent when multiple antigens are employed if one or more is present in excessive concentrations (52); the antibodies produced are limited to those antigens employed in greatest amounts.

Effect of Adjuvants upon Antibody Production. Immunologic adjuvants are substances which, if mixed with antigens, cause an increase in antibody responses. These substances are usually nonantigenic themselves. Some, such as alum and calcium phosphate, are routinely employed in the preparation of certain vaccines for human use; others, including water-in-oil emulsion and staphylococcus toxin, have been restricted almost entirely to experimental animals.

The use of extraneous substances for the intensification of antibody responses originated with Pasteur (53). A large variety of materials has been examined for this property since then, including unrelated bacteria, foreign proteins, metallic salts, various lipids and oils, and absorbents. Some of the more useful of these are described in the following paragraphs.

1. Alum. Aluminum potassium sulfate was first shown to enhance antigenicity with diphtheria toxoid (54). At first the toxoid was precipitated by the alum and the entire suspension mixture employed. Later it was estab-

lished that in addition to enhancing antigenicity, precipitation with alum afforded a means for the concentration of the toxoid and the elimination of extraneous proteins in the original solution (55). This adjuvant is still used chiefly with toxoids, both diphtheria and tetanus, but has also been employed clinically with bacteria, notably *H. pertussis,* in mixtures with the toxoids (56).

The effectiveness of alum-precipitated vaccines in eliciting higher and more enduring antibody titers has been repeatedly proved both in experimental animals and in man for diphtheria (57), for tetanus (58) and for mixed vaccines (59). For this more satisfactory level and persistence of antibodies it has been found that a smaller number of injections suffices; thus, for diphtheria prophylaxis two injections of alum-precipitated material provide a somewhat better result than do three injections of fluid toxoid, and in the case of pertussis vaccine a relatively small dose of bacteria precipitated with alum provides responses equal to those obtained with very heavy emulsions of bacilli in salt solution.

2. Aluminum hydroxide (aluminum cream). Aluminum hydroxide has been employed for many years as a protein precipitant, and has been shown also to bolster antigenic stimuli in experimental animals (60). This material is reported to be a very satisfactory adjuvant with scarlet fever toxoid in human beings (61) and with diphtheria and tetanus toxoids and the typhoid bacillus in experimental animals (62). There is evidence in the case of diphtheria and tetanus toxoids that aluminum hydroxide may be a more suitable substance than alum, resulting in higher and more enduring levels of antitoxin (63).

3. Water-in-oil emulsions. Some years ago it was found that paraffin oil potentiates antigenic activity. The first observations with mineral oil were made in France (64). Freund (65) modified the original procedure by emulsifying water-in-oil with the aid of lanolin. The antigens in such a mixture are contained in water droplets surrounded by the oil. Favorable results with respect to levels and persistence of antibodies (65, 66) have been reported from the use of such preparations in animals and man.

The addition of killed tubercle bacilli to such emulsions increases their adjuvant effect markedly (67). This striking effect is caused by a lipopolysaccharide extractable from the bacillus (68); other lipids from the same bacterium or from a variety of other cellular sources have been found by the present author to lack this ability. This same tubercle bacillary substance has other marked influences upon immunologic responses (see Chapter 14).

4. Other adjuvants. Mention might be made of one or two other examples of adjuvants. Salk (69) has employed calcium phosphate with influenza viruses. This substance, like alum, serves to concentrate and purify the virus preparation in addition to enhancing its antigenicity. Staphylococcus toxin has been reported also to increase immunologic responses (70). Other substances have also been employed, including metallic salts.

The mechanism of the adjuvant effect is not well understood. Presumably adsorbents and emulsions may protect antigens so that they remain in the body longer than would otherwise be the case, and the antigen may also become more widely distributed through the tissues and thus more accessible to antibody-forming cells (71).

Normal Antibody. In relation to the preceding discussion of antibody production it is pertinent to consider the possible reasons for the existence of naturally occurring antibodies in the sera of various animal species. Those antibodies which may be found in human beings and animals as a result of immunization by subclinical infection, or by absorption of antigenic material from the gastrointestinal or the respiratory tracts, do not fall under this heading. These latter are of course **acquired** through a spontaneous process of vaccination; they are not native to the body. The native antibodies are those which do not depend upon an antigenic stimulus and which are, in general, characteristic for a particular species of animal. The difficulty comes in attempting to distinguish these two groups, and the question is whether normal antibodies as such exist or whether all are the result of some esoteric process of vaccination.

As mentioned before, there is one example of native antibodies which almost precludes debate, the human blood group isoagglutinins. These antibodies, found also in certain of the higher anthropoids, are complementary in an inverse sense to the blood group antigens which an individual may possess. The presence of a particular antigen or antigens in the erythrocytes automatically excludes the possibility of a corresponding antibody, but just as automatically assures the presence of antibodies against the blood group factors which the individual lacks. In this case there is little basis for entertaining the notion that antigenic stimulation may account for the antibodies, though the possibility exists (72a).

Aside from these blood group agglutinins, there may be found in animals of all species a variety of antibodies reacting with bacterial and other cells, and it is the origin of these which is often difficult to account for. Opportunities for unnoted stimuli by environmental antigens are certainly good, and the particular bacterium or other cell against which the antibodies are found need not even itself provide that stimulus. A chemically similar or heterogenetic antigenic constituent of an entirely unrelated agent would serve just as well. For illustration we might take the example of the Forssman antibody which occurs almost universally in the sera of human beings. This antibody is most conveniently demonstrated by its activity upon sheep erythrocytes in which the Forssman antigen (a complex substance—a lipo-carbohydrate-protein) occurs in the cell stroma. This antigen occurs also in many bacteria, in a variety of edible plants, and it is widely present in the animal kingdom. It may be inferred then that subclinical or overt infections with any of the bacteria containing the substance may result in this antibody response (72b). Add to this the fact that the antigen is heat stable and is present in foods of plant and animal origin, and the possibility becomes evident that slight but repeated adsorption from the gastrointestinal tract may keep antibodies in almost continuous production (73). It seems improbable that people should escape frequent contacts with this antigen in one of its biologic envelopes. Yet this assumption does not prove that the Forssman antibody in the human being may not be a native substance. The difficulties of conclusive proof in either direction are obviously considerable.

One might suppose that the time of appearance of antibodies in young animals would shed some light on the general problem, since the native antibodies might be present earlier than those requiring an antigenic stimulus. This is not the case, however, for even the blood group isoagglutinins appear only after several months in the infant, at a time when he has already become capable of responding to foreign antigenic stimuli.

The rationale which most convincingly suggests that certain of the antibacterial and anticellular antibodies may indeed be native to an animal species is based on the regularity of their occurrence in all individuals of that species, and their absence in other species which should have equal opportunities to become spontaneously vaccinated. Furthermore, such antibodies often show differences from deliberately stimulated antibodies in that they are very sluggishly absorbed from the serum by the cells upon which they act, and in their relatively low-grade specificity (73).

In summary, we know that the blood group antibodies of the human being and certain other primates constitute one example of physiologically determined antibodies. We know also that the widespread occurrence of other antibodies in man and animals may often be clearly related to subclinical infection or to the ingestion or inhalation of antigens. Certain features of some antibodies—their ubiquity in individuals of one species and their absence from others, their serologic behavior—suggests that they also, like the isoagglutinins, may be determined by physiologic rather than antigenic factors. It is interesting to speculate that such antibodies may be native to the animal as an accident of serum globulin formation, i.e. the arrangement of polar forces on the normal globulin molecules characteristic for a particular species of animal may by chance be such that the molecule is specifically oriented to the determinant groups occurring in certain bacterial and other cells.

BIBLIOGRAPHY

1. Brieger, J., and Ehrlich, P.   Ztschr. f. Hyg. u. Infektionskr., 13:336, 1893.
2. Hektoen, L., and Welker, W. H.   J. Infect. Dis., 57:337, 1935.
3. Dean, G.   Tr. Path. Soc. London, 51:15, 1899.
4. Cole, R. I.   Ztschr. f. Hyg. u. Infektionskr., 46:371, 1904.
5. Burnet, F. M.   The Production of Antibodies, Melbourne, Macmillan and Co., 1941, pp. 9-16.
6. Cannon, P. R.   J. Lab. & Clin. Med., 28:127, 1942.
7. Hektoen, L., and Welker, W. H.   Science, 86:592, 1937.
8. Lewis, P. A., and Loomis, D.   J. Exper. Med., 47:437, 1928.
9. Carlinfanti, E.   J. Immunol., 59:1, 1948.
10. Sako, W., Trueting, W. L., Witt, D. B., and Nichamin, S. J.   J.A.M.A., 127:379, 1945; J. Pediat., 30:29, 1947.
11a. Toyama, I.   J. Biol. Chem., 38:161, 1919.
   b. Jameson, E., Alvarez-Tostado, C., and Sortor, H. H.   Proc. Soc. Exper. Biol. & Med., 51:163, 1942.

c. Smith, E. L., and Holm, A. J. Biol. Chem., 175:349, 1948.

d. Famulener, L. W. J. Infect. Dis., 10:332, 1912.

e. Freund, J. J. Immunol., 18:315, 1930.

12. Gormsen, H. Personal communication to the author, 1950.

13. Thomsen, O., and Kettel, K. Ztschr. f. Immunitätsforsch. u. exper. Therap., 63:67, 1929.

14a. Baumgartner, L. J. Immunol., 27:407, 1934.

b. Grasset, E. Pubs. S. African Inst. Med. Research, 24:1171, 1929.

15a. Bjørneboe, M. Acta path. et microbiol. Scandinav., 20:221, 1943.

b. Boyd, W. C., and Bernard, H. J. Immunol., 33:111, 1937.

16. Schmidt, E. S., and Schmidt, C. L. A. J. Immunol., 2:343, 1917.

17a. Avery, O. T. J. Exper. Med., 21:133, 1915.

b. Felton, L. D. Boston Med. Surg. J., 190:819, 1924.

18. Goodner, K., and Horsfall, F. L., Jr. J. Exper. Med., 66:413, 425, 437, 1937.

19a. Biscoe, J., Hercik, F., and Wyckoff, R. W. G. Science, 83:602, 1936.

b. Heidelberger, M., and Pedersen, K. O. J. Exper. Med., 65:393, 1937.

c. Kabat, E. A. J. Exper. Med., 69:103, 1939.

d. van der Scheer, J. J. Immunol., 41:349, 1941.

e. ———— Wyckoff, R. W. G., and Clarke, F. H. J. Immunol., 39:65, 1940.

f. Tiselius, A., and Kabat, E. A. J. Exper. Med., 69:119, 1939.

20. Treffers, H. P., Heidelberger, M., and Freund, J. J. Exper. Med., 86:95, 1947.

21a. Deutsch, V. Compt. rend. Acad. d. sc., 208:603, 1939.

b. Deutsch, H. F., Alberty, R. A., Gosting, L. J., and Williams, J. W. J. Immunol., 56:183, 1947.

22. Paic, M. Bull. Soc. chim. biol., 21:412, 1939.

23. Koprowski, H., Richmond, G., and Moore, D. H. J. Exper. Med., 85:515, 1947.

24. Pappenheimer, A. M., Jr., Lundgren, H. P., and Williams, J. W. J. Exper. Med., 71:247, 1940.

25a. ———— J. Exper. Med., 71:263, 1940.

b. Heidelberger, M., Treffers, H. P., and Mayer, M. J. Exper. Med., 71:271, 1940.

c. Treffers, H. P., Heidelberger, M., and Freund, J. J. Exper. Med., 86:83, 1947.

d. Hooker, S. B., and Boyd, W. C. Ann. New York Acad. Sc., 43:107, 1942.

26a. Ando, K., Kee, R., and Manako, K. J. Immunol., 32:83, 1937.

b. ———— Kee, R., and Komiyama, T. J. Immunol., 32:181, 1937.

c. ———— Manako, K., Kee, R., and Takeda, S. J. Immunol., 33:27, 1937.

d. ———— J. Immunol., 33:41, 1937.

e. ———— Manako, K., and Takeda, S. J. Immunol., 34:295, 1938.

f. ———— Takeda, S., and Hamano, M. J. Immunol., 34:303, 1938.

g. Treffers, H. P., and Heidelberger, M. J. Exper. Med., 73:125, 1941.

27a. Stillman, E. G. J. Exper. Med., 51:721, 1930.

b. Julianelle, L. A. J. Exper. Med., 51:449, 1930.

c. Derick, C. L., and Swift, H. F. J. Exper. Med., 49:615, 883, 1929.

28. Heidelberger, M. J. Exper. Med., 86:77, 1947.

29. Dubos, R. J., and MacLeod, C. M. J. Exper. Med., 67:791, 1938.

30. Freund, J., and Bonanto, M. V. J. Immunol., 40:437, 1941.

31a. Cooke, R. A., Barnard, J. H., Hebald, S., and Stull, A. J. Exper. Med., 62:733, 1935.

b. Loveless, M. H. J. Immunol., 41:15, 1941.

32. Heidelberger, M., MacLeod, C. M., Kaiser, S. J., and Robinson, B. J. Exper. Med., 83:303, 1946.

33a. Ledingham, J. C. G. J. Hyg., 7:65, 1907.

b. Felton, L. D. J. Infect. Dis., 43:543, 1928.

c. Ornstein, O. Klin. Wchnschr., 7:1081, 1928.

34a. Raffel, S., Pait, C. F., and Terry, M. C. J. Immunol., 39:317, 1940.

b. ———— and Terry, M. C. J. Immunol., 39:337, 349, 1940.

35a. Tiselius, A. Biochem. J., 31:313, 1464, 1937; J. Exper. Med., 65:641, 1937.

b. ———— and Kabat, E. A. Science, 87:416, 1938.

c. Witebsky, E., Mohn, J. F., Howles, D. J., and Ward, H. M. Proc. Soc. Exper. Biol. & Med., 61:1, 1946.

   d. Moore, D. H., van der Scheer, J., and Wyckoff, R. W. G. J. Immunol., 38:221, 1940.

36. Svedberg, T., and Pedersen, K. O. The Ultracentrifuge, Oxford, The Clarendon Press, 1940.

37a. Kabat, E. A. J. Exper. Med., 69:103, 1939.
   b. Moore, D. H., van der Scheer, J., and Wyckoff, R. W. G. J. Immunol., 38:221, 1940.

38a. Kekwick, R. A., Knight, B. C. J. G., MacFarlane, M. G., and Record, B. R. Lancet, I:571, 1941.
   b. ——— and Record, B. R. Brit. J. Exper. Path., 22:29, 1941.

39. Kabat, E. A. J. Immunol., 47:513, 1943.

40. Madden, S., and Whipple, G. H. Physiol. Rev., 20:194, 1940.

41. Cannon, P. R. Am. J. Clin. Path., 19:99, 1949.

42. Kabat, E. A., Moore, D. H., and Landow, H. J. Clin. Investigation, 16:571, 1942.

43. Katzenelbogen, S. The Cerebrospinal Fluid and its Relation to the Blood, Baltimore, Johns Hopkins Press, 1935.

44. Morgan, I. M. Am. J. Hyg., 45:390, 1947.

45. Walsh, T. E., and Cannon, P. R. J. Immunol., 35:31, 1938.

46. Oakley, C. L., Warrack, G. H., and Batty, I. J. Path. & Bact., 61:179, 1949.

47a. Ørskov, J., and Andersen, E. K. Ztschr. f. Immunitätsforsch. u. exper. Therap., 92:487, 1938.
   b. Hartley, G., Jr. J. Infect. Dis., 66:44, 1940.

48. Burnet, F. M., and Fenner, F. The Production of Antibodies, 2nd ed., Melbourne, Macmillan and Co., 1949.

49a. Walzer, M. J. Immunol., 14:143, 1927.
   b. Wilson, S. J., and Walzer, M. Am. J. Dis. Child, 50:49, 1935.
   c. Ratner, B., and Gruehl, H. L. J. Clin. Investigation, 13:517, 1934.

50a. Ross, V. J. Exper. Med., 51:585, 1930; 54:875, 899, 1931.
   b. Cooper, M. L., and Keller, H. M. Proc. Soc. Exper. Biol. & Med., 64:422, 1947.

51. Hektoen, L., and Boor, A. K. J. Infect. Dis., 48:588, 1931.

52a. Glenny, A. T. J. Path. & Bact., 28:241, 252, 1925.
   b. ——— and Waddington, H. J. Path. & Bact., 31:403, 1928.

53. Pasteur, L., and Joubert, G. Compt. rend. Acad. d. sc., 85:107, 1877.

54. Glenny, A. T., Pope, C. G., Waddington, H., and Wallace, U. J. Path. & Bact., 29:38, 1926.

55a. ——— and Barr, M. J. Path. & Bact., 34:118, 1931.
   b. Wells, D. M., Graham, A. H., and Havens, L. C. Am. J. Pub. Health, 22:648, 1932.

56a. Daughtry-Denmark, L. Am. J. Dis. Child., 63:453, 1942.
   b. Kendrick, P. L. Am. J. Hyg., 38:193, 1943.
   c. Miller, J. J., Jr. J.A.M.A., 134:1064, 1947.

57a. Glenny, A. T., and Barr, M. J. J. Path. & Bact., 34:31, 1931.
   b. Poditzky, O. R. Am. J. Hyg., 29:89, 1939.
   c. Volk, V., and Bunney, W. E. Am. J. Pub. Health, 32:690, 1942.

58a. Bergey, D. H. J. Infect. Dis., 55:72, 1934.
   b. Jones, F. G., and Moss, J. M. J. Immunol., 30:115, 1936.

59. Miller, J. J., Jr., and Saito, T. N. J. Pediat., 21:31, 1942.

60. Hektoen, L., and Welker, W. H. J. Infect. Dis., 53:309, 1933.

61. Menten, M. L., Finlay, H. H., and Andersch, M. A. J. Immunol., 51:45, 1945.

62. Mann, L. S., and Spinka, I. M. J. Immunol., 53:209, 1946.

63. Miller, J. J., Jr., Humber, J. B., and Dowrie, J. O. J. Pediat., 24:281, 1944.

64. LeMoignic, and Pinoy. Compt. rend. Soc. de biol., 79:201, 352, 1916.

65a. Freund, J. Ann. Rev. Microbiol., 1:291, 1947.
   b. ——— Am. J. Clin. Path., 21:645, 1951.

66a. Halbert, S. P., Mudd, S., and Smolens, J. Proc. Soc. Exper. Biol. & Med., 60:17, 1945.
   b. Henle, W., and Henle, G. Proc. Soc. Exper. Biol & Med., 59:179, 1945.
   c. Rist, N. Bibliotheca Tuberculosea, 5:91, 1951.

67. Landsteiner, K., and Chase, M. W. Proc. Soc. Exper. Biol. Med., 49:688, 1942.

68a. Raffel, S.   J. Infect. Dis., 82:267, 1948.
 b. ———— and Forney, J. E.   J. Exper. Med., 88:485, 1948.
 c. ———— Arnaud, L. E., Dukes, C. D., and Huang, J. S.   J. Exper. Med., 90:53, 1949.
69. Salk, J. E.   Proc. Soc. Exper. Biol. & Med., 46:709, 1941; Science, 101:122, 1945.
70. Marsh, H. C.   Yale J. Biol. & Med., 17:359, 1944.
71a. Rist, N.   Ann. Inst. Pasteur, 61:121, 1938.
 b. Ehrich, W. E., Halbert, S. P., Mertens, E., and Mudd, S.   J. Exper. Med., 82:343, 1945.
 c. Holt, L. B.   Brit. J. Exper. Path., 30:289, 1949.
72a. Wiener, A. S.   J. Immunol., 66:287, 1951.
 b. Shorb, M. S., and Bailey, G. H.   Am. J. Hyg., 19:148, 1934.
73a. Dunlop, E. M.   J. Path. & Bact., 31:769, 1928.
 b. Gordon, J., and Carter, H. S.   J. Path. & Bact., 35:549, 1932.

7

MECHANISMS OF ACQUIRED IMMUNITY

THE MECHANISM OF ANTIGEN ANTIBODY REACTIONS

LATTICE HYPOTHESIS

In 1934 Marrack (1) proposed a concept describing the reaction between antibody and antigen. This was elaborated in quantitative terms by Heidelberger and his co-workers (2), and is generally referred to as the lattice hypothesis. The essential mechanisms of reaction embodied in this hypothesis will be seen to follow logically from preceding discussions of the characteristics of antibodies and antigens.

The proposed mechanism can most clearly be diagrammed in terms of the precipitation system. Heidelberger's earlier studies made use of purified III pneumococcal SSS and its antiserum. Various quantities of the ingredients were mixed, the resultant precipitates were washed free of adhering nonspecific serum constituents, and the total nitrogen contents of the precipitates were determined by Kjeldahl analysis. Since this particular antigen is practically free of nitrogen, all the nitrogen of the precipitate derives from the antibody; precise values could thus be obtained for quantities of antibody globulin reacting with known amounts of antigen at various points in the reaction range. Later, methods were devised for equally quantitative investigations of protein antigens and their antibodies.

A result of these studies has been the quantitative demonstration that precipitates vary in their composition depending upon the proportions in which the two components are mixed. If antibody is present in excess the precipitate will contain relatively more molecules of this, while the addition of excess antigen results in precipitates made up of fewer antibody molecules than molecules of antigen. Thus, if a constant amount of antibody is placed in a series of tubes and to them increasing amounts of antigen are added, an analysis of the resultant precipitate will reveal decreasing values for the ratio of antibody to antigen in the successive tubes of the series. The point is best illustrated by diagrams. Figure 19 represents a bivalent molecule of antibody and Figure 20 a multivalent molecule of antigen. In both figures the circles represent reactive sites on the molecules. Most molecules of anti-

gen have more reactive sites than do antibodies, which are possibly limited
to two.

When two such molecules react the antibody may attach to antigen through
one or both of its reactive sites as shown in Figures 21 and 22 respectively.
If the antibody attaches by one reactive site only it is left with a free valence
which may then serve as a link to combine with more antigen. If, on the other
hand, the antibody combines with antigen through both its sites it is expended
and of course cannot longer serve to attach to other antigen molecules.

Fig. 19. Diagrammatic representation of antibody molecule with two
combining sites.

Fig. 20. Diagrammatic representation of a molecule of antigen with
four determinant groups.

Fig. 21. Reaction between antigen and antibody through one combining
site on each molecule.

Fig. 22. Reaction between antigen and antibody through two combining
sites on each molecule.

The antigen, on the other hand, has many combining sites and can attach
to many molecules of antibody. For these reasons the possible combinations
between multivalent antigen and antibody are elastic depending upon the
proportion in which these substances are mixed. This point is illustrated in
Figure 23 portraying six tubes to which a constant amount of antibody has
been added along with serially increasing concentrations of antigen. The figures drawn within the tubes illustrate the variable compositions of the precipitates formed, and the heavy lines drawn across the tubes indicate the proportion of the total antibody precipitated by the addition of the different
quantities of antigen.

In tubes 1 and 2, the quantities of antigen added are small. Antibodies
are therefore in excess and crowd themselves onto each available antigen
molecule, making use of only one combining site for the attachment. As the

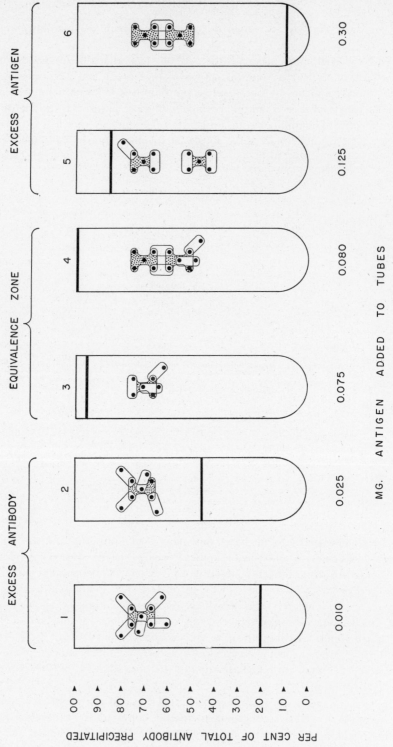

Fig. 23. Antigen-Antibody reactions.

result of this crowding effect the basic unit of combination consists of anti-body:antigen in the ratio 5:1 and 4:1. It is seen that the second combining sites of all the antibodies are still free, and these could serve as links for other antigen molecules if they were available. The cross lines reveal that the small amounts of antigen added to these two tubes, even though they spread themselves to combine with as many antibody molecules as possible, were able to remove only a portion of the total antibody available; 18 per cent in tube 1 and 45 per cent in tube 2. In these mixtures therefore uncombined antibodies remained in the supernatant fluid. This zone of reaction is termed the region of antibody excess.

More antigen was added to tube 3, and the proportions of reactants here approach immunologic equivalence. In this case a more natural combination occurs in that the combining sites of both molecules are more fully utilized. The ratio of antibody:antigen molecules here is 3:1, and two of the antibodies have attached to antigen through both combining sites, leaving only one antibody with a free valence to serve as a link for other antigen molecules. In this case almost all the antibody has been removed from solution, about 95 per cent. It should be noted that in this tube three times the quantity of antigen used in the preceding tube removed only twice as much antibody; this again is a reflection of the difference in composition of the precipitate.

A slight increase in the amount of antigen added to tube 4 keeps this in the equivalence region, but here there is sufficient antigen to combine with all the antibody. Again there is a change, but a lesser one, in the combining ratio of antibody with antigen. Here it is 5:2, and again only one antibody molecule retains a free combining site to serve as a link for further antigen. The antigen also of course is still free to combine with other antibody molecules. In this case all antibody as well as antigen has been removed from solution.

Tube 5 represents the beginning region of excess antigen. Now the antibody begins to spread itself thinner, the ratio to antigen falling to 2:1. In the upper picture in this tube one antibody molecule still possesses a free combining group, so that aggregates could be built up by combination of this with additional antigen. However, only about 85 per cent of the total antibody is precipitated from this mixture and the failure of complete precipitation is probably due to the formations of other units such as the one pictured below, in which both antibodies are fastened to antigen through both their combining sites, leaving no bridging link available. This is the beginning of what is called the zone of inhibition which occurs in the region of antigen excess.

Tube 6 is well into the inhibition zone; here only about 12 per cent of antibody has been precipitated. A further shift in the ratio of antibody:antigen has occurred here bringing the proportion to 3:2. Practically all the antigen-antibody complexes formed here are incapable of reacting further to build up larger aggregates because, as illustrated, the antibody combining groups are entirely saturated by antigen and no bridging links are available. These complexes therefore remain in solution. Antigen-antibody union has occurred without precipitate formation.

Although it might be supposed that the ratio of antibody to antigen in mixtures of excess antigen would reverse itself so that one molecule of antibody might combine with two of antigen, this does not seem to occur in the systems which have so far been studied.

Complexes of the types illustrated are the basic units for the building up of lattices of precipitate in all except tube 6, where the soluble complexes lack free combining groups to attach to additional antigen or to other similar complexes. Samples of such lattices of aggregated antigen-antibody are shown in Figures 24, 25 and 26. These would of course be three-dimensional in actuality.

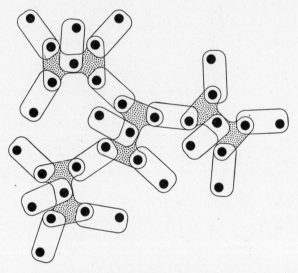

Fig. 24.   Lattice formed with excess antibody.

Figure 24 represents a lattice formed in the region of antibody excess (e.g. tube 1 or tube 2 in Fig. 23). Residual combining sites remain free on many of the antibody molecules.

Figure 25 illustrates the kind of lattice which might form at the beginning of the equivalence zone (tube 3 in Fig. 23). Only a few antibody combining sites remain free since in these proportions the combination between antigen and antibody satisfies most of the reactive groups on both molecules.

In Figure 26 the reaction has taken place at the beginning of the inhibition zone where antigen is in excess (tube 5 in Fig. 23). No free antibody combining sites remain, but many uncombined sites are still present on the antigen molecules.

Now of course this mode of combination of two substances to form a compound of variable composition according to the proportions in which they are mixed has no counterpart among chemical reactions between crystalloids.

The mixture of two bivalent atoms results in a new compound of constant composition regardless of the proportions in which the reactants have been brought together. $Ba^{++} + SO_4^{=} \rightleftharpoons BaSO_4$ no matter how much Ba^{++} or $SO_4^{=}$ has been added. The **amount** of $BaSO_4$ which precipitates however will

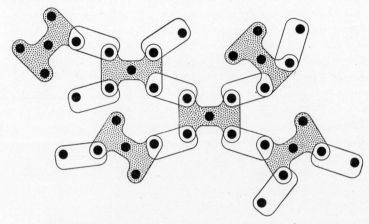

Fig. 25. Lattice formed at the beginning of the equivalence zone.

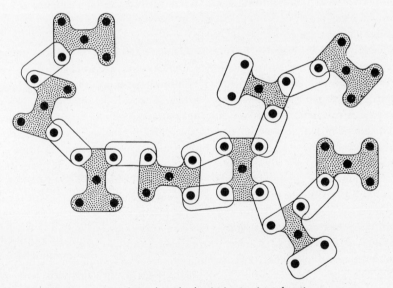

Fig. 26. Lattice formed in the beginning region of antigen excess.

vary with differences in the relative amounts of the reactants in accordance with the law of mass action. Obviously then the antigen-antibody reaction cannot be simply hung onto the framework of the law of mass action. Neither, as Heidelberger (2) has pointed out, can it be characterized by adsorption isotherms which govern the reactivities of colloidal substances, for these also contain a term for **concentration and not for composition** of the reaction product.

By making certain simplifications however, Heidelberger has been able to derive a relation from the law of mass action which accounts quantitatively for the behavior of many precipitating systems. The reaction is considered as a series of successive bimolecular reactions, i.e. antibody first combines with antigen to form a simple complex, and this is followed by competing reactions in which the complex reacts with another molecule of antibody (in the region of antibody excess) or with another complex, and so on until the large aggregates pictured hereto are built up.

For the derivation of the equations expressing these relations the reader is referred to Heidelberger's review (2) and to a series of papers by Heidelberger and co-workers appearing chiefly in the Journal of Experimental Medicine between 1929 and 1937. The reader is also referred to objections to the lattice theory which have been pointed out by Hooker and Boyd (3). Other theories describing the quantitative aspects of antigen-antibody reactions have been formulated by Boyd (4), Haurowitz (5), How (6), Hershey (7) and Teorell (8).

Although the lattice concept suffers from the deficiency of being applicable in a quantitative sense only to a limited region of reaction—the zone of antibody excess—unless modifications are introduced, nevertheless it seems to provide the most reasonable working hypothesis available on the basis of present information.

Specificity of Aggregate Formation. The reader may recognize that this picture of the reaction between antigen and antibody represents it as occurring in two continuous stages; primary **combination** is followed by the **aggregation** of small complexes to form a lattice. The validity of such a stepwise distinction is revealed by the fact that the first stage of union will occur under circumstances in which aggregates fail to build up. One such circumstance is the absence of electrolyte from the solution in which antigen and antibody are mixed. If one employs a particulate antigen, which can later be centrifuged out of the mixture, and adds antibody to it, the physical condition of the antigen is not visibly changed in the absence of electrolyte. If the still evenly distributed antigen is now sedimented from the mixture it can be shown that the antibody has come along with it, for the supernatant fluid no longer has the ability to aggregate additional antigen even if salt is added. Furthermore, if the sedimented particles of antigen are now resuspended in saline they quickly flocculate. For this effect a minimal concentration of 0.005 N sodium chloride equivalent is necessary.

Other subsidiary factors appear also to enter into the aggregative phase of the reaction. Thus, Hartley (9) indicated some years ago that the lipids present in antibody-containing sera are of importance to the formation of precipitates, and more recently Horsfall (10) demonstrated that the thorough extraction of lipids from pneumococcus antisera abolished their ability to precipitate SSS or to agglutinate the bacterial cells. Lecithin was found to be the essential lipid in horse serum, cephalin in rabbit serum. Extracted sera could still combine with antigen (a situation analogous to the absence of electrolyte), and upon readdition of these substances to the sera their ability to flocculate antigen reappeared.

Information of this kind has led many investigators to believe that the aggregate phase of the precipitation reaction may be entirely unspecific, depending upon such chemical and physical factors as a decrease of the surface electric charges of both antigen and antibody as the result of combination, with consequent decreases in their mutual repulsion as well as their solubility in water. This viewpoint of course stands in direct opposition to the lattice hypothesis which stresses heavily the importance of specific union between antigen and antibody combining sites in the building up of aggregates. As Heidelberger (2) points out, the fact that the primary complexes formed in the region of excess antigen remain soluble (e.g. tube 6, Fig. 23) is itself evidence that physical factors alone cannot account for flocculation. According to his viewpoint, these complexes of combined antigen-antibody remain soluble because there are no free antibody combining sites to provide bridging links for lattice formation. The same conclusion is suggested by the fact that univalent antibody combines with antigen without causing aggregation despite optimal chemical and physical conditions in the medium, because of the lack of bridging groups on these antibodies.

There is an experimental approach to this question which has been utilized by a number of investigators. If two different antigen-antibody systems are mixed in the same tube, the formation of mixed aggregates would be expected if aggregation is unspecific, whereas aggregates of two distinct types should occur if this stage is specific. Both results have as a matter of fact been reported (11) but the preponderance of evidence favors the view that flocculation is specific. Nevertheless, it is apparent that under some circumstances mixed aggregates occur in experiments of this kind. It seems reasonable to conclude for the present, as suggested especially by the work of Duncan (11e) and of Lanni (11f) that the flocculative phase is specific, but is abetted by physicochemical factors. In the case of electrolyte, Heidelberger (2) suggests that this aids the building of aggregates by decreasing electrostatic effects due to the presence of ionized groups on the surfaces of the primary complexes formed. The function of serum lipid may be a mechanical one, providing nuclei for aggregates in a manner analogous to the action of dust particles in promoting crystallization in a supersaturated solution.

Dissociation of Antigen-Antibody Compounds. The reaction equilibrium between antigen and antibody may be shifted by variations in salt concentration. Heidelberger and his co-workers (12) have shown that in the reaction between antipneumococcal SSS and antigen, the compound formed in the presence of high concentrations of sodium chloride contains less antibody than that formed in an isotonic medium. Furthermore, if the reaction is permitted to proceed first in isotonic saline, and the concentration of salt is subsequently raised to 15 per cent, the originally formed compound dissociates to reach a new equilibrium and free antibody appears in solution. As mentioned earlier, this method has been employed to purify antipneumococcal antibodies from the sera of several species of animals.

Danysz Effect. An early observation by Danysz (13) called attention to the peculiarities of neutralization of diphtheria toxin by antitoxin according to the way in which these substances were mixed. Amounts of toxin and antitoxin were chosen which resulted in a nontoxic mixture when the two were mixed all at once. If however the same total amount of toxin were split into several portions and these were added to antitoxin in series, the resulting mixture was still toxic. This effect follows from the earlier description in this chapter of the manner of interaction between multivalent antigen and multivalent antibody, and applies to other serologic systems (using molecular antigen) in which the reactants are both multivalent. Reference to Figure 23 will recall that the addition of antigen to antibody in a single dose in equivalent proportions (tube 3) results in virtually complete combination, while the addition of one-third as much antigen to the same quantity of antibody (tube 2) removes one-half as much antibody. This is of course simply another way of stating that the ratio of combined antibody:antigen is greater in the region of antibody excess. If now successive small quantities of antigen were added to tube 2 it is evident that the first addition would remove about 50 per cent of the antibody, the second addition most of the remainder, and that the antigen added as the third dose would remain largely uncombined for lack of residual antibody. In order for this effect to be seen it is necessary that the precipitate formed after each addition of antigen should be removed, for otherwise the molecules could regroup themselves to form a lattice of the equivalence type after all the additions of antigen had been made.

The Danysz effect with diphtheria toxin and antitoxin can be described in precisely the same terms. The particular point which requires clarification in respect to this system is why, after all the additions of toxin have been made, a rearrangement of the toxin-antitoxin combination does not remove free toxin from the mixture. A simple explanation for this is available (14). It was stated earlier that diphtheria antitoxin produced by the horse has the peculiar serologic property of flocculating with toxin in a very narrow range of proportions, corresponding to the equivalence zone. This means that in the demonstration of the Danysz effect the first addition of toxin is followed by a reaction in the region of antibody excess, and here soluble complexes are formed. It has been found that these soluble complexes form very rapidly, but that on the contrary the insoluble floccules built up in an equivalent mixture of toxin and antitoxin form very slowly. Therefore if one tests the mixture resulting from serial additions of small portions of toxin soon after the mixing has been completed there has not been sufficient time for floccules to form and the mixture is found to be toxic. If one waits for an interval however the proper rearrangement of toxin-antitoxin molecules occurs, floccules form, the mixture becomes nontoxic, and the Danysz effect spontaneously disappears.

Ehrlich Phenomenon. During the course of Ehrlich's extensive studies of the diphtheria toxin-antitoxin system, troubling inconsistencies were found to occur in the titration of units of toxin and antitoxin by the inoculation of guinea pigs. Ehrlich first established a minimal lethal dose (M.L.D.) of toxin for this animal. It was later proposed that 1 unit of antitoxin be the least amount which, when mixed with 100 M.L.D. of toxin, completely neutralizes its toxicity. Subsequently a more convenient unit of toxin was established for the purpose of antitoxin standardization. This was called the L_0 (limes nul) dose, the largest amount of toxin which, added to 1 unit of antitoxin, would completely neutralize this as determined by injections into guinea pigs.

It would be naturally supposed then that if one added to such a mixture an additional amount of toxin consisting of 1 M.L.D., this mixture should become lethal for guinea pigs. In fact, however, Ehrlich found that it was often necessary to add many minimal lethal doses to such a mixture before it became lethal. An explanation of this phenomenon again lies in the description of antigen-antibody combination illustrated in Figure 23. If we consider tube 4 in this figure as representing the addition of the L_0 quantity of toxin to 1 unit of antitoxin, it is evident that the small increase of antigen represented by a single additional M.L.D. would occasion only a trivial change in the molecular ratio of antibody combined with antigen. The added toxin would readily build itself into the lattice, and it might take the addition of a considerable amount of toxin in excess of the original L_0 dose before sufficient remained free in solution to be lethal for the guinea pig.

Zone of Inhibition. It has been mentioned that precipitation is inhibited in the presence of excess antigen. In this circumstance the reaction proceeds only so far as the formation of small complexes (as pictured in tube 6, Fig. 23), because no antibody links remain available to bring about further aggregation. It might be expected that an analogous failure of aggregation should be the case under the reverse situation where antibody is in excess, since here no free antigenic groups would be available to serve as links for precipitate formation. However, antibody excess inhibition does not occur in the precipitin reaction; instead a very small amount of antigen will pull out of solution as much antibody as it can combine with. The reason for this is not clear, but Marrack (15) has suggested that the difference may depend upon the manner in which antigen or antibody can pack around molecules of the other kind. In the region of antibody excess, globulin so completely covers the multivalent antigen molecule that many polar groups—aside from the specific reactive groups—are covered up. Consequently the complex loses its affinity for water, and flocculation occurs. This would not be true in the case of excess antigen because antigen molecules could not pack about antibody which may have only two reactive sites. Such complexes thus retain their solubility and fail to flocculate.

Reactions Involving Univalent Antibody or Antigen. 1. UNIVALENT ANTIBODY. Antibody molecules with only one reactive site for antigen cannot take part in the building up of a lattice structure because they lack the links

necessary to bring together molecules of antigen. Such antibodies can however become incorporated in a lattice as it forms in the presence of multivalent
antibody and antigen. The presence of both kinds of antibody in a single
sample of serum may be noted under the conditions of the Danysz experiment.
If antigen is added to the serum in small successive portions, a part of the
antibody is precipitated from solution with each addition, and it is found at
the completion of the experiment that all the avid antibody has been removed
but a residuum of nonprecipable antibody remains. If however all antigen
is added to the serum at once, the nonprecipitable antibody becomes included
in the total aggregate and it also is removed from solution (16).

One would suppose that under the special conditions of excess antibody
even univalent antibody might precipitate with antigen because of the packing
effect just described. That this does not occur reveals the inadequacies of our
present information in explaining all phases of the reaction.

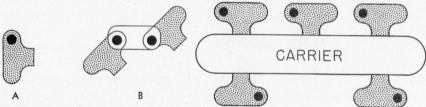

Fig. 27. A, univalent antigen-hapten. B,
limited complex formed by hapten and   Fig. 28. Diagrammatic representation of haptens
bivalent antibody.   coupled with a carrier.

2. UNIVALENT ANTIGEN. The reverse of the case just described might be
imagined to occur with an antigen which possesses only a single reactive group.
Such is indeed the case with the simplest haptens; these combine with antigen
but fail to provide binding sites for aggregate formation, as pictured in Figure
27. However, simple haptens with more than one combining site do not always
form aggregates either. Boyd (17) suggests that in these cases the spatial
relationships of reactive groups on the hapten may determine the failure,
since by steric hinderance they may block combination with more than one
molecule of antibody.

Simple haptens which combine with but do not precipitate antibody inhibit the subsequent reaction of the antibody with a complete antigen in which
the hapten functions as a determinant group. This inhibitory reaction is also
illustrated by Figure 27. The antibody is no longer available for combination
with the complete antigen which is represented by Figure 28 and which ordinarily reacts with antibody to form a lattice as shown in Figure 29.

Mechanism of the Agglutination Reaction. The same kind of equation
which described the precipitin reaction is applicable also when the antigen
is part of a bacterial cell (18). Although inhibition of flocculation in the
region of excess antibody does not occur in precipitation systems, it does take

place in the case of bacterial agglutination. No ready explanation for this difference is available. The zone phenomenon is much more strikingly evident in some bacterial systems than in others. In the case of the brucellas it is so common an occurrence that diagnostic agglutination tests must be arranged with the possibility in mind that a negative result in tubes containing higher concentrations of serum may be due to an excess of antibody rather than to its absence (19). Perhaps in these bacteria the antigenic groupings on the surface of the cell are relatively sparse, so that antibody excess is attained even with a moderately potent antiserum.

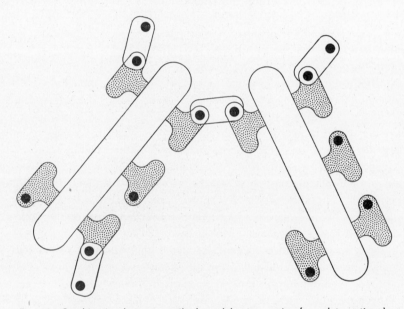

Fig. 29. Combination between antibody and hapten-carrier (complete antigen).

Alterations of Antibody Activities through Aging and Chemical and Physical Treatment. The activity of antibody may become modified spontaneously or through various manipulations. Simple aging of a serum sometimes results in the formation of antibodies which have lost their ability to agglutinate bacterial cells, but continue to combine with them. Mild heating of a serum may produce an analogous effect (20) as will also certain chemicals (21) and exposure to ultraviolet light (22).

Generally speaking such studies have not yet clarified which specific structures of the antibody molecule may be involved in serologic reactions, but they have provided some practical results in permitting the purification of antibodies for human use. For example, trypsin and pepsin may remove from horse antitoxin an inactive portion of the antibody molecule. The resultant antitoxic preparation is more active and at the same time its nitrogen content is considerably diminished over the original (23).

SUMMARY OF ANTIGENS, ANTIBODIES AND THEIR REACTIONS

Antigens are substances of protein or polysaccharide nature which, upon injection into animals, stimulate antibody responses. In order to qualify as an antigen a molecule must have a minimal molecular weight of about 10,000 and, probably more important, it must bear upon its surface a repetition of certain chemical groupings. These determine the antigenic specificity of the molecule; it is against these groups that the specific antibody response is directed.

The constituent of a group most important in determining its specificity is an acid radical. A degree of specificity may be possessed by groups which have no such radical. Of subsidiary importance in respect to specificity are the position of radicals in the group, the position of double bonds, and stereo-isomeric properties.

Antibodies are plasma globulin molecules, frequently the same as normal gamma globulin in all respects except for their ability to react specifically with antigen. The **physicochemical** properties of antibody globulin are not always the same, varying in an interrelated fashion with the species of animal undergoing vaccination, with different antigens employed for the vaccination of a single species, with the route of administration of antigen, and with the duration of the vaccination period and the intensity of treatment. The **serologic** properties of antibodies produced by one animal against a single antigenic substance are likewise variable. Antibodies produced early in the course of immunization have, in general, less ability to react with antigen, and are more highly specific in their reactivity. Later in the course of vaccination the antibodies produced are usually less specific, possessing now reactive sites with broader combining patterns. The later antibodies are also more avid for antigen because each molecule possesses multiple combining sites. An antiserum obtained at any particular point during the course of vaccination will reveal antibodies of all degrees of avidity, but the preponderance of poorly or highly reactive molecules will generally coincide with the duration and intensity of vaccination to which the animal has been subjected. In certain special cases, as exemplified by the vaccination of the horse with diphtheria toxin and other protein antigens, only antibodies of narrow reactive ability are produced at any time, but even here variations in avidity are found to occur in the antibodies contained in a single sample of serum.

This elasticity of physicochemical and serologic properties of antibodies depending upon such fairly well defined circumstances as nature of antigen and route of administration lead to the suggestion that different cells of the body may be able to produce antibody globulin depending in part upon these circumstances. Currently, there is evidence that three specific cell types may take part in the process of antibody manufacture: the cells of the reticuloendothelial system, lymphocytes and plasma cells. Whether future evidence will confirm this role for all these cells remains to be seen. Meanwhile, it seems worth considering that antibody production may be an even more general property of cells than would be indicated by these three possibilities.

The reaction between antibody and antigen is most simply explained at the present time on this basis: both are multivalent and the possession of multiple combining sites provides mutual bridging links so that a three-dimensional lattice structure of antigen-antibody may be built up. The occurrence of zone reactions, and of nonflocculating combinations when one or both of the components in the system is univalent, are discussed from this viewpoint.

These basic observations and hypotheses will enter later into the discussions of acquired resistance to infectious agents, and will be referred to also in the interpretation of certain of the aspects of hypersensitivity.

68054

BIBLIOGRAPHY

1. Marrack, J. R. The Chemistry of Antigens and Antibodies, London, His Majesty's Stationery Office, 1934.
2. Heidelberger, M. Bact. Rev., 3:49, 1939.
3. Hooker, S. B., and Boyd, W. C. J. Immunol., 33:337, 1937.
4. Boyd, W. C. J. Exper. Med., 75:407, 1942.
5. Haurowitz, F. Chemie der Antigene und der Antikörper, in Fortschritte der Allergielehre, ed. by P. Kallós, Basel, S. Karger, 1939, Chap. 2, p. 19.
6. How, A. E. J. Immunol., 37:77, 1939.
7. Hershey, A. D. J. Immunol., 42:455, 1941.
8. Teorell, T. J. Hyg., 44:227, 237, 1946.
9. Hartley, P. Brit. J. Exper. Path., 6:180, 1925.
10. Horsfall, F. L., Jr. J. Bact., 35:207, 1938.
11a. Hooker, S. B., and Boyd, W. C. J. Immunol., 33:337, 1937.
  b. Boyd, W. C., and Hooker, S. B. Proc. Soc. Exper. Biol. & Med., 39:491, 1938.
  c. Topley, W. W. C., Wilson, J., and Duncan, J. T. Brit. J. Exper. Path., 16:116, 1935.
  d. Wiener, A. S., and Herman, M. J. Immunol., 36:255, 1939.
  e. Duncan, T. J. Brit. J. Exper. Path., 19:328, 1938.
  f. Lanni, F. J. Exper. Med., 84:167, 1946.
12a. Heidelberger, M., Kendall, F. E., and Teorell, T. J. Exper. Med., 63:819, 1936.
  b. ———— and Kendall, F. E. J. Exper. Med., 64:161, 1936.
13. Danysz, J. Ann. Inst. Pasteur, 16:331, 1902.
14a. Healey, M., and Penfield, S. Brit. J. Exper. Path., 16:535, 1935.
  b. Pappenheimer, A. M., Jr., and Robinson, E. S. J. Immunol., 32:291, 1937.
15. Marrack, J. R. The Chemistry of Antigens and Antibodies, 2nd ed., London, His Majesty's Stationery Office, 1938.
16. Heidelberger, M., and Kendall, F. P. J. Exper. Med., 62:467, 1935.
17. Boyd, W. C. J. Exper. Med., 75:407, 1942.
18. Heidelberger, M., and Kabat, E. A. J. Exper. Med., 65:885, 1937.
19. Spencer, R. R. Pub. Health Rep., 45:2383, 1930.
20a. Eisenberg, P., and Volk, R. Ztschr. f. Hyg. u. Infektionskr., 40:155, 1902.
  b. Kleczkowski, A. Brit. J. Exper. Path., 22:44, 192, 1941.
21a. Eagle, H., Smith, D., and Vickers, P. J. Exper. Med., 63:617, 1936.
  b. ———— J. Exper. Med., 67:495, 1938.
22a. Tyler, A. J. Immunol., 51:157, 329, 1945.
  b. ———— and Swingle, S. M. J. Immunol., 51:339, 1945.
23a. Parfentjev, I. A. U. S. Patent 2,065,196, 1936.
  b. Pope, C. G. Brit. J. Exper. Path., 19:245, 1938.
  c. Northrop, J. H. J. Gen. Physiol., 25:465, 1942.

8

MECHANISMS OF ACQUIRED IMMUNITY

SEROLOGIC MANIFESTATIONS OF ANTIBODY ACTIVITY

Although our chief concern here is with immunity rather than serology, the serologic aspects of antibody activity may give us clues to the nature of the potential protective activities of antibodies in vivo. These reactions are of course of a great deal of usefulness in their own right also, providing diagnostic methods for the existence of infection and for the identification of infectious agents, and serving as well to identify antigens or antibodies unrelated to infectious disease.

The antibody produced in response to a single chemical substance may bring about a variety of observable effects. The nature of the specific union of antibody with antigen was described in the preceding chapter. Subsequent to this combination a number of visible reactions may occur, depending upon subsidiary conditions. Soluble antigens may **precipitate**, and if the antigen is in particulate form as part of a bacterial or other cell, the analogous aggregation which occurs is called **agglutination**. Certain cells, bacterial and others, may undergo **lysis** through the activity of antibody plus a component of normal serum called **complement**. When bacteria have combined with antibody they may be phagocytized by leukocytes and macrophages much more effectively than would be the case in the absence of antibody. Sensitization to phagocytosis by antibody is called **opsonization**. Almost any antigen combined with antibody will absorb complement even though the union be an invisible one, and this reaction is called **complement fixation**. These are the five major manifestations of antibody activity in the test tube, and these and related effects will be discussed in the present chapter.

For a long time after their discovery there was a tendency to ascribe these reactions to the activities of individual antibodies, each especially fitted to bring about a particular end result. It is common still to see references to "complement-fixing" or "agglutinating" antibodies produced during the course of one or another infection, and such terminology perpetuates the notion that separate antibodies are responsible for any one, in distinction to another, serologic manifestation.

UNITY OF ANTIBODY. It would seem a rather peculiar biologic stratagem if a single antigenic substance were actually to stimulate the production of a series of antibodies, all performing different functions. That this does not happen harmonizes with reason as well as with experimental evidence. Several of the early workers in immunology believed that the various serologic reactions were expressions of the same antigen-antibody reaction, and Zinsser epitomized these views in 1921 under the term unitarian theory (1). This hypothesis states simply that against a **single antigen** in a pure state, one variety of antibody is produced. This is present in the form of a serum constituent specifically capable of uniting with the antigen. The reactions which may follow the combination of the antigen with this antibody are determined by other substances present, such as complement or leukocytes, and by the environmental conditions under which the observations are made.

This viewpoint does not of course imply that only one antibody is produced in response to a bacterium or any other cell, since every cell is a mixture of antigens. But for each antigen of the cell there is produced one antibody with the capacity to combine with it, and to show any of a number of subsequent serologic events depending upon conditions.

This simple concept was not formulated earlier chiefly because the various serologic manifestations of an antiserum usually fail to show parallel titers, and it was generally considered that if all activities were due to a single antibody, then the same measure of its concentration should be obtained in any reaction into which it entered. There were several reasons for this misconception. To begin with, most early observations were made with complex antigens such as cells or protein mixtures, so that the activities of antibodies against more than one antigen were observed simultaneously. There are many sources of error in such systems; for example, an antibody which agglutinates bacteria by acting upon their flagella would obviously, for physical reasons, be incapable of causing lysis of the bacterial body in the presence of complement. There might be another antibody present in the same serum, directed against the cell body, which could bring about lysis, but this would be an independent antigen-antibody phenomenon, hence not to be compared quantitatively to the degree of flagellar agglutination. Perhaps a more striking reason for differences in titers of a serum in the different serologic reactions depends upon the nature of antibody and its reactivity with antigens. Thus, an antiserum containing a large proportion of univalent antibody might be able to aggregate an antigen only poorly, while the simple fact of combination could result in extensive fixation of complement. In both cases the same number of antibody molecules have reacted with the antigen, but the observable end result which each of these tests is designed to reveal suggests a discrepancy which is apparent rather than real. Titration differences of this kind will be discussed in more detail in later sections of this chapter.

Convincing evidence that the same antibody may bring about a variety of serologic reactions comes from experiments such as this: If a single pure soluble antigen is employed to stimulate antibody production, this antibody will precipitate the antigen in its soluble form and will combine with it to fix complement. If the soluble antigen is adsorbed to particles such as collodion, these can be agglutinated by the same antibody, and if phagocytes are added to such a mixture, the particles are also found to be opsonized. If now the original precipitating antibody is removed from the serum by permitting it to react with the antigen in soluble form and then centrifuging out the precipitate, all the other serologic abilities of the serum vanish with it (2).

The necessity for certain qualifications in regard to the unitarian viewpoint is apparent from previous discussions of the variations in physicochemical and serologic properties of antibodies produced in response to single antigens. Such antibodies are not single in the sense of all being perfect casts of the mold. But the variability which they display is not related to the serologic reactions in which they partake except insofar as an early-produced univalent antibody, for example, will not be able to cause aggregation because it lacks bridging groups. Even so it may be capable of causing opsonization, lysis and fixation of complement. The fact that some antibodies may lack the capacity to accomplish all the serologic manifestations of which antibodies in general are capable does not alter the viewpoint that all such reactions can be the expression of the activity of one antibody. This is certainly distinct from the viewpoint that there is, for any one antigen, an antibody for precipitation, another for agglutination, a third for lysis, and so on.

Other apparent exceptions to the unitarian theory occur also. For example, it is well known that antibody produced by the horse against pneumococcal capsule and other antigens readily precipitates these, but these combinations do not fix complement. On theoretic grounds, an antibody which is of sufficiently good quality to aggregate antigen should be able to perform in the other serologic reactions also. The explanation for this anomaly however probably resides in the complement rather than the antigen-antibody complex itself, for the complements of all animal species do not enter equally into antigen-antibody reactions, and when one fails another may succeed (see page 111).

MEANING OF TITER. Serologic tests are carried out to determine the suspected presence of antibodies or antigens. In the first case the test is set up with a known antigen; in the second, with known antiserum. Tests for antibodies usually account for their relative concentration as well as their existence in a serum. This additional information is ordinarily obtained by diluting the antiserum serially in a row of tubes. To these are added constant and arbitrarily fixed amounts of antigen and whatever other ingredients, such as complement or leukocytes, as may be necessary. The mixtures are incubated for an appropriate interval, usually at 37° C., and then scanned for the results called for by the particular test being conducted. The last tube in the series showing this effect is considered to contain one reacting unit of antibody, and on the basis of this tube the **titer** of the serum is determined. Titer is (or should be) an expression of the number of antibody units per unit volume of the undiluted serum. The logical unit volume is 1 milliliter. Thus, if the last tube showing a positive reaction contains 1 ml. of serum diluted 1:1,000, the titer of the serum is 1,000 (units of antibody per milliliter). Simple as this sequence is, it is not universally followed. Titer is often expressed as a function of dilution without reference to unit volume. As a result, the titers reported by different laboratories are often not to be compared at all, unless sufficient data are given to permit conversion to a unit volume basis.

In succeeding sections the various manifestations of antibody-antigen reaction in vitro are taken up. The description of methods is limited to those which clarify principles involved in the reactions. Various procedures to facilitate the setting up of tests and the reading of results are well described by Kabat and Mayer (3).

Precipitation. The precipitation reaction refers to the aggregation of soluble antigens by the action of antibody. Soon after the discovery of this activity of antibody, it was found that titration could not be carried out in the ordinary way by dilution of serum with addition of a fixed amount of antigen to all tubes in the series, because the tubes containing the higher dilutions of serum failed to show precipitation despite the presence in them of antibody. It was thought at one time that serum lipids might lend bulk to the precipitate, and that the dilution of serum would thin this nonspecific component to a point where precipitation could not occur, but this widely quoted view has found no confirmation (4). The precipitate is usually composed chiefly of antibody globulin and antigen, although certain normal serum lipids in small amount are necessary for precipitation as well as agglutination (see Chapter 7). Presumably serum which has been too far diluted fails to precipitate antigen for the simple reason that an excessive amount of antigen is generally used in the test. Zinsser (5) has pointed out that a number of molecules of antigen in solution, each exposing to antibody perhaps several combining groups, would constitute an antigen excess, whereas the same amount of antigen adsorbed to collodion particles would have some of the combining groups oriented to the adsorption surface and unavailable to antibody, so that in this physical state the same amount of antigen would not be in excess. Martin (6) has shown that if a properly small dose of soluble antigen is employed for the precipitation test, dilutions of serum will precipitate with it and titers may be obtained by the serum dilution method. For some odd reason however these facts have been widely ignored, and as the result of the early difficulties with precipitation titrations a reversed procedure was adopted and is still very often used, namely, titrating a constant amount of serum against graded dilutions of antigen. Unfortunately this procedure does not measure antibody; instead it indicates the concentration or purity of the antigen, and the results of "antibody titrations" obtained on the basis of this test have no meaning.

Other methods for measuring the precipitating ability of antibody are useful and shed light on the nature of the reaction as well. The quantitative procedure of Heidelberger described in the preceding chapter provides precise values for precipitating antibody and also yields information concerning its avidity for antigen. A less exact but very interesting procedure for obtain-

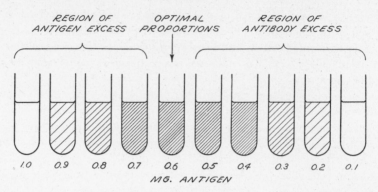

Fig. 30. Optimal proportions flocculation test.

ing a relative measure of concentration and combining power is based upon observations made some years ago by Opie (7) and Dean and Webb (8). If a constant amount of serum is placed in a row of tubes and decreasing amounts of antigen are added to these, then by observing the tube which shows first flocculation one determines the mixture in which antibody and antigen exist in **optimal or immunologically equivalent** proportions. The tubes on either side of the optimal proportions tube flocculate successively, spreading from the center. The most voluminous precipitate usually occurs to the left of the optimal proportions tube, in the region of slight antigen excess. But the best conditions for rapid lattice formation occur in the tube where combining sites of antigen and antibody molecules are equivalent. This is shown diagrammatically in Figure 30. The supernatant fluid in the optimal tube, when tested for residual antigen and antibody, is found either to be

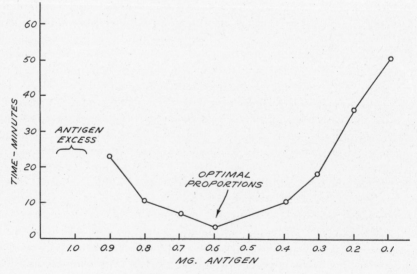

Fig. 31. Flocculation-time curve

free of both, or to show both in traces. In the tubes to the left of this the supernatants contain residual antigen; in those to the right, residual antibody only. The first tube in the diagram has failed to precipitate at all because of too great an excess of antigen; this is a so-called postzone of inhibition. Not all antigen-antibody systems show optimal proportions for flocculation at the neutral point. Most do, but in some cases this may occur in the presence of excess antibody (9) or antigen (10).

If the times at which flocculation occurs are plotted against the concentrations of antigen in the various tubes, a curve is obtained of the kind shown in Figure 31.

Now, if the same serum is set up in several rows of tubes, keeping the amount of antibody constant in each row but varying the dilution in successive series, and these are set up against varying amounts of antigen, the optimal proportions tube is found in each set to be that one showing the same ratio of antigen to antibody. This is shown in Table 2, where the optimal tube in each case is encircled.

Table 2. Tubes showing optimal proportions in series containing various dilutions of antibody

Antibody Dilution	Antigen Dilution										
	Un- diluted	1:2	1:4	1:8	1:16	1:32	1:64	1:128	1:256	1:512	1:1024
Undiluted	4+	4+	(4+)	3+	3+	2+	+	+	+		
1:2	2+	4+	4+	(3+)	3+	2+	+	+	+		
1:4		+	+	3+	(3+)	2+	+	+	+		
1:8			+	3+	(3+)	2+	+	+			
1:16				+	2+	(3+)	+	+			
1:32					+	2+	(2+)	+			
1:64							+	(2+)	+		
1:128								+	(+)	+	
1:256									−	−	−

This test gives a relative idea of the antibody potency of a serum when compared with other sera of the same kind. Thus, if two antisera against the same antigen show optimal flocculation, in one case in the tube containing 0.6 mg. of antigen (Fig. 30), and in the second case in the tube containing 0.3 mg. of antigen, the first serum is roughly twice as good as the second. The over-all result depends upon the relative quantities and qualities of antibodies in the two sera. An idea of the relative multivalencies of the two sera can be gained from these tests also. If the sera are employed in amounts adjusted so that the optimal proportions tube is the same in both cases, that is, the same amount of antigen is optimally combined with, then we know that the same over-all combining power of antibody is operating in both sera. If one of these contains antibody of good quality and the other contains antibody of poorer valence, this difference will reveal itself in the rates of flocculation, for the multivalent antibody should bring together antigen molecules into a lattice more efficiently and rapidly than antibody of poorer average combining ability. As shown in Figure 32, different flocculation curves will be obtained with these two sera, differing not only in the speed but also in the range of flocculation with varying amounts of antigen. The multivalent antibody also shows broader equivalence zones as may be determined by titrating the supernatants of these tubes for residual antigen and antibody.

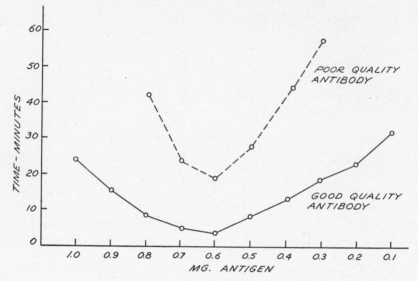

Fig. 32.   Comparative time-flocculation curves.

The serum indicated by the solid line flocculates in 2 minutes in the tube containing 0.6 mg. of antigen, but the tubes on either side of this come down quickly also because the antibody has a sufficient number of combining sites so that a moderate disproportion of antigen or antibody molecules does not unduly delay lattice formation. The serum portrayed by the broken line, although it flocculates optimally with the same amount of antigen, does so more slowly, and because the antibodies in this serum are poorer in numbers of combining sites, the disproportion of antigen and antibody molecules has a greater delaying effect on lattice formation, and the curve of flocculation is narrower and steeper, and the region of flocculation is narrow also.

The Ramon flocculation test for the quantitative estimation of diphtheria toxin or antitoxin (11) employs a similar scheme except that antigen is held constant while antibody is varied. This procedure is applicable to other toxin-antitoxin systems also, including tetanus and staphylococcus.

A procedure described recently for visualizing precipitation reactions takes advantage of an automatic optimal proportions adjustment between antigen and antibody as they diffuse at right angles to each other through an agar base. Mixed systems can be set up in a single preparation, since each system will show its own line of precipitation in the agar along the optimal proportions gradient. Thus, the relationship of two antigens or antibodies may be investigated. The method described by Elek (12) is shown in Figure 33; variations have also been employed very successfully (13).

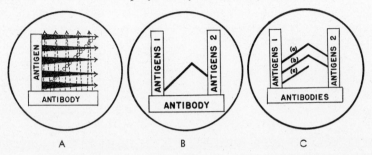

A   B   C

Fig. 33. A, diffusion of antibody and antigen through agar to form a band of precipitate in the zone of optimal proportions. B, loop of precipitate when a common antigen in two preparations react with the same antibody. C, reaction of a mixed antibody-containing serum with a mixture of antigens.

Strips of filter paper are soaked in antibody and antigen and embedded in agar in a Petri plate, as shown in Figure 33A. The arrows indicate by their thickness the dwindling of concentrations of antigen and antibody as these diffuse away from their respective sources. At points along the paths of their cross-diffusion antigen and antibody will be at optimal proportions, and the small circles represent the line of precipitate which forms in the agar at these points.

Now if a second antigen of unknown but suspected relationship to the first is also incorporated in this plate the result will be as shown in Figure 33B, if the relationship exists. A continuous band or loop of precipitate forms between the two strips, for whatever the relative concentrations of the antigen in the strips, they must meet at a common point. In the illustration Antigen 1 is more concentrated than Antigen 2, since it comes to optimal proportions with the common antibody in the area where antibody is more concentrated, i.e. close to its source of diffusion.

A mixed antibody-containing serum may also be employed with separate mixtures of antigens, for distinct lines of reaction will segregate each system, the common antigens in the mixtures forming loops ([a] and [b] in Figure 33C), the unrelated antigens single lines only ([c] in Figure 33C).

Diffusible toxins may be detected by streaking the suspected bacterium in the position occupied by the antigen-containing paper strip. As the toxin spreads through the agar it will meet with antitoxin diffusing from the paper strip to give patterns similar to those just described.

Agglutination. The reaction of agglutination is in principle like that of precipitation; both are aggregative, but in this case particulate rather than soluble antigens are brought together by antibody. Since values for the precipitating activity of antibody are sometimes troublesome to establish, especially when the antibody content of a serum is low so that optimal proportions and other tests are difficult to read, a method has been suggested for converting such titrations to more readily visualized agglutination reactions by adsorbing the soluble antigen to collodion particles. The particulate antigen is then mixed with dilutions of serum. This is based on the fact that an antigen adsorbed to a particulate surface exposes only a small part of its reactive groups to the antibody, so that inhibition by excess antigen is avoided. A further advantage lies in the greater visibility afforded by weakly aggregated particles as compared to lightly flocculated molecules of soluble antigen (2b, 14).

Titrations of the agglutinating activities of antisera are ordinarily carried out by the serial dilution of serum and the addition of a constant quantity of antigen suspension to all dilutions. A reading is made of the final dilution aggregating the arbitrarily appointed unit of antigen. Optimal proportions titrations may also be carried out with cellular antigens however (15), and Heidelberger's application of the quantitative technic has already been mentioned.

In the case of living bacterial antigens, the viability of the cells is not impaired as a result of agglutination per se, even in those cases where motile bacteria are brought to rest. This point will be of importance to the later discussion of the protection afforded by antibody against infection.

CONGLUTINATION PHENOMENON. Ehrlich, and Bordet and Gay early in the century described a peculiar ability of normal bovine serum to increase the agglutination of erythrocytes or bacteria in the presence of antibodies and complement, and this was suggested as a method for detecting antibody too weak to cause agglutination.

No particular application of this observation was made until 1945, when Wiener (16) suggested a somewhat analogous procedure for the detection of nonagglutinating Rh antibodies (see Chapter 32). It was found that incomplete or univalent antibody incapable of agglutinating Rh positive erythrocytes in routine tests could often cause agglutination if serum dilutions were made in normal plasma instead of saline. The normal plasma contains conglutinin, the nature of which is indicated by the ultracentrifugal studies of Pedersen (17) who has found in concentrated plasma an X-protein, a high-molecular-weight dissociable complex of albumin and globulin containing large amounts of lipid and probably also of carbohydrate. This substance is apparently absorbed by antibody-coated erythrocytes, causing them in some way to stick together without the necessity for bridging antibody groups. Dilution of plasma causes dissociation of this complex into albumin, gamma globulin and lipid; hence an antibody-containing serum itself, serially diluted in saline, cannot supply the conglutinin. The conglutinin activity may be produced by mixing solutions of albumin and gamma globulin in vitro (18).

Hole and Coombs (19) object that this phenomenon seen with Rh erythrocytes is not actually the conglutination phenomenon because the latter requires the presence of complement. Further clarification of the relationship between these two manifestations of the activity of plasma colloid upon sensitized cells in vitro is necessary.

Lysis and Complement. The activity of antibody which results in the lysis of cells introduces a new element into the consideration of antibody activity. The reaction is still a rather mysterious one on at least two counts. First, because the antibody alone cannot produce this effect but needs for the completion of the process a component of normal serum which is called complement, and second because this particular activity of antibody with complement is not a general one; it is limited to erythrocytes and a few species of bacteria. None of the gram-positive organisms are so affected, and among the gram-negative forms only the cholera vibrio, the typhoid bacillus, and to a less marked degree the paratyphoid organisms, the colon and dysentery bacilli, *Pseudomonas,* probably *Brucella* and *H. influenzae* are susceptible to lysis by antibody and complement.

Since complement is an essential ingredient in the production of antibody lysis, a description of its nature and activities is inserted here. It will be seen to take part also in the subsequently described reactions of complement-fixation and opsonization.

COMPLEMENT. Complement is a substance of mixed globulin composition which occurs in the plasma of all normal animals. It enters into immunologic reactions; generally speaking it is absorbed by any combination of antigen with antibody, though the extent and firmness of this absorption may vary considerably with the particular antibody concerned as well as with the complements of different species of animals.

The most spectacular effect of complement is in the lysis of cells which have been previously sensitized by antibody. It may have other effects as well, upon the opsonizing activity of antibody, upon the viral neutralizing activity of antisera in some cases, and upon the precipitation and agglutination reactions also. In the aggregative reactions the presence of complement is said to interfere with their full development (20), but in all other cases complement is helpful, as will be described in the sections devoted to these reactions. These effects may all presumably occur in vivo, since complement has been seen to act upon sensitized erythrocytes injected into the blood stream of frogs by observation of the vessels of the foot web. There is however some question about this point since it may be that complementing activity is activated by the processes which result in blood coagulation (21). Even if this is the case, complement activity would become manifest in areas of inflammation where the clotting mechanism comes into play; this is evidenced by the visible lysis of susceptible bacteria in the peritoneal cavities of guinea pigs (the Pfeiffer phenomenon). Complement may therefore have a part in protection against infection as well as in serologic diagnosis. Purely from the standpoint of diagnostic application in vitro, complement is used to test for suspected antibody or antigen in the so-called complement-fixation test and its variations, as discussed in later sections of this chapter.

In its nature, this substance has no resemblance to antibody. Its concentration in the serum is rather constant for each species of animal, although its level may sometimes increase as the result of infection (22). In the human being complement is usually present at birth, though in somewhat lower concentration than in the adult (23). The guinea pig possesses higher levels than other laboratory animals or man, and in consequence guinea pig serum is widely employed as a source of the substance. Such serum contains between 0.25 and 0.40 mg. of complement protein per milliliter, or about one-half per cent of the total serum proteins. In terms of the quantity necessary for the lysis of a single sheep erythrocyte, Heidelberger has estimated 25,000 molecules of complement with about 500 molecules of antibody (24). The components of human complement are substitutive with those of the guinea pig (25).

The chemical characterization of complement has been difficult because of its complex nature. At the present time four components are recognized on the basis of hemolysis; not all these components are necessary for simple absorption by an antigen-antibody complex. The components are termed $C'1$, $C'2$, $C'3$ and $C'4$. $C'1$ and $C'2$ separate on dialysis, the first appearing in the sediment (euglobulin), the second in the supernatant (muco-euglobulin). Both are heat labile. The third and fourth components are recognized in a negative way, i.e. by their selective removal or inactivation. $C'3$ is removed by yeast and $C'4$ is destroyed by treatment with ammonia (26). Both these components are heat stable. These involved relationships are shown in the diagram.

THE COMPONENTS OF COMPLEMENT (C')

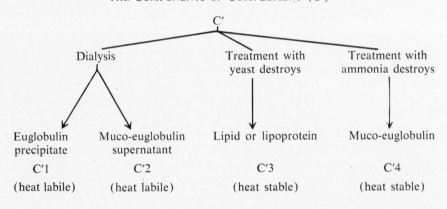

By proper juggling of these methods so as to add or eliminate components individually, it has been possible to characterize the complements of various species (27). It has thus been found that some complements, including those of the horse, cow, sheep and mouse, lack $C'2$ and so are nonhemolytic (28). These complements may however be well absorbed by antigen-antibody combinations as will be mentioned later in connection with the conglutination complement absorption reaction. More details about the chemical nature of complement may be found in the literature on immunochemistry (3, 24, 25) in addition to other references already cited.

A well known characteristic of complement is its rapid deterioration after withdrawal from the body. Potency dwindles rapidly, within 24 hours at room temperature, and after a few days at refrigerator temperatures. Preservation may be accomplished by the addition of high concentrations of sodium chloride, or more practically by the storage of freshly collected serum at low temperature ($-25°$ C.), or by lyophilization. At $56°$ C. the lytic activity is completely destroyed in 20 minutes due to the lability of C'1 and C'2, and this procedure is routinely employed for ridding an antiserum of its normal content of complement before using it in serologic tests. If it is required, known amounts of complement can then be added to such tests.

The same complement of any one species of animal enters into all antigen-antibody reactions, but the usual effects of complement activity are not always obvious. Hemolytic and bactericidal activity fails to occur entirely with some complements (28, 29), while in other cases a complement may enter into lysis with the antibody produced by one species of animal, but not with that of another (30). The more basic reaction of absorption can vary considerably, so that one complement may be poorly absorbed by a particular antigen-antibody system whereas another is firmly bound. Thus, Scholtens (31) has found that combinations of rabbit antibodies with typhoid and dysentery bacilli fix guinea pig complement well, whereas human antibodies combined with these same antigens fix this complement poorly. In these cases therefore there are wide divergencies between the results of agglutination and complement-fixation tests carried out with human sera. Similar earlier-described examples are also well known (30, 32), and recently Coombs and Hole have been adding to our information along this line (19, 33) and have suggested methods for choosing the best-absorbed complement for particular antigen-antibody systems (see conglutinating complement absorption test, page 118).

The mechanics by which complement is absorbed by antigen-antibody complexes are not yet appreciated. Complement does not combine with antigen alone. It has a loose affinity for antibody, but a much stronger affinity for the finished combination between these two elements. Neither is there a settled opinion regarding the mode of its action in producing lysis. One viewpoint regards this activity as an enzymic one (25), while another suggests that it is the antibody which may react over and over again like enzyme, while complement appears to act as a cofactor (34a).

LYTIC REACTION. The essential mechanism by which antibody and complement cause a cell to lose its contents is not known. For lysis of erythrocytes to take place it is apparent from quantitative considerations that only isolated areas of the stroma, less than 0.1 per cent of the surface, need be combined with antibody molecules. About 50 times as much complement as antibody is necessary. In erythrocytes undergoing lysis, the cell stroma retains its form, but alterations in it permit the hemoglobin to escape. The hemoglobin itself is not changed by the reaction. Figure 34 depicts sheep erythrocytes immediately before and immediately after lysis has occurred, as observed in the darkfield. The cell membrane appears to remain intact after lysis, but a sudden narrowing of the refractile rim of the cell is seen at the moment when lysis occurs.

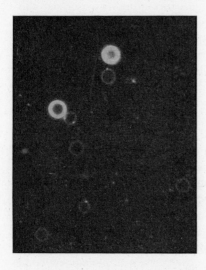

Fig. 34. Darkfield photograph of lysis of erythrocytes by antibody and complement. The cells with wide rims are unlysed; those with narrow rims have just undergone lysis.

TITRATION OF LYTIC ACTIVITY. The relationship of lysis to other antibody effects is somewhat unpredictable. It might be inferred that since the lytic reaction does not require antibodies to serve as links as in aggregation, much smaller quantities of antibody might suffice for this effect than for agglutination. This is apparently the case with the commonly employed antisheep cell sera produced by the rabbit. Such sera contain two main antibodies, one directed against the Forssman antigen, a second against a protein of the stroma. These sera always continue to cause lysis in dilutions far beyond those which produce agglutination. In contrast however an antibody against another stroma antigen of the sheep erythrocyte—the antibody produced by human beings with infectious mononucleosis—agglutinates cells in higher dilutions than it causes lysis. Human isoagglutinins are also more effective in causing agglutination than lysis of their corresponding red cells. In these instances it may be that complements other than that of the guinea pig would cause lysis to occur with smaller amounts of antibody; tests of this point have apparently not been made. Or the location of the antigen molecules in the stroma may be concerned as is suggested by Coombs' findings with various samples of bovine erythrocytes some of which are readily agglutinable while others are refractory, though all undergo hemolysis equally well ([34b], see also page 490). Whatever the reasons, such differences in relative lytic and agglutinating activities of various antierythrocyte antibodies are still difficult to predict and to explain.

Titrations of the lytic activities of antisera are carried out by the serum dilution method. The serum is first deprived of its normal content of complement by heating at 56° C. for 15 or 20 minutes, so that fixed amounts of complement from an outside source may be employed for the test. In lytic tests three variables must be dealt with: antigen, antibody and complement; and two of these must be fixed in order that the third may be determined. The unit of antigen is fixed arbitrarily; in the case of erythrocytes, for example, this is often designated as 0.5 ml. of a 2 per cent suspension. If antibody is to be titrated, then the unit of complement must also be fixed arbitrarily. This introduces a flexible source of error since antibody and complement exhibit a considerable mutual interdependence in their activities, a deficiency in one being made good by an excess of the other. Thus, if the amount of normal serum chosen to serve as the unit of complement contains more than the usual concentration of this, the hemolytic unit of antibody determined will be small, i.e. the potency of the antiserum titer will appear to be high, and vice versa. In practice however this consideration does not cause much difficulty. Normal guinea pig serum is the usual source of complement and its content is fairly constant. Constancy is even better assured if the sera of a number of animals are pooled for use. A quantitative chemical determination of complement can be made, but the procedure is not simple and this degree of accuracy is unnecessary for general serologic purposes.

If complement is to be titrated it becomes necessary to fix the unit of lytic antibody, and this is done on the basis of the titration just described. Obviously, the performance of the routine type of lytic test requires a certain degree of faith, since each of two variables is fixed with reference to the other. Continuity can be established by titrating new batches of antibody with previously used complement, and fresh pools of complement with previously employed antiserum.

The lysis of bacteria is determined by a somewhat different method, since the easily visible result afforded by the liberation of hemoglobin has no counterpart in the case of bacteria. Mixtures of antibody, bacteria and complement are incubated and then incorporated in agar to make a pour plate. The result is determined by colony counts after appropriate incubation of these cultures. A source of error here lies in the possibility that rapid agglutination of the bacteria may occur without lysis. Each clump of cells will then give rise to a single colony on the plate, and the consequent sparsity of colonies may falsely suggest bacteriolysis.

Zones of inhibition may occur in the region of antibody excess in lytic tests, most frequently in bacteriolysis. The reason probably lies in the method employed here; in order to obtain countable numbers of colonies thin suspensions of bacteria are used as antigen. The addition of even a moderately potent antiserum to a scant suspension of antigen is apt to result in antibody excess in the first tubes of the series.

This zonal effect is referred to as the Neisser-Wechsberg phenomenon, or the deviation of complement, because it was at one time thought that excess free antibodies might deviate complement from antigen-antibody complexes, and thus account for the failure of lysis. Since complement does not combine well with antibody alone however, some other explanation must be sought. One possibility is that, in the presence of a sufficiently great excess of antibody, complete dissociation of the antigen-antibody union may occur. Another possibility which may sometimes apply is the complement-destructive effect of certain antisera. A nonspecific anticomplementary activity of antisera may be due to a number of causes such as bacterial contamination or simple aging, and sometimes is present for no apparent reason at all. If this exists in small degree it would be evident only in those tubes containing the greatest concentrations of serum.

Complement Fixation. The diagnostic use of the complement-fixation reaction is limited to relatively few diseases, but because this is the basis for the Wassermann reaction it is one of the most frequently performed serologic tests. The technical aspects of this reaction are relatively unwieldy and exacting. However, it frequently supplies information which is not obtainable from other serologic tests, for reasons to be discussed later.

ESSENTIAL STEPS IN THE COMPLEMENT-FIXATION REACTION. This test is based on the fact that complement enters into combinations formed between soluble or particulate antigens with antibody even when the combination does not become visible as an aggregate. In testing for a suspected antibody or antigen, the essence of the test is to determine whether or not complement is taken up by the mixture of these two substances. As in all serologic procedures, one of the two substances must be known in order that the other may be tested for.

Serum, antigen and complement are first mixed and incubated. After the proper interval, a second antigen-antibody system is added; its purpose is to indicate what has been the fate of the complement in the first mixture. To be useful as an indicator this second system must be an easily visualized one, and consists of erythrocytes (usually sheep cells) mixed with rabbit anti-red cell antibody.

Now if, in the test mixture, complement has been taken up then none remains available to cause lysis of the red cells of the second system. This result constitutes a positive complement-fixation test. If on the other hand no reaction has occurred between the serum and antigen in the first mixture the complement remains free, and on addition of the sensitized red cells it enters into this reaction to produce hemolysis. Lysis then constitutes a negative complement-fixation test. There are of course gradations of positivity, for only a portion of the complement may be used up in the first part of the test. The following is a summary of the procedures in this test:

> Step 1. Mix: suspected (or known) antiserum
> suspected (or known) antigen
> complement
> Incubate

Step 2. Add: sheep erythrocytes + antibody
Incubate

Read for hemolysis:
no lysis = **positive** fixation in Step 1
lysis = **negative** fixation in Step 1

CHOICE OF COMPLEMENT FOR THE TEST. Guinea pig complement is ordinarily used, but neither this nor the complements of other species necessarily behave in the same way with respect to different antigen-antibody systems. Certain complements fail to cause hemolysis though they may be absorbed by antigen-antibody systems; others may be fixed by antigens combined with the antibodies of one species but not those of another, and in some cases a complement which is hemolytic may be only weakly absorbed by antigen-antibody systems (28, 29, 30, 31, 32). The failure may lie either with the inability of the antibody to adsorb complement, or with the presence of a nonspecific substance in serum which inhibits fixation (33b). The factor of choice of complement is of particular importance in experimental procedures where there is no precedent established for the proper ingredient to be employed, since false negative results may be obtained. Rice has suggested an indirect test to ascertain that this kind of occurrence does not pass unnoticed (35). A description of this follows the present discussion.

The choice of complement available for tests is limited since the non-hemolytic complements (horse, cat, pig and mouse) are unsuited for the complement-fixation reaction. To circumvent this limitation a different procedure, the conglutinating complement-fixation reaction, has been suggested (33); this permits the use of nonhemolytic complements, as described in a succeeding section.

Another aspect of complement that requires careful attention in the performance of these tests is its marked susceptibility to all kinds of deleterious influences. The antiserum being tested may be anticomplementary as a result of bacterial contamination or for other reasons, so that a control tube must be included with every test to rule out the possibility of nonspecific destruction of complement. This control consists of serum incubated with complement in the absence of antigen. Similarly, the antigen must be tested for its possible anticomplementary activity by mixing it with complement in the absence of serum. After incubation in both cases sensitized erythrocytes are added to the tubes and if complement has not been destroyed complete lysis should occur.

NATURE AND MECHANICS OF THE COMPLEMENT-FIXATION REACTION. The usefulness of the complement-fixation test centers in the fact that complement may enter into the antigen-antibody complex at the earliest stage of combination. Since subvisible complexes can fix complement, this reaction may be expected to occur (*a*) when the proportions of antibody and antigen are unfavorable for flocculation, (*b*) when the amount of antibody or antigen is so small that a visible flocculate is not produced, or (*c*) when the quality of antibody is too poor to bring about aggregation. Generally speaking, these expectations are fulfilled (36) as illustrated by the data in Table 3 from published experiments of Goodner and Horsfall (37).

Table 3. Precipitation and complement fixation of rabbit antipneumococcal capsule serum with purified capsular polysaccharide

| DILUTION OF SSS | DILUTION OF SERUM | | | |
| | 1:10 | | 1:50 | |
	PRECIPITATION	COMPLEMENT FIXATION	PRECIPITATION	COMPLEMENT FIXATION
1:2,500	—	3+	—	—
1:12,500	+	4+	—	—
1:62,500	3+	4+	±	+
1:312,500	2+	4+	—	4+
1:1,562,500	+	4+	—	4+
1:7,812,500	—	3+	—	4+
1:39,062,500	—	—	—	±

The serum diluted 1:10 illustrates the broader range of complement fixation as compared with precipitation, extending into the regions of antigen and antibody excess. The serum diluted 1:50 precipitates minimally with only one of the dilutions of antigen, while complement fixation with this small amount of antibody continues to occur through decreasing amounts of antigen to about 1/600 of that which precipitates. The ability of nonprecipitating (univalent) antibody to fix complement, though not shown here, can also be demonstrated.

For these reasons, all revolving about the pivotal fact that complement enters into antigen-antibody complexes in the early stage of combination, the complement-fixation test may be positive earlier in the course of an infectious disease than the agglutination reaction, at a time when antibody is perhaps scant and largely univalent. For analogous reasons it may be the only in vitro diagnostic test available in certain virus infections, because the etiologic agent cannot be cultivated in large amounts for use as antigen, and antibody responses in the infected host may also be poor.

Not only is complement adsorbed by small complexes of antigen and antibody, but it appears to be more effectively taken up at this stage than later in the course of aggregation in systems where flocculation eventually occurs. This is apparently a matter of relative surface area available for fixation of complement; obviously this will be greater in the early stage of antigen-antibody combination when complexes are small. As correlaries to this information, the complement-fixation reaction is found in general to proceed most extensively under the following conditions:

1. Mixture of the ingredients in a definite order—antibody, complement, antigen—so that complement is present at the inception of combination between antigen and antibody.

2. Incubation of the test at low temperature (4° C.) for a prolonged period (18 hours). The complement-fixation test for syphilis proceeds optimally under this condition, possibly because the rate of complex formation is retarded (38).

As mentioned before, some serologic systems fail entirely to fix guinea pig complement. This is true for example of horse antibodies against a variety of antigens including pneumococcal SSS, anthrax bacillus carbohydrate and the influenza bacillus. The complements of other species may enter into such combinations however. In the following paragraphs alternative procedures are described which may succeed in instances where the conventional test fails.

INDIRECT COMPLEMENT FIXATION TEST. When the sera of various animal species are being surveyed for the presence of an antibody by the complement fixation method, negative results may in some instances be due to a failure of a particular antibody-antigen combination to fix the complement being employed. Rice (35) has suggested the following procedure to obviate the possibility that positive sera will not be overlooked on this basis. The test is set up in duplicate, as shown in the chart. Set 1 is an ordinary direct test. Set 2 contains the same initial mixture of test serum, antigen and complement, but after incubation a second antiserum is added of known ability to combine with the antigen and to fix complement; this is referred to as standard antiserum.

	Set 1		Set 2
1. Mix:	test serum antigen complement		test serum antigen complement
		Incubate	
2. Add:	saline		standard antiserum
		Incubate	
3. Add:	sensitized erythrocytes		sensitized erythrocytes
		Incubate	

Read for hemolysis:

1. No hemolysis = + fixation
2. Hemolysis = (a) − fixation or   If 2(a): no hemolysis
   (b) failure of this antibody-antigen combination to fix complement   If 2(b): hemolysis

If the result of the direct test is positive, the second set may be ignored. If the result of the direct test is negative however, it may be due either to the lack of antibodies in the test serum or to the failure of antibodies in this serum to fix complement after combination with the antigen. If the first is the case, then the indirect test will show a positive result (no hemolysis), for the standard antiserum combines with antigen to fix complement. If the second is the case then the indirect test will show a negative result (hemolysis) for the test serum by combining with antigen has made this unavailable to the standard antiserum and complement fixation cannot occur. Thus, when the test serum possesses antibody but this is incapable of fixing complement with the antigen in question, both sets in this test show hemolysis.

CONGLUTINATING COMPLEMENT-ABSORPTION TEST. In those cases where guinea pig complement fails to be fixed, other hemolytic complements may prove successful, but the number of these is limited as pointed out before. Coombs and Hole (19, 33) have recently suggested a complement-fixation test based upon the conglutination reaction (see page 108); this requires the absorption of complement in order for agglutination to become evident. For this test a nonhemolytic complement is employed, and that of the horse has been found to be well absorbed in several systems where guinea pig complement is only weakly taken up.

The first stage of the test is the same as that in the conventional fixation test, i.e. antigen is mixed with suspected antiserum (or vice versa) in the presence of the conglutinating complement. After a proper interval to permit fixation, the indicator system is added, and this differs from that of the ordinary fixation test. It consists of sheep erythrocytes mixed with heat-inactivated bovine serum. The bovine serum contains normal antibodies against sheep cells as well as conglutinin. If complement has not been fixed in the first stage, the added sheep cells are agglutinated by the combination: antibody, conglutinin, complement. If complement has been fixed, no agglutination takes place, since bovine conglutinin can act only in the presence of complement and antibody. These steps may be summarized as follows:

Step 1. Mix: suspected (or known) antiserum
          suspected (or known) antigen
          horse complement

Incubate

Step 2. Add: sheep erythrocytes + inactivated bovine serum
          (containing normal antisheep cell antibody
          and conglutinin)

Incubate

Read for agglutination:
          no agglutination = **positive** fixation in Step 1
          agglutination = **negative** fixation in Step 1

Opsonization. Another of the serologic manifestations of antibody is opsonization, the preparation of bacteria for phagocytosis. Although phagocytosis of most particular matter ordinarily occurs without the necessity for any particular intervening mechanism, it has been described in Chapter 3 that many pathogenic bacteria resist ingestion because of a repellent activity of surface antigens upon leukocytes which is especially evident in fluid medium. In such cases sensitization of the microbes by antibody markedly increases their engulfment. It bears repeating that this activity of antibody is simply another of its manifestations; there is no special immune body responsible for opsonization. The determining factors are the presence, along with antibody, of leukocytes and complement.

OPSONINS AND BACTERIOTROPINS. A confusion in terminology persisting from the early days of immunology requires clarification. This arises from the use of two terms, opsonin and bacteriotropin, to describe the activity of antibody which sensitizes bacteria to phagocytosis. Wright and Douglas in 1904 (39) first observed that the fresh serum of normal animals promoted the phagocytosis of various bacteria, and they applied to this serum element the name opsonin. They found that opsonin was a heat-labile element of the serum, and it was soon considered by other workers that opsonin and complement might be identical. A short time later Neufeld and Hüne (40) found a similar but much more powerful effect with specific bacterial antisera resulting from vaccination. The sensitizing activity in this case was found to be heat stable and thus apparently independent of complement for its activity, and to differentiate it from opsonin, the term bacteriotropin was introduced.

Now in reality the process of phagocytosis in the presence of antibody is greatly aided by complement, whether the antibody is normal (as in the case of Wright's work) or acquired. In the first case Maaløe (21b) has shown with *Salmonella breslau* that complement is essential for phagocytosis in the presence of normally occurring antibody. His experiments have indicated further that very small concentrations of complement, 1:1,000 or less, suffice; and that the technical methods available to Neufeld for washing leukocytes free of serum were such that he probably retained complement in sufficient concentration to account for his findings in its assumed absence. The activity of complement with more potent sera resulting from vaccination has been ascribed to an increase in the rate of phagocytosis, not in its eventual extent (41).

There is thus no valid reason for the differentiation implied by the terms opsonin and bacteriotropin, and since the former is a more convenient one it will be used here.

OPSONIZING EFFECT OF ANTIBODY. The chief reasons for increased engulfment by phagocytic cells subsequent to sensitization by antibody appear to be these: Bacteria which discourage leukocytes because of their surface antigens are, after combination with antibody against these substances, at least partially coated with a layer of globulin. This effect is illustrated by the behavior of bacteria at an oil-water interface before and after treatment with antibody. Lipoidal bacteria, such as the acid-fast forms, move into the oil from the interface; after treatment with antibody they move into the water phase. The surfaces of antibody-treated bacterial cells take on the cataphoretic and iso-electric properties of plasma globulin (42). It is evident that this surface is more congenial to the phagocyte than is the bacterial surface itself, but the reasons for this are not clear. The precise role of complement in this mechanism is also not understood at present. Recent studies of

Delaunay and Pages (43) indicate that complement stimulates the respiratory metabolism of leukocytes.

TITRATION OF OPSONIC ACTIVITY. The titration of antibody by observing its effect on phagocytosis is not a frequently employed procedure. For diagnostic purposes its most frequent use is in undulant fever, where the so-called opsonophagocytic index may be a worthwhile adjunct to other methods of laboratory diagnosis. Two chief objections to the method are the difficulties in the technical procedure and in assessing the results quantitatively. Nonetheless, as a method for determining the over-all degree of acquired resistance developed against an organism this procedure may be of value, especially when carried out with fresh uncoagulated whole blood.

Tests in vitro may be done either with antiserum plus added leukocytes, or with whole blood, in which case the immune animal supplies the phagocytic cells also. Bacteria are added to such preparations and after an incubation period samples are removed to slides and stained. The polymorphonuclear leukocytes are examined for their content of bacteria. A comparison is made with a parallel control preparation in which normal serum or blood has been employed. The **phagocytic index** is determined for the experimental and control preparations; this value expresses the average number of bacteria per phagocyte. The **opsonic index** is the ratio of the immune to the normal phagocytic index. If for example it were found that the blood under test revealed 30 bacteria per leukocyte, while the normal preparation showed 5 per cell, the opsonic index would be 6. In other words there is six times as much phagocytosis in the presence of antibody as in normal serum or blood.

Serologic Reactions Revealing Univalent Antibody or Antigen. Several methods are available for demonstrating indirectly in vitro the combining activity of antibody which is not good enough in quality to cause aggregation of antigen. Analogously, the combination between a univalent antigen or hapten and its antibody may be demonstrated by means of the inhibition test.

The inhibition test has been used extensively by Landsteiner (44a) in studies with simple chemical haptens. This reaction depends upon the fact that the union of antibody with hapten results in the formation of soluble compounds, the single antigenic group in this case providing no link for building up a lattice of antibody with antigen. In order to reveal that such a combination has occurred, a complete antigen of which the hapten is a component is added to the mixture. Precipitation of the complete antigen is inhibited by the prior attachment of hapten to the antibody. An interesting alternative method has been suggested by Coombs (44b) wherein the hapten is coupled with a serum containing nonagglutinating antibodies against erythrocytes. The hapten can then be attached to the red cells by permitting the antiserum to react with them. The test for antibodies against the hapten may then be visualized through the agglutination of the red cells.

The blocking reaction is analogous to the inhibition test, but it is employed in the reverse circumstance where antibody is univalent. This reaction was demonstrated with bacteria some years ago (45) but was little used until rather recently when Wiener (46a) and Race (46b) independently observed the presence of nonagglutinating antibodies against Rh antigens in maternal sera, and applied the blocking test to their demonstration. When serum containing nonagglutinating or incomplete Rh antibody is mixed with Rh positive erythrocytes, union occurs but there is no agglutination. There is thus no visible evidence that antibody is present in the serum. If now there is added another antiserum with known agglutinating power it is found that agglutination still fails to occur because the incomplete antibody of the first serum has combined with all available antigenic groups in the erythrocyte stroma, i.e. has blocked the subsequent attachment of agglutinating antibody. If the first serum had contained no antibody, addition of the second serum would have resulted in agglutination.

The developing test is an interesting application of serologic engineering. This again is a revival of an earlier demonstration for current usefulness with Rh antigen-antibody systems (47). The cells and serum under study are mixed so that the nonagglutinating antibody, if it is present, may attach to the cell surfaces. The erythrocytes are then washed free of nonspecific serum constituents by centrifugation. The specifically combined univalent antibody globulin however remains attached to the red cells. These cells are now resuspended in saline and then exposed to an antiserum produced in rabbits against globulin itself. The antiglobulin antibodies function as antiantibodies, aggregating the red blood cells by attaching to the incomplete antibodies on the surfaces of the red cells. The purpose of this test is the same as that of the blocking reaction; to demonstrate the presence in sera of antibodies incapable of causing agglutination of erythrocytes containing the homologous Rh antigen. This test is the most delicate of the procedures available for the purpose.

The events in this procedure are illustrated in Figure 35.

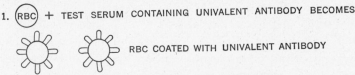

1. (RBC) + TEST SERUM CONTAINING UNIVALENT ANTIBODY BECOMES

RBC COATED WITH UNIVALENT ANTIBODY

2. RBC WASHED FREE OF NONSPECIFIC SERUM PROTEINS

3. THE ADDITION OF ANTIGLOBULIN ANTIBODY ◺ CAUSES AGGREGATION OF ERYTHROCYTES BY ATTACHMENT TO THE UNIVALENT ANTIBODY GLOBULIN ON THEIR SURFACES

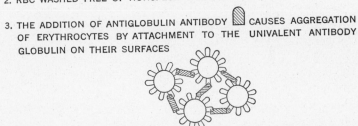

Fig. 35. Diagrammatic representation of the Coombs developing reaction.

The demonstration of univalent antibacterial antibodies in human serum has also been successfully made with this procedure (48). This should prove to be a useful method in dealing with the question of the relationship of antibodies to resistance in various infectious diseases where a correlation is not obvious.

The conglutination phenomenon has been described earlier in this chapter in conjunction with the agglutination reaction. It also may be applied in instances where it is desired to reveal weakly agglutinating antibody.

Other specific tests will be described in relation to the Rh antigen-antibody systems (see Chapter 32).

Neutralization. NEUTRALIZATION OF TOXINS. Antibodies are produced against a variety of diffusible bacterial toxins—diphtheria, tetanus, botulinus, scarlatinal and others—as well as antigenic venoms of snakes and certain insects, such as bees. These antibodies, when they combine with the poisonous antigens, fortunately neutralize their toxic properties, perhaps by reacting with the same portion of the toxic molecule as does the tissue substrate, perhaps by simply eliminating the poison from the body fluids, or preventing its entrance into cells (48d). This is a reversible neutralization as evidenced by dissociation of the antigen-antibody union under appropriate conditions.

Antitoxins produced in the horse against diphtheria and other toxins precipitate only in very narrow ranges of proportions, corresponding to the equivalence zones. This was pointed out before as a characteristic of the antibody response of the horse to certain types of antigens, nontoxic as well as toxic (see Chapter 6). On either side of the flocculation zone, however, soluble compounds of toxin-antitoxin are formed, and these are nonpoisonous to the degree that sufficient antitoxin is present. Since visible evidence of this effect does not appear in vitro, injection of mixtures into susceptible animals is used to make the demonstration.

NEUTRALIZATION OF VIRUSES. Many filterable viruses when mixed with the serum of an individual recovered from infection, or following vaccination, are found to be inhibited in their ability to cause infection in a fresh host. The nature of this inactivation is not clear; the possibility of a direct virucidal effect is countered by the fact that certain manipulations, such as dilution of a neutral serum-virus mixture, may result in the reappearance of infectious virus in the mixture (49). Morgan (50), however, has observed with western equine encephalomyelitis virus that neutralizing antibodies may be virucidal if complement is present.

In the case of larger viruses, including those of psittacosis, lymphogranuloma venereum, vaccinia, lymphocytic choriomeningitis and influenza, soluble antigens may be obtained from suspensions of the viral particles which react with antisera in complement-fixation and in some cases in precipitation tests. The antibodies concerned in these serologic reactions however represent merely the response of the body to multiple antigenic substances of which the viruses are composed; they do not appear to be the same as those which neutralize viral infectivity, and which may be more closely related to acquired resistance than the antibodies active in the ordinary serologic tests.

NEUTRALIZATION OF VIRAL HEMAGGLUTININS. Mention has been made before (in Chapters 2 and 3) of the ability of a variety of viruses and rickettsias to cause agglutination of the normal erythrocytes of different species of animals. In the case of influenza virus there is some evidence that the hemagglutinating activity may be related to infectivity, the virus acting like an enzyme upon specific erythrocyte receptors as substrate. It has been found that the hemagglutinating activity of these infectious agents is inhibited by antisera, and in the case of the influenza virus at least, the antibody which causes agglutination-inhibition is considered by many workers to be the same as that which neutralizes viral infectivity. Opinion on this matter is not entirely settled however (see Chapter 28).

This reaction is a useful diagnostic one in determining the existence of humoral responses to viruses. Whether it measures also protective resistance is a question which depends upon the relationship of resistance to neutralizing antibody, and this question cannot be answered in general terms at the present time. It will be considered in individual cases in the later chapters dealing with infectious diseases.

BIBLIOGRAPHY

1. Zinsser, H.   J. Immunol., 6:289, 1921.
2a. Felton, L. D., and Bailey, G. H.   J. Immunol., 11:197, 1926.
  b. Jones, F. S.   J. Exper. Med., 46:303, 1927; 48:183, 1928.
  c. Mudd, S., Lucke, B., McCutcheon, M., and Strumia, M.   J. Exper. Med., 52:313, 1930.
  d. Avery, O. T., and Goebel, W.   J. Exper. Med., 54:437, 1931.
  e. Delves, E.   J. Infect. Dis., 60:55, 1937.
  f. Heidelberger, M., and Kabat, E. A.   J. Exper. Med., 63:737, 1936.
3. Kabat, E. A., and Mayer, M. M.   Experimental Immunochemistry, Springfield, Ill., Charles C Thomas Co., 1948.
4. Marrack, J., and Smith, F. C.   Brit. J. Exper. Path., 12:30, 1931.
5. Zinsser, H.   J. Immunol., 18:483, 1930.
6. Martin, D. S.   J. Lab. & Clin. Med., 28:1477, 1943.
7. Opie, E. L.   J. Immunol., 8:19, 1923.
8. Dean, H. R., and Webb, R. A.   J. Path. & Bact., 29:473, 1926.
9. Burnet, F. M.   J. Path. & Bact., 34:471, 1931.
10. Malkiel, S., and Boyd, W. C.   J. Exper. Med., 66:383, 1937.
11. Ramon, G.   Compt. rend. Soc. de biol., 86:661, 1922.
12. Elek, S. D.   Brit. J. Exper. Path., 30:484, 1949.
13a. Oudin, J.   Ann. Inst. Pasteur, 75:30, 1948.
  b. Ouchterlony, O.   Lancet (Feb. 29), 1:346, 1949.
14. Cannon, P. R., and Marshall, C. E.   J. Immunol., 38:365, 1940.
15. Duncan, J. T.   Brit. J. Exper. Path., 13:498, 1932.
16. Wiener, A. S.   J. Lab. & Clin. Med., 30:662, 1945.
17. Pedersen, K. O.   Ultracentrifugal Studies on Serum and Serum Fractions, Uppsala, Almqvist and Wiksells Boktryck, A. B., 1945.
18. Wiener, A. S., Hurst, J. G., and Sonn-Gordon, E. B.   J. Exper. Med., 86:267, 1947; J. Lab. & Clin. Med., 33:181, 1948.
19. Hole, N. H., and Coombs, R. R. A.   J. Hyg., 45:480, 490, 497, 1947.
20. Heidelberger, M.   J. Mt. Sinai Hosp., 9:897, 1943.
21a. Wadsworth, A., Maltaner, F., and Maltaner, E.   J. Immunol., 33:297, 1937.
  b. Maaløe, O.   On the Relation between Alexin and Opsonin, Copenhagen, E. Munksgaard, 1946.
22. Osborne, T. W. B.   Complement or Alexin, New York, Oxford University Press, 1937.

23a. Adair, F. L.   Tr. Am. Gynec. Soc., 40:427, 1915.
  b. Wassermann, P., and Alberts, E.   Proc. Soc. Exper. Biol. & Med., 45:563, 1940.
24. Heidelberger, M.   Am. Scientist, 34:597, 1946.
25. Ecker, E. E.   Ann. Rev. Microbiol., 2:255, 1948.
26a. Omorokow, L.   Ztschr. f. Immunitätsforsch. u. exper. Therap., 10:285, 1911.
  b. Gordon, J., Whitehead, H. R., and Wormall, A.   Biochem. J., 20:1028, 1926.
27a. Pillemer, L., Ecker, E. E., Oncley, J. L., and Cohn, E. J.   J. Exper. Med., 74:297, 1941.
  b. Bier, O. G., Leyton, G., Mayer, M. M., and Heidelberger, M.   J. Exper. Med., 81:449, 1945.
28a. Hegedus, A., and Greiner, H.   Ztschr. f. Immunitätsforsch. u. exper. Therap., 92:1, 1937.
  b. Brown, G. C.   J. Immunol., 46:319, 1943.
29a. Dingle, J. H., Fothergill, L. D., and Chandler, C. A.   J. Immunol., 34:357, 1938.
  b. Shrigley, E. W., and Irwin, M. R.   J. Immunol., 32:281, 1937.
30. Muir, B.   J. Path. & Bact., 16:523, 1912.
31. Scholtens, R. T.   J. Hyg., 45:50, 1947.
32. Noguchi, H., and Bronfenbrenner, J.   J. Exper. Med., 13:78, 1911.
33a. Coombs, R. R. A., and Hole, N. H.   J. Hyg., 46:296, 1948.
  b. Blomfield, A. N., Coombs, R. R. A., and Hole, N. H.   J. Hyg., 48:73, 1950.
34a. Mayer, M. M., Croft, Ch. C., and Gray, M. M.   J. Exper. Med., 88:427, 1948.
  b. Coombs, R. R. A., Gleeson-White, M. H., and Hall, J. L.   Brit. J. Exper. Path., 32:195, 1951.
35a. Rice, C. E.   J. Immunol., 60:11, 1948.
  b. Hilleman, M. R., Haig, D. A., and Helmold, R. J.   J. Immunol., 66:115, 1951.
36a. Dean, H. R.   Proc. Roy. Soc. Med., 5:62, 1911-12.
  b. Goldsworthy, N. E.   J. Path. & Bact., 31:220, 1928.
  c. Platt, A. E.   Australian J. Exper. Biol. & Med. Sc., 14:101, 1936.
37. Goodner, K., and Horsfall, F. L. Jr.   J. Exper. Med., 64:201, 1936.
38. Dean, H. R.   J. Path. & Bact., 21:193, 1916-17.
39. Wright, A. E., and Douglas, E. R.   Proc. Roy. Soc., London, s.B., 72:357, 1904.
40. Neufeld, F., and Hüne, G.   Art. Kaiserl. Gesundh.-amt., Berlin, 25:164, 1905.
41a. Ward, H. K., and Enders, J. F.   J. Exper. Med., 57:527, 1933.
  b. Welch, H., Brewer, C. M., and Hunter, A. C.   J. Immunol., 38:273, 1940.
42a. Mudd, S., and Mudd, E. B. H.   J. Exper. Med., 36:173, 1927.
  b. Eagle, H.   J. Immunol., 18:393, 1930.
  c. Jaffe, E. W.   J. Gen. Physiol., 18:615, 1935.
43. Delauney, A., and Pages, J.   Rev. d'immunol., 10:33, 1946.
44a. Landsteiner, K.   The Specificity of Serological Reactions, 2nd ed., Cambridge, Mass., Harvard University Press, 1945.
  b. Coombs, R. R. A., Mynors, L. S., and Weber, G.   Brit. J. Exper. Path., 31:640, 1950.
45a. Coca, A. F., and Kelly, M. F.   J. Immunol., 6:87, 1921.
  b. Jones, F. S.   J. Exper. Med., 47:245, 1928.
46a. Wiener, A. S.   Proc. Soc. Exper. Biol. & Med., 56:173, 1944.
  b. Race, R. R.   Nature, London, 153:771, 1944.
47a. Moreschi, C.   Zentralbl. f. Bakt., 46:49, 1908.
  b. Coombs, R. R. A., Mourant, R. E., and Race, R. R.   Brit. J. Exper. Path., 26:255, 1945.
48a. Morgan, W. T. J., and Schütze, H.   Brit. J. Exper. Path., 27:286, 1946.
  b. Stewart, F. S., and McKeever, J. E.   J. Hyg., 48:357, 1950.
  c. Schuhardt, V. T., Woodfin, H. W., and Knolle, K. C.   J. Bact., 61:299, 1951.
  d. Marrack, J. R.   Internat. Arch. Allergy and Applied Immunol., 2:264, 1951.
49. Andrewes, C. H.   J. Path. & Bact., 31:671, 1928.
50. Morgan, I. M.   J. Immunol., 50:359, 1945.

9

MECHANISMS OF ACQUIRED IMMUNITY

THE PROTECTIVE EFFECTS OF ANTIBODY

Conclusive evidence for the role of antibody as the chief instrument of acquired resistance is available only for some of the infectious diseases. Such evidence however is often tacitly assumed in instances where an analysis of data does not support the conclusion. In still other infections even a casual appraisal of evidence indicates that the relationship of antibody and immunity is so obscure, if one exists at all, that conclusions are by general consent left in abeyance. The experimental inquiry into the possibility of a relationship of antibodies to resistance in any individual infectious disease can involve many difficulties; this question is discussed in general terms in the final portion of this chapter, and in specific cases in Section Three.

Among the bacterial diseases the best proven cases of the occurrence of antibody-resistance are those in which a superficially located antigen serves as a virulence factor for the etiologic organism. This is the case with the pneumococcus, the group A hemolytic streptococci, the influenza bacillus, and the salmonellas. When antibodies combine with such antigens they neutralize the virulence effects, chiefly by rendering the cells more susceptible to phagocytosis. In some of these instances the microbes may also be made ready for lysis by the intervention of complement.

This sequence does not always follow however, for in other cases the external virulence antigen induces antibodies which are not protective. The capsular antigen of the anthrax bacillus provides such an example; the antibodies formed by the rabbit against this substance have no part in resistance. Instead a response of still unknown nature but of obvious effectiveness against some other constituent or product of the bacillus constitutes acquired immunity (see page 288). The resistance acquired by guinea pigs to the plague bacillus is also directed against some deep-lying substance of the cell, rather than the superficial envelope antigen (see page 297). Thus, the simple straightforward neutralization of a virulence antigen does not supply a general answer to the question of acquired immunity in bacterial infections.

In some bacteria, as was pointed out in Chapter 3, the existence of antigens related to virulence has not even been established. If such factors do not exist, obviously we must seek for some other explanation for acquired protection than the one we have just discussed.

Regardless of how general the principle of antibody mediation in acquired resistance may eventually prove to be, at the present time it is the mechanism of defense about which we have most definite information. Our object now is to look into the various ways in which antibodies may act in vivo to protect the body against infectious agents and their toxins **in those cases where it is known to function as an instrument of protection.**

Agglutination in Relation to Protection. Early evidence of the nature of one protective function of antibody stems from several observations made in the last century. Charrin and Roger in 1889 noted that when *Pseudomonas aeruginosa* was cultivated in a fluid medium containing the serum of a vaccinated animal, it failed to grow diffusely, as it ordinarily does, but instead formed small masses which remained at the bottom of the tube. Metchnikoff described the same kind of occurrence with a vibrio and with the pneumococcus. Then Theobald Smith and Moore in 1892 found that normal rabbits infected subcutaneously with the swine plague bacillus rapidly developed fatal septicemia; in contrast, animals which had previously received inoculations of vaccine formed local abscesses at the site of infection and lived much longer than the controls. These essential observations suggest the concept that agglutination of bacteria, as seen in the test tube, may serve in the body to localize the organisms at least temporarily at the portal of entry. It is interesting that these points were made before the reaction of agglutination itself was formally described in 1896 by Gruber and Durham. These historical developments are discussed by Bailey (1a) and Cannon (1b).

Agglutination in itself does not impair the viability of bacteria (2). Some further activity on the part of the body is necessary to eliminate them as an element of danger. Again certain early investigations made this clear. Sawtschenko and Melkich in 1901 found that in recurrent fever in the human being agglutinating antibody for the causative spirochete appeared in the blood during the afebrile periods between recurrences. During these same periods Metchnikoff observed that the disappearance of organisms from the blood was coincidental with extensive phagocytosis in the spleen. The initial activity of antibody appeared then to be an agglutinative one; this prepared the spirochetes for phagocytosis in two ways: by sensitizing (opsonizing) them for the activity of phagocytic cells, and by presenting aggregates rather than single individuals to the appropriate cells for more efficient engulfment.

Direct observations of in vivo aggregation of bacteria have been made many times. In a series of studies summarized by Bailey (1a), Bull described direct observations of the clumping of pneumococci, typhoid bacilli and other organisms in the blood stream shortly after intravenous injections into actively and passively immunized animals. In some cases naturally insusceptible animals were shown to have the same ability owing to their normal antibody. In all cases Bull was impressed by the rapidity of agglutination in the blood stream, and by the fact that this occurred in the presence of small concentrations of antibody which might be totally ineffective in causing agglutination in the test tube.

Several detailed investigations later revealed in a stepwise fashion the effect first of agglutination in localizing organisms in the tissues, and subsequently of opsonization and phagocytosis in delivering the *coup de grâce* in acquired resistance to the pneumococcus (3) and the staphylococcus (4) in experimental animals. Of these, the immuno-pathologic study of Rich and McKee (3b) has been chosen for description.

Rabbits were inoculated intradermally with virulent pneumococci, and the development of lesions was studied by the periodic examination of excised injection sites and by blood cultures. In normal animals the bacteria were seen to proliferate rapidly in the area of injection, soon invading the circulation to cause the fatal termination characteristically seen in this host. In immune rabbits on the other hand the pneumococci remained at the site of inoculation, and although they proliferated in this area there was no extension of the infection during the time necessary for the leukocytes to mobilize, ingest the bacteria, and put an end to the infection.

It was evident from these observations that the agglutinative tendency of the sensitized bacteria, not only to each other but to the tissues as well (5), constitutes the first localizing maneuver of the immune host (1b).

Opsonization in Relation to Protection. In order further to distinguish the steps in the resistance process to the pneumococcus, Rich and McKee employed another group of immune rabbits which had been deprived of their leukocytes by treatment with benzol, a substance poisonous to the bone marrow. After the blood leukocyte counts of such animals had been brought from the normal level of 8,000 to 10,000 per cubic millimeter to the neighborhood of 100, these animals were given intradermal inoculations of pneumococci. Again the bacteria were found to be localized in the area of injection in the skin, but with ineffective numbers of leukocytes there was no check on microbial proliferation. Tissue sections revealed the development of large masses of bacteria at the site of their deposition in the skin. Eventually these broke into the lymph and blood channels, and the animals developed septicemia and died. The sera of these animals were potent in passively protecting normal rabbits against the organisms, so that there was no question of the benzol treatment having had a deleterious influence on the production or nature of the circulating antibody.

The obvious conclusion from these experiments is that antibody performs the important function of preventing the immediate spread of pneumococci through the tissues. Simultaneously it makes them more amenable to the phagocytic activity of the leukocytes by reason of its opsonizing effect, and because the agglutinated organisms can be dealt with by the phagocytes in numbers rather than singly. These experiments illustrate graphically the inferences drawn from the work of earlier investigators.

Precipitation in Relation to Protection. Although the precipitation of soluble antigen by antibody is less easily demonstrable in vivo than is the aggregation of larger particles such as bacteria, it has been shown to occur in the tissues (6). The effectiveness of this kind of antibody activity within the body as a protective device is not so readily apparent as is bacterial agglutination. The disease-producing agents of a size small enough to enter into precipitation reactions are the viruses and various bacterial and other antigenic toxins. In the former instance, neutralization of the infectivity of viruses by antiserum occurs in the absence of precipitation. The detoxifying activity of antitoxins is also manifest outside the range of flocculating proportions; simple combination of antibody with toxin is sufficient for its neutralization as was discussed in Chapter 8.

There are however certain other instances in worm infestations in which precipitation within the body is related to acquired protection. This effect has been described in the case of a hookworm-like helminth, *Nippostrongylus muris,* of the rat. Following an original infestation, the rat becomes resistant to this worm and succeeds in ridding itself of the parasite. If fresh larvae subsequently penetrate the skin they are found to be impeded in their growth and, after having become established in the intestinal tract, in their ability to lay eggs. The reason for these deficiencies is the precipitation by an antibody of proteinaceous secretions and excretions at the various orifices of the worm. The host thus specifically protects itself by causing an "acute intestinal obstruction" in the parasite (7). The same mechanism has been found to be active against other worms, such as *Trichinella,* as well as insect larvae (8).

Antibody Lysis in Relation to Protection. Although the lysis of organisms implies a finality which is more spectacular than the mechanisms just described, nature perversely limits its occurrence to only a few bacteria so that its importance in defense must automatically be a restricted one. Lysis in vivo can occur with the bacteria enumerated before: the cholera vibrio, some of the gram-negative enteric bacilli, and probably the brucellae and *H. influenzae.* Since the smooth virulent variants of many of these susceptible bacteria are less easily lysed than the rough avirulent forms, the area of effectiveness of this antibody activity in protection is even further restricted than would be the case if the virulent forms were more effectively attacked.

The antibody-complement lytic effect was observed to occur in vivo some time before the nature of the reaction was appreciated. In 1894 Pfeiffer and Issaeff found that when cholera vibrios were injected intraperitoneally into immunized guinea pigs, the organisms shortly deteriorated. Later it was shown that the same effect could be produced in the test tube with serum from such animals, and that heating the serum at 60° C. vitiated the effect. Bordet clarified the relationship of antibody contained in the serum to the heat-labile complement necessary for lytic activity. The actual role of lysis in resistance to this organism is obscure (page 307). It is known that large amounts of antibody administered to an infected animal may cause the rapid release of so much toxic bacterial cytoplasm as to prove fatal to the host; a far cry from protection. Such a circumstance would presumably not occur in the prophylactically vaccinated individual exposed to the organism in nature, since the infective dose would be relatively small and any protective effects conferred by lysis would probably become manifest before a large number of bacteria had the opportunity to accumulate.

The bactericidal activity of normal blood for various bacteria early described by Nuttal (9) was probably mediated in some cases through the action of normal antibody with complement, for heating destroyed this property. Similar conclusions are implied by more recent descriptions of bactericidal activities of normal blood upon the brucellae and *H. influenzae* (10).

The lytic effect of antibody probably goes on concomitantly with the agglutinative and opsonic effects of antibody where it occurs at all, so that the acquired resistance conferred by antibody may include this possibility within the limitations discussed.

A Reproduction-Inhibiting Substance, ABLASTIN, in Relation to Protection. The various antibacterial activities so far discussed lead to the destruction of the microbe either directly by lysis or, more remotely, by the intervention of phagocytes. There is no clear-cut instance of an intermediate activity which might interfere with the progress of a bacterial infection in some more subtle way, such as by discouraging reproduction. Humoral bacteriostasis has cropped up in discussions of antibacterial immunity from time to time. However, it is difficult to demonstrate that its apparent occurrence is not rather the result of a partially effective bactericidal activity which allows the maintenance of a more or less balanced population (11). A chief difficulty is the lack of a criterion by which to distinguish in vivo between a static population of bacterial cells, and a balanced rate of multiplication and death.

This difficulty is evaded in dealing with infections caused by the protozoa that have definite morphologic features characteristic of various stages of division and growth. It has thus been possible with certain blood flagellates, the trypanosomes of the *Trypanosoma lewisi* group, to demonstrate an inhibition of reproduction occurring in the host with acquired immunity. As will be discussed, this acquired property is a humoral one with some of the characteristics of antibody, but whether it actually is antibody remains to be decided.

T. lewisi causes a nonlethal self-limited infection in the rat, thus distinguishing itself from its fellow trypanosomes which in general produce serious and progressive infections in human beings and a range of animal hosts. The difference in pathogenesis is owed chiefly to the fact that during the course of infection the rat elaborates an antibody which restricts the ability of *T. lewisi* to reproduce.

At the beginning of an experimental infection the trypanosomes which appear in the blood stream divide by longitudinal fission, producing multiple parasites called rosettes (see Fig. 36, dividing stages). These separate into young forms of variable sizes, the growth stages portrayed in the figure. If measurements of a number of these single forms are made the variability of length (called coefficient of variation) is found to be greater the more active the multiplication. On the third or fourth day of the infection the coefficient of variation is high, and meanwhile the total number of parasites in the blood has continued to rise steadily; these two points are illustrated in Figure 37. A day or two later, however, the rosettes and variable growth forms begin to disappear from the picture, and by the tenth day the coefficient

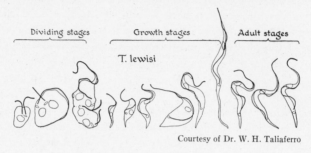

Courtesy of Dr. W. H. Taliaferro

Fig. 36.   Developmental stages of *T. lewisi* in the rat.

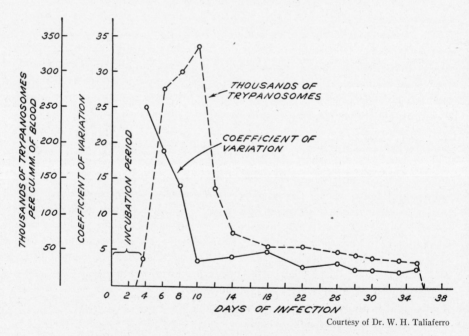

Courtesy of Dr. W. H. Taliaferro

Fig. 37.   Course of the blood infection by *T. lewisi* in the rat.

of variation has fallen to a low point, while the total number of parasites has reached a peak (see Fig. 37). At this time blood films reveal only adult forms of uniform length, as shown in Figure 36. The population has attained its ultimate in numbers, but babies are no longer being produced.

At about this same time a precipitous fall in the total number of trypanosomes is apt to occur; this results from the appearance of an antibody which (with complement) causes their lysis and phagocytosis. The survivors of this crisis live on in the blood without hope of progeny for perhaps a month, during which time there is a slow but steady depletion of numbers. Finally all the organisms disappear from the blood stream and the infection is terminated (see Fig. 37).

The inhibition of reproduction which occurs during the first days of the infection is due to the acquisition of a humoral substance which Taliaferro has named **ablastin** (12). This factor can be passively transferred to normal animals, and in them it is active against multiplying parasites. It separates from the serum with the globulin portion, and it can be induced to appear by vaccination with killed organisms. In these respects it appears to qualify as an antibody. In another major respect however it fails to act like antibody; it cannot be absorbed from serum by the organisms against which it is directed. As was described in the preceding chapter, even those antibodies incapable of bringing about manifest serologic changes nonetheless have the capacity to **unite** with their antigens. This ability would seem to be a minimal expectation to be met by a substance which is to fall within the definition of antibody.

It is interesting that in at least two other cases, *B. anthracis* (see page 288) and a tapeworm of the rat (13), nonabsorbable humoral factors acquired by the host as the result of immunization also account for resistance. These and other examples will be discussed more fully in the next chapter in dealing with possible avenues of acquired defense other than antibody.

Viral Neutralization in Relation to Protection. With a variety of viruses it is easy to demonstrate that the admixture of serum from a previously infected or vaccinated individual can inhibit the infectivity of the agent when the mixture is subsequently injected into test animals. The nature of this neutralization is not yet appreciated. The virus is not usually killed by the neutralizing factor, for it may be caused to dissociate by simple dilution or filtration of the mixture, and the virus then again becomes infectious (14, 17a).

For some years there was serious doubt that the viral neutralizing factor was actually antibody, because it was difficult to demonstrate its absorption by the etiologic agent. It seems apparent now however that the combination of the neutralizing factor with virus is demonstrable when proper quantities are employed as antigen (15). This evidence has been reinforced by the demonstration that even a bacterium and its antibody may show the same phenomena of dissociation with dilution and apparent failure of absorption in experiments appropriately set up for the purpose (16). In some instances also complement promotes the viral neutralizing effect of antisera; this has been described for the viruses of mumps and encephalitis and this also constitutes evidence that the neutralizing factor is antibody (17).

There have been various doubts also that the neutralizing antibodies are the protective mechanism concerned in the resistance of the immune body to viruses, for in some cases at least it has not been possible to reveal a relationship between resistance and the presence or absence of the humoral neutralizing substance. This is not a question which can be blanketed by generalization. In some cases it seems certain that the humoral mechanism is the chief, perhaps the sole, basis for acquired resistance, as in those instances where immunity may be transferred passively to normal individuals by means of serum. In the human being it is possible to modify or inhibit the occurrence of measles, and perhaps mumps and chickenpox in this way, and the infant may be protected for some months after birth against herpes simplex by antibodies passively supplied in utero by the mother (18). In other instances cogent evidence for the importance of humoral resistance has been obtained by culturing cells from immunized animals in vitro, and demonstrating that such cells are susceptible to virus in the absence of serum, and regain their immunity when serum is added to the preparation. Andrews (19) has carried out such experiments with herpes simplex and virus III of rabbits, and Goodpasture and Anderson (20) have reached similar conclusions concerning fowlpox by grafting skin from immune hosts to normal hosts, and to the chorio-allantoic membranes of chick embryos.

Nevertheless there are instances in which the possibility exists that an alteration in susceptible cells themselves may account for acquired resistance to viral agents. This question will be considered again in the next chapter, and in the discussions of individual diseases in Section Three. The fact pertinent to the present discussion is the ability of neutralizing antibody to function as the chief instrument of resistance against certain viruses at least, though the manner in which this occurs is not presently known.

Antitoxin in Relation to Protection. The antitoxic activity of antibody in vitro was discussed in the preceding chapter, and there is little to add with regard to its protective effect against toxins in vivo. In addition to the more notorious diffusible toxins elaborated by the bacteria causing diphtheria, tetanus, scarlet fever and botulism, many other antigenic bacterial poisons are equally well neutralized by their appropriate antibodies. Examples are streptokinase, leukocidins, and hyaluronidase (21a, 21b), substances which may be concerned in the virulence of the bacteria which elaborate them (see Chapter 3). Whether the neutralizing antibody actually combines with the toxic group of a toxin is a moot point. Marrack (21c) points out that urease loses its toxicity for animals after combination with antibody, but it is still able to break down urea to ammonium salts, and it is this process which endows the enzyme with its toxicity in the first place. In this case the function of antibody in protecting against toxicity lies in removing the enzyme from the body fluids. It seems dubious that nonprecipitating diphtheria antitoxin could accomplish this; Marrack suggests that perhaps it prevents toxin from entering cells.

The diffusible bacterial toxins which have so far been characterized chemically have proved to be proteins. These substances were for many years referred to as exotoxins, as distinct from endotoxins or cytoplasmic poisons released by certain bacteria only after cell death. Of the properties conventionally evoked to distinguish these two classes of toxins, an outstanding one was the difference in their antigenicity and capacity to be neutralized by antibodies produced against them. Exotoxins were considered to be potent antigens, readily neutralized by their corresponding antibodies. Endotoxins on the other hand were classified as poor antigens, relatively insusceptible to neutralization, for the sera of animals vaccinated against highly toxic cells proved to be only slightly effective in opposing their poisonous properties.

A good deal has been learned about the nature of one important group of endotoxins in the past 15 years, and it is interesting to consider anew the possible reasons for their stubborn behavior with regard to induction of antibodies capable of acting against them. Among the salmonellas and shigellas, two genera in the forefront of the endotoxic bacteria, antigenic complexes may be extracted from the cells by any of a variety of simple methods (22). These complexes are composed of carbohydrate, lipid and protein. These substances, antigenically specific for species and in some cases for types of bacilli, are the major antigenic factors of the organisms, and account as well for their high level of toxicity. Of interest, however, is the fact that the carbohydrate moiety of the complex is chiefly concerned with its antigenic property, while the protein portion is only poorly antigenic but highly toxic (23). It seems very probable that this information provides the answer to the mysterious inability of antisera to neutralize these toxins; the complex is a good enough antigen, but antibodies are not directed against that part of it which poisons animal tissues.

Complement Fixation in Relation to Protection. Of the various serologic manifestations of antibody activity described in the preceding chapter, this particular one has no relationship per se to the functioning of acquired resistance. When complement enters into antigen-antibody reactions to produce lysis, or to activate the opsonic or viral neutralizing effects of antibody, its activity may be of importance to resistance, but the serologic reaction of complement-fixation itself is simply a technical procedure devised to take advantage of the ability of complement to attach to almost any union between antigen and antibody, and thus to demonstrate the presence of one or the other of these factors in unknown samples of material.

SUMMARY OF THE ROLE OF ANTIBODY IN ACQUIRED RESISTANCE

There is little question that most of the activities of antibody demonstrable in the test tube—agglutination, precipitation, lysis, opsonization, toxin neutralization—can be concerned also in protecting the animal body against infectious agents. In addition an activity less well defined in its nature, the neutralization of viral infectivity, is of prime importance to resistance against at least some of these filterable agents. Finally we must tentatively include here a reproduction-inhibiting action of a transferable humoral factor which which may or may not be antibody, but which is of obvious importance in acquired resistance to certain protozoa, perhaps to some of the metazoal parasites, and possibly also to certain bacteria. Some of these activities of antibody no doubt occur simultaneously in the body with resistance, since a single type of antibody combining with its substrate may lead to a variety of sequelae, such as agglutination, opsonization and lysis.

FACTORS MODIFYING THE PROTECTIVE ACTIVITIES OF ANTIBODIES. In those cases where antibody is capable of functioning in a protective capacity there are various circumstances which may modify or vitiate its effectiveness without in any way impugning its intrinsic ability in the absence of these factors.

The spirochetes of recurrent fever (genus *Borrelia*) and several species of trypanosomes invade the blood of experimental animals and multiply, often attaining a large number. After an appropriate interval of days a sudden release of antibodies is followed by a dramatic clearing of the invading agents from the blood stream, largely through opsonization and the intercession of phagocytes. This lull is shortlived however; soon organisms again appear in the blood and begin to proliferate, in the continued presence of antibody by which they are now unaffected. These antibody-resistant survivors, presumably mutants, are antigenically distinct from the parent strain. Eventually another antibody crisis occurs, to be followed by the same sequence of events. Now two distinct antibodies may be shown to be circulating along with the second relapse strain. Several such crises and relapses may occur before the animal finally succumbs (24). The obviously effective antibodies in these instances rarely if ever complete a cure because of the emergence of antigenic mutants.

In certain bacterial infections in which the protective antibody is directed against a capsular antigen, the solubility of this substance in body fluids may impede the action of antibodies upon the organism itself. This may be the case in lobar pneumonia caused by the pneumococcus, for example. In the case of the type III organism particularly the concentration of capsular polysaccharide dissolved in the sputum and affected lobes of the lungs may be in excess of 1 per cent, and large quantities may also occur in the circulating blood (25). The free antigen can of course combine with much or all of whatever antibodies have been formed by the host, diverting them from the infectious agent itself. The same thing may happen with other bacteria also, and in this connection the soluble substance is sometimes called an aggressin, since it assists the progress of the microbe in the immune host (26).

Infections in which the causative agents are superficially located with relation to the tissues may provoke antibody responses which could be effective if they were able to reach the microbe. The reverse circumstance of a very intimate relationship with cells, such as is characteristic of the viruses, may lead to the same end result, for the virus may so quickly attain its intracellular locale in the new host as not to be subjected sufficiently to the antibodies in the body fluids. It is obvious then that even in those instances where a **potential** relationship of antibodies to acquired immunity has been proven, their **actual** role is not always entirely clear cut.

Nature of Evidence Necessary to Establish the Relationship of Antibody to Acquired Resistance. In view of the difficulties which so often attend the effort to find out how far antibodies may contribute to acquired resistance in any particular infectious disease, it seems worth while to consider here in a general way the question of how such information may be arrived at, and what some of the difficulties may be. Offhand the process would seem straightforward, largely a matter of applying the proper questions experimentally to each individual disease, and coming out with a series of answers. The fact that after years of thought and effort on the part of many investigators only a few such answers are available makes it evident that complications exist.

It is often tempting to infer a relationship of antibodies to immunity from observations which suggest that they put in their appearance coincidentally. This is an insufficient basis for judgment for various reasons: first, because antibody production per se signifies nothing more than a pattern of response of the animal body to foreign antigenic substances of whatever source, and can just as well be induced by injections of milk as by a pathogenic microbe. Several antibodies may be produced by a host in response to the antigens of a bacterial cell, and we know from available examples that only one of these will be of significance insofar as protection is concerned. Without definite proof, we cannot know but that all of them may be useless; obviously then valid inferences cannot be made on the basis simply of coincidental appearance. Further, a particular antibody which may seem to be protective may not have access to the organism in its tissue locale, as was pointed out earlier in this chapter. We must look further for a satisfying analysis of the function of humoral antibody in acquired resistance in any particular instance of host-parasite relationship.

The essential criteria to be met before we can assign a protective role to humoral antibody seem to the author to be the following:

1. The demonstration that antibodies against the agent are present in the blood of the immune animal.

2. The demonstration that the serum from such an animal is capable of transferring resistance passively to a normal animal, preferably of the same species.

These two demonstrations will establish the existence of antibodies and the existence of a humoral protective factor. In order to ascertain that these are synonymous, i.e. that the protective factor is not some substance other than the antibody, a third criterion is suggested.

3. The demonstration that the protective property can be absorbed from the serum by the organism in question, and that the serum then loses its ability to transfer resistance.

The reasons for this choice of criteria, and the pitfalls which may be involved in their realization, are as follows.

1. The demonstration of the presence of antibodies against the infectious agent in the blood of immune animals. As the result of vaccination or infection humoral antibodies usually appear. There may be several, each directed

against a different component of the microbe. One of these may be related to resistance while the others are entirely adventitious by-products of reactivity to antigenic substances. The fact that antibodies may agglutinate a bacterium in vitro is not in itself evidence of a protective function in vivo. An illustration of this is afforded by the antiflagellar antibodies produced in response to the typhoid bacillus; although these cause aggregation (H agglutination) of the organisms in the test tube, they have been shown to be without significance to resistance (27). To go a step further, in another instance involving the anthrax bacillus, not one of the readily manifest antibodies produced by the rabbit vaccinated with the entire bacterial cell has been shown to have any relationship to resistance, although these may cause capsular swelling, agglutination and other effects when mixed with the bacteria in vitro (see Chapter 8). Once the demonstration of antibodies has been made, however, presumptive evidence exists that one of these may be related to resistance, and the second criterion can be investigated.

In some cases the difficulty arises that antibodies cannot be revealed in immune animals by the serologic tests commonly employed for the purpose. This failure in itself does not provide proof of their absence, for they may be present in small concentration, or they may be of poor reactive quality, or both. A very low level of circulating antibody can in some instances provide appreciable protection (28) and it is not always the best serologically reactive antibody which is most protective. Thus Horsfall and Goodner have fractionated horse antipneumococcal serum and found that the fraction which best precipitates capsular polysaccharide is not best in protecting mice against the organism (29). It is sometimes necessary then to employ more delicate tests for the presence of antibodies. One such procedure is the Pfaundler thread reaction (1a). If bacteria are grown in the serum of vaccinated or previously infected animals they are seen to remain clumped as they multiply, although the serum may not be capable of bringing together isolated bacteria presented to it in the usual agglutination test. Other methods may be better; for example, the developing reaction (30) or the blocking test (31) both of which have been successfully used with various bacteria. These and other tests are described in Chapter 8.

In this first step, the demonstration of antibodies in the sera of immune animals, their presence still requires proof of their relationship to immunity, and their apparent absence requires thorough study by sensitive methods before their existence can be ruled out, especially in view of the findings, already mentioned, that small amounts of antibody may in some instances confer resistance.

2. The passive transfer of immunity. Whether or not antibodies have been successfully demonstrated in the serum of the immune animal, it is necessary next to find out if such serum confers protection against the infectious agent upon normal individuals. If antibodies have not been discovered even by precise technics the existence of a humoral protective property may be revealed by passive tests.

Let us suppose that such an experiment proves successful. This shows us that the serum contains a protective element and that this may presumably be one of the antibodies that have been demonstrated. What considerations can cause us to question this result?

If the test is carried out in an animal species other than the one supplying the serum, the infectious agent may not have the same pathogenic relationship to the test host as to the serum donor. For example, human antityphoid sera are tested for their protective abilities in mice. The mouse however is not susceptible to infection with the typhoid bacillus, so that in order to carry out the test it is necessary to incorporate the bacteria in a protective coating of mucin and to inject this mixture intraperitoneally. Under these conditions the bacilli will multiply in the peritoneal cavity until sufficient toxic cytoplasm has accumulated to kill the mouse. We are hardly justified in assuming that the antibody which is protective under these artificially established conditions, in an unnatural host-parasite relationship totally different from that existing in typhoid fever in man, is also the mechanism through which acquired immunity functions in the natural host.

Wherever possible therefore passive resistance tests should be carried out in members of the same species as that supplying the antibodies. When this can not be done, the best alternative is the use of a test animal in which the infectious agent at least produces a true infection, and the more similar this is to the evolution of the infection in the immune host, the more meaningful will be the results of the passive resistance test, for it is desirable to know whether mechanical factors such as walling off or exposure to humoral currents give the antibody as much opportunity to act upon the agent in one case as in the other. Variations of this question may arise according to the infectious agent, the host species involved, and the conditions under which infection takes place, and they must be weighed individually in the particular instance under consideration.

Now let us suppose that a passive resistance test has not been successful. What conclusions may be drawn from this? A negative result does not necessarily preclude a relationship of antibodies to the immunity of the donor animal, for certain technical difficulties may account for the failure. Thus, in a chronic infection such as tuberculosis it may be difficult to know what quantity of serum administered over how long a period of time may suffice to provide significant evidence of its ability to transfer resistance. If the serum of one species of animal is employed in recipients of another species, and especially when such tests are prolonged, the species difference in itself may account for a failure to transfer resistance, for the recipient may within a few days produce antibodies against the serum proteins being administered, and these may completely vitiate the protective effects of antibodies in the serum.

In summary then, a passive protection test has greatest significance in evaluating the role of antibody in resistance if the test is carried out in an animal of the same species as the one supplying the serum, or failing that, if the test is carried out in a species which is susceptible to true infection with a resultant disease which has some similarity to that produced in the species supplying the serum. In addition, the factors of chronicity of the disease under test, and of production of antiantibodies by the recipient animal in tests requiring prolonged administration of serum, must be kept in view.

3. Absorption of the passive protection factor from the serum with the infectious agent. If antibodies have been shown to be present in the serum of the immune animal, and if passive transfer under appropriate conditions reveals a protective capacity of the serum, the suggestion is strong that these two phenomena are related. To question this deduction may seem quibbling, but there is sufficient evidence of nonantibody humoral protective factors to justify further inquiries on this point. The humoral protective element in rabbits immune to the anthrax bacillus does not fit our conception of antibodies, neither in its mode of action in the immune individual nor in its failure to be removed from the serum either by the soluble bacillary substance which induces it or by whole living bacilli (see page 288). Perhaps the reproduction-inhibiting factor active upon certain species of trypanosomes may be included in the category of nonantibody substances, since it also has no affinity for the organisms which induce its formation (see Chapters 8 and 10). These possibilities suggest that there may be acquired humoral properties of immunity which are not antibody in nature; at least, further evidence will be necessary to establish that they are. If antibodies have been demonstrated under point 1, and if passive transfer of resistance has been accomplished, then the absorption of antibodies by the infectious agent with simultaneous removal of the protective properties of the serum proves that the antibodies are responsible for protection.

OTHER LINES OF EVIDENCE CONCERNING THE RELATIONSHIP OF ANTI-BODIES TO ACQUIRED RESISTANCE. In view of the considerable complexities which may attend efforts to meet these various proofs, individual instances may warrant other methods for obtaining evidence on the question of the relationship of antibody to resistance. For example, if points 2 and 3 are difficult to meet, refinements under the first point may supply significant evidence. Thus, if antibodies against a bacterium are demonstrable one might try to find out whether a particular one of the antibodies occurs always in resistant animals, and never in animals vaccinated with a preparation of the same bacterium which fails to induce resistance. The pneumococcus is useful to illustrate this point, although with this organism there is no difficulty in supplying evidence to satisfy all the criteria discussed.

Let us suppose that one group of animals has been vaccinated with S forms of this bacterium, and another group with R forms. Both groups may be found by serologic tests to possess antibodies against the homologous vaccines, but infection tests with virulent pneumococci reveal that only the group treated with the S vaccine is immune. If now serologic tests are carried out with both kinds of sera against the **component antigens** of the successful vaccine the immune group is found to possess antibodies reacting with nucleoprotein, Forssman antigen, somatic carbohydrate and capsular polysaccharide; the nonimmune group on the other hand has antibodies only against the first three of these antigens. The importance of these three antibodies to immunity can then be discounted, since they occur in animals which lack resistance. By inference, the fourth antibody, against the capsular substance, is related to immunity. Carrying through such a project depends upon employing chemical procedures which will not change the responsible antigen so much as to leave it unreactive with antibody. Negative results from such a line of experimentation may mean simply a deficiency in the technical methods employed.

In the chapters dealing with acquired resistance to individual infectious diseases, these various criteria have been applied to an analysis of our current information about mechanisms of immunity.

BIBLIOGRAPHY

1a. Bailey, G. H.   Newer Knowledge of Bacteriology and Immunology, edited by Jordan, E. O., and Falk, I. S., Chicago, University of Chicago Press, 1928.
 b. Cannon, P. R.   Physiol. Rev., 20:89, 1940.
2. Sevag, M. G., and Miller, R. E.   J. Bact., 54:88, 1947.
3a. Tsuda, S.   Virchows Arch. f. path. Anat., 247:123, 1923.
 b. Rich, A. R., and McKee, C. M.   Bull. Johns Hopkins Hosp., 54:277, 1934.
 c. Catron, L.   J. Exper. Med., 61:735, 1935.
 d. Cannon, P. R., and Hartley, G., Jr.   Am. J. Path., 14:87, 1938.
4. ——— and Pacheco, G. A.   Am. J. Path., 6:749, 1930.
5a. Manwaring, W. H., and Coe, H. C.   J. Immunol., 1:401, 1916.
 b. Taliaferro, W. H., and Cannon, P. R.   J. Infect. Dis., 59:72, 1936.
6. Opie, E. L.   J. Immunol., 8:55, 1923; 9:247, 255, 1924.
7a. Sarles, M. P., and Taliaferro, W. H.   J. Infect. Dis., 59:207, 337, 1936.
 b. Taliaferro, W. H., and Sarles, M. P.   J. Infect. Dis., 64:157, 1939.
8a. Oliver-Gonzalez, J.   J. Infect. Dis., 69:254, 1941.
 b. Otto, G. N.   J. Parasitol., suppl. 25, p. 29, 1939.
 c. Blacklock, D. B., Gordon, R. M., and Fine, J.   Ann. Trop. Med. Hyg., 24:5, 1930.
 d. Trager, W.   J. Parasitol., 25:57, 1939.
9. Nuttal, G. H. F.   Blood Immunity and Relationships, London, Cambridge University Press, 1904.
10a. Dingle, J. H., Fothergill, L. D., and Chandler, C. A.   J. Immunol., 34:357, 1938.
 b. Shrigley, E. W., and Irwin, M. R.   J. Immunol., 32:281, 1937.
 c. Ecker, E. E., Seifter, S., and Dozois, T. F.   J. Lab. & Clin. Med., 30:39, 1945.
11a. Ascoli, A.   Ztschr. f. physiol. Chem., 48:315, 1906; Centralbl. f. Bakt., 46:178, 1906.
 b. Dochez, A. R., and Avery, O. T.   J. Exper. Med., 23:61, 1916.
12. Taliaferro, W. H.   Bact. Rev., 12:1, 1948.
13. Campbell, D. H.   J. Immunol., 35:205, 465, 1938.
14a. Todd, C.   Brit. J. Exper. Path., 9:244, 1928.
 b. Andrewes, C. H.   J. Path. & Bact., 31:671, 1928.
 c. Schultz, E. W., Gebhardt, L. P., and Bullock, L. T.   J. Immunol, 21:171, 1931.
 d. Sabin, A. B.   Brit. J. Exper. Path., 16:70, 1935.
15a. Burnet, F. M., Keogh, E. V., and Lush, D.   Australian J. Exper. Biol. & M. Sc., 15:227, 1937.
 b. Salaman, M. H.   Brit. J. Exper. Path., 18:245, 1937.
16. Enders, J. F., and Shaffer, M. F.   J. Immunol., 32:379, 1937.
17a. Morgan, I. M.   J. Immunol., 50:359, 1945.
 b. Whitman, L.   J. Immunol., 56:97, 1947.
 c. Leymaster, G. R., and Ward, T. G.   J. Immunol., 61:95, 1949.
18. Dodd, K., Johnston, L., and Buddingh, G. J.   J. Pediat., 25:105, 1938.

19. Andrewes, C. H.   Brit. J. Exper. Path., 10:273, 1929; J. Path. & Bact., 33:301, 1930.
20. Goodpasture, E. W., and Anderson, K.   Arch. Path., 30:212, 1940.
21a. Friou, G. J., and Wenner, H. A.   J. Infect. Dis., 80:185, 1947.
   b. Thompson, R. T.   J. Lab. & Clin. Med., 32:1407, 1947.
   c. Marrack, J. R.   Internat. Arch. Allergy and Applied Immunol., 2:264, 1951.
22a. Boivin, A., and Mesrobeanu, L.   Compt. rend. Soc. de biol., 113:490, 1933; 114:302, 307, 1933.
   b. Freeman, G. G., Challinor, S. W., and Wilson, J.   Biochem. J., 34:307, 1940.
   c. Morgan, W. T. J., and Partridge, S. M.   Biochem. J., 34:169, 1940.
23. Perlman, E., and Goebel, W. F.   J. Exper. Med., 84:223, 1946.
24. Culbertson, J. T.   Immunity Against Animal Parasites, New York, Columbia University Press, 1941.
25a. Tripp, J. T., Frisch, A. W., Barrett, C. D., Jr., and Pidgeon, B. E.   J. Exper. Med., 76:497, 505, 1942.
   b. Bukantz, S. C., de Gara, P. F., and Bullowa, J. G. M.   Arch. Int. Med., 69:191, 1942.
26. Boivin, A., and Delaunay, A.   Ann. Inst. Pasteur, 71:168, 1945.
27a. Arkwright, J. A.   J. Path. & Bact., 30:345, 1927.
   b. Perry, H. M., Findlay, H. T., and Bensted, H. J.   J. Roy. Army M. Corps, 62:161. 1934.
28. Walsh, T. E., and Cannon, P. R.   J. Immunol., 31:331, 1936.
29. Horsfall, K., and Goodner, F. L., Jr.   J. Exper. Med., 66:413, 425, 437, 1937.
30. Morgan, W. T. J., and Schütze, H.   Brit. J. Exper. Path., 27:286, 1946.
31a. Coca, A. F., and Kelly, M. F.   J. Immunol., 6:87, 1921.
   b. Jones, F. S.   J. Exper. Med., 47:245, 1928.
   c. Griffitts, J. J.   Pub. Health Rep., 62:865, 1947.
   d. Cox, C. D., and Kutner, L. J.   Science, 111:545, 1950.

10

MECHANISMS OF ACQUIRED IMMUNITY

NONANTIBODY DEFENSE MECHANISMS

The point has been made several times before that the mediation of acquired resistance through the action of antibody is not always apparent. Antibodies with significant agglutinating properties which may effect localization of infectious agents in the tissues are not found in some diseases (e.g. tuberculosis) or if they are produced have no evident relationship to resistance (e.g. anthrax). The opsonizing effect of antibody may be rendered meaningless in the case of infectious agents which are able to persist inside phagocytes. Lysis is restricted to some of the gram-negative bacilli only. For these reasons it seems worth-while to consider the possibility of other mechanisms in attempting to evaluate the nature of resistance in the cases where this is not yet clear. This chapter deals with such possibilities in general; other specific suggestions gleaned from an analysis of current work are discussed under individual diseases in Section Three.

1. Humoral Factors. Protective substances in the blood and tissue fluids which do not seem to fit the description of antibody are acquired against several parasites, including a bacterium and certain viruses, protozoa and helminths. Among the bacteria, *B. anthracis* so far provides the best example suggesting the existence of a nonantibody type of humoral resistance. Many years ago Ascoli (1) spoke of an antiblastic humoral resistance to this bacillus, preventing its germination from spores and inhibiting the formation of capsules. A recent detailed study of anthrax infection and immunity has resulted in evidence which may supplement some such viewpoint. It was found that bacilli deposited in the immune rabbit undergo extracellular destruction some hours later, an effect which cannot be ascribed to any known activity of antibody **acting upon gram-positive bacteria.** Furthermore, although the serum can be shown to possess this antibacterial property by passive transfer to normal animals, the protective factor cannot be removed from the serum by treatment with component antigens of the bacillus, by the living bacillus itself, or by a diffusible factor of the growing cell which is known to induce the antibacterial immunity. These negative features cast serious doubt upon the antibody nature of the protective substance (see Chapter 19 for details).

Further support for this tentative conclusion is provided by the fact that killed vaccines prepared from virulent anthrax bacilli are ineffective for immunization while **living avirulent** bacilli serve this purpose well. This is a different state of affairs from that seen in those cases where a specific antigenic component of the bacterial cell is necessary for the induction of antibody-mediated resistance, e.g. in the case of the pneumococcus, for here the absence of the antigenic component from the avirulent cell renders it useless as a vaccinating agent. The immunizing efficacy of living avirulent anthrax bacilli could mean that the resistance-inducing substance is a product of actively metabolizing cells rather than a fixed chemical constituent of the bacillus, and there is good evidence for this viewpoint (2). The immune response to such a substance could of course be an antibody (for example, an antienzyme; other examples of this are known [3]), but in view of the evidence that the immune factor has no affinity for the substance which induces it, it seems improbable that this is the case.

Immunity in anthrax then differs from the known examples of antibody resistance in three major respects: resistance is not directed against a morphologically fixed antigen of the cell, the immune factor is not absorbed from serum by the substance which induces it, and the nature of its antibacterial action differs from ordinary antibody effects.

The antitrypanosomal factor (ablastin) which inhibits the propagation of *Trypanosoma lewisi* and *T. duttoni* (4) shares certain characteristics with the antianthrax substance, in particular its failure to be removed from serum by the organisms upon which it acts (see Chapter 9). Moulder (5) has evidence that ablastin interferes with the oxidative assimilation of glucose by trypanosomes, and that this may account for the inhibition of reproduction and growth of the organisms. It has been suggested (6) that ablastin may be an oxidative enzyme in which pantothenic acid serves as the active prosthetic group.

In the case of an avian malarial parasite, *Plasmodium lophurae,* a humoral reproduction-inhibiting and lethal substance appears to account for the native resistance which appears in chickens with increasing age. Trager and McGhee (7) present evidence that acquired immunity depends largely upon an increase in the concentration of this nonantibody factor in the blood.

In a study of resistance of two species of rat tapeworm, Campbell (8) has found a protective humoral factor produced by infected animals which fails to be absorbed from serum by whole worms or ground worm suspension. Since this protective substance appears only after several weeks of infection, and not at all following vaccination with killed worms, the suggestion is made that it may be an antibody induced by some metabolic product of the worm which accumulates slowly during the period of infestation, and which might not be present in sufficient quantity in the parasites at any one time to effect absorption of the corresponding antibody in an in vitro test. On the other hand the author points out that the nonabsorbable serum factor may not be an antibody but some other kind of protective response.

In regard to certain viruses there is also evidence that inhibitory substances of nonantibody nature may account for acquired immunity. Enders

(9) has recently called attention to two such possibilities. Antiviral substances have been extracted from the tissues of animals infected with lymphogranuloma venereum and Theiler's mouse encephalitis viruses by French and Swedish workers. In the latter case the factor is resistant to heat and proteolytic enzymes, and neither substance is identifiable with antibody (9b).

What the nature of these various protective responses may be, if they are not antibody, can only be speculated on. They may be of the nature of enzymes adapted to a substrate provided by the infectious agent, or competing with an enzyme system of the organism itself, and necessary for its survival. They may be substances, which, like penicillin, interfere in some as yet obscure manner with amino acid utilization, or with the utilization of some other metabolite, by the infectious agent. Some interference with metabolic activity seems indicated by certain of the examples just cited. In contrast, studies with protective antibodies against the pneumococcus and the typhoid bacillus have revealed no interference with oxygen consumption (10) except insofar as agglutination may decrease the surface contact between bacteria and medium (3, 11).

2. **Cellular and Tissue Factors.** A. PHAGOCYTES IN ACQUIRED RESISTANCE. As described in the preceding chapter, the phagocytic cells play the essential role in antibody immunity of efficiently ingesting microbes which have been prepared by antibody. Most studies of this activity in vitro have left no doubt that phagocytes supplied by normal animals can function as well as those from the immune subject which supplies the antibody. On the other hand there are in some cases indications that the phagocytes themselves may acquire special abilities to deal with infectious agents, and these are worth attention.

Metchnikoff's early efforts to stretch the capacities of phagocytes to account for acquired resistance on the basis of these cells alone led him to suggest a process of "education" or adaptation to the immunizing agent. This view was ridiculed by contemporary pathologists as an attempt to endow somatic cells with attributes of the psyche. Physical "learning" as exemplified by the appearance of adaptive enzymes in the presence of an appropriate substrate was still unknown.

In recent years several examples have suggested that Metchnikoff's idea may have some merit. There is evidence that in certain infections there may occur (a) increased phagocytic activity independently of antibody and (b) an improved ability of phagocytes to destroy ingested organisms. In the first instance Lurie (12) has found that the macrophages of rabbits immune to the tubercle bacillus engulf unrelated particles such as India ink and staphylococci more avidly than do the cells of normal animals. In the case of the tubercle bacillus it is difficult to see how this particular acquisition may serve the host to advantage, since this microbe is readily taken up by phagocytic cells even in the normal body. The difficulty is that they do not ordinarily die in this locale.

As regards the second possibility, that phagocytes of the immune body may acquire an increased ability to destroy ingested organisms, Lurie (13) studied the fates of tubercle bacilli inside the macrophages of normal and immune animals which had been transplanted to the anterior chambers of normal rabbit eyes, away from the influence of possible humoral protective factors. His observations indicated that virulent bacilli die in monocytes derived from resistant animals. These experiments supplement the common observation that tubercle bacilli disappear from epithelioid cells in the body of infected immune animals and human beings, and suggest that some alteration distinguishes the phagocytes of the resistant individual with respect to the tubercle bacillus (see Chapter 23).

B. OTHER BODY CELLS IN ACQUIRED RESISTANCE. The question whether cells other than phagocytes may take part in acquired resistance is particularly interesting with respect to virus diseases. The reasons for this are: First, a relationship of humoral antibody to the immune state is not always seen; and second, these agents exist in intimate metabolic relationship with host cells, and an alteration in the cell itself may be expected to influence the ability of the virus to propagate.

As regards the first of these points, the failure of relationship of the presence of antibody to resistance, the same considerations in general apply here as were discussed in Chapter 9. The **absence** of antibodies in the presence of resistance may mean simply an inadequacy in the methods for revealing antibodies. On the other hand instances occur in which humoral antibodies are present without concomitant resistance, and this situation is more difficult to reconcile with a humoral mechanism of immunity, since appropriate tests prove that these antibodies can neutralize viral infectivity. It may be of course that immunity depends upon the presence of a high concentration of antibodies in those areas attacked by the virus. There is some evidence that this may be the case in poliomyelitis and equine encephalomyelitis, where immunity has been correlated with higher concentrations of inhibiting antibody in the central nervous system than in the blood steam (14) although this possibility is not a settled one (14c, see also page 390). Analogously, the presence of antibodies in surface bathing fluids, such as nasal mucus, may even in small concentrations affect the virus at its portal of entry (15), but it is possible that this situation may not always obtain even when humoral antibodies are demonstrable. In any case, the possibility remains open for consideration that in instances where immunity-antibody relationships are not forthright, resistance may depend upon cellular modifications.

The second point, the fact that viruses depend for their own welfare upon the metabolic activities of the host's cells (16), suggests that acquired resistance may sometimes depend upon subtle alterations in the physiologic activities of these cells. Further, the intracellular location of viruses may shield them from potentially protective humoral antibody (17), in this case restricting the functioning of antiviral activity to virus which is enroute via blood or lymph pathways to its cellular habitat. Even this possibility may go by the board however if, as seems possible, certain viruses invade the cells of predilection directly after introduction to the surface or deeper tissues (e.g. the axons of nerve cells) and thus escape effective exposure to body fluids.

Only one definite instance seems to be available in which an obvious alteration in cells following upon a primary viral infection is correlated with resistance to reinfection. The intranasal instillation of influenza virus in ferrets and mice results in desquamation of the superficial epithelium, and during repair a low transitional type of cell appears. This epithelium is refractory to infection with the same virus before antibody appears in the blood. When the normal ciliated epithelium returns, susceptibility to infection returns also (18).

Despite the paucity of proved examples in relation to acquired resistance, observations of other kinds concerning the changed reactivity of cells to viruses are sufficiently suggestive to warrant discussion in this connection.

(a) The influence of the metabolic state of the host upon susceptibility to viruses. It has been described in relation to native resistance (see Chapter 2) that the nutritional status of a host may influence virus infections in a manner contrary to conventional expectations. Hosts deficient in certain vitamins may be less susceptible than normal animals to some viruses, apparently because the metabolic processes of the deficient cells, upon which the viruses depend for their own proliferation, are impaired. An example already quoted is that of mouse poliomyelitis (19). Animals deficient in thiamine chloride are found to be less susceptible to this virus than normal mice. The function of this vitamin is to activate the co-carboxylase system of nerve cells and when this function is interfered with the virus suffers along with the host. Along this same line, Rivers (20) has observed that malnourished rabbits show less reaction to vaccinia virus than do normal animals, and similar observations have been made with respect to fowl sarcoma virus (21) and to foot and mouth disease virus in guinea pigs (22).

(b) The interference phenomenon. For some years evidence has accumulated to reveal that the injection of one virus into an animal may lead to a refractory state with respect to infection by another unrelated virus (23a). Hoskins (23b) first showed the protective effect of neurotropic against pantropic yellow fever virus in monkeys. The same effect was then demonstrated with two entirely unrelated viruses, the yellow fever neurotropic agent protecting against Rift Valley fever when the two were simultaneously inoculated into mice (24). In the case of influenza virus, even the inactivated agent inoculated into the allantoic sac of chick embryos can prevent the subsequent development of active virus (25). Similar findings had been made earlier with certain plant viruses. Many other examples of interference are now established.

It is well known that certain viruses may exist together in the same cell (26), presumably because they fit into the physiologic mechanisms of the cell at different points. When interference occurs, the interfering virus may compete with the infecting virus for some cellular component essential for its propagation (27). Analogously, a polysaccharide obtained from *Klebsiella pneumoniae* type B injected into experimental animals prevents the multiplication of mumps virus or pneumonia virus of mice, apparently by blocking an essential intracellular metabolic system of the host (28).

(c) Hemagglutination by viruses. The erythrocyte agglutination reaction first described by Hirst (29) for influenza virus and chicken red cells has been found to occur with a variety of viral and rickettsial agents, and different erythrocytes (30). In certain instances the hemagglutinating factor is a soluble substance separable from the virus itself. But in another group of viruses, including mumps, influenza and Newcastle disease, the hemagglutinating factor appears to be part of the viral particle, and in these cases also the reaction between virus and red cell appears to be comparable to an enzyme-substrate reaction. The erythrocytes have specific receptors for the virus, and the destruction of these receptors makes the cell subsequently inagglutinable by the virus. Other host cells have similar receptors, and when these are destroyed the cells become refractory to infection; this is seen to happen with influenza virus for example (30, 31). Here again then there is tentative evidence that a cellular alteration—the loss of a receptive substrate—may in some instances interfere with subsequent infection. Eventually receptors may regenerate and when this happens susceptibility to infection returns.

These three lines of evidence have been described in juxtaposition because they all point toward the common conclusion that various modifications in cells may have the effect of rendering these cells refractory to infection by a virus to which they are normally susceptible. Though such evidence by no means proves that acquired resistance to viruses depends upon analogous changes, it provides a pattern which, in the present state of inconclusive information, has at least the virtue of suggesting plausible paths of study.

3. General Tissue Immunity. The idea of a generally altered reactivity of the tissue cells which might help explain acquired resistance has been bandied about in the literature of immunology for many years. That various body cells can participate in the immunologic response under certain conditions is indicated by their reactivity to antigen in infectious hypersensitivity; this occurs entirely independently of humoral antibodies (see Chapter 14). It is difficult to see however how an acquired altered reactivity of tissues could in itself affect the fate of bacteria, since these are for the most part intercellular parasites. It seems hypothetically possible that tissues might acquire immunity to soluble toxins, and that certain cells might become modified in their susceptibility to viruses, as already discussed, but tissue immunity has ordinarily been described as a localizing and bactericidal influence in a more general sense. Some of the lines of thought on this question are briefly outlined in the following discussion.

Over a half century ago Cobbett observed a mild degree of increased local resistance to streptococci within a day following cutaneous vaccination, but an equal degree of resistance could be induced with chemical irritants. Studies since then (32) have reiterated these findings. These results, however, are attributable not to a specific local tissue immunization, but rather to the incitement of local inflammation by the vaccine or other agent employed. The mild benefits which inflammation can provide against virulent organisms are manifested in test animals if the challenge infection is a lenient one.

Besredka erected a structure of immunologic theory on the basis of a local immunity of tissues for which a particular bacterium has special affinity, the tissue in which, in his terms, the microbe shows "selective localization." According to this view, resistance to the typhoid bacillus depends upon an immunity of the intestinal mucosa; this is called a portal immunity. In this scheme antibodies played a very subordinate role (33). In more recent times Kahn (34) has carried out extensive studies of tissue immunity also, chiefly with diphtheria toxin. All such experiments suffer from the difficulty in distinguishing a localizing effect of tissues from the early concurrence of antibodies, and the burden of proof still remains with the proponents of this viewpoint.

Perhaps a more promising example of a possible acquired antitoxic resistance of tissues has been described by Burrows and his co-workers (35). A lipoidal cellular toxin of the cholera vibrio increases the permeability of isolated intestinal strips to the passage of fluids. Though antibodies are formed against this toxin, they do not protect intestinal strips from the permeability effects of the toxin. On the other hand strips removed from actively immunized animals are resistant to this toxic effect. Burrows suggests that intracellular antibodies within macrophages of the intestinal wall may be responsible for neutralization, but an alternative possibility may be an acquired resistance of mucosal cells to the toxic substance.

4. Allergic Inflammation in Acquired Resistance. As the result of exposure to antigenic substances the body may become hypersensitive to further contact with the specific antigenic agent. Subsequently, if this antigen enters the tissues to provoke a hypersensitive response, an intense inflammatory reaction may occur as a result of the irritating effect of this reaction. The immunologic reaction of hypersensitivity is the primary event, and the inflammation follows upon this. The **increased intensity** of this inflammatory process is thus an acquired phenomenon though the occurrence of inflammation in itself is not, for even in the nonsensitized subject the foreign antigenic substance is bound to cause some degree of inflammation.

Hypersensitive states are generally classified into two major categories, the immediate or anaphylactic type and the delayed or infectious type. (The detailed differences between these are discussed in Chapter 14). In the first case the hypersensitive state is related to the presence of humoral antibodies against the antigen, and it has been demonstrated repeatedly that if antigen is injected into the skin of a properly sensitized animal, the localization of antigen to the site is a function of these antibodies. The intense inflammatory reaction (Arthus reaction) is a consequence of the antigen-antibody reaction, not the cause of the localization (36).

The second type of reaction, the delayed type, is characteristically induced by infectious agents including bacteria, viruses, and other parasites as well. In this case there is no relationship of the hypersensitive state to circulating antibodies; instead, various tissue cells become specifically reactive to antigen upon an immunologic basis the nature of which is not yet clear. In this case there is some reason to anticipate that the acquired cellular reactivity may account for resistance to the infectious agent which has induced the hypersensitive state.

On what bases could this cellular reactivity prove to be a protective one? It may be so by virtue of some immunologic process whereby the reactive cells in some way localize, and perhaps destroy, the agents which gain access to the tissues, though as already stated it is difficult to imagine how tissues would bring this about. Or it may depend upon the intensified inflammation which follows upon the allergic reaction itself, as was discussed in regard to anaphylactic sensitivity.

For the first viewpoint there exists no positive evidence; in every individual instance so far investigated the results have shown that the delayed allergic response is directed against an antigen of the organism other than the factor which induces resistance; obviously then the two are separate responses. The case of tuberculosis is one which has occupied the attention of many workers for years (see Chapter 23). It is known that infectious hypersensitivity in this disease is directed against the protein antigens of the bacillus. With appropriate methods tuberculous hypersensitivity can be induced in animals with substances isolated from the bacillus, but this is not accompanied by immunity (37). Other methods may also be used to demonstrate the divergence of the antiprotein allergic state from the resistant state (38). In another case, that of the pneumococcus, it is found that delayed allergic reactivity of the tissues is also directed against nucleoprotein of the organism, while acquired resistance depends upon antibodies against the capsular polysaccharide.

So far as the second point is concerned—the possibility that the intensified inflammation secondary to the hypersensitive reaction itself may act as a protective mechanism—the inadequacy of this viewpoint is indicated by the evidence just presented. Animals in which allergic reactivity to the tubercle bacillus has been induced by the use of isolated antigens fail to show resistance to the organism, yet they develop the intensified inflammatory response resulting from contact with the bacilli as well as do immune animals. The question has been put to test more directly however by studies of the ability of intense inflammations to hinder the dissemination of bacteria. It has been found in the first place that the inflammation resulting from an allergic reaction comes on too late to prevent effectively the dissemination of agents through the lymphatics. Further, if microbes are introduced into a previously prepared area of intense inflammation resulting from an induced allergic reaction, localization is still ineffective, and in fact the forcefulness of the passage of exuded fluids through the tissues may serve to distribute organisms, vitiating whatever beneficial effect a milder degree of inflammation may have had

(38, 39). Intensification alone of the normal process of inflammation has thus not been proved to be an instrument of acquired resistance. The ordinary protective attributes of inflammation do not increase with more inflammation; in fact, the reverse may be the case.

It appears then that acquired tissue immunity does not occur on the basis of hypersensitivity to infectious agents, or if it does, this has not yet been adequately demonstrated.

SUMMARY

In the present state of information concerning acquired resistance mechanisms we are confronted with many instances of immunity which have not been successfully explained on the basis of antibody mediation. Efforts should of course continue toward gathering evidence that antibody may be concerned in these still undefined instances, but our preoccupation with the economy of nature should not be permitted to obscure the possibility that other processes may be operative.

In this chapter various nonantibody possibilities to account for acquired resistance have been considered: that humoral factors other than antibody may be acquired by the resistant animal, that specific alterations may occur in phagocytes which enable them to destroy microbes more effectively, and that modifications in other cells which are ordinarily susceptible to viruses may account for their failure subsequently to support viral propagation. The possibilities are also considered that the tissues generally may participate in acquired immunity, and that the inflammation resulting from hypersensitive reactions may sometimes determine resistance. Available evidence eliminates certain of these possibilities entirely, but in the first three cases the data at hand seem sufficiently suggestive to warrant continued consideration and study.

BIBLIOGRAPHY

1. Ascoli, A.   Ztschr. f. physiol. Chem., 48:315, 1906; Centrlbl. f. Bakt., 46:178, 1908.
2. Gladstone, G. P.   Brit. J. Exper. Path., 27:394, 1946.
3. Sevag, M. G.   Immuno-catalysis, Springfield, Ill., Charles C Thomas Co., 1945.
4. Taliaferro, W. H.   Bact. Rev., 12:1, 1948.
5. Moulder, J.   J. Infect. Dis., 83:42, 1948.
6. Becker, E. R., and Gallagher, P. L.   Iowa State Coll. J. Sci., 21:351, 1947.
7. Trager, W., and McGhee, R. B.   J. Exper. Med., 91:365, 1950.
8. Campbell, D. H.   J. Immunol., 35:205, 465, 1938.
9a. Enders, J. F.   Federation Proc., 8:625, 1950.
  b. Gard, S.   Acta med. Scandinav., 119:27, 1944.
10. Sevag, M. G., and Miller, R. E.   J. Bact., 55:381, 1948.
11a. Blake, F. G.   J. Exper. Med., 26:503, 1917.
  b. Barber, M. A.   J. Exper. Med., 30:569, 589, 1919.
12. Lurie, M. B.   J. Exper. Med., 69:579, 1939.
13. ——— J. Exper. Med., 75:247, 1942.
14a. Morgan, I. M.   J. Immunol., 62:301, 1949.
  b. Schlesinger, R. W.   J. Exper. Med., 89:491, 507, 1949.
  c. Sabin, A. B., and Steigman, A. J.   J. Immunol., 63:211, 1949.

15a. Amoss, H. L., and Taylor, E.   J. Exper. Med., 25:507, 1917.
  b. Howitt, B. F.   J. Infect. Dis., 60:113, 1937.
  c. Bell, E. J.   Am. J. Hyg., 47:351, 1948.
  d. Hammon, W. McD.   Bact. Rev., 13:135, 1949.
16a. Parker, R. F., and Smythe, C. V.   J. Exper. Med., 65:109, 1937.
  b. Smadel, J. E., and Hoagland, C. L.   Bact. Rev., 6:79, 1942.
17a. Rivers, T. M., and Pearce, L.   J. Exper. Med., 42:523, 1925.
  b. Andrewes, C. H.   J. Path. & Bact., 31:671, 1928.
  c. Rivers, T. M., Haagen, E., and Muckenfuss, R. M.   J. Exper. Med., 50:673, 1929.
18a. Francis, T., Jr., and Stuart-Harris, C. H.   J. Exper. Med., 68:789, 803, 813, 1938.
  b. Straub, M.   J. Path. & Bact., 50:31, 1940.
19. Clark, P. F.   Ann. Rev. Microbiol., 4:343, 1950.
20. Rivers, T. M.   Viral and Rickettsial Infections of Man, J. B. Lippincott, Phila-
       delphia, pg. 9, 1948.
21. Rous, P.   J. Exper. Med., 13:397, 1911.
22. Olitsky, P. K., Traum, J., and Schoening, H. W.   Report of the Foot and Mouth
       Disease Commission of the United States Dept. of Agriculture, Tech. Bull.,
       76:93, 1928.
23a. Lennette, E. H.   Ann. Rev. Microbiol., 5:277, 1951.
  b. Hoskins, M.   Am. J. Trop. Med., 15:675, 1935.
24. Findlay, G. M., and MacCallum, F. O.   Brit. J. Exper. Path., 44:405, 1937.
25. Henle, W., and Henle, G.   Science, 98:87, 1943.
26a. Anderson, K.   Am. J. Path., 18:577, 1942.
  b. Syverton, J. T., and Berry, G. P.   J. Exper. Med., 86:145, 1947.
27a. Schlesinger, R. W. in Viruses, 1950, edited by M. Delbrück, California Inst. Tech.,
       1950.
  b. Henle, W.   J. Immunol., 64:203, 1950.
28a. Ginsberg, H. S., and Horsfall, F. L., Jr.   J. Exper. Med., 89:37, 1949.
  b. Anderson, S. G.   Federation Proc., 8:631, 1950.
29. Hirst, G. K.   J. Exper. Med., 76:195, 1942.
30. ——— in Viruses, 1950, edited by M. Delbrück, California Inst. Tech., 1950.
31. Stone, J. D.   Australian J. Exper. Biol. & M. Sc., 26:287, 1948.
32a. Gay, F. P., and Rhodes, B.   J. Infect. Dis., 31:101, 1922.
  b. Amoss, H. L., and Bliss, E. A.   J. Exper. Med., 45:411, 1927.
  c. Gray, D. F.   J. Path. & Bact., 59:235, 1947.
33. Besredka, A.   Local Immunization, Baltimore, Williams and Wilkins Co., 1927.
34. Kahn, R. L.   Tissue Immunity, Springfield, Ill., Charles C Thomas Co., 1936.
35a. Burrows, W., Mather, A. N., Wagner, S. M., and McGann, V. G.   Proc. Soc. Exper.
       Biol. & Med., 57:308, 1944.
  b. ——— Proc. Soc. Exper. Biol. & Med., 57:306, 1944.
  c. ——— Wagner, S. M., and Mather, A. N.   Proc. Soc. Exper. Biol. & Med., 57:311,
       1944.
36a. Opie, E. L.   J. Immunol., 9:259, 1924.
  b. Culbertson, J. T.   J. Immunol., 29:29, 1935.
37. Raffel, S.   J. Infect. Dis., 82:267, 1948; Experientia, 6:410, 1950.
38. Rich, A. R.   The Pathogenesis of Tuberculosis, Springfield, Ill., Charles C Thomas
       Co., 1944.
39a. Cannon, P. R., and Hartley, G., Jr.   Am. J. Path., 14:87, 1938.
  b. Menkin, V.   Physiol. Rev., 18:366, 1938.
  c. Miles, A. A., and Miles, E. M.   Brit. J. Exper. Path., 24:95, 1943.

11

GENERAL AND EPIDEMIOLOGIC ASPECTS OF IMMUNITY

It has been the aim in preceding chapters to examine the basic mechanisms of native and acquired resistance, and of pathogenicity, unencumbered so far as possible by considerations of host-parasite relationships as observed in spontaneously occurring diseases, or of applied immunizing procedures. The intention has been to establish a pattern of ground rules as these emerge from controlled experiments. The present chapter will be devoted to the general relationship of these rules to events as they occur in nature.

As a first step the following chart sets forth the conventional classification of immunities, native and acquired, and the intrinsic factors which may determine their effectiveness.

NATIVE RESISTANCE	ACQUIRED RESISTANCE
Species	Species
Race	Race
Individual	Individual

1. Actively acquired resistance
   a. Through infection (natural means)
   Clinical
   Inapparent
   b. Through vaccination (artificial means)

2. Passively acquired resistance
   a. Congenital (natural means)
   b. Through serum transfer (artificial means)

INTRINSIC FACTORS INFLUENCING
NATIVE AND ACQUIRED RESISTANCE

Heredity
Age
Sex

151

Native resistance implies the effective operation of the mechanisms discussed in Chapter 2, probably along with other unrecognized factors, all of which are inherent in the anatomic and physiologic make-up of the animal. As was already discussed, these inherent defense mechanisms are endowments of the species as a whole, but modifications may occur in a race within the species, and some differences always exist among individuals in the ability to resist a particular microorganism to which the species as a whole is susceptible. Acquired resistance, on the contrary, is especially associated with the individual, since each member of a species must in person undergo the experience which results in his specific immunity. Whereas heredity is the central determinant of native resistance, it is only a modifying influence in acquired resistance. Thus, the factor of race enters in that the members of one race may be genetically better able to acquire a particular immunity than the members of another race within the species. Analogously, one species may be more proficient in acquiring resistance than another. These generalizations are suggested in the chart by means of the boxes of varying thicknesses enclosing "species," "race," and "individual." These and other points listed in the chart are discussed in detail later.

NATIVE RESISTANCE

Species Differences in Native Resistance. Native resistance may be **absolute** for a particular microbe or toxin; of this there are many examples (see Chapter 2). In fact we may regard the general relationship of animals to all saprophytic organisms as instances of absolute native immunity, a point which has been made before. **Relative** differences in resistance are also frequently observed among animal species, one being subject to much milder parasitization or intoxication by an agent than another. A case in point is the mildness of infection with the human type tubercle bacillus in the rabbit as compared with its seriousness in the guinea pig. Similar differences exist in respect to susceptibility to toxins. It is well known that the rat and mouse are almost insensitive to large amounts of diphtheria toxin so that the rat withstands doses up to 1,000 times that lethal for the guinea pig.

Racial Differences in Native Resistance. All or none differences in native immunity are not seen among races within a species. The differences here are of degree. A number of investigators, through the inbreeding of mice (1), rats (2), guinea pigs (3), rabbits (4) and other animals (5), have succeeded in deriving strains with markedly differing susceptibilities to various infectious organisms. Striking as these differences may be they remain relative ones, as illustrated in Table 4, from data supplied by the work of Webster and Schneider (1b). It is interesting that selected resistant strains are in most cases resistant only to a particular agent, though sometimes a relationship among immunities to several different microbes is seen (5).

The racial segregations shown here are of course not likely to occur in nature (6) either in human beings or animals. But in a much modified way

Table 4. Varying susceptibilities of strains of mice to a bacterium and a virus

Mouse Strain	Test Pathogen	Survival
Bacteria-resistant, virus-resistant	S. enteritidis	92
	St. Louis encephalitis virus	76
Bacteria-susceptible, virus-resistant	S. enteritidis	2
	St. Louis encephalitis virus	88
Bacteria-resistant, virus-susceptible	S. enteritidis	82
	St. Louis encephalitis virus	2
Bacteria-susceptible, virus-susceptible	S. enteritidis	2
	St. Louis encephalitis virus	3

these experimental findings undoubtedly have their counterpart in human beings. A disease which has been documented extensively from the genetic standpoint in tuberculosis. A difficulty in evaluation in this case is one common to all chronic infections, i.e. whether apparent differences in native immunity may not actually be expressions of differences in ability to **acquire** resistance, for the slow evolution of the infectious process could permit its eventual suppression to depend upon acquired immunity (7). If we are willing to assume however that the ability of human beings to handle tubercle bacilli on a first exposure depends in part at least upon their native resistance, certain occurrences are very instructive.

In Caucasians primary tuberculous infections even in young children are most often self-limited, restricted to the original (usually pulmonary) focus and to the lymph nodes which drain it. In contrast, Negroes are much more apt to develop progressive disseminated disease. This tendency has been strikingly manifested in several instances exemplified by the Senegalese troops serving in France during World War I, and in South African Negroes brought together as laborers in British mining enterprises. In these groups the morbidity was extremely high, the course of disease was toxic and acute, and dissemination throughout the body was a common occurrence. The lesions were massive and rapidly caseous, with none of the fibrotic tendency seen in the white races. Presumably Caucasians owe their relative resistance to generations of selection. This process is probably under way now in American Negroes, but at the present time the tubercle bacillus still constitutes a greater hazard for this group than for whites, social and economic factors being accounted for (8a). The question of primitive tuberculosis is dealt with most interestingly by Cummins (8b).

Individual Differences in Native Resistance. When we come to consider the individual in respect to native immunity, differences are again relative ones. The fact that varying degrees of susceptibility exist among individuals is a matter of common observation. In almost any experiment in which a series of normal animals of the same weights and sexes and subjected to the same environmental influences are inoculated with an equal dose of an infectious agent, differences are observed in the length of life and even in the final outcome, whether survival or death. Many factors difficult to control (e.g. equality of distribution of infectious particles and the exact location of the dose deposited in the tissues) may influence such differences, but individual divergences in inherent resistance mechanisms are no doubt chiefly responsible. Actually to prove this point however it would be necessary to do what Webster, Lurie and others have done: to demonstrate the existence of an inheritance trait by drawing it out in the progeny of individuals with differing susceptibilities.

Influence of Age upon Native Resistance. Considerations of native resistance, and of the virulence of pathogenic agents, are always referred to the events which occur in the normal host. A strict delimitation of normality is of course impossible, for if factors of general well-being are equal so far as they can be judged, the question of individual genetic constitution remains open, and the matter of age introduces a continually changing variable. It is well recognized that age can modify very markedly the susceptibility of animals to various infectious agents; an example was mentioned in Chapter 2 in reference to Sabin's studies of encephalitis-producing viruses in mice and guinea pigs (9) and other similar examples are known (10) in which differences in clinical picture as well as susceptibility occur. It is common knowledge that young animals and human beings are less reactive to foreign agents than older ones. Their inflammatory reactions are relatively poor; because of this they frequently fail to respond to toxin skin tests despite the absence of specific antitoxins. Culbertson (11) has found that the macrophages of suckling animals are much less actively phagocytic than are those of older animals. It is not uncommon for massive fatal infections of infants to run their course very rapidly, almost without warning of their presence.

Old age is also a time of waning ability to withstand infections. Certain mechanical defections, including tissue atrophies and enfeebled circulation, facilitate the progression of bacterial invasions which in younger individuals would not even get started. Thus, any injury or illness necessitating prolonged bed-rest carries with it the danger of bronchopneumonia because the pulmonary circulation is embarrassed in recumbency. Bladder infections are common in old men because prostatic hypertrophy interferes with complete emptying, and residual urine serves as a culture medium for bacteria. In the female the vaginal epithelium atrophies, the local reaction becomes less acid, and a mixed bacterial flora is permitted to grow and may give rise to infection (12).

Certain obstacles limit the carrying out of satisfactory studies of the variable course with age of native resistance to any particular infectious disease in human beings. One such factor is the matter of opportunities for exposure, i.e. whether apparent insusceptibility in a particular age group may not be due to shielding from sources of infection. This is generally the case with infants and young children, for example. On the other hand shielded infants may sometimes be subjected to more massive exposure than adults, for if a source of infection exists in the household itself they will be constantly under its influence and in addition will reap the disadvantages of kissing, cuddling and all the other close contacts to which babies are liable. Obviously the factors of the **existence and degree** of exposure must remain entirely matters of chance in dealing with statistics on human populations, and for this reason we cannot consider native resistance from the simple standpoint of ability to withstand infection entirely, as we could do with a herd of experimental animals all subjected to the same challenge with an infectious agent under the same conditions. A person with good native resistance may be overwhelmed by a heavy infective dose, while another individual with poorer resistance powers may never be subjected to appreciable numbers of organisms and thus never develop an infection.

Since the criterion of ability to withstand infection is not applicable in most human studies, the next best basis for judging native powers of resistance is the ability to suppress the disease once it has started. This eliminates the question of whether or not exposure has occurred, but of course still leaves unknown the factor of degree of exposure. Nonetheless, it is the best that can be done in human studies of this kind, and limited data are available from morbidity and mortality reports to permit a partial evaluation of age-resistance relationships.

The disease chosen for discussion as an example is tuberculosis, for which statistical information is relatively good. The trouble with this instance however is that the disease is a slow-moving one, and there is some question whether the capacity to suppress the primary infection actually depends upon **native** immunity, or rather upon the ability to **acquire** immunity. From this standpoint one of the acute infectious diseases would be better for illustration, but comparable data are not available for these. Therefore the discussion which follows must be qualified by appreciation of these facts: that it does not reveal the ability to ward off bacilli entirely, that it ignores the factor of size of infective dose, and that it assumes that the ability to overcome a primary tuberculosis infection is a function of native resistance rather than of an eventually acquired specific immunity.

Rich (7, p. 217) presents a table compiled from the U. S. Registration Area for 1940 which shows roughly the percentages of the population in succeeding age groups which become infected with the tubercle bacillus, as revealed by tuberculin surveys. It shows also the estimated mortality among those infected, rather than in the population as a whole. By arrangement of these data an attempt has been made, in Figure 38, to indicate how successfully the infected members of successive age groups are able to survive tuberculous infection. Obviously some of those dying in one age group will have become infected in a preceding one, but again this is one of the imponderables which must be accepted in these data.

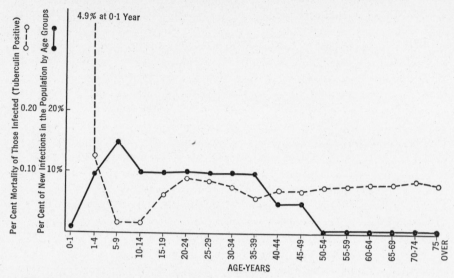

Fig. 38.   Tuberculous infection and mortality among human beings in successive age groups.

It is seen that in the first year of life the incidence of infection is low (0.5 per cent); this is undoubtedly due to lack of opportunities for exposure. But the mortality at this age is very high (4.9 per cent); indeed, this is the age of greatest mortality risk. (Note that this may depend partly also upon **heavy exposure** from a household source.).

In the one to four year period the number of children infected increases considerably, but the percentile mortality among these drops to 1/40 its earlier level and would probably be lower except that some deaths occur here as the result of infection in the zero to one year period. Apparently a very marked ability to withstand tubercle bacilli appears during this time, but the danger from infection remains a considerable one.

In the five to nine year period the largest single increase of infections occurs because of further increased opportunities for exposure, but the mortality figure at this time drops to its lowest point and this level continues during the next five year period, up to the time of adolescence. The years between 5 and 15 then appear to be the years of greatest ability to discourage bacillary progression.

Beginning with adolescence another change takes place, this time in the direction of greater infection hazard. The higher mortality persists through the remainder of the life span, rising with advancing years. Marked differences in mortality in males and females begin to show up at this time also, as will be discussed later.

There appear then to be three differing levels of native immunity to the tubercle bacillus between birth and middle age. Infancy and early childhood is a time of least ability to cope with the organism, the years between 5 and 15 are most favorable for the host, and in succeeding years the balance

again swings to favor the parasite. Whether this last change reflects physiologic alterations accompanying adolescence, or the emergence of various
stresses to which younger children are not subjected, or both, is difficult to
know. Possibilities are discussed by Long (13), Pinner (14) and Rich (7).
The general shape of this curve is maintained in a series of age-mortality
graphs for successive decades since 1900 in the United States despite the
continuing decrease in total mortality from tuberculosis (14), and it holds
quite well also for other countries at different times (15). An interesting
exception occurs in the case of Hungary where statistics for 1934 revealed a
steady sharp rise in mortality between the ages of 5 and 15. The reasons
for this would be interesting to know.

Figures for several acute infectious diseases including measles, mumps,
whooping cough and scarlet fever have been compiled by Collins (16), extending only as far as the 14 or 15 year period. Like the data for tuberculosis
these show in all cases by far the highest mortalities in infants, and a considerably improved ability to cope with these diseases from about the age of
three onward. In the case of measles alone there is a significant recurrence
of higher mortality at about 10 to 14 years of age.

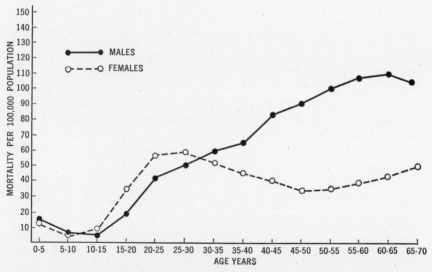

Fig. 39. Male and female mortality from tuberculosis in successive age groups.

Variation of Native Resistance with Sex. Sex is not so significant a determinant of susceptibility to infectious disease as it is to various organic illnesses, but here also it may play a part. Morbidity and mortality due to
whooping cough are higher in females than in males, and this is seen also
with meningococcal infection (16a). Again the more complete available statistics relate to tuberculosis and as shown in Figure 39 these reveal, between
the ages of 15 and 30 or 35, an earlier and more abrupt increase in mortality

among females although the incidence of infection in both sexes is about the same (7, 14b, 15). In succeeding age periods however a reversal occurs, with a sharp decrease in the numbers of female deaths and a continuing rise in male mortality. The divergence in favor of males between the ages of 20 and 35 may perhaps be accounted for by the detrimental effects of the child-bearing period upon women, and the subsequent reversal of the curves to favor females may reflect the cessation of this stress and a generally easier way of life while males continue to be subjected to the tumult and strifes involved in earning a living. However, the earlier years between 15 and 20 would appear to be largely free of these factors, and the lesser ability of females to overcome bacillary progression during this period is probably ascribable to the physiologic differences between the sexes which become accentuated at this time.

ACQUIRED RESISTANCE

Species Differences in Acquired Resistance. Species differences in ability to acquire resistance to disease-producing agents are not well known. There are however obvious differences in the abilities of various species of animals to form humoral antibodies. Among laboratory animals the rabbit is especially proficient, while guinea pigs and rats are notoriously poor in their responses. Yet there is no indication that the latter species is any less able to acquire resistance to various infectious agents than is the rabbit.

Racial Differences in Acquired Resistance. Racial differences in respect to acquired immunity on the other hand are known. Considering antibody production as an index of acquired resistance, it was described in Chapter 6 that strains of animals particularly adept at forming antibodies may be segregated by inbreeding. If we examine the question from the broader viewpoint of proved resistance to disease agents, there is evidence from studies of human beings that Negroes have less capacity to **acquire** resistance to tuberculosis than whites as judged by the fact that they not infrequently show pathologic evidence of two successive primary types of infection, i.e. a repetition of the nonlocalized infection which occurs in the absence of acquired immunity (7).

Individual Differences in Acquired Resistance. The major determinant of acquired resistance rests in the **individual.** It does not exist except as the result of an individual's previous exposure to a specific microbe or toxin. Exceptions to this might occur in cases where antibody mediates acquired resistance, and this could conceivably be elaborated against some other substance (bacterium, food) which shares a common antigen with the pathogenic agent in question. This possibility is discussed under Normal Antibody on page 81. Individuals may vary considerably in their ability to form antibodies against a particular antigen, as is commonly observed in any vaccination experiment or program (17), and a single individual may be proficient in producing antibodies against one antigen, but not against another (18). Again we are speaking of the production of antibodies and only presumptively of resistance, but certainly individual variations in ability to resist challenge infections are also seen frequently in actively immunized animals, whatever may be the mechanisms of acquired resistance involved in any particular case under study.

Influence of Age upon Acquired Resistance. Age markedly influences the ability to produce antibodies in man and lower animals at the two extremes of life (19; see also Chapter 6). These groups would therefore be at a disadvantage in acquiring a resistance dependent upon antibody mediation. There are very scant data concerning age-acquired immunity relationships based directly upon ability to resist infection rather than upon measurement of the development of antibodies; consequently little can be said with respect to the acquisition of resistance in various age periods in instances where antibody may not necessarily be the primary factor concerned. The fact that early childhood is the time when many of the immunities which persist through life are usually acquired would indicate that young children are very able in this respect, while the evidence available implies that infants or nursing animals are probably at a disadvantage (20).

Variation of Acquired Resistance with Sex. It has not been pointedly demonstrated that sex influences the acquisition of immunity, but certain indirect evidence infers that this can be the case. Thus, in syphilis the course in females is said to be much more benign than in males (21) and this may be due to a better ability of the female to acquire immunity to *Treponema pallidum*.

The various categories of acquired resistance are discussed in accordance with the outline shown in the chart at the beginning of the chapter.

Actively Acquired Resistance. RESISTANCE ACQUIRED THROUGH OVERT CLINICAL INFECTION. Many infections leave in their wake a highly effective and durable resistance; others are succeeded by only a relative and short-term immunity. The first group is represented by the exotoxic diseases diphtheria and scarlet fever, by the primarily bacterial diseases typhoid fever and pertussis, by the viral diseases smallpox, yellow fever, mumps, measles and chickenpox, and by the rickettsial diseases typhus fever and the spotted fever group. Second attacks of any one of these may occur of course, but generally speaking convalescence ushers in lasting and effective protection. In the second group are found pneumococcic lobar pneumonia, in which reinfection with the same type is said to occur rather commonly (22), bacillary dysentery which may recur repeatedly (23), the common cold which, epidemiologic studies suggest, leaves resistance of only a few months duration, and influenza which apparently also bequeaths a resistance measured in months only.

The reasons for these wide differences of impress upon the host by the infectious agent are not entirely clear, but certain possibilities come readily to mind.

First, wherever strains of antigenic diversity occur in a single species of infectious agent, protective antibodies will be effective only against the strain which has stimulated their manufacture. Among the pneumococci there are

75 known antigenic types, among the paradysentery bacilli probably 19 types, and several strains of influenza virus are recognized.

Second, as was discussed in Chapter 10, potentially protective antibodies may not come into play against the reinfecting agent because of its superficial relationship to the tissues, or at the other extreme, because it is shielded from antibodies by an intracellular habitat. Francis (24) has pointed out that in virus diseases of man lasting immunity follows those infections in which the agents go through a blood phase in the process of invasion. Thus, yellow fever and encephalitis viruses are introduced by biting insects, and measles, chicken pox and smallpox viruses enter through the respiratory tract and are carried via the blood to their eventual loci in the skin and mucous membranes. The virus of reinfection in these cases should consequently be exposed thoroughly to circulating antibodies. In contrast, the poorly immunizing viruses are parasites of superficial tissues, not readily reached by antibodies unless these are present in the fluids bathing the portals of entry, such as the mucus of the nasal passages. It may be noted however that these fluids have been shown to contain virus-neutralizing substances, but perhaps their concentration is not adequate.

Third, the mechanism of acquired immunity against certain agents may not be effectively invoked because the disease is short-lived. An extension of this viewpoint would suppose that certain agents persist in the tissues after recovery from the diseases which they cause, and that this may account for enduring immunity. This possibility is discussed later in more detail.

Fourth, it is conceivable that frequency of exposures with opportunities for restimulation of immunity may influence its duration and effectiveness. Such opportunities will of course be most frequent in the case of pathogenic agents which are endemic in a population. The question of the effectiveness of exposures in restimulating resistance is closely bound up with type variations in antigenicity, for a particular type or strain of an organism will invoke responses to itself alone.

Finally it may be speculated that in some instances where antibody is ineffective, the host is simply incapable of developing any specific defense.

Persisting Infection in the Presence of Acquired Resistance. It is an odd fact that certain infections may continue to run their course even though the body has acquired a refractoriness to reinfection from without. This seems to be the case in typhoid fever, where the antibodies presumably associated with resistance appear a week or 10 days following onset, but the disease continues for some additional weeks. The host with tuberculosis, even while the disease progresses to a fatal termination, shows evidence of acquired resistance in its ability to localize bacilli newly introduced into the tissues (25). Syphilis and undulant fever are examples of the same phenomenon. Among the viruses, herpes simplex is thought to persist in the tissues during the lifetime of the individual infected at an early age, and to be activated at times by various factors such as trauma, gastrointestinal upsets and menstruation (26). Concomitantly, virus neutralizing antibodies circulate in the blood. It may be of course that without the immunity these infections would run their courses entirely unbridled, but the point is that they may progress even in its presence while reinfection from outside is strongly discouraged.

In certain other special instances it is easy to see why infection should persist in the presence of acquired immunity, for the parasites are extremely labile genetically under the influence of acquired antibodies. Various trypanosomes cause infections in laboratory animals in which the parasites multiply in the blood stream. The parasites reach a high number and then suddenly disappear from the blood coincidentally with the appearance of an antibody which is active against them, and which in fact is the reason for their disappearance. A few days later parasites again appear in the blood in increasing numbers, in the continued presence of the antibody but entirely unaffected by it because these new organisms are antigenically different from the parent strain. Several such incidents may occur during the course of a single infection, and it is eventually possible to demonstrate the coincident presence of a series of antibodies of distinct specificities along with freely proliferating parasites of an antigenic type which is unaffected by any of them. Fortunately, such genetic instability in antigenic character is not a common occurrence among infectious agents generally, for spontaneous variations in antigenicity with the retention of virulence may obviously put the host at a tremendous disadvantage in dealing with an infectious agent.

"Nonsterile" Immunity. Since it is evident that parasites may persist in the body in the presence of acquired resistance, the question arises whether the durable postinfection immunities may not be the result of the continuous latent residence of the infecting agent in the body for years after the clinically apparent disease has disappeared, perhaps for the lifetime of the individual. The idea is an old one, but it cannot yet be settled as a generalization, as perhaps it should not be. Certainly in the chronic infectious diseases such as tuberculosis, syphilis and undulant fever, the agent may remain in the body for many years during which no progression of the disease occurs. Certain acute diseases also are followed by carrier states in which viable organisms persist after all clinical evidence of the disease process has passed. This occurs rather frequently following diphtheria and typhoid fever. An interesting instance of persistence in the body of a bacterium for years following recovery from infection has been described in the case of a laboratory worker who contracted tularemia in 1919 during investigations of the disease. Since that time there have been recurrent local infections of the fingers at the sites of minor injuries, with regional lymph gland involvement but no further extension or systemic symptoms (27).

In the case of the virus diseases which induce enduring immunities in human beings, adequate evidence has not been established for the persistence of the viral agent in the body. This holds true for smallpox, measles and chickenpox (24). Rivers (28) points out however that with these agents there are opportunities for new encounters throughout life, and this might account for periodic restimulations of immunity. In contrast, there are no such opportunities in the case of regional diseases once an individual has left the area where they are endemic. Yellow fever provides such an example, and humoral antibodies have been found in people who have been away from all possible sources of reinfection for 50 or 75 years after an attack of the disease. Either this virus has a most striking ability to impress itself upon antibody-producing cells, or it can persist in the tissues of the once-infected individual indefinitely. Rivers (28) inclines toward the latter viewpoint because various other viruses have been recovered from immune experimental hosts (29), and because intracellularly located agents are in an optimal position for remaining in their nests indefinitely provided that they refrain from killing the cells which harbor them. A reasonable tentative conclusion would seem to include the possibility, therefore, that enduring immunities may in some instances depend upon the persistence of the causative agent in the host.

IMMUNITY ACQUIRED THROUGH INAPPARENT INFECTION. Unrecognized subclinical or inapparent infections may result in the acquisition of immunities as solid as those which follow overt attacks of disease. The proof for this in animals is settled (30), but similar proof for the spontaneous occurrence of inapparent infection-immunity in man has been difficult to establish since it has had to come from epidemiologic studies, and these perforce leave questions to be answered by deduction rather than from controlled experiment. One such question is: what constitutes satisfactory evidence that inapparent infections have occurred which might account for immunity? A second question is: what constitutes reasonable proof that resistance to the agent under study has been acquired?

The satisfactoriness of the answer to the first question varies with different infectious diseases. In some cases fairly good visual evidence of symptomless infections may be obtained, as with the chest x-ray for tuberculosis. The evidence for the existence of this infection in the absence of clinical symptoms can be broadened considerably by the use of tuberculin tests, for these will be positive even when small lesions are invisible in films. Sometimes, in certain of the bacterial and virus diseases, surveys are based upon serologic tests, the presence of antitoxic or neutralizing antibodies being taken as evidence that the agent has at some time resided in the body. It has been objected that the antibodies so determined may signify an immunologic maturation rather than the acquisition of a specific response to an antigenic stimulus. Hirszfeld (31) especially has favored this viewpoint, maintaining that the increasing incidence of antibodies against various agents found in progressive age groups is primarily due to the maturation of "biochemical organs" in a sense analogous to anatomic and physiologic maturation. The fact that the human blood group isoagglutinins are most probably determined genetically rather than by antigenic stimulus lends sufficient credence to the possibility of the maturation thesis so that it cannot be ignored without some proof to the contrary. The evidence which is at hand leaves no reasonable doubt that inapparent infections may occur in large segments of populations in which the infectious agents are endemic. A clear discussion of this evidence for a variety of bacterial and viral diseases is to be found in Topley and Wilson's volumes (32). One example has been chosen for illustration here, dealing with the diphtheria bacillus in human populations. This disease is a particularly favorable one for study on several counts. The bacillus is spread by air-borne droplets so that information about its distribution can be easily gotten by cultural methods. Supplementary information can be obtained from the presence of circulating antitoxin as revealed by a simple skin test, the Schick test. Determinations of small antitoxin concentrations may be established by using the sera of individuals for protection tests against very small doses of toxin in the skin of guinea pigs. Finally, the fact that diphtheria toxin is antigenically a homogeneous substance permits these tests to be employed without any confusion occasioned by the question of strain and type specificities as is so frequently the case with other infectious agents.

These facts have been applied in the following ways to the point under discussion, that inapparent infections may be sufficiently widespread to account for acquired immunity. With the cultural method, studies of the carrier rate of virulent diphtheria bacilli among elementary school children in London over a 10 year period have revealed positive cultures in 2.5 to 5.0 per cent of the subjects at various times (33). This figure could easily account for an eventual blanketing of the entire group with inapparent infections. An application of the Schick test carried out by Dungal (34) in Reykjavik has also indicated rather clearly the relationship between opportunities for spread and the occurrence of latent infections. In 1921 in that city there was a peak in the number of clinical cases of diphtheria which had been occurring in moderate number for some years before. In succeeding years a rapid subsidence in the number of cases occurred throughout Iceland. Twelve years later, in 1933, Dungal carried out a Schick test survey on 814 school children, and found that while the incidence of negative reactors stood at 17.24 per cent in the 11 year old group, it was over twice as frequent in the 13 year group, 37.5 per cent. Thus, these children who had experienced the epidemic year of 1921 showed the effects of increased opportunities for inapparent infections.

In view of these and other similar findings, the rising curve of antitoxin producers in succeeding age groups of human populations (Fig. 40) can reasonably be assigned to the occurrence of inapparent infections beginning in early childhood.

The second question relates to the evidence that the population in which latent infections have occurred has been immunized by them. This question must be answered individually for every disease studied. If it is known that antibodies are the mechanism of immunity in a particular disease, and if these can be demonstrated, the evidence is at hand. Or the conclusion may be based upon comparative actuarial data concerning morbidity and mortality in populations exposed to an agent with and without the benefit of previous inapparent infections. Sometimes controlled experiments in human beings have been carried out upon a small number of individuals selected from both groups, challenging all with the same dose of the infectious agent.

In the case of diphtheria the question of what constitutes immunity is a clear cut one; antitoxin without doubt affords the major and probably the only protection against the disease (35). The Schick test which is employed to test for previous exposure to the diphtheria bacillus indicates a level of antitoxin which has been found to correlate statistically with the immune state (36), and this epidemiologic evidence has been bolstered by a small controlled experiment carried out with a group of human volunteers. Guthrie (37) swabbed the throats of four negative and four positive Schick reactors with a culture of diphtheria bacilli. The positive reactors (lacking antitoxin) all developed the disease while the four negative reactors remained well.

Thus the data portrayed in Figure 40, based on a study by Zingher (38), can be interpreted as revealing not only the widespread occurrence of inapparent infections, but the resulting incidence of acquired immunity to the disease as well.

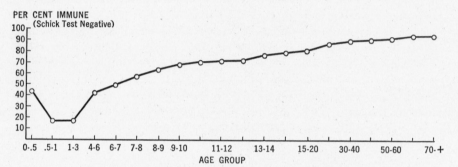

Fig. 40. Schick negative reactors in successive age groups.

The high figure for immunity during the first few months of life shown in this graph is due in part to congenitally transmitted antitoxin; in part to the incapacity of infants to respond to stimuli with inflammation as dependably as do adults. In the period between one-half to three years of age children have for the most part lost this passive congenital immunity and are on their own, and subsequent events are determined by exposures to the bacillus. The large jump in the number of immune children in the four to six year period reflects increased opportunities for such exposures with the beginning school years, and from this time on there occurs a progressive rise in the number of immune individuals with the passage of years until, in the ages between 15 and 20, over 80 per cent of the population upon which this study was based failed to react positively to the Schick test dose of toxin.

IMMUNITY ACQUIRED THROUGH VACCINATION. Deliberate immunizing procedures are in general less effective than infections as stimulators of acquired resistance. Not only are the resultant immunities in some cases less effective, but what is more generally true, they are less durable. There remain still a few diseases for which satisfactory vaccination is not possible at all though infection itself bestows resistance. It seems likely however from the strides which have been taken recently that an understanding of what constitutes an adequate vaccine and how it should be administered will result before long in making artificial prophylaxis available (though not always necessary nor practical) for all those diseases to which immunity can be acquired.

The following discussion lists the general factors which need consideration in the preparation of satisfactory vaccines. Not all these points apply to all vaccines; this discussion is intended to be general, embracing the various possibilities.

1. The occurrence of strains and types of infectious agents. Strains of diverse antigenicity occur among bacteria and viruses, and wherever such types specifically determine protective responses this factor is of utmost importance in the preparation of vaccines. This point has been discussed in various connections before and needs no further belaboring here.

2. The loss of protection-inducing substances during cultivation. This may occur in organisms in which the surface antigens are the important immunizing substances. The superficially situated Vi antigen of the typhoid bacillus and other salmonellas which is present at the time of isolation from the host rapidly disappears on subculture. The Boivin (surface somatic) antigens of these bacilli as well as the capsules of pneumococci, streptococci and other bacteria may also disappear during cultivation in vitro. Vaccines prepared from microbes which have lost these factors are practically useless as prophylactic agents.

3. The alteration or destruction of protection-inducing substances resulting from the method employed in killing the organism for vaccine preparation, or from the chemical treatment used for the extraction of an immunizing substance.

4. The possibility that in some instances relatively large masses of vaccine may be necessary for adequate immunization as is true in the case of pertussis and plague prophylaxis.

5. The possibility that certain agents could be effective if their toxicities were so reduced as to permit the use of adequate vaccinating dosage. Work on this point is currently proceeding with the Boivin (somatic) antigen of *Shigella paradysenteriae.*

6. The regulation of the dosage schedule and the vaccination period. In recent years it has been found that gas gangrene toxoid, a notoriously poor immunizing agent, regularly induces good levels of antitoxin if the injections are spaced over a period of months rather than weeks. This entails no increase in either the concentration of toxoid or the number of doses employed.

7. The possibility that a living agent may be necessary for one or more of the following reasons:

(a) Because the substance which induces protection is not a fixed constituent of the microbial cell, but is produced as a diffusible product of metabolizing organisms. The immunizing factor of *Bacillus anthracis* is an example of this.

(b) Because it may not be feasible to provide sufficient quantities of nonviable minute agents such as viruses to serve as effective stimulators of immunity. A small concentration of a living agent can propagate within the vaccinated subject to overcome this deficiency.

(c) Because of the possibility that certain agents may induce immunity in the host by modifying the cells which they parasitize, and nonviable agents may fail to do this.

(d) Because it may be essential for the maintenance of resistance that the infectious agent reside in the body continuously (see Nonsterile Immunity, page 161).

8. The possibility, which is just coming to be appreciated, that different constituents or products of a single agent may be necessary for the induction of resistance in different species of animals. There is evidence that one antigen of *Pasteurella pestis* immunizes rats and mice while another induces protection in guinea pigs (39). In the case of the anthrax bacillus there is a strong suggestion of an analogous situation. A diffusible product of the living bacillus immunizes rabbits while for the induction of resistance in mice a fixed cellular constituent, the capsular polypeptide, appears to be the essential substance. The choice of test animals in evaluating the efficacy of a vaccine for human beings is obviously of paramount importance in such cases.

Further details and references relating to the various examples cited are to be found in the chapters dealing with individual diseases.

Effective Vaccines for Immunizing Human Beings. The various kinds of vaccines employed for human immunization are described briefly here in relation to the factors just discussed. More detailed information will be found in Section Three and in the books of Rivers (28), of Parish (40a) and of Dubos (40b).

The general kinds of vaccines used are these: (1) the soluble toxins of microorganisms used as such or, whenever possible, detoxified with antigenic properties intact (toxoids); (2) infectious agents killed by physical or chemical means (killed vaccines); (3) substances isolated from infectious agents; and (4) living attenuated microbes. The vaccines chosen for discussion are those for which there are good indications of usefulness.

1. Toxoids. The soluble toxins of the **diphtheria, tetanus** and **gas gangrene** bacilli can be converted to toxoids by the use of formalin and moderate heat. These are administered in fluid form or precipitated on alum. The levels and durabilities of immunity attained with these preparations are generally good. **Scarlatinal** toxin in contrast does not lend itself to toxoid formation, so that graded doses of the toxin itself must be used. For this reason, and because this toxin is not antigenically homogeneous, and because the resultant immunity to the toxin is only mediocre, and because resistance to the toxin still leaves the subject open to the ravages of the hemolytic streptococcus itself, this immunization procedure is not much employed.

2. Killed vaccines. Certain bacterial vaccines consist of cultured organisms killed by heat (usually 60° C. for one hour), by ultraviolet irradiation, or by chemicals (phenol, alcohol, formalin). The salmonellae vaccine is ordinarily

made up of a mixture of *Salmonella typhosa, S. paratyphi* and *S. schott-muelleri* (called TAB, i.e. typhoid and paratyphoid A and B). **Pertussis** vaccine is frequently mixed with diphtheria and tetanus toxoids for the immunization of children. **Cholera** vaccine is also a nonviable preparation. A killed plague vaccine was used by the American armed services in the recent war years, but a viable attenuated preparation is believed to be superior to this.

Among the viruses, the **rabies** vaccine consists of infected nerve tissue treated with virucidal chemicals such as phenol, ether or formalin, or by ultraviolet irradiation. The original Pasteur vaccine, prepared by drying infected spinal cords of rabbits, contains viable virus; this remains in use in some parts of the world. **Influenza** vaccine is harvested from the allantoic fluid of chick embryos. **Eastern** and **western equine encephalomyelitis** vaccines are cultivated also in chick embryos and treated with formalin; these have proved useful especially in laboratory workers. **Mumps** virus vaccine prepared from monkey parotid gland or fertile eggs gives promise of value but is still in the experimental stage.

For the rickettsial diseases **epidemic typhus fever** and **Rocky Mountain spotted fever** vaccines are prepared from infected yolk sacks of fertile eggs. The organisms are inactivated by formalin and induce very significant protection in human beings and animals.

3. Substances isolated from infectious agents. The combined capsular polysaccharides of the most prevalent pneumococcal types have been employed in human beings with favorable results. The isolated somatic antigens of *S. typhosa* and *Sh. paradysenteriae* are currently being examined for their effectiveness in human beings. The protection-inducing diffusible factor of the anthrax bacillus has been isolated and is effective in rabbits.

4. Attenuated living vaccines. For protection against some infections living organisms are found to be superior to killed or, what is more often the case, they constitute the *sine qua non* of immunity induction. Among the bacteria, living avirulent **anthrax** bacilli have been employed for the immunization of sheep and cattle since Pasteur's original demonstration of the efficacy of such a vaccine. The recently isolated product of bacillary growth just mentioned may eventually supersede this. The BCG vaccine (Bacille-Calmette-Guérin) for **tuberculosis** is the outstanding example of a living bacterium employed in human beings. This is an attentuated derivative of an initially virulent bovine type bacillus. Avirulent **plague** bacillary vaccines are also employed; these are probably more effective than the killed preparations although the data required to ascertain this point are not sufficiently in hand.

The viruses provide two examples of viable preparations which are in common use. The classic vaccination procedure for **smallpox** (variola) is performed with living cowpox (vaccinia) virus obtained from calf lymph. This virus is not entirely without virulence for the human being, for generalized vaccinial pox may occur, and very rarely encephalitis may follow vaccination. It is not clear however that the latter is a direct result of infection of nerve cells; it may be one of the demyelinating diseases which seem to depend upon an immunologic response of the body to its own slightly altered nerve tissue (41, see also page 458). Viable virus is also employed for vaccination against **yellow fever.** The virus employed, the 17D strain, has been attenuated by prolonged cultivation in tissue culture. The vaccine itself is prepared in fertile eggs and harvested from the pulped embryo juices. The immunity induced by it probably persists for several years.

It should be noted parenthetically that vaccines prepared from viruses cultured in fertile eggs carry with them the danger of sensitization to egg proteins.

Passively Acquired Resistance. Passive immunity is that which is transferred to a nonimmune individual by the blood or other body fluids of an actively immunized one. The term would be equally apt of course if immunity were transferred via cells or tissues. In a sense analogous to the acquisition of active immunity spontaneously (through infection) or artificially (through vaccination), passive immunity may also come about spontaneously or artificially. In the first case this occurs by the transmission of humoral factors from the mother to the fetus through the placenta, or to the newborn child by way of the milk. The artificial transfer of immunity is accomplished by the injection of serum obtained from an immune donor.

NATURALLY TRANSMITTED PASSIVE IMMUNITY. It has been known for many years that antibodies can be transmitted from mother to fetus through the placenta (42). This occurs in man as well as in certain of the lower animals, and may be of considerable significance for the protection of the infant against various infectious diseases such as diphtheria (43), as shown in Figure 40, as well as measles, mumps and others. Ehrlich (42) also demonstrated that newborn mice are additionally endowed with antibodies by the mother through suckling. The globulin-rich colostrum contains especially high concentrations of whatever immune bodies may be present in the maternal circulation, and the newborn is able to absorb these into its blood stream from the gastrointestinal tract in the early hours after birth, either because it lacks digestive enzymes or possesses a high absorptive ability, or both (44). A striking demonstration of both these points is afforded by the events which take place in human beings when a developing fetus possesses an erythrocytic antigen which the mother lacks (see Rh factor, page 499). Antibodies against the Rh factor are produced by the mother and transmitted to the fetus where they act upon erythrocytes and other cells to cause various forms of hemolytic disease. This situation may be greatly aggravated postnatally if the infant is nursed. It is apparent from this one example that in the human being both placental and colostral transmission of antibodies may occur. This is not the case in all mammalian species. Placental transmission depends to some extent upon the number of tissue layers interposed between the maternal and fetal circulations; the more layers, the less passage of antibodies. Examples of animals with multiple tissue layers include the pig, ruminants and carnivores; species with fewer layers include various rodents, apes and man (44, 45).

It is an interesting and curious fact that in man at least not all antibodies are transmissible through the placenta. For some reason which still defies explanation, the atopic antibodies elaborated by individuals who become spontaneously sensitized to pollens and other environmental antigens are not passed to the fetus. Another striking example is provided by the isohemagglutinins of the major blood types, the α and β agglutinins. Since the fetus is very often of different blood type than the mother, the placental passage of these antibodies could be disastrous, but injury to the fetus on this basis is rare because the antibodies fail to penetrate to the fetal circulation. In this particular instance a possible explanation may be afforded by the fact that the antibodies are of large molecular size (46a), but this seems not too probable because it has been found that diphtheria antitoxin molecules split by enzymes fail to pass the placenta, while the larger untreated antibodies do so (46b). Another striking instance of selective placental impermeability in the human being is shown by the Rh antibodies just mentioned. Maternal serum may contain agglutinating antibodies of the usual type against the Rh factors, but these are not transmitted to the fetus. However the nonagglutinating, so-called incomplete antibodies, also produced by the mother, enter the infant's circulation and cause cellular damage (47).

The congenital transmission of antibodies in fowls occurs through the yolk. This receives a supply from the maternal blood and later gives it up to the embryo (48).

ARTIFICIALLY TRANSMITTED PASSIVE IMMUNITY. The transfer of immunity by means of injections of serum is almost always carried out as a therapeutic procedure, when a disease is already under way and it is desirable to give the patient the advantages of immediate specific resistance. It is most frequently employed now in the treatment of the exotoxic diseases, especially diphtheria and tetanus, as well as in other intoxications caused by the antigenic poisons of various insects and reptiles. The extensive use of serum for the treatment of certain of the bacterial infections, notably those caused by the pneumococcus and the meningococcus, practiced a few years ago has been largely supplanted by the use of chemotherapeutic and antibiotic agents.

In certain circumstances passive immunization is employed prophylactically. Thus if susceptible children are intimately exposed to a case of diphtheria, antitoxin may be administered for interim protection and active immunization started as early as possible. Similarly tetanus antitoxin is routinely given to the nonvaccinated individual who has suffered a wound which, because of its nature and the circumstances under which it was incurred, may favor the proliferation of *Clostridium tetani*. Antibody is here given during the presumptive incubation period. Immune bodies for the viruses of measles and mumps are also employed in the same way in the first few days following exposure, before these parasites have settled finally in the tissues of predilection.

The sera of animals (generally horse and rabbit) when injected into a human being may persist in the circulation in diminishing concentrations for periods of one to three weeks. This means of providing immunity is thus designed to meet a short-term emergency. Efforts to provide protection for longer periods with the sera of heterologous species of animals may be complicated by the manufacture of antibodies against the foreign serum by the recipient, i.e. of antiantibodies.

BIBLIOGRAPHY

1a. Webster, L. T.   J. Exper. Med., 65:261, 1937.
  b. Schneider, H. A., and Webster, L. T.   J. Exper. Med., 81:359, 1945.
  c. ——— J. Exper. Med., 89:529, 1949.
2. Irwin, M. R.   J. Immunol., 24:285, 297, 313, 319, 329, 1933.
3a. Lewis, P. A.   Eugenics, Genetics and the Family, 1:178, 1923.
  b. ——— and Loomis, D.   J. Exper. Med., 47:449, 1928.
4a. Lurie, M. B.   Proc. Soc. Exper. Biol. & Med., 39:176, 181, 1938; Am. Rev. Tuberc. (Suppl.), 44:1, 1941.
  b. ——— Abramson, S., and Heppleston, A. G.   Federation Proc., 8:361, 1949.
5a. Gowen, J. W.   Ann. Rev. Microbiol., 2:215, 1948.
  b. Hill, A. B.   The Inheritance of Resistance to Bacterial Infection in Animal Species, Med. Res. Council (Great Britain), Spec. Rept. Ser., No. 196, 1934.
6. Schneider, H. A.   J. Exper. Med., 84:305, 1946.
7. Rich, A. R.   The Pathogenesis of Tuberculosis, Springfield, Ill., Charles C Thomas Co., 1944.
8a. Roth, R. B.   Am. Rev. Tuberc., 38:196, 1938.
  b. Cummins, S. L.   Primitive Tuberculosis, London, John Bale Medical Publications, Ltd., 1939.
9. Sabin, A. B., and Olitsky, P. K.   J. Exper. Med., 66:15, 35, 1937; J. Exper. Med., 67:201, 229, 1938; Proc. Soc. Exper. Biol. & Med., 38:597, 1938.
10a. Bowman, M.   Canad. J. Pub. Health, 36:199, 1945.
  b. Casals, J.   J. Exper. Med., 72:445, 1940.
11. Culbertson, J. P.   Arch. Path., 27:212, 1939.
12. Te Linde, R. W.   J.A.M.A., 110:1633, 1938.
13. Long, E. R.   Arch. Path., 32:122, 1941.
14a. Pinner, M.   Pulmonary Tuberculosis in the Adult, Springfield, Ill., Charles C. Thomas Co., 1945.
  b. Palmer, C. E.   Personal communication regarding a study in Kansas City, Missouri, for 1939-1946.
15. Redeker, F.   Ztschr. der Internat. Vereinigung gegen die Tuberc., Leipzig, J. A. Barth, 15:46, 1942.
16a. Collins, W.   Pub. Health Rep., 44:763, 1929.
  b. Norton, K. F., and Gordon, J. E.   J. Prev. Med., 4:207, 1930.
17. Jones, F. G., and Moss, J. M.   J. Immunol., 33:173, 1937.
18. Carlinfanti, E., and Cavalli, L. L.   Boll. d. Ist. sieroterap. milanese, 24:215, 1945.
19. Felton, L. D., Prescott, B., Kauffmann, G., and Ottinger, B.   Federation Proc., 6:427, 1947.
20a. Culbertson, J. T., and Kessler, W. B.   Am. J. Hyg., 29:Sec. C., 33, 1939.
  b. Morgan, I. M., and Lavin, G. I.   Proc. Soc. Exper. Biol. & Med., 47:497, 1941.
21. Frazier, C. N., and Hung-Chiung, L.   Racial Variations in Immunity to Syphilis, Chicago, Ill., University of Chicago Press, 1949.
22. Finland, M., and Winkler, A. W.   Am. J. M. Sc., 188:309, 1934.
23. Shaughnessy, H. J., Olsson, R. C., Bass, K., Frieiver, F., and Levinson, S. O.   J.A.M.A., 132:362, 1946.
24. Francis, T., Jr.   Bact. Rev., 11:147, 1947.
25. Koch, R.   Deutsche med. Wchnschr., 16:1029, 1890.

26. Burnet, F. M. Virus as Organism, Cambridge, Mass., Harvard University Press, 1945.
27. Rosebury, T., and Kabat, E. A. J. Immunol., 56:7, 1947.
28. Rivers, T. M. Editor, Viral and Rickettsial Infections of Man, Philadelphia, J. B. Lippincott Co., 1948.
29a. Olitsky, P. K., and Long, P. A. J. Exper. Med., 50:263, 1929.
  b. Zinsser, H. Am. J. Hyg., 20:513, 1934.
30. Meyer, K. F. J. Bact., 31:109, 1938.
31a. Hirszfeld, L. Ergeb. Hyg. Bakt. Immunitätsforsch. Exptl. Therap., 8:367, 1926.
  b. Hirszfeld, H., and Hirszfeld, L. Ztschr. f. Immunitätsforsch. u. exper. Therap., 54:81, 1927.
32. Topley, W. W. C., and Wilson, G. S. Principles of Bacteriology and Immunity, revised by G. S. Wilson and A. A. Miles, Baltimore, Williams and Wilkins Co., 1946, Volume II.
33a. Dudley, S. F. Med. Res. Council (Great Britain), Spec. Rept. Ser., No. 75, 1923.
  b. Forbes, G. Med. Res. Council (Great Britain), Spec. Rept. Ser., No. 115, 1927.
34. Dungal, N. Brit. J. Exper. Path., 13:360, 1932.
35. Raffel, S. Ann. Rev. Microbiol., 3:221, 1949.
36. Ipsen, J. J. Immunol., 54:325, 1946.
37. Guthrie, G. C., Marshall, B. C., and Moss., W. L. Bull. Johns Hopkins Hosp., 31:388, 1921.
38. Zingher, A. Am. J. Dis. Child., 25:392, 1923.
39a. Meyer, K. F. Ann. New York Acad. Sc., 48:429, 1947.
  b. Baker, E. E., Sommer, H., Foster, L. E., Meyer, E., and Meyer, K. F. Proc. Soc. Exper. Biol. & Med., 64:139, 1947.
  c. Meyer, K. F. J. Immunol., 64:139, 1950.
40a. Parish, H. J. Bacterial and Virus Diseases. Antisera, Toxoids, Vaccines and Tuberculins in Prophylaxis and Treatment, Baltimore, Williams and Wilkins Co., 1948.
  b. Dubos, R. J. Editor, Bacterial and Mycotic Infections of Man, Philadelphia, J. B. Lippincott Co., 1948.
41. Rhodes, A. J., and van Rooyen, C. E. Textbook of Virology, New York, Thomas Nelson and Sons, 1949.
42. Ehrlich, P. Ztschr. f. Hyg. u. Infektionskr., 12:183, 1892.
43. Smith, T. J. Med. Research, 13:341, 1905.
44. Mason, J. H., Dalling, T., and Gordon, W. S. J. Path. & Bact., 33:783, 1930.
45a. Schneider, L., and Szathmáry, J. Ztschr. Immunitätsforsch. u. exper. Therap., 95:169, 177, 189, 1939.
  b. Kolodny, M. H. Am. J. Hyg., 30:Sec. C, 19, 1939.
  c. Fenner, F. Brit. J. Exper. Path., 29:64, 1948.
46a. Pedersen, K. O. Ultracentrifugal Studies on Sera and Serum Fractions, Uppsala, Almqvist and Wicksells A.B., 1945.
  b. Hartley, P. Proc. Roy. Soc., London, s.B., 138:499, 1951.
47. Wiener, A. S., and Gordon, E. B. J. Lab. & Clin. Med., 33:181, 1948.
48a. Ramon, G. Compt. rend. Soc. de biol., 99:1473, 1928.
  b. Schmidt, S., Ørskov, J., and Steenberg, E. Ztschr. f. Hyg. u. Infektionskr., 118:455, 1936.
  c. Andrewes, C. H. J. Path. & Bact., 48:225, 1939.

12

FACTORS INFLUENCING IMMUNITY

Various extrinsic factors—extrinsic in the sense of not being innate to the host's development as are sex, age and hereditary influences—may affect native or acquired resistance or both. These factors may be ordinarily environmental ones such as temperature and humidity, or extraordinary ones such as industrially employed chemicals, or abnormal organic states of the body as exemplified by diabetes mellitus. By their effects upon the animal body these influences may alter the host-parasite relationship for better or worse through these general activities:

1. Interference with a defense mechanism of the potential host (e.g. destruction or stimulation of leukocytes, inhibition or enhancement of antibody production).

2. Provision of an altered environment in vivo for potential parasites, more or less favorable than that which ordinarily exists. This would be the case for example when a deficiency of a vitamin so alters a tissue anatomically and physiologically that it may become subject to infections which would not normally occur.

The operation of many of the factors to be discussed takes place within a genetic framework, that is, they may have more or less influence depending upon the hereditary background of the individual. Schneider (1) has pointed up this fact in his studies of the influence of nutritional factors upon susceptibility to infection. Mice maintained on a natural complete diet and a synthetic supposedly complete diet showed different susceptibilities to a *Salmonella,* the latter group surviving the infection less successfully. When however mice which had been inbred for resistance or susceptibility to this organism were exposed to it the diet made no difference in end results in either group. The dietary influence upon susceptibility thus revealed itself only in a population which is analogous, in respect to genetic heterogeneity, to ordinary human populations.

Native and acquired resistance will be taken up individually in respect to the various influences affecting them. Obviously any factor which alters the function of such a mechanism of native resistance as the phagocytes will modify also the efficacy of the individual's acquired resistance to agents against which antibodies and phagocytes act jointly.

With respect to acquired resistance extrinsic factors may make themselves felt only in the process of acquisition (as in influencing the formation of antibodies), or only in the functioning of an immunity already present, or both. It is not always possible to discuss these facets separately because of scarcity of available data, but the effort will be made wherever possible.

NUTRITIONAL FACTORS

1. **General Malnutrition.** The adverse effect of general malnutrition upon susceptibility to infectious diseases is generally taken for granted, but on close scrutiny the matter is more complex than it would seem to be. Starvation among human beings is often a by-product of periods of stress, such as wars, when many other factors such as extreme fatigue and exposure to the elements may account for the observed results. One of the clearer instances of the untoward effects of malnutrition in human beings was provided by Denmark during World War I (2). Since this country remained neutral it was not subjected to the physical stresses which ordinarily accompany war, but a good deal of the country's food was exported. Between 1914 and 1917 the tuberculosis mortality rate rose from 138 to 176 per 100,000. Other infectious diseases also increased to a considerable extent during this time, especially enteritis, bronchopneumonia and otitis media. In 1917 food exports were curtailed by the German blockade and the shortage ended. In the following year the mortality from tuberculosis fell back to the prewar level of 138 and continued to decline subsequently. Not all epidemiologic observations have been interpreted in this same way however. Keys (3) cites morbidity and mortality statistics for infectious diseases derived from areas of mass starvation in western Holland, Greece, and other regions during World War II to suggest that the level of sanitation rather than malnutrition determined the extent of pestilence. Leyton (4) in discussing the effects of chronic starvation in Russian prisoners of war was not able to find evidence that the liability to acute infections was much increased, though other physiologic changes were obvious enough.

In experimental animals it has been found repeatedly that an inadequate diet may be correlated with increased susceptibility to a variety of bacterial diseases (5) and in part this may be due simply to a deficiency of calories (6). Sabin (7) in studies of the development in mice of age barriers to infection by vesicular stomatitis virus found that general malnutrition during the period of rapid growth of the animal hindered the development of this native mechanism of resistance. Spies and his co-workers have made an interesting approach to this question (8). They developed a basal diet for rats similar to that upon which persons observed by them in an area of endemic malnutrition developed mixed deficiencies. The diet was deficient in protein, vitamins and minerals, and rats fed on it suffered loss of weight, of appetite and of hair. During periods of two to five months studies were made of the differential blood pictures, and of the activity of the blood phagocytes of these animals. The leukocyte counts dropped to one-third to one-half the normal level, and the cells were considerably poorer in phagocytic activity than were those of normal rats. No test was made of the relative abilities of deficient and normal animals to resist infectious agents.

As in the human epidemiologic studies, evidence obtained from experimental animals has not been unanimous by any means in showing a deleterious effect of malnutrition upon native immunity. In the case of the viruses especially experiments have shown that malnutrition may actually favor the host with respect to susceptibility. Rous (9) found that sick or malnourished fowl were more resistant to fowl sarcoma virus than normal controls; Olitsky and others (10) made similar observations with foot and mouth disease virus in guinea pigs, and Rivers (11b) and Sprunt (11a) have noted the same effect with vaccinia virus in malnourished rabbits. Similar findings have been made with certain of the neurotropic viruses (see Thiamin Chloride, page 178). It is generally believed that these rather surprising examples are in fact in accord with the view that the propagation of the viral agent depends upon normal metabolic function of the host's cells; if malnutrition undermines this the parasite may also suffer. There is thus no generalized answer to the question of the influence of starvation upon susceptibility to infection, either from human studies or animal experiments. Susceptibility to most potential parasites is undoubtedly increased; in some cases perhaps there is no particular effect at all, for as Clark (12) points out, there appears to be no distinction between well-nourished and malnourished children in susceptibility to the common infectious diseases of childhood; and in the special instances just cited malnourishment appears to favor the host.

The acquisition of resistance may be interfered with by starvation in some cases. The rats studied by Spies (8) formed agglutinins to bacterial vaccines poorly, and analogous findings have been noted in mice vaccinated with western equine encephalomyelitis virus (13). This is perhaps referable to the effect of protein deficiency upon antibody formation.

2. Protein. Although we will be concerned here chiefly with the effects of a deficiency of protein in the diet, many other situations may result in subnormal concentrations of proteins in the blood of man and animals. Hypoproteinemia is in general a consequence of dietary lack, of loss, or of inability to assimilate. It may result from malnutrition, fever, hemorrhage, hypothyroidism, liver disease, neoplasm, serious wounds or burns, acute infectious disease, surgical operations, and gastrointestinal disease when normal intestinal absorption is impaired. There may be a direct loss of protein through the urine in nephrosis and nephritis. Thus there are multiple circumstances in which an insufficiency of circulating protein occurs and it is the generally accepted opinion that a dynamic equilibrium exists between dietary, circulating and tissue proteins (14). Since this is the case, hypoproteinemia from any cause might influence native and acquired immunity similarly, although most of the evidence described here is taken from studies of dietary deficiency.

INFLUENCE ON NATIVE RESISTANCE. It is the general opinion that susceptibility to infection is heightened when hypoproteinemia exists. Human beings with extreme deficiency of blood proteins often die with pulmonary edema and pneumonia (15). Dogs deprived of plasma proteins become susceptible to a variety of infections including abscesses, enteritis, endocarditis, septicemia and respiratory disease (16). Koerner and associates (17) maintained rats for several generations on diets containing 15, 25 and 40 per cent protein, and tested these groups for their abilities to cope with intravenously injected tubercle bacilli. The high-protein group fared best, showing better localized and less extensive infection, a tendency toward regression, and longer life. Rats on low protein diets show increased susceptibility to murine typhus (18) and similar observations have been made in rats tested with pneumococci (19), with a *Salmonella* (20), and with the Friedländer bacillus (21).

It is interesting to know how protein insufficiency may interfere with native resistance to infection. Cannon states that there is a decrease in the number of potential phagocytes from the mesenchymal tissues, and there appears to be as well a depressed production of new granulocytes and lymphocytes (22). In addition to this quantitative decrease, the activity of the phagocytes also seems to be impaired (23). Finally there is evidence (6) that the normal bactericidal activity of body fluids may be impaired. From the mechanistic viewpoint there seem then to be adequate explanations for the observed deleterious effects of protein deprivation upon susceptibility to certain of the bacteria, at least to those susceptibile to phagocytic destruction.

The consequences of deficient protein intake or utilization so far as infection is concerned constitutes a vicious cycle, since the deficiency predisposes to infection and on the other hand infection is well known to retard plasma protein regeneration. In addition, if the infection is sufficiently severe and the plasma protein level falls to a low point, intestinal edema may further interfere with the absorption of protein.

The refeeding of protein to deficient animals reinstates their normal levels of resistance. For this purpose animal proteins are superior to those of vegetable origin (24).

INFLUENCE ON ACQUIRED RESISTANCE. Most of the controlled observations of the effect of protein deprivation upon the ability to **acquire** specific resistance indicate again a deleterious effect. In the case of bacteria, Wissler (19b, 25) has found that rabbits and rats vaccinated to pneumococcus while on protein-deficient diets are subsequently incapable of resisting challenge infections as well as do controls. It was pointed out however that a caloric as well as a protein deficiency was involved in these studies. Impoverished antibody responses were the chief factor concerned, though of course the loss of phagocytic efficiency also enters into such results with this microbe (26). Similar findings have been made with *Klebsiella pneumoniae* in rats (21). In the parasitic worm infections caused by *Nippostrongylus muris* (27) and *Trichinella* (28) in rats, acquired immunity is appreciably lowered in the presence of protein deficiency, and it has been suggested that this may explain the epidemiologic picture of human hookworm infection in the economically retarded areas of this country where chronic disease occurs (27). Otheɪ analogous observations concerned with protozoa are described by Clark (29).

Now again we inquire as to mechanisms. The previously cited work concerned with native resistance gives evidence of impairment of the systems of phagocytes, and these are in certain instances of paramount importance to acquired as well as to native resistance. Evidence is also available with respect to antibody formation. In the first place, it is necessary to ascertain how directly dietary protein may influence the manufacture of plasma globulins. As was mentioned earlier, Whipple has evolved the concept of equilibrium between dietary, plasma and tissue proteins, and Heidelberger and co-workers (30) have found by feeding radioactive leucine to rabbits and rats undergoing vaccination that the half-life of a globulin molecule is two weeks, and that antibody takes part in metabolic reactions involving exchange with dietary nitrogen. This would make it seem likely that protein deficiency should soon be reflected by an impoverished antibody synthesis. Oddly enough however there have been repeated observations over a period of years that in experimental hypoproteinemia induced by feeding deficient diets, the globulin level remains intact for weeks after the albumin has sunk to low values (31, 32), and this implies that antibody globulin formation might not be impeded even by prolonged protein deficiency. The truth of the matter must be sought directly by studies of antibody formation in deficient animals. Cannon and his co-workers (33) have found in rabbits and rats after prolonged periods of protein deprivation a loss of the ability to synthesize antibody. The refeeding of protein restores this ability provided that high quality proteins or amino acid mixtures are used (34). There is some evidence also that hypoproteinemia in human beings may interfere with antibody formation (35).

How may one correlate this effect of protein deprivation upon antibody formation with the observations regarding the persistence of globulins even in advanced hypoproteinemia? The answer seems to depend upon the interval during which the protein deficiency is maintained. It has been reported that a significant depression of antibody formation in rats does not occur for perhaps a month after the deficient diet has been instituted (36a). We can only conclude then that there must be a very serious deficiency of building blocks before antibody production becomes seriously compromised (36b), and there is some question as to how frequently this may occur in malnourished human beings except perhaps under conditions of prolonged starvation (37).

There is no evidence to suggest that the intake of protein in amounts above body requirements increases either native or acquired resistance beyond their normal levels.

3. **Vitamins.** A good deal of interest has for some years been centered upon the possible influence of the vitamins upon susceptibility to infectious disease. The metabolic functions of many of these accessory food factors are known now, and deficiencies of these substances result in recognizable clinical syndromes in man or animals.

Generally speaking, when a vitamin deficiency causes specific pathologic changes the tissues affected become liable to secondary infection. This is probably a nonspecific consequence of cellular damage, and occurs in several deficiencies. There is some evidence also that the lack of certain vitamins may lower resistance in more specific ways, by interfering with known mechanisms of defense such as the phagocytic cells, or bactericidal enzymes, or the antibody producing cells.

VITAMIN A. A deficiency of this fat-soluble substance causes a variety of effects in the human being including night blindness, xerophthalmia, drying and scaliness of the skin, and keratinizing metaplasia of epithelial tissue including that of the respiratory, alimentary and genito-urinary tracts. As a result of the last-named alteration the epithelium comes to resemble that of epidermis regardless of the previous structure or function of the part involved.

Fifteen or twenty years ago a great deal of effort went into work designed to reveal a relationship of vitamin A to native and acquired resistance. For a time this was referred to as the anti-infective vitamin. Subsequent events have not upheld this viewpoint; there is no convincing evidence that a deficiency in this factor results in anything other than enhanced susceptibility of the tissues particularly damaged, especially those of the respiratory tract. Infections in this location associated with atrophy of the epithelium may occur long before keratinizing changes can be seen. As a matter of fact, vitamin A deficiency does not ordinarily become severe enough in human beings to cause marked tissue changes, but when the pancreas is diseased so that the fat-splitting enzymes no longer empty into the duodenum, the absorption of fats and of fat-soluble vitamins is greatly impaired. This is what happens in children with chronic cystic fibrosis of the pancreas and the resultant celiac syndrome (38). A consequence of this disease is a deficiency in vitamin A. In young children it happens that the epithelium of the trachea and bronchi is earliest affected by the deficiency; consequently the upper respiratory tract first becomes highly susceptible to bacterial infection. Pneumonia, commonly of the interstitial or peribronchial type, is then a frequent sequel to the pancreatic disease.

A variety of observations in deficient animals has indicated increased susceptibility to *Salmonella* infections (20) and to intestinal worm infestations (39a), and in human beings there is beginning to emerge evidence that deficiencies in vitamins A and C may increase susceptibility to tuberculosis (39b).

With regard to acquired immunity, earlier reports that antibody formation might be impaired by deficiency have not been confirmed in recent years, nor is there evidence that other possible mechanisms of acquired resistance may be interfered with.

VITAMIN B. The vitamin B complex is made up of a variety of food factors and the list grows longer almost by the month. Among the substances which comprise the B complex are thiamin chloride (B_1), riboflavin (B_2), pyridoxine (B_6), nicotinamide, pantothenic acid, pteroylglutamic acid (folic acid), B$_{12}$, biotin, inositol, choline, para-aminobenzoic acid and adenylic acid. Of these, thiamin chloride is the antineuritic or antiberiberi factor in man. Deficiency of riboflavin results in oral and ocular lesions. The need for pyridoxine has not been established in human beings but it may play some part in specifically acquired resistance. Nicotinamide is concerned with the prevention of pellagra, a disease marked by dermatitis, glossitis and other changes. The usefulness of pantothenic acid, biotin and the other members of the complex are not evident at the present time so far as human beings are concerned, but their lack in animals has been correlated with certain changes in susceptibility to infection. Depletion of the folic acid factor of the B complex leads to macrocytic anemia, and because of its activity upon bone marrow it may be related to the maintenance of the normal level of native resistance. These various factors will be taken up separately. It should be pointed out that deficiency of any one of these substances is not necessarily the direct cause of whatever modifications may be seen in native or acquired resistance. A severe deficiency of one element may disturb other aspects of metabolism.

Thiamin Chloride. There appears to be some correlation between deficiency in this vitamin and lowered resistance to certain experimental bacterial infections. Deficient rats are more susceptible to rat leprosy (40), and mice maintained on amounts subminimal for growth requirements are more susceptible to intranasal and intratracheal infection with pneumococcus type I (41) and to S. typhimurium (42). Rats receiving one-twentieth the optimal amount of thiamin are more susceptible than normal rats to murine typhus (43). On the other hand, the past few years have provided evidence that a lack of this food substance may actually increase resistance to certain virus diseases and perhaps to other infections also. Foster and her co-workers (44) found that mice with thiamin deficiency responded to inoculations of poliomyelitis virus with a lengthened incubation period and a lower incidence of paralysis and mortality than control animals. Similar results have been reported by others with the Lansing poliomyelitis as well as the Theiler's mouse encephalomyelitis viruses (45), and there is a similar indication in the case of herpes simplex (46). A peculiar effect in which the infection progresses with few encephalitic symptoms but with unaltered mortality has been seen with the virus of western equine encephalomyelitis (47).

Since nerve cells are deleteriously affected by thiamin chloride deficiency it is tempting to attribute decreased susceptibility to an inability of poorly metabolizing cells to support the proliferation of these parasites. This viewpoint may be correct but if so there are qualifying factors, for monkeys, unlike mice, are not favorably affected in their susceptibility to poliomyelitis by thiamin deficiency (48), and in other virus diseases of the nervous system the effect of deficiency may be adverse, as reported for the age resistance to vesicular stomatitis virus in mice (7).

In several other diseases deficiency of B complex (rather than individual factors) has also been found favorable to the host. A better ability to withstand certain protozoa has been described in rats; the diseases include trypanosomiasis (*Trypanosoma equiperdum*) and coccidiosis (*Eimeria nieschulzi*) (49, 50). In most cases however B deficiency has been found to have an adverse effect upon susceptibility to larger parasites (39).

There is no good evidence that antibody formation or acquired resistance to infection itself is affected in any direction by thiamin deficiency.

Pantothenic Acid. As with thiamin chloride there are indications here also that deficiency may in some cases increase native susceptibility to experimental infections, in others decrease it. Deficient rats are more susceptible than controls to murine typhus (43), but no effect could be determined in the development of pneumococcal infection in the same host (41b, 51). On the other hand an advantage for the host has been reported with Theiler's virus in mice (29) and in the development of malarial parasites (*Plasmodium gallinaceum*) in the erythrocytes of chickens (52).

There is some indication that this vitamin may have an influence upon acquired resistance. The production of hemagglutinins is said to be impaired in deficient rats (53), and these animals are not as well able as normal rats to handle the ordinarily benign parasite *T. lewisi* apparently because the reproduction-inhibiting substance, ablastin, is not effectively produced (54).

Riboflavin. This member of the B complex forms the Warburg yellow enzyme, concerned in tissue oxidations. Deficiency is usually associated with greater susceptibility to infections. In human beings with pellagra (due to mixed B deficiency) the staphylococci and hemolytic streptococci may be frequently isolated from cheilotic and ocular lesions, and these bacteria disappear quickly with riboflavin therapy (55). Animal experiments have also revealed the deleterious effect of deficiency upon the native resistance of involved tissues. Mice become more susceptible to spontaneous salmonellosis (56), and deficient rats show a marked susceptibility, beyond the normal, to murine typhus. Pinkerton and Bessey (57) have reported that restoration of the vitamin will pull these animals back from the verge of death to recovery in 24 hours. The explanation proposed for this spectacular effect is interesting; these investigators believe that since rickettsias multiply best within cells metabolizing at a low respiratory level they flourish in the absence of a vitamin so important to cellular respiration, while the restoration of the vitamin halts their progress very suddenly.

As with other members of the B complex, reports here also indicate that in certain instances deficiency may be of advantage to the host in dealing with infectious agents. Malarial parasites of the chicken and the monkey develop in fewer erythrocytes of deficient animals than of those on normal diets (58).

The author is aware of but one study dealing with the effect of riboflavin deficiency upon antibody formation and it suggests that this is decreased in rats vaccinated with human erythrocytes (59).

Pyridoxine (B_6). This vitamin is concerned with the metabolism of protein, acting as a coenzyme for the decarboxylation and transamination of certain amino acids, notably tryptophane. It seems also to take part in the metabolism of unsaturated fatty acids. In rats it is an antidermatitis factor and in dogs a deficiency leads to microcytic anemia.

The relationship of pyridoxine deficiency to a mouse pneumonia virus infection (PVM) seems to be a fluctuating one. Young mice deprived of the vitamin for several days following infection showed decreased susceptibility to the virus, but the opposite effect was seen if the deficiency were inaugurated earlier and maintained for a longer time. The reasons for these differences are not yet appreciated (60).

With respect to acquired resistance, Stoerk and others (61) have reported that pyridoxine-deficient rats form antibodies against sheep red blood cells only poorly, and this is correlated with a decreased concentration of alpha and gamma globulins in the serum. The fact that other workers had found defective antibody formation in man and animals with B complex deficiency (62) suggests that the lack of pyridoxine may have been specifically responsible in those cases also. This viewpoint is contested by another report however, (60b) so that more work will be necessary before a stabilized opinion can be formed.

Nicotinamide. Nicotinamide is the functional group in coenzymes which act as hydrogen carriers in the body. A deficiency of this substance leads to pellagra. Among the symptoms traditionally associated with pellagra are inflammation of the tongue, gums, and membranes of the mouth and pharynx. The organisms of Vincent's angina become very abundant wherever the mucous membranes are involved, and several reports indicate that they disappear following treatment with the vitamin. Here again, a heightened susceptibility to parasitic invasion occurs in tissues which, because of the nutritional deficiency, undergo pathologic changes. It does not seem likely that such deficiencies interfere with specific mechanisms of defense, but some impairment of antibody formation has been described (61c).

Folic Acid. Pteroylglutamic or folic acid is related chiefly to the macrocytic anemias associated with sprue, pregnancy, pellagra, the anemia of infancy, and pernicious anemia. It is essential for the conversion of megaloblasts into erythrocytes. In certain animals, including the monkey and the rat, a deficiency of this substance also depresses granulopoiesis so that only a small number of leukocytes are manufactured. It is not clear that this effect occurs in human beings. It might be imagined that the depression of leukocyte formation would favor susceptibility to a variety of microbes, and this has been found to be the case in monkeys tested with a streptococcus. Saslaw and his co-workers (63) have worked with a group C streptococcus which, when administered intranasally to rhesus monkeys, produces very slight evidence of infection. In monkeys deficient in folic acid, however, the granulocytic response to infection was very slight, and in the absence of the leukocytes most animals developed erysipelas or died of septicemia. Administration of folic acid resulted in a prompt return of ability to resist this organism even after infection was under way. The same investigators (64) found the susceptibility of deficient monkeys to influenza type A to be increased also, possibly as the result of epithelial changes in the respiratory tract. A similar decrease in native ability to resist has been seen with avian malaria in folic acid-deficient fowl (65).

In the experiments with monkeys it was found that immunologic responses to the infectious agents were precisely the same in the folic acid deficient monkeys as in normal animals. Acquired immunity as reflected by antibody response was thus not impaired in this particular instance (see, however, Ludovici and Axelrod [61c]).

Para-aminobenzoic Acid. In all cases so far described, whatever effect a vitamin may show with respect to susceptibility to infectious disease has been the result of a deficiency of the substance in the host. PABA is exceptional in that although a deficiency does not affect susceptibility to murine typhus (50), excessive amounts are beneficial in rickettsial infections of animals and man (66). This effect may be the result of stimulation of the metabolism of the host's cells, for rickettsias propagate optimally when cellular respiration is at a low level.

Biotin. Deficiency of this substance causes increased susceptibility of rats and mice to a *Salmonella* (67), and may also depress the formation of antibodies (68).

VITAMIN C. This vitamin (1-ascorbic acid) is necessary for the proper formation and maintenance of intercellular material, such as the collagen of all fibrous tissues, the cement substance of endothelial tissues and especially that of the capillaries, and the matrix of bone and cartilage. The syndrome of deficit is scurvy. As in the case of vitamin A, some years ago a great deal of enthusiasm attended the possible role of this vitamin in various processes of both native and acquired immunity, but time has so altered the perspective that now even its most sanguine proponents no longer refer to it as an anti-infectious vitamin. Because gingivitis accompanies the early stages of scurvy and because the mouth normally maintains a rich flora of microbes, there is an increased tendency for infection of the pathologically affected tissues in early ascorbic acid deficiency. There may be also a more general tendency to susceptibility because of a defect in the leukocytes, at least in scorbutic guinea pigs. Nungester and Ames (69) studied the relation between leukocyte fragility, phagocytic ability and vitamin C levels in the peritoneal fluids of these animals, and found a marked increase in fragility and an impairment of phagocytosis at low vitamin levels. In the presence of serum however these adverse effects were considerably reduced, leaving some question as to the significance of the deficiency to phagocytosis in vivo.

In some infections, of which tuberculosis is an outstanding example, the ascorbic acid requirement may be considerably greater in infected than in normal individuals. The deficiency, however, is the result of infection rather than vice versa, and although infection and deficiency may perhaps constitute a vicious cycle, it is now obvious that the deficiency cannot be given an etiologic status in favoring the onset of the disease.

The other well-defined vitamin factors, D, E, K, and P at the present time have no clear status with respect either to innate or acquired immunity processes.

In summary, the known influences of vitamin deprivations upon native resistance extend to (a) a decrease in the ability of pathologically altered tissues to resist potential parasites, (b) some rather sparse indications that specific mechanisms of native resistance may in certain instances be impaired, notably the number and quality of leukocytes in deficiencies of folic acid and perhaps of ascorbic acid, and (c) in the case of thiamin chloride, and perhaps other members of the B complex, evidence that deprivation may increase native resistance. As for acquired immunity, only in the case of pyridoxine is there serious evidence that a deficiency may interfere with antibody formation, though certain other members of the B complex may also be involved in the effective functioning of acquired resistance. This evidence is so far scanty and must therefore be considered tentative.

In only one case has there been any indication that quantities of these food factors in excess of the normal requirements have any influence upon immunity. The exception is in the effect of paraaminobenzoic acid upon rickettsial infections; it seems probable that the therapeutic efficacy in this instance depends upon an alteration in the metabolic functioning of host cells.

4. **Minerals.** In the past few years a beginning has been made in assessing the role of dietary minerals in the functioning of resistance. A general reduction of the mineral content of the diet has been found to decrease native resistance to salmonellas in mice (20), an effect which Church relates to the deficiency in calcium (70). The Wisconsin group of nutritionalists and bacteriologists has looked into the effect of deprivation of each of a series of minerals upon native susceptibility to Theiler's encephalomyelitis virus in mice, and has determined that the ability to resist is **increased** when the diet is freed of either potassium or phosphorus. Lack of sodium, calcium, magnesium or chlorine had little or no effect upon susceptibility in either direction (71).

There has apparently been no study made of the possible influence of mineral deficiencies upon acquired immunity.

INFLUENCE OF PHYSICAL ACTIVITY

INFLUENCE ON NATIVE RESISTANCE. The factor of fatigue as related to resistance is not readily measurable. Nevertheless, appreciation of such a relationship is probably as old as human observation itself. It is difficult to determine for any individual what constitutes physical overstrain or fatigue and what may be simply healthful exercise. Probably the factor of time is an important differential here; physical exertion which may ordinarily be of no harm to the body could be deleterious to native resistance if engaged in during the incubation period of an infectious disease, and this is what Boycott and Price-Jones (72) found to be the case in experimental animals. Fatigue induced in rats in advance of test infection with *S. enteritidis* by mouth made little apparent difference to the course or outcome as compared with infection controls. If, however, animals were fatigued at intervals during the incubation period or early after obvious disease had begun there was a pronounced effect, manifested in early generalization of infection and increased mortality. Bailey has made observations similar in principle concerning intratracheal and intra-nasal pneumococcus type I infection in rabbits (73). One factor which may help to explain these observations is found in the depressing influence of fatigue upon the number of circulating leukocytes (74). In some instances there may be more direct reasons for not taxing the body when an infection is under way. Rich (2b) points out that in pulmonary tuberculosis, for example, the increased movement of the lungs resulting from exertion may act mechanically to rupture partly caseous blood vessels and the necrotic margins of lesions, and this may lead to hemorrhage and the mechanical spread of the bacilli. Analogous considerations may apply to other infections; thus, there is some evidence that fatigue predisposes to poliomyelitic paralysis in man (75).

INFLUENCE ON ACQUIRED RESISTANCE. The results of tests of the effect of fatigue upon antibody formation have been variable. Bailey's work with rabbits already vaccinated to pneumococcus have shown that fatigue induced before or after test infection by a natural route did not vitiate the effectiveness of the acquired resistance (73). Undoubtedly this result depends upon the solidity of an acquired immunity, and would vary with different animal species and infectious agents. A review of this subject has been made by Baetjer (76).

INFLUENCE OF TEMPERATURE AND HUMIDITY

INFLUENCE ON NATIVE RESISTANCE. Many observations have been made in experimental animals as well as in human beings concerning the influence of environmental temperature upon susceptibility to infections. The host-parasite relationships which may be affected by temperature and temperature variations fall into these general categories:

1. Instances in which animals are innately resistant to an infectious agent, but can be made susceptible by a change in environmental temperature great enough to influence the body temperature.

2. Instances in which a superficial tissue—the skin—is susceptible to infection because of its lower temperature, and in which the host-parasite relationship can be changed by modifications of environmental temperature.

3. Instances in which general tissue susceptibility is already present, but may be increased or decreased by changes in environmental temperature.

There are several examples of the first kind. Pasteur attributed the resistance of chickens to anthrax to the high body temperature of this fowl. By immersing the bird's feet in cold water and thus eventually lowering its body temperature it could be made susceptible, lethally so, to the anthrax bacillus (77). At the other end of the scale are cold-blooded animals, including the frog, which owe their innate resistance to the same bacillus to their usually low body temperatures. These may be made susceptible by increasing the environmental temperature to the neighborhood of 37° C.

The type III pneumococcus fails to cause progressive infection in rabbits because the body temperature of that animal, once an incipient fever is under way, is too high to support growth of the microbe. If rabbits are placed in a cold environment they become susceptible to this pneumococcus to the degree of developing fatal septicemia (78).

With influenza virus, Saslaw and co-workers (64) have found that monkeys ordinarily respond to its intranasal administration with very slight signs of disease. When these animals were kept at 4° to 6° C. after instillation of virus they became lethargic and weak, developed respiratory distress, and three of four so treated died of pneumonitis.

Thus, the effect of lowering the environmental temperature, and as a consequence the body temperature, in all these instances involving warm-blooded animals proved deleterious to the host.

In the second category of host-parasite relationships influenced by environmental temperature are instances in which susceptibility to infection is limited to superficial tissues because these are at a lower temperature than the deeper tissues. The agents involved apparently possess all the requisites for parasitism except the ability to proliferate at the internal temperature of mammalian hosts. Thompson (79) has found that the viruses of infectious fibromatosis and infectious myxomatosis of rabbits can be inhibited in their epidermal development if the skin temperature is raised by sojourn at a temperature of 36° to 40° C.

Several years ago MacCallum and his associates (80) in Australia uncovered a mycobacterium (*Myco. ulcerans*) responsible for cases of ulceration of the skin in human beings. This strongly acid-fast bacillus grows optimally at 33° C., hence will not infect the deeper tissues either of man or animals. It would be interesting to know whether a depression of body temperature by a sufficient cooling of the environment might alter the relationship between the host and parasite in this case.

In the third group fall those instances in which general susceptibility to infection exists but for various reasons may be altered by variations in external temperature. Thus, mice infected with typhus rickettsias and kept at 18° to 22° C. all die, while of animals maintained at 29° to 37° C. only one-tenth succumb. This finding is consistent with the knowledge that lower temperatures are favorable to the intracellular growth of rickettsias. The same effect may be operative in favoring the development of the scrotal reaction after the intraperitoneal injection of rickettsias into experimental animals, for the temperature of the scrotum is below that of the body proper (81).

In man it has been recognized for many years that the air-borne infections, such as pneumonia and epidemic meningitis, are most prevalent in

cold climates and during cold seasons when they may assume epidemic proportions. This could be due to factors which increase effective spread of the
organism, such as greater exposure opportunities in closed rooms. On the
other hand there may in addition exist factors related to increased susceptibility, and there is evidence that this is so. Sulkin (82) worked with influenza
virus in mice kept in cool, moderate, and hot (95° F.) environments, and
though these different temperatures had little effect upon mortality there was
decidedly less lung involvement in animals kept consistently at the high temperature. Consistency of temperature in itself seems to be an important point
as might be expected from ordinary human experience. Animals kept by Mills
(83) either at 68° F. or 90° F. developed spontaneous pneumonia very infrequently, whereas of those maintained at the variable temperatures of a
laboratory room about 20 per cent died of pulmonary infections. When in
addition humidity is brought into the picture it has been generally observed
that both extremes of temperature, if associated with high humidity, are
most deleterious to native resistance (84). A lead to the reasons for this may
be supplied by Cralley's (85) finding that animals subjected to inhalation of
bacteria in droplet nuclei are ordinarily able to dispose of 80 per cent of the
organisms reaching the lungs in the first hour, while at extremes of temperature and humidity only about 30 per cent are removed. The mechanisms
which might be impaired were not studied. Nungester (86) has shown that
chilling makes rats more susceptible to pneumonia because of interference
with closure of the glottis. As a consequence there is a greater tendency to
aspirate infectious material from the upper respiratory passages.

Not only in the case of air-borne infections may temperature and humidity affect susceptibility. In mice exposed to *S. enteritidis* by the oral route
low temperatures and high humidities favored severe infections, and it has
been suggested that the seasonal epidemicity of typhoid fever in Palestine, the
area in which the study was undertaken, might be accounted for by these observations (87).

Susceptibility to overt infection by various agents existing in a latent state
in man and lower animals may be altered by various environmental influences,
including temperature changes. The virus of herpes simplex appears to reside
in human beings from early childhood, breaking into prominence in the form
of fever blisters when resistance is temporarily impaired. Heat among other
factors may induce such attacks (88). The resistance disturbed here may be
of the acquired variety, since virus-neutralizing antibodies generally occur in
the sera of latently infected individuals. In various laboratory animals inapparent pneumotropic viruses occur commonly, two or more sometimes
existing simultaneously, all capable of causing pneumonia when the host-
parasite equilibrium is upset by various stimuli such as intranasal instillation
of fluids. Such stimuli are by far most commonly effective in winter (89),
a fact which may depend upon temperature, although other seasonal factors
may also be of importance.

Susceptibility to the effects of toxic substances also varies with changes in environmental temperature which are sufficiently great to influence the body temperature. This is especially striking in poikilothermic animals. Thus a lizard, the desert iguana, responds to tetanus toxin with convulsions and death within 24 hours at 38° C., with death in seven or eight days at 27° C., and without apparent symptoms at 10° C. (90). Even in mammals differences in susceptibility are met with; mice are less resistant to the effects of dysentery (Shiga) toxin in winter than in summer (91).

INFLUENCE ON ACQUIRED RESISTANCE. With respect to the acquisition of resistance, certain interesting studies indicate an influence of environmental temperature also, especially striking in cold-blooded animals. Frogs, eels and fish produce antibodies to vaccines when kept at ordinary room temperature, but do so sluggishly or fail entirely at temperatures of 10° C. or below (92). This may lead to interesting host-parasite relationships. Thus Bisset (93) has found that certain water bacteria parasitize fish, causing symptomless but persistent infections at 10° C. At 20° C. innate susceptibility to these bacteria increases so that some fish die, but most of them, now able to produce antibodies, clear themselves entirely of the infection as a consequence of their acquired antibody immunity.

In mammals subjected to high environmental temperatures, sufficient to cause fever, antibody production may be impeded (94), and this is true also when the body temperature is forced down to 5° C. below normal by transection of the spinal cord. If the heat loss is made good in such animals by warming the environment, normal antibody formation is resumed (95).

What the influence of temperature may be upon the functioning of an acquired immunity which is already present is only scantily dealt with by existing information. In the case of rabbits immune to a pneumococcus, however, lowered body temperature was found not to interfere with the effectiveness of this resistance (101a).

INFLUENCE OF IRRADIATION

Effect of Sunshine and Ultraviolet Irradiation. It is generally believed that exposure to sunshine in moderate degree induces a condition of well-being which may be associated with less likelihood of spontaneous infection. The difficulty in evaluating this factor in relation to resistance is indicated by the variety of conflicting reports. Thus, English workers (96) have observed that exposure of animals to ultraviolet light increases the native bactericidal activity of their blood against streptococci and staphylococci, and it has also been found experimentally that irradiation tends to modify subsequent lesions produced by the vaccinia virus in rabbits if exposure is carried out shortly before or after infection (97). Attempts which have been made to reproduce such experiences in human beings, however, have been disappointing. Observations of children and of university students and older adults for the effects on the incidence of colds of ultraviolet irradiation given at frequent intervals for periods of months have been uniformly negative (98).

Effects of Short Wave Irradiation. INFLUENCE ON NATIVE RESISTANCE. Studies have been carried out over a period of years upon the effects of x-rays and other ionizing radiations upon native and acquired immunity. A recent article by the Taliaferros reviews this information (99). Many reports indicate an impairment of native defenses to various infectious agents, and others suggest the opposite effect, in both instances presumably on the basis of an influence of the radiations upon phagocytic cells (injury or stimulation) and upon the capacity to develop inflammatory responses. In general large doses of irradiation have been found deleterious to the host, small doses either without effect or sometimes beneficial. One report (100) concerned with the sequelae of the atomic bomb explosions in Japan describes the very general occurrence of injury to bone marrow occasioned by gamma radiation. The consequent leukopenia favored the development of septic lesions of the gums, pharynx and other tissues, as in agranulocytosis from other causes (see page 127).

INFLUENCE ON ACQUIRED RESISTANCE. The acquisition of antibodies is likewise adversely affected by large amounts of radiation administered during the time when vaccination is being carried out. Small doses however may enhance the production of antibodies according to the experience of some workers (99).

INFLUENCE OF DRUGS AND CHEMICAL SUBSTANCES

Alcohol. Ethyl alcohol is one of the more common chemicals to which the human body is repeatedly subjected. The common observation that pneumonia frequently follows bouts of drunkenness ending up in the gutter has been shown experimentally to be due largely to the intoxication itself, although exposure and chilling contribute to increased susceptibility. Alcohol itself however favors the generalization of pneumococci even in animals with acquired resistance. This effect is due to the paralyzing activity of alcohol upon blood vessels so that inflammatory responses become sluggish and few leukocytes appear in the tissues to take up the struggle (101). In addition to this simultaneous interference with the functioning of native and acquired immunity, it seems probable that the formation of antibodies is also interfered with by the administration of alcohol during the period of vaccination (102).

Chronic alcoholism introduces in addition the factor of malnutrition with its possible influences upon susceptibility to various infectious agents.

Ether Anesthesia. Ether has an effect very similar to that of alcohol upon susceptibility to pneumococcus infections in rabbits (101a). Interesting examples of the reverse effect of ether upon susceptibility are presented by the neurotropic viruses of equine encephalomyelitis and St. Louis encephalitis. Mice etherized immediately after the intracerebral inoculation of these viruses were found in some instances to survive, in contrast to controls. Although ether destroys these viruses in vitro, the workers who related these observations suggested that the in vivo effect was not due to direct virucidal activity, but rather to an alteration by the anesthetic agent of the metabolism of the cortical cells for which these viruses have affinity (103).

Bone Marrow Depressants. A variety of chemical substances have the effect in some individuals of injuring the bone marrow. Damage to the parent cells from which blood leukocytes are derived results in leukopenia, and this may be followed by greatly enhanced susceptibility to various microbes of the environment, including some which would be without infectious properties in the normal body. Certain of the commonly used drugs may occasionally bring about this intense leukopenia or agranulocytosis in individuals whose myeloid tissue apparently becomes hypersensitive to these substances. Examples are the aminopyrines, arsphenamine, barbiturates, sulfonamides and thiouracil. Agranulocytosis in itself is not a very serious affliction, for after a time regeneration of the stem cells in the bone marrow takes place. The factor which in the past accounted for a high mortality in affected individuals was the almost invariable occurrence of intercurrent infections permitted by the inadequacy of circulating polymorphonuclear neutrophils (104). The advent of antibiotics has therefore made a great difference in the prognosis for this disease, not by altering its course, but by controlling the septic complications.

Benzol Poisoning. Poisoning by benzol fumes is an occupational hazard in various chemical industries. This substance induces a depression of the bone marrow which is followed by a pronounced decrease of erythrocytes and leukocytes in the circulating blood. The serious oral and pharyngeal infections which so regularly accompany agranulocytosis are less common in this disease because the leukocyte depression is generally less. It has been clearly demonstrated experimentally however that the leukopenia induced by this compound may have serious effects upon resistance to certain infections. This is well illustrated by the work of Rich and McKee with rabbits subjected to experimental infection with the pneumococcus (see page 127). Even animals which had received the benefits of prophylactic immunization were unable to cope with the microbes if deprived of most of their circulating leukocytes as the result of poisoning with benzol.

Silicosis. A unique example of the effect of a chemical substance upon susceptibility to a disease and its subsequent progress is provided by silica in relation to tuberculosis. Exposure to silica dust occurs among those engaged in mining, quarrying, the grinding and polishing of cutlery and the fabrication of pottery. The result of such exposure is pulmonary fibrosis; the clinical syndrome is termed silicosis. It has been known for some years that individuals with silicosis become extraordinarily liable to serious infection by the tubercle bacillus, or if already infected, that the advent of silicosis worsens the disease. It does not influence other pulmonary infections in the same way.

This relationship has been examined experimentally with very interesting conclusions. It has been found that the native resistance of guinea pigs to attenuated tubercle bacilli is undermined (105, 108), and that the native resistance of rats and mice to human virulent bacilli is similarly impaired (105c, 106). Thus, an attenuated strain of the human tubercle bacillus which ordinarily produces only a local regressive tubercle at the site of inoculation in guinea pigs causes progressive and metastatic disease in animals subjected to inhalation of silica dust. The same thing happens if attenuated bacilli are injected intraperitoneally along with silica dust.

The acquired resistance which may be induced in guinea pigs by vaccination is also vitiated by silicosis (105b, 108). Silicosis is thus deleterious to native as well as acquired immunity.

The mechanism of this activity of silica is not known. It seems improbable that there is an effect upon the bacillus itself, for in the test tube there is no clear evidence that silica stimulates bacillary proliferation (105a, 107). Attenuated bacilli isolated from silicotic guinea pigs with progressive lesions and inoculated into normal animals show their usual nonprogressive characteristics (105b, 108). Nevertheless the majority opinion of those who have carried out such experiments is that some factor favoring growth of the bacillus may be produced in vivo, for fibrosis caused by other methods does not similarly influence the development of bacilli in the body (105a, 105b). The answer to this question remains to be settled.

An interesting practical aspect of this situation concerns the use of BCG vaccine in individuals who are exposed to silica dust. As might be expected from this discussion, this has proved to be a dangerous procedure in guinea pigs, for animals given vaccinating doses of BCG and subjected to quartz inhalation develop progressive and fatal pulmonary disease (108).

INFLUENCE OF INTERCURRENT INFECTIONS

One infectious agent may predispose the body to more serious infection by another, or both may act conjointly. This is especially evident in respiratory disease in which the virus of influenza may act concomitantly with a bacterium to cause serious pulmonary infection. It seems probable that such a relationship existed in the influenza pandemic of 1918 when various bacteria, notably beta hemolytic streptococci, staphylococci, pneumococci, and *Hemophilus influenzae,* were cultured from human pulmonary infections. Since the primary cause of that pandemic was not ascertained, and a similar pandemic has not recurred, it is not possible to state with certainty that that lethal plague resulted from a virus-bacterial relationship. There are however certain models which have been studied since and which lend credence to this belief. Shope (109) found influenza in hogs to be the product of the joint action of swine influenza virus with *H. influenzae suis.* Attempts to duplicate this experience with human influenza viruses and the *Hemophilus* in hosts (mice, ferrets) susceptible to these have not been successful, but an analogous situation has been created in monkeys infected with human influenza A virus and a hemolytic streptococcus of group C (110a). Rhesus monkeys are only slightly disturbed by this virus after its intranasal instillation, but they develop a characteristic leukopenia. The streptococcus employed also causes very mild infection when given intranasally. However, when monkeys were treated with the virus and about two weeks later were exposed to the streptococcus, serious respiratory infections frequently resulted. It appears that the leukopenia caused by the virus inhibits the leukocytic response which would ordinarily greet the streptococcus, and in the absence of a large number of white cells the bacterium produces severe infection. Interestingly from the epidemiologic standpoint, the leukopenic potentiality of the virus continued effective for as long as 17 days after recovery from the primary stage of leukopenia. Damage to respiratory tract epithelium by virus as well as the presence of edema fluid have been suggested as contributing factors in lowering resistance to the bacterium (110). It is interesting that staphylococcal pneumonia in human beings is not commonly found apart from influenza (111).

The activity of influenza virus upon blood cells has been ascribed to a toxic property which can be separated from other properties of the virus such as the hemagglutinating and the antibody-inducing substances, but this effect has been observed only upon the lymphocytes (112).

INFLUENCE OF ORGANIC FACTORS

Diseases Affecting Phagocytic and Lymph Cells. Influence on Native Resistance. In the leukemias which involve the phagocytic cells, i.e. the myelogenous and monocytic types, the circulating immature cells are found to have little phagocytic activity, but mature forms are apparently normally active in this respect (113).

Influence on Acquired Resistance. In leukemias of all types— myeloid, lymphoid and monocytic—the ability to form antibodies is seriously impaired, sufficiently so that the absence of Forssman's antibody has been suggested as diagnostic evidence for these diseases (114). Human beings ordinarily possess appreciable levels of these antibodies which act upon sheep erythrocytes (see page 447).

A blood dyscrasia which is of particular interest from the immunologic standpoint is infectious mononucleosis. This disease is of unknown though probably infectious origin, and unlike the leukemias it is self limited. Hematologically it is marked by the presence of circulating lymphoblasts. An antibody active against sheep and ox erythrocytes appears in most patients with this disease (115). What the relationship of this antibody may be to the unknown etiologic factor has not been determined. In any case, this syndrome is marked by the pronounced ability of the affected individual to produce this particular type of antibody, and in addition it is not uncommon for such patients to develop a variety of other antibodies; e.g. false positive Wassermann reactions may occur and antibodies in diagnostic concentrations against brucellas and other bacteria sometimes appear (116). Native susceptibility to sepsis tends to increase in this disease, at least insofar as oral infection with Vincents' organisms is concerned. In view of the propensity of the affected individual to form antibodies it would be interesting to know how the disease may influence acquired resistance. Evidence upon this point is not available.

Diabetes Mellitus. INFLUENCE ON NATIVE RESISTANCE. It has long been appreciated that poorly controlled diabetes mellitus favors the establishment of various pyogenic infections as well as tuberculosis, and that conversely infection in the presence of this disease adversely affects its proper control. The older and natural assumption that a heightened susceptibility to infection might be the result of excessive glucose favorable for microbial growth in the body fluids is not supported by the studies which have been made on this point. The addition of glucose to normal blood to attain a concentration comparable to that of diabetic blood does not increase its capacity to support bacterial growth (117). It appears instead that the bactericidal property of the blood of diabetics or of depancreatized animals is inferior to that of normal blood (118, 119). In addition to this alteration in the normal humoral defenses the phagocytic powers are also impaired (120). Rich (2b) points out that this might be expected in view of the excessive deposits of glycogen found in the leukocytes of the diabetic subject.

INFLUENCE ON ACQUIRED RESISTANCE. With regard to the acquisition of resistance there are observations to indicate that the diabetic is less able to form antibodies than is the normal person (117, 121). It is known that in untreated or poorly regulated diabetes large quantities of nitrogen are excreted in the urine as the result of increased gluconeogenesis (conversion of protein to carbohydrate). As a consequence a large protein deficit may occur, and in view of the findings outlined earlier in this chapter concerning the relationship of protein deficit to defective antibody production it seems possible that the inferior ability to produce antibody may be related to this occurrence. Recent tests of the ability of hypoproteinemic and normoproteinemic diabetics to respond to *S. typhosa* showed the former to be relatively poor in forming H agglutinins (122).

Sex Hormones. In the normal course of bodily development the sex hormones appear to influence susceptibility to tuberculosis as revealed by the relative mortality statistics for this disease in adolescent males and females discussed in the preceding chapter. Differences in death rates from other infections vary with sex also. The mechanisms affected in these instances are not known. Lurie (123) has found administered estrogen to increase resistance to tuberculosis in a genetically susceptible race of rabbits, presumably because this hormone reduces vascular permeability and so perhaps retards bacterial dissemination. A similar effect has been found in the case of vaccinia virus (124). Chorionic gonadotropin has an opposite effect upon native resistance which may correlate with its tendency to increase vascular permeability (125). In view of the ramifications in the activities of endocrine substances it seems very possible that other mechanisms also may be involved in the influences of these hormones upon innate immunity.

Local infections of the vagina may sometimes depend upon hormonal influences. In infancy and after the menopause vaginal epithelium is more susceptible to infection than in the years between, when it is highly resistant. During this period the epithelium is many cell layers thick, contains much glycogen, is acid in reaction, and the bacterial flora is dominated by organisms which flourish in an acid medium, notably the Doederlein bacillus. Most microbes are unable to establish themselves in this environment.

In infancy and during the postmenopausal years these cells are poor in glycogen and the local pH is lower. In both circumstances bacterial infections can more easily occur, and in both instances the administration of estrogen restores glycogen, increases acidity, and helps to eliminate infection (126).

Adrenal Cortical Hormones. The exciting new appreciation of the influence of adrenal cortical hormones upon resistance and hypersensitivity is still in the early stage of evaluation, but it seems evident that fundamental information will come from studies of these substances. The substances best studied at this time have been cortisone, representing Kendall's compound E of the adrenal cortex, and anterior pituitary adrenocorticotrophic hormone, or ACTH.

INFLUENCE ON NATIVE RESISTANCE. As regards native resistance, it is not yet known what effects, if any, these may have upon susceptibility to environmental infectious agents. Since however the adrenal cortex and cortisone may influence phagocytic activity (127) and depress the inflammatory response, and possibly also reduce the function of the reticulo-endothelial system (128), in addition to its other striking physiologic effects, the near future may yield knowledge on this point.

The ability to resist experimentally established infections has been studied to some extent and with variable results. Treatment with cortisone is described as being deleterious to guinea pigs and rats infected with the tubercle bacillus, resulting in a wider distribution of lesions than ordinarily occurs (127a, 127c); this has also been the experience of Freeman and others with pulmonary tuberculosis and the administration of ACTH. A feeling of well-being and subsidence of toxicity was associated with a spread of infection (129). Perhaps this outcome depends upon the inhibition of the inflammatory reaction and the eventual production of protective fibrosis. On the other hand Lurie and his co-workers have found that although cortisone-treated rabbits develop more tubercles following inhalation of bacilli than controls, and the caseous contents of these swarm with bacilli, the tendency to dissemination is lessened (127b). Obviously more study will be required before the question receives a clear answer. There is some evidence that pneumococcus infection in human beings may be benefited by ACTH (130).

INFLUENCE ON ACQUIRED RESISTANCE. The evidence presently available upon the question of acquired immunity concerns the ability of human beings and animals to form antibodies during the time when these substances are being administered. In rabbits, suppression of antibody formation has been reported as virtually complete with cortisone and partially so with ACTH (131). However, patients with pneumococcal pneumonia or vaccinated with pneumococcal polysaccharides while under treatment with cortisone or ACTH proceeded to produce antibodies (130). Antibodies present as the result of previous vaccination decrease by perhaps 25 per cent under the influence of cortisone (132) suggesting that the effect of this substance upon an immunity already acquired may be deleterious if this immunity depends upon antibody activity. Again, this question is presently too much in flux to permit conclusions.

It is not feasible to attempt a summary of the influences of the various factors discussed in relation to native and acquired resistance. In most instances it is difficult to provide a capsule of conclusions even for a single factor for its effect in different infections may vary considerably, depending among other things upon the nature of the relationship of parasite to host (whether intracellular, for example) and the mechanisms of resistance effective against a particular parasite. The first point is exemplified by the influence of thiamin chloride deficiency upon susceptibility to various bacterial infections in contrast to its influence in mice *vis-à-vis* poliomyelitis virus. The second point refers to such a possibility as this: that a depression of leukocytes which is of undoubtedly serious consequence to a host dealing with infectious agents against which phagocytes constitute an important mechanism of innate as well as acquired immunity, may be of little or no import in respect to a parasite against which leukocytes are of no avail as defensive agents.

BIBLIOGRAPHY

1. Schneider, H. A.   Bact. Rev., 13:99, 1949.
2a. Ledingham, J. C. G.   A System of Bacteriology in Relation to Medicine, London, His Majesty's Stationery Office, 6:31, 1931.
  b. Rich, A. R.   The Pathogenesis of Tuberculosis, Springfield, Ill., Charles C Thomas Co., 1944.
3. Keys, A.   J.A.M.A., 138:500, 1948.
4. Leyton, G. B.   Lancet, 2:73, 1946.
5. Watson, M.   J. Hyg., 37:420, 1937.
6. Guggenheim, K., and Buechler, E.   J. Hyg., 45:103, 1947.
7a. Sabin, A. B., and Duffy, C. E.   Science, 91:552, 1940.
  b. ———— J. Pediat., 19:596, 1941.
8. Berry, L. J., Davis, J., and Spies, T. D.   J. Lab. & Clin. Med., 30:684, 1945.
9. Rous, P.   J. Exper. Med., 13:397, 1911
10. Olitsky, P. K., Traum, J., and Schoening, H. W.   Report of the Foot and Mouth Disease Commission of the U. S. Dept. of Agriculture, Tech. Bull., 76:93, 1928.
11a. Sprunt, D. H.   J. Exper. Med., 75:297, 1942.
  b. Rivers, T. M.   Editor, Viral and Rickettsial Infections of Man, Philadelphia, J. B. Lippincott Co., 1948.
12. Clark, P. F.   Ann. Rev. Microbiol., 4:343, 1950.
13. Ruchman, I.   J. Bact., 51:403, 1946.
14. Whipple, G. H., and Madden, S. C.   Medicine, 23:215, 1944.
15. Thompson, W. H., McQuarrie, I., and Bell, E. T.   J. Pediat., 9:604, 1936.
16a. Whipple, G. H.   Am. J. M. Sc., 203:477, 1942.
  b. Madden, S. C., Winslow, P. M., Howland, J. W., and Whipple, G. H.   J. Exper. Med., 65:431, 1937.
17. Koerner, T. A., Getz, H. R., and Long, E. R.   Proc. Soc. Exper. Biol. & Med., 71:154, 1949.
18. Fitzpatrick, F. K.   J. Bact., 53:802, 1947.

19a. Sako, W. S.   J. Pediat., 20:475, 1942.
  b. Wissler, R. W.   J. Infect. Dis., 80:264, 1947.
20. Ross, J. R., and Robertson, E. C.   Am. J. Dis. Child., 43:547, 1932.
21. Woolridge, R. L.   Federation Proc., 8:376, 1949.
22a. Cannon, P. R.   J.A.M.A., 128:360, 1945.
  b. Asirvadham, M.   J. Infect. Dis., 83:87, 1948.
23a. Mills, C. A., and Cottingham, E.   J. Immunol., 47:503, 1943.
  b. Steffee, C. H.   J. Infect. Dis., 86:12, 1950.
24a. Robertson, E. C., and Doyle, M. E.   Proc. Soc. Exper. Biol. & Med., 35:374, 1936.
  b. Guggenheim, K., and Buechler, E.   J. Immunol., 54:349, 1946; 58:133, 1948.
25. Wissler, R. W.   J. Infect. Dis., 80:250, 1947.
26. Skinsnes, O. K., and Woolridge, R. L.   J. Infect. Dis., 83:78, 1948.
27. Donaldson, A. W., and Otto, G. F.   Am. J. Hyg., 44:384, 1946.
28. Taliaferro, W. H., Woolridge, R. L., and Benditt, E. P.   Science, 109:443, 1949.
29. Clark, P. F., and others.   Bact. Rev., 13:99, 1949.
30. Heidelberger, M., Treffers, H. P., Schoenheimer, R., Ratner, J., and Rittenberg, D.
        J. Biol. Chem., 144:555, 1942.
31a. Frisch, R. A., Mendel, L. B., and Peters, J. P.   J. Biol. Chem., 84:167, 1929.
  b. Cutting, W. C., and Cutter, R. D.   Proc. Soc. Exper. Biol. & Med., 32:1053, 1935.
  c. Weech, A. A., Goettsch, E., and Reeves, E. B.   J. Exper. Med., 61:299, 1935.
  d. Elman, R., Sachar, L. A., Horwitz, A., and Wolf, H.   J. Lab. & Clin. Med.,
        27:1183, 1942.
  e. Allison, J. B., Seeley, R. D., Brown, J. H., and Ferguson, F. P.   Proc. Soc. Exper.
        Biol. & Med., 63:214, 1946.
32. Zeldis, L. J., Alling, E. L., McCoord, A. B., and Kulka, J. P.   J. Exper. Med.,
        82:157, 1945.
33a. Cannon, P. R., Chase, W. E., and Wissler, R. W.   J. Immunol., 47:133, 1943.
  b. ——— Wissler, R. W., Woolridge, R. L., and Benditt, E. D.   Ann. Surg., 120:514,
        1944.
  c. Wissler, R. W., Woolridge, R. L., Steffee, C. H., Jr., and Cannon, P. R.   J. Im-
        munol., 52:267, 1946.
34. ——— Woolridge, R. L., and Steffee, C. H.   Proc. Soc. Exper. Biol. & Med.,
        62:199, 1946.
35. Wohl, M. G., Reinhold, J. G., and Rose, S. B.   Arch. Int. Med., 83:402, 1949.
36a. Benditt, E. P., Wissler, R. W., Woolridge, R. L., Rowley, D. A., and Steffee,
        C. H.   Proc. Soc. Exper. Biol. & Med., 70:240, 1949.
  b. Miles, J. A. R.   Brit. J. Exper. Path., 32:285, 1951.
37a. Bieler, M. M., Ecker, E. E., and Spies, T. D.   J. Lab. & Clin. Med., 32:130, 1947.
  b. Balch, H.   J. Immunol., 64:397, 1950
38. Andersen, D. H.   Am. J. Dis. Child., 56:344, 1938.
39a. Trager, W.   Bact. Rev., 13:99, 1949.
  b. Getz, H. R., Long, E. R., and Henderson, H. J.   Am. Rev. Tuberc., 64:381, 1951.
40. Badger, L. F., Masunaga, E., and Wolf, D.   Pub. Health Rep., 56:1027, 1940.
41a. Wooley, J. G., and Sebrell, W. H.   J. Bact., 44:148, 1942.
  b. Robinson, H. J., and Siegel, H.   J. Infect. Dis., 75:127, 1944.
42. Guggenheim, K., and Buechler, E.   Proc. Soc. Exper. Biol. & Med., 61:413, 1946.
43. Fitzpatrick, F.   Am. J. Pub. Health, 38:676, 1948.
44. Foster, C., Jones, J. H., Henle, W., and Dorfman, F.   Proc. Soc. Exper. Biol. &
        Med., 51:215, 1942; J. Exper. Med., 79:221, 1944.
45. Rasmussen, A. F., Jr., Waisman, H. A., Elvehjem, C. A., and Clark, P. F.   J. Infect.
        Dis., 74:41, 1944.
46. Cutting, W. C., Dreisbach, R. H., Halpern, R. M., Irwin, A. I., Jenkins, D. W.,
        Proescher, F., and Tripi, H. B., 1947, J. Immunol., 57:379, 1947.
47. Kearney, E. B., Pond, W. L., Plass, B. C., Maddy, K. H., Elvehjem, C. A., and
        Clark, P. F.   J. Infect. Dis., 82:177, 1948
48. Clark, P. F., Waisman, H. A., Lichstein, H. C., and Jones, E. S.   Proc. Soc. Exper.
        Biol. & Med., 58:42, 1945.
49. Reiner, L., and Paton, J. B.   Proc. Soc. Exper. Biol. & Med., 30:345, 1932.
50. Becker, E. R.   J. Parasitol., 28:18, 1942.
51. Day, H. G., and McClung, L. S.   Proc. Soc. Exper. Biol. & Med., 59:37, 1945.

52. Brackett, S., Waletsky, E., and Baker, M.   J. Parasitol., 32:453, 1946.

53. Ludovici, P. P., Axelrod, A. E., and Carter, B. B.   Proc. Soc. Exper. Biol. & Med.,
     72:81, 1949.

54a. Becker, E. R., Taylor, J., and Fuhrmeister, C.   Iowa State Coll. J. Sci., 21:237,
     1947.

  b. ———— and Gallagher, P. L.   Iowa State Coll. J. Sci., 21:351, 1947.

55. Riddle, J. W., Spies, T. D., and Hudson, N. P., Proc. Soc. Exper. Biol. & Med.,
     45:361, 1940.

56. Kligler, I. J., Guggenheim, K., and Buechler, E.   Proc. Soc. Exper. Biol. & Med.,
     57:132, 1944.

57. Pinkerton, H., and Bessey, O. A.   Science, 89:368, 1939.

58a. Seeler, A. O., and Ott, W. H.   J. Infect. Dis., 75:175, 1944.

  b. McKee, R. W., and Geiman, Q. M.   Proc. Soc. Exper. Biol. & Med., 63:313, 1946.

59. Axelrod, A. E., Carter, B. B., McCoy, R. H., and Geisinger, R,   Proc. Soc. Exper.
     Biol. & Med., 66:137, 1947.

60a. Leftwich, W. B., and Mirick, G. S.   J. Exper. Med., 89:155, 1949.

  b. Mirick, G. S., and Leftwich, W. B.   J. Exper. Med., 89:175, 1949.

61a. Stoerk, H. C., and Eisen, H. N.   Proc. Soc. Exper. Biol. & Med., 62:88, 1946.

  b. ———— Eisen, H. N., and John, H. M.   J. Exper. Med., 85:365, 1947.

  c. Ludovici, P. P., and Axelrod, A. E.   Proc. Soc. Exper. Biol. & Med., 77:526, 1951.

62a. Morey, G. R., and Spies, T. D.   Proc. Soc. Exper. Biol. & Med., 49:519, 1942.

  b. Berry, L. J., Davis, J., and Spies, T. D.   J. Lab. & Clin. Med., 30:684, 1945.

  c. Ruchman, I.   J. Immunol., 53:51, 1946.

63. Saslaw, S., Wilson, H. E., Doan, C. A., Woolpert, O. C., and Schwab, J. L.   J.
     Exper. Med., 84:263, 1946.

64. ———— Wilson, H. E., Doan, C. A., Woolpert, O. C., and Schwab, J. L.   J. Exper.
     Med., 84:113, 1946.

65. Seeler, A. O., and Ott, W. H.   J. Infect. Dis., 77:82, 1945.

66a. Greiff, D., Pinkerton, H., and Moragues, V.   J. Exper. Med., 80:561, 1944.

  b. Yeomans, A., Snyder, J. C., Murray, E. S., Zarafonetis, C., and Ecke, R. S.
     J.A.M.A., 126:349, 1944.

  c. Ross, S., McLendon, P. A., and Davis, H. J.   J. Pediat., 2:163, 1948.

67. Kligler, I. J., Guggenheim, K., and Herrnheiser, H.   J. Infect. Dis., 78:60, 1946.

68a. Caldwell, F. E., and Gyorgi, P.   J. Infect. Dis., 81:197, 1947.

  b. Carter, B. B., and Axelrod, A. E.   Proc. Soc. Exper. Biol. & Med., 67:416, 1948.

69. Nungester, W. J., and Ames, A. M.   J. Infect. Dis., 83:50, 1948.

70. Church, C. F.   J. Bact., 34:350, 1937.

71. Lichstein, H. C., McCall, K. B., Kearney, E. B., Elvehjem, C. A., and Clark, P. F.
     Proc. Soc. Exper. Biol. & Med., 62:279, 1946.

72. Boycott, A. E., and Price-Jones, C.   J. Path. & Bact., 29:87, 1926.

73. Bailey, G. H.   Am. J. Hyg., 5:175, 1925; 9:192, 1929.

74a. Reznikoff, P.   Am. J. M. Sc., 195:627, 1938.

  b. ———— and van Duyn, J.   Arch. Surg., 37:302, 1938.

75. Russell, W. R.   Brit. M. J., 2:1023, 1947.

76. Baetjer, A. M.   Physiol. Rev., 12:453, 1932.

77. Pasteur, L., Joubert, J. F., and Chamberland, C.   Bull. Acad. de méd., Paris,
     Series 2, 7:432, 1878.

78. Muschenheim, C., Duerschner, D. R., Hardy, J. D., and Stoll, A. M.   J. Infect.
     Dis., 72:187, 1943.

79. Thompson, R. L.   J. Infect. Dis., 62:307, 1938.

80a. MacCallum, P., Tolhurst, J. C., Buckle, G., and Sissons, H. A.   J. Path. & Bact.,
     60:93, 1948.

  b. Fenner, F., and Leach, R. H.   Australian J. Exper. Biol. & M. Sc., 30:1, 11, 1952.

81a. Moragues, V., and Pinkerton, H.   J. Exper. Med., 79:41, 1944.

  b. Pinkerton, H.   Bact. Rev., 13:99, 1949.

82. Sulkin, S. E.   J. Immunol., 51:291, 1945.

83. Mills, C. A.   Ann. New York Acad. Sc., 46:97, 1945.

84a. McDowell, C.   Am. J. Hyg., 3:521, 1923.

  b. Winslow, C. E. A.   Report of the New York Commission on Ventilation, New
     York, E. P. Dutton and Co., Inc., 1923.

85. Cralley, L. J.   Am. J. Hyg., 36:303, 1942.
86. Nungester, W. J.   J. Infect. Dis., 63:94, 1938.
87. Kligler, I. J., and Olitzki, L.   Am. J. Hyg., 13:349, 1931.
88. Kidd, J. G.   J.A.M.A., 117:1327, 1941.
89. Horsfall, F. L., Jr.   Federation Proc., 5:249, 1946.
90. Cowles, R. B., and Nelson, N. B.   Proc. Soc. Exper. Biol. & Med., 64:220, 1947.
91. Blake, A. V., and Okell, C. C.   Brit. J. Exper. Path., 10:175, 1929.
92a. Smith, W. W.   Proc. Soc. Exper. Biol & Med., 45:726, 1940.
    b. Cushing, J. E., Jr.   J. Immunol., 45:123, 1942.
    c. Bisset, K. A.   J. Path. & Bact., 59:301, 1947.
93. ———— J. Hyg., 45:128, 1947; J. Path. & Bact., 60:87, 1948.
94. Ellingson, H. V., and Clark, P. F.   J. Bact., 35:29, 1938.
95. Kopeloff, L. M., and Stanton, A. H.   J. Immunol., 44:247, 1942.
96. Colebrook, L., Erdinow, A., and Hill, L.   Brit. J. Exper. Path., 5:54, 1924.
97a. Carnot, P., Camus, L., and Bernard, H.   Compt. rend. Soc. de biol., 95:457, 1926.
    b. Rivers, T., Stevens, H., and Gates, F. L.   J. Exper. Med., 47:37, 1928.
98a. Colebrook, D.   Med. Res. Council (Great Britain), Special Rept. Ser., No. 131,
    1929.
    b. Doull, J. A., Hardy, M., Clark, J. H., and Herman, N. B.   Am. J. Hyg., 13:460,
    1931.
99. Taliaferro, W. H., and Taliaferro, L. G.   J. Immunol., 66:181, 1951.
100. LeRoy, G. V.   J.A.M.A., 134:1143, 1947.
101a. Pickrell, K. L.   Bull. Johns Hopkins Hosp., 63:238, 1938.
    b. Lushbaugh, C. C.   J. Immunol., 46:151, 1943.
102. Deléarde, A.   Ann. Inst. Pasteur, 11:837, 1897.
103. Sulkin, S. E., Zarafonetis, C., and Goth, A.   J. Exper. Med., 84:277, 1946.
104a. Stenn, F.   Arch. Path., 20:902, 1935.
    b. Castle, W. B., in Pathologic Physiology: Mechanisms of Disease, W. A. Sodeman,
    Editor, Philadelphia, W. B. Saunders Co., 1950, Chapter 14.
105a. Gardner, L. U.   Am. Rev. Tuberc., 20:833, 1929.
    b. Dowd, G. R.   Am. Rev. Tuberc., 32:62, 1935.
    c. Vorwald, A. J., and Delahant, A. B.   Am. Rev. Tuberc., 38:347, 1938.
106. Gye, W. E., and Kettle, E. H.   Brit. J. Exper. Path., 3:241, 1922.
107. Cummins, S. L., and Weatherall, C.   Brit. J. Exper. Path., 12:245, 1931.
108. Vorwald, A. J., Dworski, M., Pratt, P. C., and Delahant, A. B.   Am. Rev. Tuberc.,
    62:455, 1950.
109. Shope, R. E.   J. Exper. Med., 54:349, 373, 1931; Harvey Lectures, 31:183,
    1935-36.
110a. Wilson, H. E., Saslaw, S., Doan, C. A., Woolpert, O. C., and Schwab, J. L.   J.
    Exper. Med., 85:199, 1947.
    b. Harford, C. G., Leidler, D., and Harra, M.   J. Exper. Med., 89:53, 1949.
111. Guthrie, K. J., and Montgomery, G. L.   Lancet, 2:752, 1947.
112. Henle, W.   Markle Foundation Reports, 1946.
113a. Strumia, M. N., and Boerner, F.   Am. J. Path., 13:335, 1937.
    b. Hertzog, A. J.   Am. J. Path., 14:595, 1938.
    c. Teng, C-T., and Chung, H.   Proc. Soc. Exper. Biol. & Med., 39:156, 1938.
114. Bernstein, A.   J. Clin. Investigation, 13:677, 1934.
115a. Paul, J. R., and Bunnell, W. W.   Am. J. M. Sc., 183:90, 1932.
    b. Bailey, G. H., and Raffel, S.   J. Clin. Investigation, 14:228, 1935.
116. Paul, J. R.   Bull. New York Acad. Med., 15:43, 1939.
117. Moen, J. H., and Reimann, H. A.   Arch. Int. Med., 51:789, 1933.
118. Richardson, R.   J. Clin. Investigation, 12:1143, 1933; 14:389, 1935.
119. Sweet, J. E.   Centrabl. f. Bakt., 35:259, 1904.
120. DaCosta, J. C., and Beardsley, E. J. G.   Am. J. M. Sc., 136:361, 1908.
121a. Richardson, R.   J. Clin. Investigation, 19:239, 1940.
    b. Bates, G., and Weiss, C.   Am. J. Dis. Child., 62:346, 1941.
122. Wohl, M. G., Waife, S. O., Green, S., and Clough, G. B.   Proc. Soc. Exper. Biol.
    & Med., 70:305, 1949.
123. Lurie, M. B.   Ann. New York Acad. Sc., 52:1074, 1950.
124. Sprunt, D. H.   South. M. J., 34:288, 1941.

125. Lurie, M. B.   Arch. Path., 34:151, 1942.
126a. Davis, M. E., and Pearl, S. A.   Am. J. Obst. & Gynec., 35:77, 1938.
  b. TeLinde, R. W.   J.A.M.A., 110:1633, 1938.
  c. Burpee, C. N., Robinow, M., and Leslie, J. P.   Am. J. Dis. Child., 57:1, 1939.
  d. Mazer, C., and Schechber, F. R.   J.A.M.A., 112:1925, 1939.
  e. Benson, R. A.   Arch. Pediat., 55:632, 1938.
127a. Spain, D. M., and Molomut, N.   Am. Rev. Tuberc., 62:337, 1950.
  b. Lurie, M. B., Zoppasodi, P., Dannenberg, A. M., Jr., and Swartz, I. B.   Science, 113:234, 1951.
  c. Michael, M., Jr., Cummings, M. M., and Bloom, W. L.   Proc. Soc. Exper. Biol. & Med., 75:613, 1950.
128. Antrapol, W.   Proc. Soc. Exper. Biol. & Med., 73:262, 1950.
129a. Freeman, E.   Proceedings 1st. Clinical ACTH Conference, Philadelphia, Blakiston Co., 1950.
  b. Tompsett, R., LeMaistre, C., Muschenheim, C., and McDermott, W.   J. Clin. Investigation, 29:849, 1950.
130a. Finland, M., Kass, E. H., and Engbar, S. H.   Proceedings 1st Clinical ACTH Conference, Philadelphia, Blakiston Co., 1950.
  b. Mirick, G. S.   J. Clin. Investigation, 29:836, 1950.
131a. Germuth, F. G., Jr., and Ottinger, B.   Proc. Soc. Exper. Biol. & Med., 74:815, 1950.
  b. Fischell, E. E.   Bull. New York Acad. Med., 26:225, 1950.
132. Carlisle, J. M., Gibson, A., and Schmatolla, E.   Postgrad. Med., 8:No. 2, 1950.

GENERAL REFERENCES

Rich, A. R.   The Pathogenesis of Tuberculosis, Springfield, Ill., Charles C Thomas Co., 1944.
Heffron, P.   Pneumonia, with Special Reference to Pneumococcus Lobar Pneumonia, New York, The Commonwealth Fund, 1939.

13

IMMEDIATE HYPERSENSITIVITIES

The study of hypersensitivity deals with specific reactions between antigens and antibodies just as do certain aspects of the study of acquired resistance to infections and toxic agents. There is however a difference in the point at which attention is focused in these two cases. When we are occupied with the mechanism of acquired resistance our attention is directed toward what happens to the antigen itself as the outcome of its combination with antibody—whether its infectivity is thwarted or its toxicity neutralized. The hypersensitive reactions on the other hand are side issues to the central fact of antigen-antibody combination. Our concern here is not what happens to the antigen, which may in fact be a bland egg protein or pollen constituent with no infectious or toxic properties at all, but rather with what happens to the tissues as a consequence of the antigen-antibody reaction. Effects upon host tissues may be caused by a disturbance of cells in the area where antigen and antibody meet, or by the release of a toxic substance as a result of this meeting, or by some other unknown mechanism, but in any case the host is affected as the result of the union of antigen with antibody and may reveal this in a variety of ways. These points may be stated diagrammatically as follows:

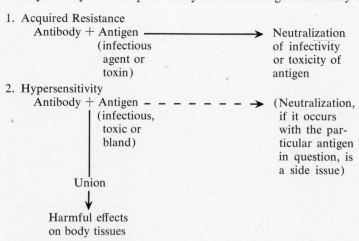

1. Acquired Resistance
   Antibody + Antigen ⟶ Neutralization
         (infectious   of infectivity
         agent or   or toxicity of
         toxin)   antigen

2. Hypersensitivity
   Antibody + Antigen - - - - - - -> (Neutralization,
         (infectious,   if it occurs
         toxic or   with the par-
         bland)   ticular antigen
                             in question, is
                             a side issue)
         Union
         ↓
   Harmful effects
   on body tissues

There is no paradox in the fact that a response of the body which may be protective—the formation of antibody which acts as in 1 in the diagram—may also result in injury to the tissues as shown in 2. The sequence shown in 1 can go on while independently a hypersensitive reaction also occurs. The viewpoint that the second reaction must also in some way share in the protection of the body is one which requires more than a teleologic justification. Evidence on the question of whether the hypersensitive reaction may also be a protective one to the body will be discussed in Chapter 15.

DEFINITION AND TERMINOLOGY OF HYPERSENSITIVITY. The meaning of hypersensitivity is well exemplified by the original description of Portier and Richet (1) who injected into dogs derivatives of sea anemones and mussels and observed, upon later reinjecting the same materials, evidence of serious illness, and sometimes death. The acquisition of a harmful sensitivity to relatively innocuous substances led these workers to describe the phenomenon as the antithesis of prophylaxis, therefore they applied the term **anaphylaxis.** Anaphylaxis has since been employed to denote acute shock-like reactions which may occur subsequent to the injection of antigens into hypersensitive man and animals.

The word **allergy** was introduced by von Pirquet (2) several years later as a more inclusive term. In its original sense this denotes a condition of altered reactivity of the body to antigenic substances. Since "altered reactivity" embraces all possible physiologic and pathologic reactions of which the body is capable, and since some of these are not concerned in the hypersensitive response at all, the word is misleading. It is very commonly used as a synonym for hypersensitivity, however. Variants of the term have been manufactured in numbers to denote quantitative differences in degree of allergy; these include anergy, hypoergy and hyperergy. It is entirely feasible to expound the subject of hypersensitivity at some length without recourse to this jargon.

Other words applied to special manifestations of hypersensitivity will be defined as they arise in subsequent discussions.

CLASSIFICATION OF HYPERSENSITIVE STATES. Our knowledge of hypersensitivity has broadened remarkably during the past half century to include many seemingly unrelated experimental observations and clinical syndromes so that some organized plan of presentation is imperative if the subject is to be made intelligible. There still remains enough misinformation and gaps in understanding so that every man can set himself up as his own taxonomist. The classification employed here is therefore neither final nor in agreement with other arrangements necessarily, but it represents what appears to the writer to be a logical survey of what we now know.

When one surveys the variety of hypersensitive manifestations in man and animals, certain cohesive facts become apparent in respect to **induction** of the hypersensitive state as well as the **occurrence of reactions** in the sensitized individual. So far as **induction** is concerned, it is found that some forms of hypersensitivity may be established by the entrance of antigens into the tissues, while others require the presence of entire infectious agents, or special conditions simulating their presence. In already sensitized subjects the **occurrence of reactions** also reveals gross differences which correlate with these differently induced sensitive states. In the type which is established by ordinary antigens alone, subsequent responses to the same antigen occur very quickly; these are called therefore **immediate** reactions. Further, there is a demonstrable relationship between this state and the presence of humoral antibody, so that the hypersensitivity may be transferred by means of serum to normal recipients who thereby become temporarily sensitized themselves. Finally, the various manifestations of this state depend largely upon changes which occur in blood vessels, smooth muscle and collagen. In contrast, in the second type of hypersensitivity the reactions to antigen are **delayed**, no relationship of the hypersensitive state to circulating antibodies has yet been demonstrated, and the hypersensitive reaction is not restricted to certain types of tissue; any cells of the body may undergo injury or destruction following exposure to antigen. A good deal will be said about these and other differences in subsequent discussions. For the present the point to be made is that the chronologic distinction in the occurrence of reaction, though it may appear to be a superficial one, provides a convenient basis for the first major step in classification of hypersensitivity into two types. These are called **immediate and delayed.**

General Mechanisms Concerned in Immediate Types of Hypersensitivity. In the subject with an immediate form of hypersensitivity, reaction to the responsible antigen follows in some fashion within seconds or minutes after contact. Sometimes the reaction is not outwardly apparent, the eventually obvious result depending upon a cumulative effect of repeated reactions as may be the case, for example, in the development of periarteritis nodosa, but presumably even here the basic reaction which eventually leads to this pathologic alteration in blood vessels begins very quickly after exposure to antigen in the sensitized individual.

Although different manifestations may become evident, the immediate hypersensitive states have in common a good deal that is basic, including (a) rapidity of response (b) relationship of reactivity to a demonstrable antibody of the blood which can transmit the hypersensitive state to a normal recipient, and (c) nonparticipation of the tissue cells per se in the reaction with antigen, but only secondarily as a result of combination of antigen with antibody. Thus, the various expressions of immediate hypersensitive responses follow a common pattern. Nevertheless, the attempt to clarify will require a certain amount of categorizing.

The facts presently at our disposal make it seem probable that the following sequence of events accounts for the induction of immediate sensitivity and for the occurrence of an immediate type of reaction in the sensitized subject:

The **induction** of the sensitive state requires a complete antigen, or a hapten which is able to combine with tissue proteins which then serve as carriers.

The route of absorption is generally of no consequence to the development of hypersensitivity.

The induction period for sensitization is about 10 days, sometimes less.

The hypersensitive state is immunologically specific in the same sense as are antigen-antibody reactions generally.

The following conditions result in the **elicitation of responses:**

The complete antigen or a hapten may be effective, as is the case in test tube serologic reactions (3).

The quantity of antigen necessary to produce a reaction is often greater than the minimal amount required to set up the hypersensitive state.

Once antigen has gained access to the hypersensitive body the following events take place:

1. Antibody reacts with antigen, in the blood or perhaps upon or within cells. This antibody is demonstrable in the circulation of the sensitized individual either by ordinary serologic tests or, in some cases where its serologic reactivity is poor, only by passive transfer to a normal recipient who becomes temporarily sensitized as a result.

This antibody in every case has resulted from a preceding stimulus by antigens injected, ingested, or inhaled, or occasionally absorbed through the skin. The relationship between the antigenic stimulus and the antibody response is sometimes a peculiar one, as in atopic sensitivity, but the basic fact of such a relationship nevertheless exists.

2. As a result of the antibody-antigen reaction certain tissues are affected, chiefly smooth muscle, blood vessels and collagen. Other cells may also be influenced in special cases, as will be discussed under appropriate headings. The responses of these tissues result in various manifestations: smooth muscle contraction may cause pulmonary difficulties and arterial constrictions; injury to blood vessels may lead to leakage of fluid into tissues (edema) as well as damage to the tissues supplied by occluded vessels; degeneration of collagen with cellular infiltration and scarring may interfere with the functions of vital structures such as heart valves.

3. The mechanisms through which these changes may be effected by the antigen-antibody reaction in vivo appear to be two.

(a) When there is a sufficient concentration of highly reactive antibody available in the body, and the injected dose of antigen is large, the resulting precipitate in itself seems to damage blood vessel walls. This may be the case in the Arthus reaction, for reasons which will be discussed more fully later.

(b) More generally, the various immediate hypersensitive responses appear to be evoked via the release of an intermediary substance as a result of the antigen-antibody reaction. For this to occur it seems sufficient that minute quantities of antibody of very low serologic activity combine with small amounts of antigen in the body. Consequently severe systemic hypersensitive reactions may take place when circulating antibody is so feeble in amount and activity as to be undetectable except by passive transfer to normal recipients. The hypersensitive manifestations which probably depend upon this intermediary mechanism include the anaphylactic, the evanescent cutaneous, and the atopic reactions, in the classification employed later.

The chief intermediary substance released by antigen-antibody reactions within the body appears to be histamine or something which acts like it and is often referred to as H-substance. This concept has developed over a period of about 40 years, since Dale and Laidlaw in 1910 first pointed out that anaphylaxis shows many points in common with the syndrome produced by the injection of histamine into guinea pigs (4), and they and Abel and Kubota (5) suggested that such a substance might be released from cells as the consequence of an antigen-antibody reaction upon (or within) them. Some years later histamine was found to be a constituent of normal tissues (6). The next step in the development of this story became entwined with the general mechanics of the inflammatory response. In 1927 Lewis (7) reported his classic observations of the "triple response" of the skin to local injury. This consists of initial erythema, the formation of a central wheal (a raised sharply delimited area of edema), and flare (the radial spread of erythema from the site of injury). This sequence of responses to injury follows a cutaneous injection of histamine also; thus Lewis was led to suggest that local injury causes the release from tissues of a histamine-like substance. Now the response of skin to local injury or to the injection of histamine finds its counterpart in the local reaction of sensitized skin to an injection of antigen (i.e. the evanescent type of response to be described). Therefore Lewis suggested further that release of H-substance accounts for the inflammatory allergic reaction also.

The first direct evidence for this viewpoint in respect to hypersensitive reactions was supplied by Dragstedt, working with anaphylaxis in dogs (8a). He was able to demonstrate the presence of a histamine-like substance in the efferent blood from the liver during shock. Code revealed such a substance also in the blood of the anaphylactic guinea pig (8b). Katz (9) and later workers demonstrated the same substance released from cells through the interaction of antigen and antibody in experiments in vitro.

Logically, the next question inquires how the union of antigen with antibody can free histamine from body cells. To this question suggestive answers have been culled from observations of sensitized animals and tissues, as well as from work with irritating and poisonous substances which reproduce the characteristics of the anaphylactic reaction in normal unsensitized animals. Thus, snake and bee venoms cause contraction of smooth muscle and produce collapse and death in laboratory animals, and these substances have been found to liberate histamine from lung tissues (10) apparently on the basis of their content of lecithinase. Lecithinase acts upon lecithin to produce lysolecithin and the latter can release histamine from tissue cells. Roche e Silva (11) has demonstrated that the enzyme trypsin, which on injection also reproduces the events of anaphylaxis, similarly liberates histamine from tissues. This investigator believes that a proteolytic enzyme is activated or liberated within cells by the antigen-antibody combination as well as by various poisonous substances, and that this enzyme in turn releases histamine which is bound to cell proteins through arginine or lysine. He thinks that the intracellular cathepsin II may be the liberated or activated cellular enzyme, since it acts upon such a substrate. In the same vein, Ungar and Mist (12) have found with sensitized guinea pigs that the addition of antigen to their serum in vitro causes the activation of a proteolytic enzyme precursor, profibrinolysin (see page 33), which may release the product directly responsible for shock.

There is experimental evidence then that a histamine-like substance circulates during anaphylactic shock, and that this arises from tissue or blood cells (13). The release of this substance may be accomplished by a proteolytic enzyme or by a lysolecithin activated by the antigen-antibody reaction. These enzymes rupture the linkage which binds histamine to the cellular constituent which is either protein (if a proteolytic enzyme is the one involved) or a lipoprotein (if lysolecithin is concerned). The histamine linkage may be through the imine radical ($=NH$) of the imidazole group (14). The toxic activity of the histamine on the other hand (11) is apparently dependent upon the amine radical ($-NH_2$).

This concept is not without serious gaps. Smooth muscle strips from sensitized animals suspended in baths in vitro have been exhausted by repeated additions of histamine so that they no longer contracted when exposed to this substance. In this state of histamine fatigue such strips responded with spasm to the addition of antigen to the bath. Such an observation obviously suggests that some other mechanism than histamine may be responsible for the contraction of hypersensitivity. However, there is evidence that a "slow reacting substance" (SRS) with muscle contracting properties is liberated in addition to histamine during anaphylactic shock (15), and it seems possible that even when reactivity to histamine has been abolished, as in the experiment described, this other oxytocic principle could still cause spasm in the muscle strip. Whether this is the answer to an experiment which otherwise puts the role of histamine in anaphylaxis into serious question remains for the future to decide. Another obstacle to the clear acceptance of the histamine concept has been the difficulty in obtaining evidence for the importance of this substance in hypersensitive reactions in the various species of animals studied. In horses, calves and rabbits the blood histamine level is actually depressed during shock (13, 16). In the case of the rabbit the explanation appears to lie in the fact that histamine is released from the blood cells themselves, and these accumulate in the pulmonary vascular bed and other end arteries during shock. Hence peripheral blood samples fail to show as much total histamine content as would normal blood with a full complement of cells. Attempts to demonstrate histamine release in man during hypersensitive reactions have also been largely unsuccessful. For example, Rose and co-workers (17) were unable to demonstrate this in blood taken by catheter from the pulmonary or femoral arteries during induced attacks of asthma. Nonetheless, there is a strong feeling among those who have studied the problem that histamine is implicated in human hypersensitive reactions for such reasons as these: that whereas normal urine contains little or no histamine, moderate to enormous amounts have been found in the urine of asthmatics, and that higher amounts of histamine have been found in upper respiratory tract mucous membranes and in lung tissues of allergic than of nonallergic subjects (18).

There is some evidence that other substances than histamine may be liberated during hypersensitive shock. The smooth muscle-contracting SRS of Kellaway has been mentioned. Heparin released from the liver may account for the defect in coagulability of the blood during anaphylactic shock (19a), though a deficiency of blood platelets may also account for this, in the dog at least (19b, 19c). Acetylcholine may be liberated in larger than normal quantities, and adenosine derivatives and potassium ions may also be freed into the circulation (20).

In résumé, the concept of histamine in relation to hypersensitive reactions of the immediate type has much to recommend it, and succeeding discussions in this chapter will often assume the truth of this viewpoint as their basis, but one should not lose sight of its shortcomings. In addition to the points already mentioned as requiring clarification the imagination balks at an easy acceptance of the sequence of events called for by this hypothesis. Does the very rapid anaphylactic response in the guinea pig, for example, wait upon a series of reactions including the union of injected antigen with antibody, then the activation of a proteolytic enzyme, then the release of histamine from cells, and finally the action of histamine upon the shock tissues to cause the observed effect? The volume and plausibility of what has been written in this connection should not obscure the questions still to be answered (147).

Types of Immediate Hypersensitivities. We begin the discussions of specific hypersensitive states with an example which appears to be the most straightforward consequence of the antigen-antibody reaction, the Arthus phenomenon. This reaction apparently stems directly from the precipitative union of antigen with antibody, presumably because the precipitate has some irritative effect upon vascular tissues. Histamine release may take part in this reaction—probably it does account for low grade manifestations—but the classic severe response does not occur except in the presence of adequate levels of precipitating antibody and relatively high doses of antigen, conditions which lack the subtlety of those sufficing for the other kinds of hypersensitive responses which will be described as stemming from the release of H-substance. Thus, whether or not H-substance is released in the circumstances producing an Arthus reaction, the fact is that the essence of the severe reaction appears to depend upon precipitate formation in vivo.

The prototypes of more delicately balanced responses which depend upon histamine release are the evanescent skin reaction, the anaphylactic reaction, and the atopic responses of human beings. All four of these manifestations have a great deal in common, but all possess distinct characteristics worthy of categorization and separate discussion.

1. ARTHUS PHENOMENON. This reaction was first described by Arthus in 1903 (21) as occurring in properly conditioned rabbits. If successive injections of an antigen are given subcutaneously or intradermally to this animal at intervals of some days, it is observed that the first injection is without effect, but subsequent to the second injection there may occur, within a half hour, a moderate degree of edema which persists for several hours. With suc-

ceeding injections the edema becomes more pronounced and prolonged, until finally, after perhaps the fifth or sixth, the reaction may progress to necrosis.

This response is of much more general occurrence than might be judged by the specific conditions set forth by Arthus. One large dose of antigen may sensitize as well as repeated smaller amounts (22). In the sensitive rabbit the reaction may be provoked in any vascularized tissue, such as the heart or brain, to which antigen has been introduced in proper amounts (23). Further, the same reactions occurs in other laboratory animals, and in man as well (24).

Mechanism of the Arthus Reaction. The Arthus reaction appears to stem directly from the reaction of antigen with circulating antibody in the tissues, as was proposed earlier in the general discussion of mechanisms. The reasons for this viewpoint are several. The antibody involved here is of the kind which enters readily into flocculative reactions in the test tube, i.e. multivalent antibody. Opie and a series of successors have shown that in rabbits the occurrence and intensity of the Arthus reaction directly parallel the level of such antibody in the blood (25). Exceptions to this point have been made (26), but quantitative studies support the existence of such a correlation. Further, it has been demonstrated that nonprecipitating (univalent) antibody will not passively sensitize guinea pigs for the development of severe Arthus reactions, although it is as good as an equal amount of precipitating antibody in sensitizing these animals to anaphylactic shock (27). Finally, the necessity for the injection of a relatively large amount of antigen in order to elicit the reaction in its intense form further suggests that the Arthus reaction results from an overt precipitative reaction in the tissues. Similar conditions regarding quality or quantity of circulating antibody and quantity of antigen need not be met for eliciting the other types of immediate reactions which depend upon the liberation of an intermediate substance as the consequence of simple combination of antigen even with poorly reactive antibody. Some factors which qualify this viewpoint are presented by Grove and Jackson (36a, 36b).

The results of union between antigen and antibody in a local area of tissue of the rabbit has been observed microscopically in living animals by Abell and Schenck (28). The primary event is contraction of the smooth muscle coats of arterioles. The endothelium of these spastic vessels as well as of capillaries and venules appears to become sticky, as do the leukocytes, so that these adhere to each other and to the vessel walls. The masses of cells may eventually completely plug the vessels. The endothelial stickiness denotes an injury which may proceed to the death of this layer of the wall, and necrosis may then extend to the rest of the wall as well. The pathologic chain of events thus includes arteriolar spasm, endothelial damage, the formation of leukocytic thrombi, and exudation of fluid and blood cells into the tissues. A severe reaction may result in the deprivation of an area of tissue of its blood supply, in which case ischemic necrosis of the area follows.

The basic elements important for the occurrence of the Arthus reaction appear thus to be two: first, the reaction of precipitating antibody with antigen, both in adequate concentrations, and second, the presence of blood vessels in the tissue where the combination takes place, since this particular hypersensitive manifestation depends chiefly upon injury to vessels, though other effects such as swelling and degeneration of collagenous fibers also occur. Further secondary damage to surrounding tissue may eventuate if the vessels are sufficiently injured. Antibody and antigen reacting in avascular tissue will not account for a reaction, as Rich and Follis and others have shown by the injection of antigen into the corneas of hypersensitive animals. The cornea is without blood supply, and an Arthus reaction does not occur here even though antibodies migrate into this tissue from the neighboring vessels at the limbus. If however the cornea is first vascularized by treatment with irritants, then the inoculation of antigen results in an Arthus phenomenon here equally as well as in any other tissue of the body. The same kind of evidence is available from studies of cells of hypersensitive animals in tissue cultures. Exposure of an explanted tissue (which of course has no blood supply) to the proper antigen results in no observable change, even if antibodies are added to the plasma medium. Cells continue to multiply actively and to migrate from the original tissue explant entirely unimpeded and undamaged (29).

Desensitization. If large amounts of antigen are injected into a sensitized animal, care being taken to avoid general shock, the circulating antibody may be diminished to the point that the skin and other tissues fail to respond to local injections of antigen. This refractory condition is only temporary; with the re-emergence of antibodies Arthus reactivity returns (30).

Passive Transfer of Arthus Reactivity. As may be inferred from the intimate relationship of circulatory antibody level to this reaction, Arthus sensitivity is readily transferable by means of serum from the hypersensitive to a normal animal. Passive transfer is characteristic generally of the hypersensitivities of the immediate type. The transfer may be effected either by systemic injections of a large amount of serum to the recipient, in which case reactions to injections of antigen may be seen wherever these are made in the skin, or by transfer of a small amount of serum to a local area of skin so that this region alone becomes reactive to subsequently injected antigen.

In view of this transferability, the question arises as to why Arthus reactions do not occur routinely in human beings following the use of therapeutic antisera for the treatment of infectious diseases. In such cases antigen is already present in the body, provided by the infectious agent, and antibodies are introduced; experimentally, this would be referred to as a reversed passive Arthus reaction. Reactions on this basis have been reported, but they seem to occur rarely, and this fortunate circumstance is difficult to account for. A possible explanation may lie in the necessity for the proper relative concentrations of antigen and antibody to produce precipitation. Since antitoxic sera have frequently been employed in human beings this point may be particularly cogent, for antitoxin produced by the horse (the usual source of such antibody) flocculates with toxin in a very limited range of proportions (see page 74).

2. EVANESCENT CUTANEOUS REACTIONS. Related to the dermal Arthus reaction are other cutaneous responses which may be elicited in sensitized men and less frequently in animals by local injections of antigen into the skin. These responses differ from the Arthus however in two features: they become visible earlier, within a few minutes, and disappear earlier, within three or four hours, and they never progress to necrosis (31, 32). Their character coincides with the wheal and flare response to histamine described by Lewis, and indeed these hypersensitive reactions appear to be the result of histamine liberation. It is in this respect that the evanescent skin reaction seems to the writer to differ from the Arthus, in which an antigen-antibody reaction, at high levels of concentrations of both, with precipitate formation, causes a more profound and longer-lasting local injury than is seen in this case, where the effects of H-substance alone are evidenced by dilatation of capillaries and increased permeability of vessel walls.

The evanescent skin reaction is analogous to or identical with (according to the experimental subject) the local hive, which will be described at more length in relation to serum sickness and the atopic sensitivities. It is brought in at this point in order that its characteristics may be directly compared with those of the Arthus response.

Other aspects of this hypersensitive manifestation are much the same as those described for the Arthus phenomenon, i.e. passive transfer may be accomplished, and desensitization is possible with variable effectiveness, however, depending upon the species of animal concerned.

3. ANAPHYLAXIS. Anaphylaxis is generally regarded as the prototype of hypersensitivities of the immediate type. It represents on a systemic scale the kind of response seen in the evanescent cutaneous reaction in that it stems from the action of H-substance. In the case of the evanescent skin response, locally injected antigen reacts in situ with antibody to give rise to the sequence of events terminating in the wheal and flare reaction. If the antigen is instead injected in a manner, preferably intravenously, which permits its rapid systemic diffusion, then anaphylactic shock may occur. In fact this can happen even when too large a dose is inoculated into the skin, for whatever antigen does not combine with antibody locally may enter lymphatics and blood vessels to disseminate through the body.

The conditions favorable for **establishing the anaphylactic state** are in general those which are favorable for the induction of antibody formation. A special point of interest however is the fact that only very small doses of antigen are required to induce this state. Wells (33) found that one twenty-millionth of a gram of egg albumin sufficed to sensitize guinea pigs so that they later showed nonfatal shock. This fact is important to the viewpoint that only a very slight antibody response is sufficient for subsequent reactivity of the anaphylactic kind in distinction to the high level of antibodies essential for the occurrence of the Arthus phenomenon.

The **elicitation of shock** in the sensitized animal follows the principles of antigen-antibody reactions generally. The haptenic portion of a complete antigen often suffices to provoke the reaction, as first shown by Tomcsik with bacterial polysaccharide (34).

Anaphylactic shock depends upon the reactions of certain types of tissue, the so-called shock tissues, comprising smooth muscle and blood vessels especially. These tissues are the same as those involved in the Arthus and evanescent skin responses. Shock consists of a sequence of events often beginning seconds after the entrance of antigen into the body, and culminating in death within minutes, although the shock may be protracted and of course need not be fatal. A central event in acute shock is contraction of smooth muscle. This takes place throughout the body and is usually made apparent to the observer by erection of hair and by the consequences of intensified peristalsis and contraction of the bladder. Actual interference with vital function is found to be most pronounced in areas of the body varying with animal species. In addition to smooth muscle contraction, other events include edema, decreased coagulability of the blood, fall in blood pressure and temperature, thrombocytopenia, general leukopenia with aggregation of white cells in the pulmonary bed, and often, pulmonary eosinophilia. The manifestations of shock depend partly upon the species of animal involved. It does not vary with respect to causative antigens.

A good deal of study has been devoted to anaphylaxis in **the guinea pig** because this animal so readily becomes sensitized and regularly develops acute and characteristic shock upon later reinjection of antigen (35). The most evident signs of anaphylaxis in this animal are respiratory. Beginning usually within seconds after injection of antigen the guinea pig appears to concentrate upon its violent efforts to breathe. Inspiratory movements are irregular and forced and are usually accompanied by convulsive leaps. The dyspnea is generally considered to be caused by contraction of the smooth muscle about the terminal bronchioles, but recent work implicates peribronchial edema also (62). Other effects of smooth muscle contraction are evidenced by erection of the hairs about the collar due to contraction of the erector pilae muscles, as well as incontinence of bladder and bowel. The blood pressure rises, then falls. Examination of the blood frequently discloses a lessened coagulability, leukopenia and thrombocytopenia. In an animal receiving sufficient antigen intravenously these signs frequently begin during the course of the injection and death through respiratory failure may come within two to five minutes. If the organs are now examined the heart is found to be still active and the lungs expanded to the limits of the thoracic cavity. The animal has filled its lungs despite the stenotic bronchioles through the aid of the voluntary muscles of inspiration. The lesser power of the muscles of expiration does not suffice to overcome this resistance.

Shock may be delayed in its appearance and protracted; this is seen sometimes after injection of antigen by a route other than the intravenous. Accumulation of antigen in the blood stream to the point of causing manifest signs and symptoms referable to pulmonary changes may require an hour or so, and the shock state, in subacute form, may persist for several hours. This usually terminates fatally.

Acute anaphylaxis which superficially resembles that in the guinea pig may also be demonstrated in **the rabbit,** though not as regularly. It is interesting that this should be so in an animal which is a much more able antibody producer than the guinea pig. The reason for this difference is not known; the relationship between the quantity of circulating antibody and the occurrence of shock is not a clearly predictable one (36).

Although the rabbit undergoes contortions during shock similar to those seen in the guinea pig, it has been believed for some years that the focus of greatest activity in this animal is not the same. Contraction of the musculature of the pulmonary arterioles leading to acute cardiac dilatation and failure is a favored explanation for the fatal event here (37a). It has been suggested alternatively, on the basis of the suddenness of collapse and death in the anaphylactic rabbit and of electrocardiographic changes, that there may occur spasm of the coronary vessels, i.e. angina pectoris (37b). However, a recent study in which electrocardiographic and ventricular pressure changes were noted along with respiratory tracings makes it appear likely that respiratory failure may actually be the lethal factor as in the guinea pig, for in most rabbits respiratory cessation followed immediately after injection of antigen (37c). The question of lethal mechanism in the rabbit thus has no clear answer now.

Other features of anaphylaxis in the rabbit are the same as in the guinea pig; there is a drop in blood pressure, and the coagulability of the blood is impaired. Leukopenia in the systemic circulation with concentration of cells in the vessels of the lungs is especially evident here.

The dog is not so readily sensitized as the guinea pig, and there are differences in the manifestations of the anaphylactic response. The syndrome in the dog usually resembles traumatic shock, with restlessness, vomiting, diarrhea, and collapse. Frequently the reaction goes through two stages; initial acute symptoms subside with later increasingly profound collapse, so that the animal may die 8 or 10 hours after injection. It has long been accepted that the liver is the central site of activity in this animal, since Manwaring showed by a series of ingenious experiments that shunting the circulation from this organ in the hypersensitive animal abolishes reactivity to subsequent injection of antigen, while joining such a liver to the circulation of a normal dog can cause shock in that animal following inoculation with antigen (38). There have been reports however that the highly sensitized dog may show shock even in the absence of the liver (39). Nonetheless, the marked engorgement of this organ and congestion of the gastrointestinal tract found at autopsy suggests that this organ plays some important part in the development of the syndrome. The work of Dragstedt (13) and Code (40) has revealed that the dog liver releases histamine, a substance which it contains in relative abundance. The histamine so liberated affects other tissues as well, and death may largely be due to increased capillary permeability throughout the body with loss of fluids from the circulation (41a). Instances of rapid anaphylactic death with a predominance of respiratory signs (41b) may also be accounted for by the large quantities of histamine released, acting upon the pulmonary musculature.

Changes in the blood are similar to those described for the guinea pig and rabbit.

Acute anaphylactic shock in **human beings** may be very much like that in any of the other species described, or there may be a combination of features (42). It resembles most often the guinea pig type of shock. It is, fortunately, an infrequent occurrence; Park reported fatal anaphylaxis in 2 of 50,000 instances following injection of horse serum, but more recent statistics indicate a somewhat greater incidence of 0.10 per cent (42a). In man also there is a fall in blood pressure and temperature, with decreased blood coagulability and eosinophilia. Shock may occur in an individual in whom sensitization has been induced by previous injections of antigen (e.g. therapeutic serum), or in those in whom sensitization has been spontaneously acquired by inhalation or ingestion of antigens (see Atopic Sensitivity, page 215), if the shocking dose is introduced parenterally. In this case the liability to shock is sometimes even greater than in induced sensitivity. People who are spontaneously sensitive to horse dander, for example, may be unusually liable to the production of shock by an injection of horse serum. This may follow from the minute quantity employed for intradermal testing.

Serum sickness occurs in over half the previously normal human beings who receive horse or rabbit antiserum (and less frequently other antigenic substances, such as penicillin, sulfonamides and other drugs) for prophylactic or therapeutic purposes. This disease is marked by the occurrence of hives, angioedema, painful joints, lymphadenopathy and fever, usually coming on about 8 to 10 days after the initial administration of the antigen, and persisting for several days. This interval from initial administration denotes the induction period for antibody formation and the hypersensitive state; at the end of the period antigen still remains in the body and as a result a reaction occurs, in which increased permeability of small vessels with edema into the skin, the joints, and other tissues is an outstanding event. This has been called protracted anaphylaxis, since there is a prolonged period of reaction permitted by the development of hypersensitivity in the continuous presence of antigen. Focal arteriolar lesions and collagen degeneration may also occur as will be described subsequently in the discussion of periarteritis nodosa and related states. The individual remains sensitive for a variable period to reinjection of the antigen, which may then produce serum sickness again after a short interval, or may cause acute anaphylactic shock (2b, 43a).

Although the serum of an individual with this syndrome will usually transmit anaphylactic sensitivity to guinea pigs and local skin reactivity to normal human recipients, humoral antibodies are not always demonstrable either by in vitro tests or by passive transfer. This may be due to their being combined with the antigen which is simultaneously present in the body. On the other hand many individuals manufacture antibodies following injections of antigens without ever developing the serum sickness syndrome (43b). Whether the latter situation depends upon a constitutional factor which may determine, for example, the reactivity of tissues to histamine, or some other protective quality, is not known.

Serum sickness is reproducible in animals. It may be provoked in rabbits and guinea pigs by single injections of large quantities of foreign serum (44). The edematous responses so characteristic of human beings are not so striking in lower animals generally, but horses are said to develop hives (45). Lesions of the periarterial type occur in some rabbits with serum disease as in some human beings.

Serum sickness is still imperfectly understood in several respects in addition to those already indicated. Thus, it occurs often after injection of foreign serum, but less frequently following other substances with good antigenic properties; for example, toxoids. This may be owed to quantitative differences in administered doses, but not entirely so, for even with horse sera it has been noted repeatedly that some samples are more apt to induce the syndrome than others.

In some respects, including the fact of formation by some individuals of antibody which transfers whealing reactivity to normal skin, this hypersensitive state partakes of the characteristics of the atopic hypersensitivities to be described later.

The rat and mouse have been generally considered stubborn to sensitizing injections of antigens, but with attention to procedure both can be sensitized rather regularly. The level of sensitivity attained by the rat is apt to be moderate at best (46). The mouse yields in the face of the proper administration and timing of doses to the extent of 70 per cent mortality (47a). McMaster and Kruse (47b) found that even in those animals which fail to show manifest signs of shock, examination of the ears and claws under magnification reveals characteristic vascular reactions consisting of arterial and venous spasms, or slowing of the blood flow, without involvement of the capillaries. The vascular changes occur quickly, often during the injection, while gross signs are more sluggish, death occurring in from 15 to 60 minutes, and sometimes not for many hours.

Anaphylaxis occurs in **other animal species** also. The sensitized monkey does not show it regularly on reinjection of antigen. When it does, manifestations are apt to occur some hours after exposure to the shocking dose, and may include pulmonary as well as digestive tract difficulties (47c). In horses and cattle respiratory obstruction is dominant, and in the latter especially there is marked spasm of the gastric musculature (47d). Anaphylaxis has been produced also in fish (teleosts), but there is some question as to the reactivity of elasmobranchs and amphibians (47e).

Passive Transfer of Anaphylactic Reactivity. As is generally true of the immediate hypersensitivities, the anaphylactic state is also passively transferable to normal recipients by means of serum. Even in the absence of antibody demonstrable by the usual test tube reactions there may be sufficient humoral substance to convey anaphylactic sensitivity. This is not surprising in view of the finding by Kabat and co-workers (48) that about 0.04 mg. of antibody protein may suffice for this purpose in the guinea pig.

It is usually advisable to permit several hours to elapse between administration of the sensitizing antiserum and the shocking antigen for most certain demonstration of anaphylaxis in the guinea pig, and it is considered that antibodies must become fixed by tissues before a reaction can occur. Whether this reason is valid seems questionable in view of the fact that with larger quantities of antiserum guinea pigs may respond to antigen given immediately after the antibody (49).

Passive transfer between different species of animals is possible in many instances, but not in all. For example, human and rabbit antisera may passively sensitize the guinea pig, and stronger sera are more effective than weaker ones for this purpose. On the other hand horse antiserum, even when it contains a high level of antibody, does not successfully accomplish this under ordinary circumstances. It has been shown however that passive sensitization with horse antipneumococcal serum is possible provided that very small doses are employed (50); there appears thus to be a zone of reaction in such transfer (51). Why this difference exists in the passive sensitizing activity of horse antiserum is not known. Failure of passive sensitization of the guinea pig is seen also with antibodies produced by the ox, chicken and rat. There may be special conditions under which these would transfer sensitivity also, but the point has not been examined.

Desensitization. Repeated small injections of antigen into a sensitive animal or a single nonfatal shocking dose results in a period of relative refractoriness to further shock. One common explanation for this effect has supposed it to be due to the saturation of antibody by injected antigen. The later return of sensitivity is ascribed to the replenishment of antibodies. There is considerable doubt that saturation of cellular antibody is in fact the correct explanation since a similar though less marked effect may follow the injection of nonspecific substances such as normal serum. Also, if an animal is sensitized to two unrelated antigens, desensitization with one results in some decrease of sensitivity to the other (52, 53).

The second explanation of desensitization was offered about 40 years ago by Weil (54), who suggested that the tissues of the hypersensitive animal may be protected from the effects of antigen if there is sufficient antibody circulating in the blood stream to combine with it. Weil injected additional antibody intravenously into sensitized guinea pigs and upon subsequent testing he found these animals to be refractory to several lethal doses of antigen. This circumstance he referred to as **antianaphylaxis.** Analogous observations were made in vitro by Dale and Kellaway (55), who found that the uterine strip of a sensitized guinea pig suspended in a bath to which antibody had been added would not contract on introduction of antigen, presumably because this was intercepted by the antibody in solution before it could reach the sensitized cells.

Logical as this second view appears, other work indicates that the protection afforded by the introduction of excess antibody is actually slight, and shock may be significantly moderated by the intravenous administration of many substances, including normal serum, shortly before the inoculation of the shock dose of antigen. Morris (56a) has shown that an excess of circulating antibody, far from functioning in a protective capacity, may sometimes lead to an increased susceptibility of the animal to anaphylaxis. Her experiments suggest that antianaphylaxis is a state of refractoriness which is due neither to excess nor depletion of circulating antibody, but depends on secondary changes the true nature of which are still not definitely established. It may be that antianaphylaxis does occur with some antigen-antibody systems and not with others (56b).

Bronfenbrenner (57) has considered the objections to both these views in his proposal of a third explanation for the desensitizing process. This supposes the refractory state to follow from temporary interference with the proteolytic enzymes which are supposed to liberate histamine from tissues.

It is apparent that there is not yet a clear explanation of the mechanism through which desensitization is attained.

Schultz-Dale Reaction; the Anaphylactic Reaction in Vitro. Sensitivity may be demonstrated also with isolated segments of smooth muscle in vitro, a fact which has already been referred to in various connotations. For example, the uterine horn of the guinea pig may be sensitized by immersion for a short interval in a bath containing antibody. If the tissue is then thoroughly washed and suspended in a balanced salt solution at body temperature, it is found that addition of specific antigen to the bath causes sharp contraction of the muscle. That this is a specific effect is evidenced by the subsequent refractoriness (desensitization) of the muscle to the same antigen while it remains responsive to other stimuli such as histamine. This kind of experiment with actively or passively sensitized isolated muscle is referred to as the Schultz-Dale reaction (58). It is demonstrable as well with intestine, lung, artery, or other tissue strips containing smooth muscle. Although sensitized tissues perfused free of blood act in this fashion, this does not necessarily mean that antigen reacts with antibody immediately attached to or within cells, for the antibodies may exist in intercellular spaces protected from the perfusion fluids (59).

Reactions of isolated strips are not as readily demonstrated with the tissues of other animal species. Rabbit smooth muscle shows this only in modified form, though Grove (60) has demonstrated satisfactory contractions of strips of pulmonary artery. Uterine strips from sensitized monkeys fail to contract upon addition of antigen to the suspension bath (61).

Mechanism of Anaphylaxis. The systemic injection of histamine reproduces many of the signs, symptoms and physiologic alterations characteristic of anaphylactic shock in various laboratory animals. This substance does not effect the lessened coagulability of the blood which ordinarily occurs during anaphylactic shock, but this particular alteration may be caused by the release of heparin from the liver, or a decrease in the number of blood platelets, also as a consequence of the antigen-antibody reaction.

In the guinea pig the antigen-antibody union which effects the release of histamine may occur in immediate contiguity with the tissues most involved. There is evidence from the injection of radioactively tagged antigen into sensitized guinea pigs that this accumulates most heavily in the lungs, in the edematous congested fibrous tissue between the bronchi and their accompanying arteries, rather than in the smooth muscle itself (62). In the rabbit it appears that combination of antigen with antibody in the blood stream may be effective, for histamine in this animal is released from cells of the blood (13).

Very small concentrations of antibody suffice to make the guinea pig reactive to subsequent injection of antigen (48), and for this purpose univalent (nonprecipitating) antibody is as effective as precipitating antibody (63). In all respects however the antibody which takes part in anaphylaxis is of the conventional type, i.e. it enters into serologic reactions with antigen either directly or, when it is poor in reactive quality, by hooking into lattice structures formed by antigen with antibody of better reacting quality (see page 96); it passes the placental membranes from mother to fetus, and it is relatively heat stable, resisting 56° C. for long periods. These points are mentioned because in the following discussion of the atopic hypersensitivities it will be seen that the antibodies involved do not possess these characteristics.

Many questions remain to be answered concerning the mechanism of anaphylaxis. We do not know why some species of animals are more readily sensitized than others, though some rough correlation exists between responsiveness to histamine and readiness of sensitization. We are uncertain also of the reasons for the more striking participation in shock of one organ in one species and a different structure in another species, or for the differences which may occur in different individuals of the same species, as in man, or the dog. The concept of histamine release is not clear in all aspects by any means, and not much is known about the other substances which may be freed from the tissues during shock. Enough remains behind the veil to occupy interested workers for many years to come.

4. ATOPIC SENSITIVITY. The fourth category under the immediate hypersensitivities introduces certain additional factors although in general outline this hypersensitivity shares the basic characteristics of the other states already discussed. Thus, an individual with the spontaneous sensitivity classified under this term will usually respond to intradermally placed antigen with an evanescent skin reaction, and if he receives an overdose of antigen he may go into anaphylactic shock. But in circumstances in which injections of antigen do not figure, the induction of this hypersensitive state, the type of antibody associated with it, and the events which transpire upon exposure to the excitant all bring to light certain differences worthy of note.

The term atopy means literally "out of place" or "strangeness." It was introduced by Coca and Cooke (64) to characterize certain hypersensitive states which they considered to be heritable and to be limited in occurrence to the human being. The term is more or less in disfavor now since attempts to pigeonhole hypersensitive states too rigorously are more likely to defeat than to help eventual understanding of these phenomena on a broad basis. Nevertheless, a certain type of immediate hypersensitivity largely restricted to the human being does possess characteristics which require special consideration, and this specific name is a useful one for convenience of discussion.

The chief manifestations of atopic hypersensitivity include asthma, hay fever, urticaria, angioedema, and probably infantile eczema. The substances most frequently responsible for clinically manifest sensitivities are pollens, feathers, animal danders, dust, milk and wheat—inhalants and ingestants. However, asthma may be caused by such simple chemical substances as aspirin on the one hand and by infestations with worms on the other.

Asthma and hay fever are affections of the respiratory tract. The former is marked by periodic dyspnea and the latter by serous effusions from the nose, sneezing, and frequently by conjunctivitis. Urticaria or hives and angioedema are closely allied conditions. The hive is a local cutaneous patch of edema surrounded by erythema. In angioedema more generalized swelling may occur in various areas of the body, often about the head and neck, and it becomes dangerous when it develops in the larynx or trachea. Atopic infantile eczema consists usually of erythematous vesicular lesions of the face, neck and the cubital and popliteal spaces, which eventually ooze and crust. Atopic eczema may occur also in older children and adults in whom the skin changes are more in the nature of thickening and pigmentation. Foods, and especially eggs, are thought to be the usual allergenic agents responsible for this form of hypersensitive manifestation. It is evident that this particular response has a more persistent character than do the immediate hypersensitive reactions so far discussed, but a quickly wrought damage may of course leave a long-lasting pathologic residue. This will be exemplified again in the later discussion of periarteritis nodosa and related syndromes. There is however some question as to the true character of allergic eczema with regard to the classification employed here. Cooke (65) believes that infantile eczema is not an atopic sensitivity but rather a coincident delayed contact type of reactivity (see page 268) which frequently develops in children who happen to be actual or potential atopic reactors also. There is at present a difference of opinion on this point (66).

The various atopic syndromes are not mutually exclusive. One or more, such as asthma and hay fever, may coexist, or one manifestation may occur at one time, another at another time in the same individual. In addition an atopic person may develop anaphylactic shock as the result of an injection of the antigen to which he is sensitive.

Characterization of Atopic Hypersensitivity. Broadly speaking, atopic hypersensitivity develops **spontaneously** as the result of casual exposure to allergens in the environment, either inhaled or ingested, or occasionally through epidermal contact. Most of the clinical states just described are not induced by the parenteral inoculation of antigen; e.g. the asthmatic state can rarely be initiated in this way. The basis for some of the other manifestations of atopic sensitivity, and especially urticaria, may however be established by parenteral injections of antigen; this has already been described as one occurrence in serum sickness for example. Thus, the line of demarcation is not an entirely sharp one between the atopic and the other categories of hypersensitive states discussed in this chapter in regard to induction, but the difference in this respect is sufficiently general as not to permit its being ignored as a unique feature.

Coca and Cooke (64) some years ago suggested several criteria by which atopic hypersensitivity may be characterized. The intervening years have proved these criteria to be fallible in some respects but they still prove satisfactory focal points for a discussion of this type of hypersensitivity. These criteria revolve about the following points:

A. The restricted occurrence of the atopic state to man.

B. The antigenic status of the substances which induce atopic reactivity.

C. The heritable character of atopic hypersensitivity.

D. The extraordinary properties of the antibodies associated with atopic hypersensitivity.

A. Occurrence of atopic hypersensitivity only in man. The initial belief that atopic hypersensitivity is limited to the human being has proved to be untenable in the strict sense because in occasional instances asthma, hay fever, angioedema, eczema and other syndromes caused by sensitization to environmental antigens have been found to occur in dogs and other animals (67). It is however true that the atopic syndromes which occur spontaneously in man are only exceptionally seen in lower animals, even though these may live in contact with the same environmental antigenic factors as do human beings. Guinea pigs may be artificially sensitized by the injection of certain substances which act as human environmental antigens—for example, horse dander or ragweed pollen—and on later exposure to these substances in nebulized form a proportion of such animals develop **anaphylactic shock** in varying degree (68). The anaphylactic state or even something very akin to the asthmatic state may be induced by subjecting guinea pigs to a heavy atmosphere of nebulized antigen (90). But this is under conditions of forced draft. It is perfectly apparent that when left to their own devices guinea pigs do not develop such sensitivity to antigens in the environment. Thus, although we cannot say that this species distinction signifies anything more basic than a greater readiness of response of some human beings to sensitization by casual contact with air-borne or food allergens, it remains a factual difference which is distinctive.

B. The special nature of the allergens involved. At the time when these criteria were formulated it was believed that many of the substances responsible for human atopic hypersensitivity, and especially the pollens, did not qualify as antigens. Expanding information about the nature of antigens and of haptens has disqualified this point, since even very simple chemical substances may combine with body protein to serve, to all intents and purposes, as complete antigens. Furthermore, it has been demonstrated that ragweed pollen extracts when absorbed to potassium alum are antigenic for experimental animals, and the same observations have been made with other pollens and with animal danders as well (69). Generally speaking the inhalant allergens are not good antigens, however, and there is certainly no reason to attribute their sensitizing ability for the human being to any exceptional antigenic power. On the contrary, their poor immunogenic properties provide reason for supposing that sensitization depends upon some peculiar ability of the affected individual to take heed of very mild antigenic stimuli, ignored by the majority of his brethren and, for the most part, by lower animals as well.

C. Familial inheritance of atopic hypersensitivity. It is very doubtful that any specific hypersensitive state in itself is inherited. This possibility was considered in the past because atopic states in infants (infantile eczema) occur on first contact with the provocative substance. A nongenetic explanation for this observation may be provided by the finding that egg proteins, which appear to be responsible for many of these cases, can pass unchanged through the intestinal wall and placenta into the fetal circulation, possibly to sensitize the fetus in utero. Antigens may also be excreted into the mother's milk to sensitize infants to foods with which, to all appearances, they have had no experience (70a).

The inheritance of a **predisposition to become sensitized** on the other hand seems unequivocal. This point has been repeatedly affirmed by various observers and is exemplified by the early statistics of Cooke and Vander Veer (70b) which reveal that almost half of a group of 504 patients studied had one or both parents with sensitivity in contrast to about 15 per cent positive antecedents among nonsensitive individuals questioned. It is not surprising that a genetic determinant should be found to play a part here. We know that inheritance plays a role in all biologic characteristics, and in relation to immunologic phenomena it has been shown to influence the level of native resistance to infectious diseases, the ability to acquire resistance, and the readiness with which experimental animals become sensitized to injections of antigens (Chapter 11 and Lewis and Loomis [71]).

About 10 per cent of the population as a whole shows some clinically manifest form of atopic hypersensitivity. The constitutional factor which determines this is as yet unexplained, but certain of the possibilities are interesting:

(a) It might be supposed that individuals with atopic sensitivity are abnormal in their immunologic responses to antigens generally. Rackemann and co-workers (72a) could find no real difference in their responses to vaccination with typhoid bacilli and other vaccines. Lately however with the use of quantitative methods for the measurement of responses to diphtheria toxoid, it has been seen that atopic individuals produce antitoxin with good neutralizing properties but with markedly inferior precipitating ability as compared with that manufactured by normal subjects. The nonprecipitating antitoxin was furthermore especially good in transferring to normal skin sensitivity to toxoid, as is true of the peculiar atopic antibodies to be described later (72b). This possibility therefore is one which warrants further study (72c).

(b) It might be inferred that some mechanical factor underlies the difference; for example, that only those individuals with mucous membranes so constructed as to permit absorption of inhaled or ingested antigenic substances can be spontaneously sensitized in this manner. But this explanation is not sufficient, since the clinical atopic states cannot be artificially induced in nonsensitive individuals by injections of antigen, a process which makes the factor of absorption superfluous. Further, an individual who is hypersensitive to one substance and thus obviously constitutionally amenable to this form of sensitization cannot be artificially sensitized to a clinical level by the injection of other antigens (73). Yet such injections can sensitize anyone, without regard to his atopic status, to subsequent anaphylactic shock.

(c) It might be thought that these individuals are more sensitive to the effects of histamine than are those not spontaneously sensitized, but no evidence has been brought forth in support of this viewpoint.

(d) There may be some peculiarity in atopic individuals in the ability of cells situated in or near mucous membranes to form antibody, and the fact that the antibody associated with atopic hypersensitivity has unique properties makes this possibility inviting. This speculation will be developed further in the discussion of the nature of the atopic antibody.

Whatever the character of the constitutional factor involved here, it serves to give distinction to this category of hypersensitivities. A genetically determined factor manifests itself in a ready sensitization of one-tenth the population as the result of casual contact with environmental antigens.

D. The special nature of the antibody involved in atopic reactions. The circulating antibodies related to atopic hypersensitivity cannot with certainty be demonstrated by any in vitro serologic test. That antibodies are present, however, is usually revealed by the ability of the serum from an allergic individual to sensitize passively the skin of a normal recipient. If a small amount of such serum is injected into a skin site of a normal subject, injection of antigen into the same area 24 hours later will result in a local hive. This is called the Prausnitz-Küstner (P-K) reaction (74a).

The activities of the atopic antibody are limited, and characteristically so, in the following respects:

(a) It fails to provide clear evidence of its presence even through the use of refined serologic technics in the test tube. It does not form a precipitate with its antigen, and Heidelberger (74b) has been unable to show that it becomes incorporated in the precipitate formed by the proper antigen combined with precipitating antibody supplied by an outside source. Ordinarily, univalent antibody will hook into such aggregates as they form (see page 96). This question of serologic activity is not entirely closed, for other workers have reported success with the precipitation and agglutination maneuvers as well as with the complement fixation test (74c, 74d, 74e). Certainly, however, this antibody is at best very restricted in serologic activities.

(b)   Unlike most other antibodies formed by the human being, this one fails to pass the placenta from mother to fetus. In line with this fact the atopic hypersensitive states, unlike anaphylaxis, are not congenitally transmitted (75).

(c)   This antibody appears to have special affinity for the skin as demonstrated by passive transfer experiments. It will not sensitize guinea pigs to anaphylaxis (i.e. smooth muscle contraction), as will sera from many human beings with serum sickness. However, there is evidence that it may attach to other than cutaneous tissues in man and monkeys, including the mucosa of the stomach, intestine and gallbladder wall (76). Subsequent ingestion of the proper antigens results in reactions in these areas marked by edema, hyperemia, and hypersecretion of mucus. By means of transfusions from allergic to normal subjects the regular establishment of temporary reactivity of the skin, nasal mucous membranes and conjunctiva has been demonstrated by Loveless (77), and some of the small group of recipients developed systemic manifestations such as asthma. But in all these cases the skin was first to show sensitivity and last to relinquish it.

(d)   This humoral substance exhibits a certain lack of specificity in the following regard. The serum of an individual reactive in skin tests to a variety of antigenic factors can transmit all of these sensitivities to the skin of a recipient. In keeping with the specific behavior of immunologic systems, each individual antigen if injected into such a passively sensitized area will cause a reaction with subsequent discharge of reactivity to that factor, i.e. the antibodies directed against this factor are neutralized. Curiously enough however the dominant antigen—that is, the substance to which the patient is clinically sensitive—will entirely neutralize the ability of the locally sensitized area to react to any of the antigens involved. An example will clarify this. Sherman and Stull (78) transferred serum from an asthmatic patient clinically sensitive to horse dander, but reacting by skin test to both horse and dog danders. Horse dander was here the dominant antigen. Injection of this into the passively sensitized area provoked a reaction, and the area became then unresponsive to subsequent injection of dog as well as horse antigen. The primary injection of dog antigen into such a sensitized area also caused a response, but the area subsequently continued sensitive to horse dander. When serum from a patient with clinical sensitivity to both danders was used in the same way, there was no dominance of antigen; each dander neutralized reactivity to itself alone. This kind of occurrence takes place without relation to structural similarities of the antigens concerned, as would be the case in ordinary cross-neutralization of antibodies.

(e)   The antibody is exceptionally heat labile, being inactivated at 56° C., usually after two hours. Ordinary precipitating antibody is not seriously modified by this treatment.

The antibody associated with atopic hypersensitivity thus possesses distinctive features sufficient for its characterization. The distinction is often made terminologically by referring to it as **reagin.** These special properties do not however set apart atopic antibody from the general class of antibodies in any sense except for purposes of recognition; there is no reason to believe that the occurrence of these antibodies of special kind creates a fundamental schism between atopic and other immunologic responses. It has been discussed in Chapter 6 that antibody responses following injection of antigens are not homogeneous in physicochemical or serologic behavior. They may show considerable variability depending upon the circumstances in which they are produced. The chief factors which influence the nature of the antibody response are: the species of animal which produces the antibody, the antigen employed, the route by which antigen is administered, and the duration and intensity of the vaccinating procedure. These factors interrelate; thus, the horse responds to diphtheria toxin (and certain other proteins) only when these are injected subcutaneously or intramuscularly, and the resulting antitoxin has special serologic and physicochemical characteristics. It flocculates with antigen in a very narrow range of proportions, and it occurs in a special globulin component of the serum which is only rarely found in normal serum of this animal. On the contrary this same animal responds effectively to pneumococcal capsular substance (and other antigens) only after intravenous injection, and the resultant antibodies in these cases flocculate over a wide range of proportions, and are often of high molecular weight, closer to 1,000,000 than the usual weight of 150,000. Other examples are cited on page 74. Against this background of information the special features of the antibodies which occur in the human being with atopic hypersensitivity cannot be regarded as having extraordinary implications which set this response apart from other immunologic responses in any fundamental sense. The fact is that small amounts of antibody of this nature have been found to be produced by laboratory animals, along with the usual precipitating antibodies, following ordinary antigenic stimulation by injections (see Evanescent Cutaneous Reactions, page 207). From these sources the antibody may be transferred to normal human skin to cause the local sensitization of the Prausnitz-Küstner type (75b, 79). Similarly, human beings with serum sickness resulting from injection of antigen may produce antibody with the properties of atopic reagin along with the precipitating type (43b, 80).

The unique feature of this antibody with regard to atopic hypersensitivity is the fact that in this case it seems to constitute the total antibody response. Upon which, if any, of the conditions previously mentioned may this depend? It depends upon the species of animal producing the antibodies only in a quantitative sense, for although man is apparently most ready to form these antibodies, other animals may do so too in more limited fashion. It does not seem to depend upon the duration or intensity of exposure to antigen, for some individuals repeatedly or continuously in contact with pollens or house dust for years never produce them, while others continue to manufacture antibody of this nature indefinitely. It does not seem to depend upon the nature of the antigen, for various pollens and animal danders if injected give rise to anti-bodies predominantly of another kind, as will be described later under De-sensitization. Occasional exceptions to this last statement may exist; one of these is exemplified by an extract of the roundworm *Ascaris* which has a peculiar ability to induce antibody apparently of this type in the majority of subjects injected (81). The point to which this antibody response appears to have most relation is **route of access of antigen** to the tissues, for although injections of various antigens may result in the formation of small amounts of such antibody in man and lower animals, it follows as the characteristic response particularly when the antigens have been inhaled or ingested, i.e. when the exposure has been a natural or spontaneous one.

In Chapter 5, in dealing with the cellular origin of antibodies, there was a discussion of the possibility that the distinctive natures of these substances resulting from variations in the type of antigen, and in route of access and other factors might suggest a multicellular origin of antibodies, one type of cell producing antibody most energetically in one set of circumstances, some other type in other circumstances. Here again available information suggests such a viewpoint. Particular cells in or contiguous to the respiratory and gastrointestinal membranes, not ordinarily concerned in the production of antibodies because injected antigens are taken in greatest amounts to lymph nodes, spleen and other depots of the lymphatic and blood streams, may take over in this case because of the concurrence of two factors. First, that the antigens are made directly available to such cells, and second and more im-portant, because in certain individuals these cells are relatively well adapted to the synthesis of antibodies. This latter point may be the genetically deter-mined constitutional factor which dictates the occurrence of atopic sensitivities. The antibody which these cells are capable of manufacturing would have the restricted serologic characteristics and peculiar physicochemical properties (including heat lability, inability to penetrate placental membranes, par-ticular affinity for certain types of tissue) which were listed before.

Some portion of an antigen injected may of course reach these cells, and this may account for the small amounts of antibody of this type found in non-atopic men and animals following inoculations of various substances. A por-tion of an antigen injected into atopic individuals likewise could reach such cells, and these people because of a special ability of the cells to respond will show a larger preponderance of antibody of the atopic type, along with ordinary precipitating antibody, as suggested by the work with diphtheria toxoid (72b).

On the other hand the possibility must also be considered that there is no special cell type concerned in producing these antibodies, but that certain individuals manufacture them because their ordinary antibody-producing cells are constitutionally attuned to such production (72b). If so, it is difficult to see why the same kind of antibodies are not manufactured by such individuals when antigens are **injected.**

Desensitization. Although the principle of desensitization applies to this class of hypersensitivities also, it cannot be so regularly accomplished as in the case of Arthus and anaphylactic sensitivity. Apparently it is not possible to diminish the concentration of circulating atopic antibody noticeably by repeated injections of the responsible antigen (82) but clinical improvement may occur in the face of this fact. A possible explanation of the desensitizing process may be found in the work first reported by Cooke and his associates (83) and since carried on by Loveless (84). Antibody from a patient with atopic hypersensitivity will sensitize a local skin area of a normal recipient so that injection of the appropriate antigen produces a wheal and flare response. If the patient has been treated by subcutaneous injections of the pollen however he produces another kind of antibody; this exhibits greater combining affinity for the antigen but lacks ability to sensitize normal skin. Thus, posttreatment serum may neutralize relatively large amounts of antigen because of its content of this new kind of antibody. This is therefore called blocking or inhibiting antibody, i.e. it blocks antigen from combining with sensitizing antibody in the tissues. This antibody has certain other features which distinguish it from atopic antibody: it is heat stable in comparison with atopic antibody (84b), and unlike the latter it crosses the human placenta to appear in the bloodstream of the fetus. This substance is also formed by the normal (nonatopic) individual who receives injections of such antigens as pollens (85), and it has been found in similarly treated cattle and sheep (79c, 86).

Loveless suggests that desensitization in the atopic states may consist in the induction of this antibody which, because of its inability to partake in hypersensitive reactions itself and its concomitant avidity for antigen, may divert inhaled or ingested antigens from sensitized tissues. The effect is analogous to the antianaphylactic state discussed earlier as a possible mechanism of desensitization in anaphylaxis. This viewpoint is not unanimously accepted because there is disagreement with the fundamental premises involved (57), and because individual correlations of the development of this antibody with clinical improvement have not been established (87), although a general correlation has been noted (84a).

The existence of this type of antibody response again brings up the question of multiplicity of cellular origins of antibodies. This substance, with distinctive immunologic and physical properties, results only from the **injection** of substances which, when they gain ingress to the body by natural routes, cause the formation of antibody of the atopic kind.

Mechanism of Atopic Reactions. The presence in the bloodstream of antibodies mediating the atopic reactions does not necessarily indicate the existence of a clinical level of sensitivity to the antigen concerned. Many individuals with clinical sensitivities to one or more pollens or danders may reveal reactivity to other substances by direct skin test and by passive transfer of sensitivity in the P-K procedure without at any time responding to these substances, as they exist in the environment, with clinical signs. This strange circumstance has no explanation as yet.

In basic mechanism, atopic reactions appear to resemble the anaphylactic type in being probably mediated by the release of H-substance subsequent to the combination of antigen with antibody in the tissues. This is not entirely clear in the human being, as discussed in a preceding section dealing with the mechanisms of immediate hypersensitive reactions and in subsequent paragraphs devoted to therapeutic agents, but sufficiently suggestive to warrant holding this viewpoint with qualifications to be clarified by later information. Walzer (88a) points out various differences in reactivity of human skin to histamine and to injected allergens.

Hay fever, urticaria and angioedema are all primarily manifestations of serous exudation from blood vessels. An increase in vascular permeability is a frequent manifestation of the immediate hypersensitive reactions in the human being. Asthma is at least superficially entirely reminiscent of anaphylactic shock in the guinea pig, and an atopic individual injected with an excessive dose of antigen will develop the typical anaphylactic syndrome. It is therefore tempting to equate asthma with anaphylactic shock involving primarily contraction of bronchiolar smooth muscle. Yet there are reasons to doubt that smooth muscle contraction is a major event accounting for the respiratory difficulties in all instances of asthma. Atopic antibody will not transfer itself to smooth muscle strips as will antibody resulting from ordinary antigenic stimuli, and the uterine muscle of a patient with atopic sensitivity shows no tendency to contract when exposed to antigen in the Schultz-Dale bath (88b). Many allergists believe that edema and hypersecretion of mucus may be the predominant factors involved in asthma, and that although histopathologic study of the asthmatic subject reveals thickening of the bronchiolar smooth muscle, this may be the result rather than the cause of long-continued respiratory distress. If hypersecretion of mucus is an important factor in the asthmatic syndrome, then one must postulate an additional effect of antigen-antibody combination in the body, this time upon the glandular epithelium of the respiratory tract. It has been pointed out also that in anaphylaxis the blood pressure falls, while in asthma it rises.

On the other side of the picture there is good evidence to suggest that the syndromes are in essence the same. Rackemann (89) has published data concerning 50 cases of death from asthma and reports that in younger individuals with asthma of extrinsic type, i.e. traceable to some definite antigenic stimulus, pathologic study revealed bronchospasm comparable to that seen in the anaphylactic guinea pig. With long persistent asthma, and especially in the asthma developing in older persons, usually without a traceable antigenic cause and hence referred to as intrinsic, autopsy of fatal cases revealed bronchial obstruction by mucus plugs. When one considers in addition experimental observations made (90) in sensitized guinea pigs the relationship between asthma and anaphylaxis becomes more striking. In this work it was shown that after induction of respiratory attacks by the intratracheal insufflation of antigen, the morphologic changes were identical with those seen in asthmatic human beings, i.e. an accumulation of eosinophils, hypersecretion of mucus, hyalinization of basement membranes and hypertrophy of bronchial musculature. Even here, however, there is a suggestion that the asthmatic-like state induced in the guinea pig differs in some respects from anaphylaxis in this animal (90b).

Although this pathologic evidence supplied by human beings and guinea pigs tentatively indicates the oneness of asthma and anaphylaxis, in view of the controversial points yet to be settled the final conclusion on this issue must wait. Certainly few would doubt that they were alike in the basic mechanisms involved. Whether the direction of blood pressure changes, the involvement of bronchiolar muscle and other possible differences are more than quantitative distinctions will eventually become clear.

The hypersensitiveness which occurs to foods further complicates our efforts to understand the atopic states. Symptoms, including abdominal pain, nausea and vomiting, occur quickly after ingestion of the responsible antigen, and these are accompanied by fluoroscopically visible occurrences such as hypomotility and hypotonicity of the stomach and spasms or dilatation of the colon (91). Yet gastrointestinal allergy usually occurs in the absence of demonstrable circulating reagin and, as a corollary to this, of positive skin responses to the offending antigen. Again it is possible by rationalization to clear this obstacle; it may be that the sensitization to food is directed against a product of digestion, hence antibodies cannot be detected when the original food substance is employed as the test material. The same thought may be applicable to the sensitizations caused by various drugs, for here also positive skin reactions and circulating antibodies cannot often be demonstrated. The drug may be combined with body constituents to serve as antigen (see page 265, and Chase [32b]).

In résumé, atopic hypersensitivity diverges from the Arthus and anaphylactic types in man and animals chiefly in these respects:

(a) Sensitization usually occurs spontaneously as the result of exposure to environmental agents.

(b) This spontaneous occurrence is almost entirely limited to man.

(c) This hypersensitivity cannot usually be reproduced by artificial (injection) methods.

(d) There is an hereditary disposition to sensitization by environmental agents. About 10 per cent of human beings are affected.

(e) The antibody associated with this response is limited to a globulin of poor combining activity for antigen, distinctive physicochemical properties, and ability to convey sensitivity to cutaneous and mucosal tissues only.

In general however these characteristics are not entirely confined to human atopic sensitivity. The distinguishing points appear to be largely distinctions of degree rather than of kind. From the fundamental immunologic viewpoint atopic hypersensitivity may be considered as similar to the other immediate types described.

5. OTHER HYPERSENSITIVE SYNDROMES OF THE IMMEDIATE TYPE. The range of clinical conditions ascribable to a hypersensitive basis is not yet sharply defined. There is some temptation to attribute almost every disease of unknown etiology to it, but without reasonable evidence it is wise to curb this temptation sharply. However, the past few years have disclosed such evidence for certain diseases of hitherto uncertain etiology. These diseases share the basic fact that they reflect injuries to vascular tissue and collagen, although they are different as categorized by clinical signs and symptoms. Vascular damage suggests that such diseases fall into the class of the immediate hypersensitivities.

Under the influence of continuous or repeated subjection to an antigen to which hypersensitivity has been established—for example, in serum sickness—certain individuals show generalized and frequently progressive vascular injury. Several of these syndromes for which the evidence is most convincing will be described. These are discussed here rather than under an earlier classification not because it was deemed desirable to segregate them, but because it was felt that the necessary descriptive detail would be distracting from the attempt to deal with basic concepts in the preceding sections.

Periarteritis Nodosa. This disease has been known for almost a century as a generalized inflammatory affection of the smaller arteries in which the lesions progress from proliferation of the intima and inflammation of periarterial structures (vasa vasorum and lymphatics) to occlusion by proliferation or thrombosis. Nodules containing polymorphonuclear cells and eosinophils form on the adventitia. Symptoms may be manifold depending upon the location of most extensive arteriolar damage.

For the past 25 years it has been surmised that periarteritis nodosa may be a disease of hypersensitivity (92). In 1942 and subsequently Rich (22, 93) capped this viewpoint with convincing clinical and pathologic evidence from human beings with the serum sickness type of response to sulfonamides and serum, as well as with experimental evidence obtained in rabbits. In these animals a single large injection of horse serum results in a modified form of serum sickness and, in about half the cases studied by Rich, in the production of generalized necrotizing arteritis. These observations have been repeatedly confirmed and there seems little doubt that in some human beings and in some animals the immediate form of hypersensitivity may eventuate in this serious interference with the circulation. The lesions may be the eventual result of the formation of wheals in the arteriolar walls about the vasa vasorum.

Although this disease is certainly not an immediate response to antigen in a literal sense, it represents presumably the eventual pathologic change resulting from repeated, or continuous, immunologic responses which are of immediate type. In other words, responses involving the vessels probably occur immediately following contact of antibody with antigen, but it takes some time for the permanent vascular alterations of periarteritis nodosa to come about.

It seems quite possible that periarteritis nodosa may result from a variety of antigenic factors in the individual who presents the proper soil for its occurrence, whatever that may be.

Rheumatic Fever. Related to the lesions of periarteritis nodosa are those seen in the heart and other tissues as the result of an attack of rheumatic fever. Collections of mononuclear and multinuclear cells occur in the periarterial connective tissue of the coronary arterioles as well as in the endocardium and the valve leaflets, and are found clustered about focal areas of degenerated collagen in the myocardium. These are called Aschoff bodies. Microscopic and sometimes macroscopic nodules of similar histologic character appear also in joint capsules and the subcutaneous tissues, where they may sometimes become palpable, especially about the elbows, knees and ankles. Here again a relationship to hypersensitivity has been hypothesized for some time partly on the basis of the similarities in structural changes seen in animals with induced sensitivities (94). In 1937 Clark and Kaplan (95) described such lesions in anaphylactically sensitized animals as well as in two cases of serum sickness in human beings, and tentatively suggested a relationship to the hypersensitive reaction. Gregory and Rich have since described in greater detail such lesions in human beings and in rabbits sensitized with horse serum and egg albumin, and others have confirmed these observations (96). The occasional occurrence of periarteritis nodosa as a complication of rheumatic fever has been reported by several observers.

The eventual etiologic factor in rheumatic fever may be more restricted than is true for periarteritis nodosa. It has long been suspected that the hemolytic streptococcus is related to this disease because the onset of rheumatic fever has been so frequently observed to follow respiratory infection with this organism (97). It is difficult to see why a hypersensitive process should depend upon a specific etiologic agent since allergic responses to different antigens may take the same form. Nonetheless, evidence has been closing in on the streptococcus for some years. In a clinical study conducted during the second World War, Rantz and others (98) instituted routine electrocardiographic examinations and cultures of the respiratory tracts of all soldiers admitted with respiratory infections to a camp hospital. It was found in some instances that electrocardiographic evidence of heart damage could become apparent shortly after the onset of an attack of acute streptococcal disease, before any clinical signs of rheumatic fever became detectable; sometimes the latter did not occur at all. In the few instances which could be followed, subsequent attacks of streptococcal infection were accompanied by more pronounced changes until overt rheumatic fever eventuated. Interestingly enough, in individuals showing this apparent sequence of developing hypersensitivity the immunologic types of streptococcus causing the succeeding respiratory infections frequently differ (99). This suggests that if hypersensitivity is established to a component of the organism itself, the capsular antigen must be excluded from consideration because this is specific for each type within the group A organisms involved. It would be interesting to know which antigenic component of the bacterium may be the sensitizing agent. The possibility exists that the responsible antigen is not a part of the streptococcus itself at all, but rather a component of the host's own tissue so altered by the activity of the microbe as to become an auto-antigen (100). This subtle point is a difficult one upon which to gather definitive evidence however, and no conclusion can be reached on the basis of that presently available. The question of autoimmunization is discussed in some detail in Chapter 31.

Until recently there was no good experimental structure to strengthen the viewpoint that the streptococcus may be related to the occurrence of rheumatic fever. Murphy and Swift (101) appear to have made up this deficiency by ingenious experiments with group A streptococci in rabbits. By carrying out multiple reinjections into the skin with organisms of different types within the group the factor of acquired immunity was evaded, and a series of infections could be established; these circumstances are presumably analogous to those obtaining in the spontaneous infections of human beings. After sustaining 2 to 10 such infections over a period of 3 to 20 months some of the animals became ill and developed elevated erythrocyte sedimentation rates, leukocytosis, loss of appetite and weight, postexertional dyspnea and, in some instances, cardiac arrhythmia. In the hearts of these animals lesions were found in endo-, myo- and epicardium; these contained no demonstrable bacteria, and in appearance they were strikingly similar to the lesions of rheumatic fever of the human being.

It is of interest that these alterations are of the immediate type, characterized by edema, vascular defects and collagen degeneration, rather than of the delayed type to be described in the next chapter.

Other syndromes may also be imputed to the hypersensitive state, including rheumatoid arthritis and disseminated lupus erythematosus. Rheumatoid arthritis has been discussed from this standpoint by Rich (22), who points out that the incidence of cardiac lesions similar to those of rheumatic fever is high in this disease and that focal degeneration of collagen is a characteristic occurrence. Inflammatory changes in arteries also occur (102). Disseminated lupus erythematosus similarly has much in common with periarteritis nodosa and rheumatic fever, including cutaneous inflammatory eruptions, necrotizing arterial lesions, focal degeneration of collagen, and focal cardiac lesions. In both cases the relationship to hypersensitivity seems to be, if not proven, well grounded, and as will be discussed later the current work with substances related to adrenal cortical hormone develops this possibility even further. Other diseases of diverse clinical manifestations may before long also be included in the category of hypersensitive syndromes; these include certain purpuric diseases and glomerulonephritis (22). These also are discussed in more detail in relation to autoimmunization in Chapter 31. This is an exciting period in the development of understanding of hypersensitivity in relation to disease.

The mechanism of production of these lesions can only be speculated upon now. Periarteritic lesions occur in only a portion of any group of rabbits sensitized with serum, and the number found to be positive in any single experiment may fluctuate widely between the extreme limits of zero to 100 per cent. The lesions have been referred to as disseminated Arthus reactions, and indeed they seem to depend upon the same essential condition as does the cutaneous Arthus response, *viz.*, a high level of circulating antibody. Thus it has been noted that these systemic lesions occur only in rabbits which develop good skin reactions of Arthus type also (102b, 130b). Since the Arthus reaction parallels quite well the level of circulating antibody, the tentative inference may be drawn that vascular lesions similarly depend upon a good antibody response by the sensitized animal. Hopps and Wissler's comment to the contrary does not seem to be justified by their tabulated data (102c).

Relationship of Eosinophils to Immediate Hypersensitive Reactions. It has been known for many years that eosinophils characteristically put in an appearance in many of the hypersensitive states with which we have been dealing. These cells may occur about local sites of reaction or they may be found in increased numbers in the blood stream, or both. They appear to be related to the hypersensitive reaction rather than to the existence of the hypersensitive state in itself. Thus, while they are not seen in abnormal numbers in sensitive guinea pigs, eosinophilia in the lungs and the blood occurs in animals which have survived an anaphylactic shock (103). Analogous findings are made in human beings; during the period of development of serum sickness eosinophilia is not met with, but once the reaction has gotten under way these cells appear in the tissues at sites of activity. Eosinophils are found in local hives, and they occur in the membranes of the respiratory tract and in the local secretions as well as in the blood of asthmatics, often only during or immediately after attacks. Atopic dermatitis is commonly associated with a significant blood eosinophilia. The lesions of periarteritis nodosa and of rheumatic fever often contain these cells. Their occurrence is so commonly related to hypersensitive reactions of the immediate type that their presence in abnormal numbers in any disease of unknown etiology (e.g. Hodgkin's disease) makes the factor of allergy suspect.

A point of interest is the fact that cortisone, which has a certain modifying influence upon diseases of hypersensitivity, causes also a decrease of circulating eosinophils in the blood. It appears that these may take refuge in the spleen, though what this means is not yet evident (104).

So far all the information about these cells is observational. There is no sound idea as to why they appear or what they do. The various theories attempting to explain their presence and function are presently merely speculations, and not especially suggestive ones.

Therapeutic Agents in Relation to the Mechanisms Concerned in the Immediate Hypersensitive States. A variety of therapeutic measures have been employed through the years in the hypersensitive states, of which a few have survived (20e). Generally speaking these agents and procedures have been based upon rationales intimately related to the fundamental viewpoints on mechanisms just described, and from this standpoint they are all worthy of consideration. A purely tentative effort has been made in Figure 41 to illustrate graphically the evolution of the hypersensitive state and reaction, from the initial entry of antigen into the tissues through the antigen-antibody union to the final action of H-substance upon susceptible types of tissue. Listed beneath this sequence are 11 substances or procedures which, in some manner, interfere with its development, or have been thought to do so. The listings have been made at the points in the sequence where the various agencies are supposed to act. It should be understood that this diagram is not intended to represent anything more than a highly simplified version of the present status of available information.

I. Agents Affecting Production of Antibody. 1. Nitrogen mustard (Fig. 41, A1). This agent (methyl-*bis* [beta-chlorethyl] amine hydrochloride) is toxic for lymphocytes, and it has been found to suppress antibody formation (105) as well as acquired resistance (106). Administration to rabbits receiving injections of horse serum has confirmed the fact of antibody suppression, and in addition the cutaneous Arthus reaction and the incidence and severity of vascular and endocardial lesions were markedly inhibited. These three evidences of diminished immunologic responsiveness showed a rather regular correlation, but this may be coincidental since nitrogen mustard affects various enzymatic and metabolic processes (107). The evidence seems suggestive however that interference with antibody formation may account for the suppression of hypersensitivity.

2. ACTH and cortisone (Fig. 41, A2). The possible influence of adreno-corticotrophic hormone and cortisone in modifying antibody responses was described in Chapter 12. The finding by Hench (108) that ACTH and 17-hydroxy-11-dehydrocorticosterone (cortisone) can dramatically alleviate the clinical courses of rheumatoid arthritis, rheumatic fever and lupus erythematosus has stimulated tremendous enthusiasm in those interested in diseases of hypersensitive origin. In clinical states in addition to these just mentioned, beneficial effects have been described in asthma, hay fever, urticaria, dermatitis, angioedema, serum sickness and gastrointestinal allergy (18a).

The mechanisms through which these beneficial activities may be mediated are far from clear. In Figure 41 this has been indicated tentatively as a suppressive activity upon antibody production, largely because some reports have revealed that antibody formation by rabbits is markedly or entirely suppressed if these substances are administered during the vaccination period (109). But there are at least two reasons for seriously questioning this mechanism. First, this conclusion with regard to antibodies is not a unanimous one, for in experimental animals (110) as well as in man (111) other workers have failed to find that these substances significantly affect antibody production, though the development of hypersensitivity (vascular lesions) in the first instance was suppressed. Secondly, the alleviatory influence of these drugs in established human hypersensitivities is prompt and encompasses relief from such profound inflammatory and degenerative changes as exist, for example, in long standing rheumatoid arthritis. It may seem more reasonable to ascribe the benefits here to the inhibition of inflammation or to some other of the physiologic alterations which these substances are known to effect, rather than to interference with an immunologic process.

Work with laboratory animals has not so far clarified this issue. As is always the case when a striking advance is made, a wave of exuberant reports is followed by a period of reflection, and eventually the status of the point at issue comes to equilibrium. The second phase with respect to cortisone and ACTH has begun at the time of this writing, and as a consequence the literature is somewhat at odds.

The information presently available indicates that in the guinea pig neither cortisone nor ACTH suppresses the development of the anaphylactic state if administered during the period of sensitization, nor does it mitigate the shock reaction itself (112). In mice on the other hand shock in already sensitized animals may be inhibited by administration of cortisone some hours before the test (113). The finding in the mouse fits other work which indicates that adrenalectomized mice are especially susceptible to anaphylactic sensitization and shock (47a).

Development of Arthus reactivity in rabbits may be suppressed by concomitant administration of these substances with the sensitizing antigen, but in animals in which sensitivity has already been established actively or by passive transfer of antibodies, these drugs do not modify the response (109). Analogously, they do not influence the skin response in patients with atopic hypersensitivity, nor in recipients of atopic serum for the Prausnitz-Küstner reaction (112e, 114). In fact, failure of diminution of the skin reaction has been seen in patients in whom the asthma, of which these tests were an index, improved considerably (115).

The vascular lesions in rabbits (analogues of periarteritis nodosa) induced by injections of serum are inhibited by treatment during the course of sensitization (110, 116); in patients also the effect of treatment upon these lesions is remarkable.

The encephalomyelitis which may be induced in laboratory animals by injecting homologous or heterologous brain emulsions is suppressed by the administration of ACTH during the period of antigenic stimulation (117a, 117b). It is possible that injury to the brain in this case stems from the development of antibrain antibodies stimulated by the injection, and the inference is made that ACTH depresses their formation (see Chapter 31).

What can we extract from these various clinical and laboratory experiences which may explain the mechanism of activity of adrenal cortical hormone in allergic disease? There is some evidence that the antibody response may be inhibited, and this would explain the beneficent activity of the hormone **if administered during the time when sensitization is being established.** This information however is not uncontested; some workers have not been able to find a significant influence upon antibody formation, and the evo-

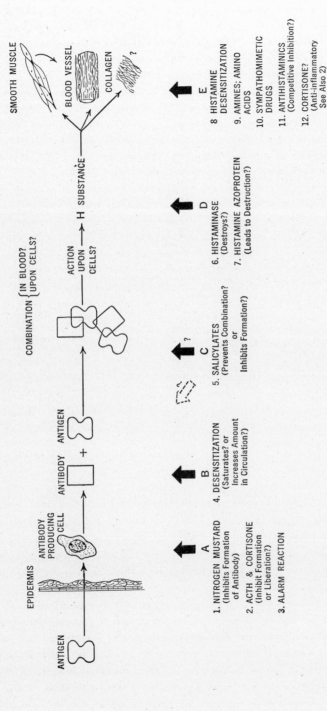

Fig. 41. Graphic illustration of possible points of suppression of immediate hypersensitivity.

lution of the classic form of anaphylactic reactivity occurring in the guinea pig is not successfully suppressed by these substances.

If we were to concede for the moment that under proper circumstances antibody responses may be abolished, this still does not clarify the effectiveness of the hormone in allergic diseases already established, e.g. in rheumatoid arthritis or asthma, in which pathologic changes already existent undergo sufficient regression to afford relief from symptoms. Interestingly, Kallós (117c) has found also in guinea pig anaphylaxis that animals which have been subjected to repeated shocks are eventually protected by ACTH, whereas those subjected to their first exposure to antigen are not.

It is evident that we cannot come to conclusions now. The effects of these hormones in the body are multiple; perhaps one activity is more pronounced in one instance, another in other circumstances. Some of the suggested mechanisms by which they may ameliorate hypersensitive conditions have been these:

(a) Inhibition of protein synthesis to explain the nitrogen loss and antibody suppression (?) following cortisone administration (118).

(b) Inhibition of the inflammatory response may modify lesions. Thus, complete suppression of the Shwartzman reaction (see page 272) has been reported (119). This is a hemorrhagic necrotic reaction which is not hypersensitive in nature. However, Arthus and atopic whealing reactions do not seem to be modified, as related earlier.

(c) Layton (120) has suggested that cortisone may inhibit the synthesis of chondroitin sulfate, thereby reducing the amount of connective tissue ground substance in the collagen diseases.

These and other suggestions (121) fail still to hit the mark convincingly. Conclusions must therefore remain for the future.

3. Alarm reaction (Fig. 41, A3). The alarm reaction of Selye (122) is mentioned in this connotation because a feature of the "syndrome of adaptation" of the animal body to traumatic influences includes stimulation of the adrenal cortex. This may conceivably intervene in the hypersensitive sequence as does an injection of cortisone. The adrenalectomized mouse is much more susceptible to anaphylactic shock than is the normal animal (47a). Perhaps it is upon the basis of temporary *hyper* function of the adrenals that the relative refractoriness to anaphylactic shock occurs following the injection of nonspecific substances.

II. AGENTS AFFECTING ANTIBODY ITSELF. 4. Desensitization (Fig. 41, B4). The use of specific antigens in the treatment of hypersensitive states is thought to influence antibody, possibly by combining with it and thus removing the agency of sensitization, or alternately by causing the production of an excess of antibodies which, present in the body fluids, may prevent the combination of antigen with antibody present upon or within cells. These possibilities have been discussed earlier; conclusive evidence for or against both is still lacking.

III. AGENTS AFFECTING ANTIGEN-ANTIBODY COMBINATION. 5. Salicylates (Fig. 41, C5). Derivatives of salicylic acid have been employed for years in the treatment of rheumatic fever, and are said to have some favorable influence upon the course of serum sickness also (123). In more recent work these drugs have been credited with protecting rabbits against the development of allergic arteritis (124) and anaphylactic shock (125). Some moderate influence has been noted also in the protection of animals against the encephalomyelitis which usually follows injections of brain emulsion with adjuvant (126). These beneficial effects have not been the experience of all investigators however (130).

There has been interest in delineating the process through which these effects may come about. Earlier experiments which indicated an inhibition of antibody formation (123, 127) have been affirmed as well as denied by others (128). There seems to be more support for the viewpoint that these drugs may inhibit the combination of antibody with antigen. This has been demonstrated to occur in vitro (129) but the amount of salicylate necessary is greatly in excess of the concentrations attained in the body with even large therapeutic doses. The issue is not yet clear, for salicylates have other activities, prolonging the blood coagulation time, increasing the sedimentation rate, and probably acting in other ways in the body. The effects upon hypersensitivity may depend upon an indirect influence rather than a direct activity upon the immunologic sequence (130).

IV. AGENTS AFFECTING HISTAMINE. 6. Histaminase (Fig. 41, D6). Best and McHenry (131) demonstrated in 1930 that an enzyme active upon histamine exists in animal tissues, and that this destroys histamine in the test tube. There is no evidence however that it can do the same in the body (132), and it is not surprising therefore that this enzyme has proved without value in experimental and clinical hypersensitivities (133, 135). This conclusion does not necessarily impugn the concept that H-substance mediates various hypersensitive reactions, for if the enzyme will not act upon histamine which is injected into the body there is no reason to expect it to influence a similar substance released by the antigen-antibody reaction.

7. Histamine-azoprotein (Fig. 41, D7). A similar rationale—the destruction or neutralization of histamine—underlaid trials several years ago of a conjugated histamine in the form of histamine-azoprotein (134). The attempt to interfere with the intermediary H-substance was in this case less direct. By means of repeated injections of this conjugate antibodies could be stimulated against the histamine hapten. It was hoped that these antibodies might be available to act upon the intermediary substance released by other antigen-antibody reactions. Vaccination of guinea pigs with histamine-azoprotein caused them to become refractory to injections of histamine, and partially so to anaphylactic shock. Nevertheless there has been little to recommend its use from experiences so far gained in human beings (133, 135). It is thus difficult to know how to evaluate evidence derived from the use of this sub-

stance with respect to the histamine concept of immediate hypersensitive reactions.

Although it does not figure in the chart, an observation concerning the effect of d-catechin upon anaphylaxis in the guinea pig is of interest (143). Administration of this substance to 14 sensitized animals resulted in the inhibition of shock in all. The mechanism of its activity is thought to be in preventing the formation of histamine by inhibiting the histidine decarboxylase of the tissues.

V. AGENTS AFFECTING HISTAMINE ACTION ON SHOCK TISSUES. 8. Histamine desensitization (Fig. 41, E8). The repeated injection of histamine itself into animals has been said to result in a partial refractoriness to this substance. The effect here is not supposed to be an immunologic one, but rather an accustoming of responsive tissues to histamine so that their reactivity to this substance is dulled (135). This kind of tolerance, of dubious occurrence in animals, does not seem to take place in human beings at all, and Cooke (133) believes along with others that there is no evidence for the use of this substance.

9. Amines (Fig. 41, E9). Various amines, e.g. arginine, histidine and cysteine, seem to protect guinea pig smooth muscle from the effects of histamine itself as well as against the contractile activity of antigen if the muscle is sensitized (18b). The ratio of arginine to histamine necessary for a counteractive effect however is 250,000:1. To fulfill this requirement in the animal body is utterly out of the question, since 50 to 100 gm. of arginine would be necessary for the protection of a guinea pig against one lethal dose of histamine. Roche e Silva (18b) believes that this factor may explain the inefficacy of arginine in tests on guinea pigs and dogs, and its lack of significance in the treatment of hypersensitive states.

10. Sympathomimetic drugs (Fig. 41, E10). Epinephrine has pronounced effects upon blood vessels and bronchial smooth muscle directly opposed to those of histamine. Whereas histamine induces bronchospasm, adrenalin in small concentrations causes relaxation, and while histamine produces dilatation and increased permeability of peripheral vessels, epinephrine constricts these and prevents leakage of fluid from them. Through these activities, adrenalin may protect the body from anaphylactic shock or it may ameliorate an attack of asthma or urticaria. Other drugs with similar activities may be effective in milder degree but for more prolonged periods. Of these, ephedrine is an especially useful member.

Certain xanthine derivatives act directly upon smooth muscle to effect relaxation. A most useful one for the relief of asthmatic attacks is aminophylline, a mixture of theophylline and ethylenediamine.

The effectiveness of these substances in allaying hypersensitive reactions of the immediate type in which smooth muscle spasm and edema are the major phenomena cannot be ascribed to any specific interference with the effects of histamine or any similarly acting substance which may result from an antigen-antibody reaction. Their effects will counteract bronchospasm and edema due to any cause, and their efficacy in mitigating hypersensitive manifestations therefore does not add to our understanding of the mechanism through which such reactions are mediated.

11. Antihistaminic drugs (Fig. 41, E11). This class of compounds has contributed more than any other to an understanding of the mediation of certain of the immediate hypersensitive reactions. The antihistamine drugs were introduced in 1933 by Fourneau and Bovet in France (136), and literally hundreds of variants have been tested since. The chemical and pharmacologic properties of many of these have been discussed especially in the Journal of Allergy for the past few years. For present purposes these substances will be dealt with as a class.

Many of these drugs are ethylenediamines or aminoethyl ethers with the essential structure:

$$R-X-\overset{|}{\underset{|}{C}}-\overset{|}{\underset{|}{C}}-N\big<$$

in which X is nitrogen, oxygen or carbon linking with the nucleus R. The central structure has some similarity to that of histamine:

$$\begin{array}{c} N-\overset{|}{\underset{|}{C}}-\overset{|}{\underset{|}{C}}-\overset{|}{\underset{|}{C}}-N\big< \\ HC \\ HN-CH \end{array}$$

Other recent compounds however have no structural similarity whatever to histamine.

Most of the data now at hand suggest that these agents block histamine by competing for the same receptor sites on sensitized cells. In this view, the activity of these drugs differs from that of the sympathomimetic substances in that the latter antagonize the effects of histamine fortuitously because they happen to exert antagonist effects upon the same tissues (137).

The thought that the antihistaminic substances are specific histamine antagonists considered together with their efficacy in suppressing immediate hypersensitive reactions provides compelling support for the concept of histamine release as the essential mechanism responsible for such reactions. Unfortunately however the two legs of the syllogism are too shaky to support the conclusion for these reasons: first, it is not proved that the drugs are specific histamine antagonists. They do not suppress all the effects of histamine in the body. The stimulation of gastric secretion caused by histamine is uninfluenced by most of these drugs, and is even apparently increased by others. Second, the abilities of these drugs to inhibit the vascular and smooth muscle effects of histamine do not parallel their abilities to suppress the anaphylactic syndrome. One drug may be only half as good as another in counteracting histamine but several times as good in suppressing anaphylaxis. It might be inferred from this that some other activity of the drugs than their antihistaminic property, or some additional effect, is necessary for antianaphylactic action (138). Third, the influence of these drugs varies considerably in different hypersensitive manifestations of animals and man. Anaphylaxis in the guinea pig can be completely suppressed by the more active compounds, and the pulmonary eosinophilia commonly present in the lungs of animals recovered from shock is not seen in treated animals (29f, 139). In the human being, these substances are quite effective against the skin manifestations of serum sickness, and in hayfever, urticaria and angioedema—to the extent of perhaps 80 per cent of instances treated. However, asthma of hypersensitive origin responds very poorly to these drugs. In experimental studies two types of manifestation appear not to be influenced by them at all. Opinion seems unanimous that the Arthus reaction in rabbits is not modified either by systemic treatment or by local injection of drug along with the reaction-eliciting dose of antigen (130b, 139). The development of lesions of the periarteritic type in rabbits appears also to remain uninfluenced by such treatment (130b). Reports to the contrary (140) are based upon small series of animals and a reduction in numbers of positive reactions which, in view of the wide fluctuations in the occurrence of such lesions even in groups of untreated animals, would seem to have little significance.

These irregularities in the efficacy of antihistaminic agents, incompatible though they appear, may still be consonant with the histamine concept of immediate hypersensitive reactions, for it is possible that the Arthus and arteritic syndromes do not stem from the release of intermediate substances as a result of the antigen-antibody reaction. Earlier in this chapter it was suggested that the cutaneous Arthus reaction may depend directly upon the union of precipitating antibody of good combining power with antigen in the tissues without the necessity for release of an intermediary substance. The effect may, as Doerr has suggested, be due to a direct action of antigen-antibody precipitate upon the cells affected (141). There are several points which suggest the independence of this reaction from histamine or other released substances. It was noted in the earlier discussion of the Arthus reaction that a parallel exists between its intensity and the concentration of precipitating antibody in the circulation. This relationship in itself suggests that a precipitative reaction in the tissues may be necessary to elicit the severe Arthus response, a viewpoint which is bulwarked by the following facts:

(a) The **quantity** of antibody necessary to sensitize a guinea pig passively for histamine-mediated anaphylaxis is about 0.04 mg. by intravenous injection. About 14 times this amount is necessary to sensitize the same animal for a minimal cutaneous Arthus reaction (27b). Almost 25,000 times as much antibody is required to induce local passive Arthus reactivity in the rabbit's skin as for the sensitization of a strip of guinea pig smooth muscle for anaphylactic contraction (25d).

(b) The **quality** of antibody (ability to precipitate with antigen) necessary for the reaction differs in the two cases also. Univalent nonprecipitating antibody will passively transfer anaphylactic reactivity to a guinea pig as well as an equal quantity (in terms of nitrogen content) of precipitating antibody. In contrast, univalent antibody cannot induce more than a very mild degree of Arthus reactivity (27b). This can be interpreted to mean that for the histamine release which results in anaphylaxis simple combination of antigen with antibody suffices; for the Arthus reaction a precipitate must form, and for this purpose univalent antibody is useless.

(c) In line with the foregoing points it is noted that the best Arthus reactions can be induced in the rabbit, which is also an excellent producer of precipitating antibody. Furthermore, the human being with atopic sensitivity may be exquisitely sensitive to antigen as revealed by liability to severe asthma, angioedema, hives and even anaphylactic shock if antigen is injected. The individual with such sensitivity however possesses antibody of very poor serologic reactivity. In agreement with this, the injection of antigen into the skin results in a local wheal and flare (the histamine type of response) but not in the destructive lesion of the Arthus type (presumably a precipitative response).

As for the disseminated vascular lesions of periarteritic type, it seems possible that these may depend upon similar antibody requirements as does the cutaneous Arthus reaction. This is suggested by observations (130b, 142) of a parallelism between the occurrence of vascular lesions and severe Arthus reactions. If this is the case then the failure of antihistaminic agents to influence the development or manifestations of both of these hypersensitive syndromes could be accounted for by reason of their independence from histamine liberation by the antigen-antibody reaction.

If this viewpoint is correct it removes a major obstacle to the thesis that the effectiveness of the drugs under discussion, in hypersensitive syndromes other than the Arthus and periarteritic, is owed to the fact that histamine is the mediator for such reactions. It does so not by interposing a fundamental gulf between the two groups of reactions, but merely by supposing that the anaphylactic type of response is delicately attuned to the simple fact of combination within the body of minute quantities of antibody and antigen, a consequent effector substance producing marked physiologic changes, while the Arthus type of reaction, typified by gross vascular damage, is the result of an antibody-antigen combination on a higher level, i.e. overt precipitation.

This discussion is not intended to force conclusions, but rather to attempt to clarify apparently contradictory observations on the basis of data presently at hand. It still leaves entirely unanswered the other questions; whether these drugs are actually antihistaminic to begin with, and why they have so poor an activity in the asthmatic state.

SUMMARY

There seems to be good reason to unify the essential mechanisms invoked in the sensitizing process and in the eventual responses in all the hypersensitive states which have been discussed. The basic fact in all cases is the primary response of the body to an antigenic substance with the formation of antibodies. When these subsequently react with the same antigen, again in the body, the union affects certain tissues, chiefly smooth muscle, blood vessels and collagen, and one or a combination of manifestations occur. Under any given set of conditions (i.e. kind and dose of antigen, route by which the sensitizing and reactive doses enter the body and species of animal) a particular kind of reaction usually follows. Thus, the parenteral injection of a sufficient dose of protein will sensitize the organism so that a subsequent inoculation given into the skin about 10 days later will cause severe inflammation and necrosis, while an injection into the blood stream is apt to result in anaphylactic shock. When certain of these conditions are varied the end result may also differ; e.g. the spontaneous sensitization of the human being by air-borne or ingested antigens results in attacks of asthma or hayfever or urticaria on subsequent exposure to the antigen by the same or a parenteral route.

An essential feature which seems to determine these differences is the nature of the antibody response induced by the antigenic stimulus. In Chapter 6 it was pointed out that antibody is far from a homogeneous entity either in its physicochemical or its serologic properties. It may have the chemical characteristics of normal gamma globulin or it may be a high molecular weight substance with different electrophoretic behavior. It may react avidly with antigen to form a lattice precipitate, or it may be capable of only the simplest combination with antigen without inducing any obvious change in it. These differences in antibody response are seen to follow especially from differences in route of entrance of antigen into the body, differences in the antigen itself, differences in the intensity of antigenic stimulation, and differences in the species of animal under consideration. These factors are interrelated, so that one species of animal may respond with antibody of one kind to certain antigens administered intravenously, and with another kind to other antigens given subcutaneously.

The mass of factual data concerning the hypersensitive reactions cannot yet be sifted to a few clear grains of truth, but the effort to do so leaves us with the tentative possibility that such differences in antibody reactivity may determine the kind of hypersensitive syndrome which can be expected.

If the antibody formed is of good reactive ability—i.e. precipitating antibody—its combination with antigen in the tissues in some way causes injury to vascular endothelium and results in the Arthus reaction. To satisfy this condition injections of substances of good antigenic properties are necessary for sensitization, and a species of animal which is preeminently proficient in developing antibody of high reactive ability also develops Arthus reactivity most readily. The same conditions may determine the occurrence of vascular lesions of the periarteritic type so far as suggestions from present evidence permit speculation.

If antibody formation is limited to a poorer combining type the effects of its union with antigen are still felt by the tissues, for the simple fact of antigen-antibody combination without precipitate formation results in the release from tissue cells of H-substance (or histamine) and possibly other physiologically active substances as well. These act upon vessels and smooth muscle; the results of such activity may be anaphylactic shock, an asthmatic attack, urticaria, angioedema, the accumulation of fluids in the joints, or the rhinitis of hayfever. Small concentrations of antibody, of poor quality, may suffice for these effects. The guinea pig with very low levels of poorly reactive antibody when injected with antigen develops anaphylaxis. The human being who is hereditarily disposed to produce antibodies in response to inhaled or swallowed substances characteristically forms antibodies of very poor combining properties, possibly because the route by which antigen gains entrance to the tissues provides only a feeble antigenic stimulus, and this to local cells which form antibodies of restricted serologic capacity only. No manifest serologic reaction with antigen takes place, but the union suffices for H-substance release. In the skin this reaction produces a hive, a fleeting response in which the vascular damage of the Arthus reaction is not seen.

In summary, there appear to be three types of antibodies involved in these various reactions:

1. For the Arthus and perhaps the periarteritic forms of manifestation, precipitating antibody.

2. For anaphylaxis, antibody of the same general kind, but this can be univalent (nonprecipitating) and a small amount suffices.

3. For atopic reactions, a peculiar antibody without manifest serologic abilities, with little capacity to neutralize antigen, and with a peculiar affinity for skin, i.e. it will not passively sensitize smooth muscle cells to the action of antigen.

The antibodies in the second and third categories affect the body, after their reaction with antigen, by causing the release of intermediary substances.

These antibody responses are not always strictly separable. The atopic human being appears to possess antibody of the third type only, but the human being who has developed serum sickness as the result of an **injection** of antigen may form all three types, so that he develops urticaria and edema and may passively transfer sensitivity of the Prausnitz-Küstner type to a normal recipient skin (antibody 3 effect), he may respond to reinjection of antigen with anaphylactic shock, and his serum may convey the anaphylactic state passively to guinea pigs (antibodies 1 and/or 2), and he may develop arterial lesions, and his serum may precipitate antigen in the test tube (antibody 1).

BIBLIOGRAPHY

1. Portier, P., and Richet, C. Compt. rend. Soc. de biol., 54:170, 1902.
2a. von Pirquet, C. F. München. med. Wchnschr., 53:1457, 1906.
  b. ———— and Schick, B. Serum Sickness, Baltimore, Williams and Wilkins Company, 1951.
3. Tomcsik, J. Proc. Soc. Exper. Biol. & Med., 24:812, 1927.

4. Dale, H. H., and Laidlaw, P. P.   J. Physiol., 41:318, 1910.
5. Abel, J. J., and Kubota, S.   J. Pharmacol. & Exper. Therap., 13:243, 1919.
6. Best, C. H., Dale, H. H., Dudley, H. W., and Thorpe, W. V.   J. Physiol., 62:397, 1927.
7. Lewis, T.   The Blood Vessels of the Human Skin and their Responses, London, Shaw and Sons, Ltd., 1927.
8a. Dragstedt, C. A.   J. Allergy, 16:69, 1945.
  b. Code, C. F.   Am. J. Physiol., 127:78, 1939.
9. Katz, G.   Science, 91:221, 1940.
10. Feldberg, W., and Kellaway, C. H.   J. Physiol., 90:257, 1937.
11. Roche e Silva, M.   J. Immunol., 40:399, 1941.
12. Ungar, G., and Mist, S. H.   J. Exper. Med., 90:39, 1949.
13. Dragstedt, C. A.   Physiol. Rev., 21:563, 1941.
14. Ackermann, D., and Wasmuch, W.   Ztschr. f. physiol. Chem., 259:28, 1939.
15. Kellaway, C. H., and Trethewie, E. R.   Quart. J. Exper. Physiol., 30:121, 1940.
16. Code, C. F., and Hester, H. R.   Am. J. Physiol., 127:71, 1939.
17. Rose, B., Rusted, I., and Fownes, A.   J. Clin. Investigation, 29:113, 1950.
18a. ———— Ann. Rev. Med., 2:155, 1951.
  b. Roche e Silva, M.   J. Allergy, 15:399, 1944.
19a. Waters, E. T., Markowitz, J., and Jaques, L. B.   Science, 87:582, 1938.
  b. Schultz, E. W.   Proc. Soc. Exper. Biol. & Med., 22:343, 1925.
  c. Krueger, A. P., and Schultz, E. W.   Proc. Soc. Exper. Biol. & Med., 22:153, 1925.
20a. Campbell, D. H., and Nicoll, P. A.   J. Immunol., 39:103, 1940.
  b. Rose, B.   Am. J. Med., 3:545, 1947.
  c. Fox, C. L., Jr., Nelson, C. T., and Freeman, E. B.   Federation Proc., 10:408, 1951.
  d. Kinsell, L. W., Kopeloff, L. M., Zwemer, R. L., and Kopeloff, N.   J. Immunol., 42:35, 1941.
  e. Herschfus, J. A., Rubitsky, H. J., Beakey, J. F., Bresnick, E., Levinson, L., and Segal, M. S.   Internat. Arch. Allergy and Applied Immunol., 2:97, 1951.
21. Arthus, M.   Compt. rend. Soc. de biol., 55:817, 1903.
22. Rich, A. R.   Harvey Lect., 42:106, 1947.
23. Seegal, I., Seegal, B. C., and Jost, E. L.   J. Exper. Med., 55: 155, 163, 1932.
24a. Gatewood, W. E., and Baldridge, C. W.   J.A.M.A., 88:1068, 1927.
  b. Tumpeer, I. H., and Cope, E. J.   Am. J. Dis. Child., 45:343, 1933.
  c. Ross, F. E.   J.A.M.A., 103:563, 1934.
25a. Opie, E. L.   J. Immunol., 9:231, 1924.
  b. Culbertson, J. T.   J. Immunol., 29:29, 1935.
  c. Cannon, P. R., and Marshall, C. E.   J. Immunol., 40:127, 1941.
  d. Fischel, E. E., and Kabat, E. A.   J. Immunol., 55:337, 1947.
26a. Seibert, F. B.   J. Infect. Dis., 51:383, 1932.
  b. Kahn, R. L.   J. Immunol., 25:307, 1933.
  c. Grove, E. F.   J. Immunol., 23:101, 1932.
27a. Kabat, E. A., and Benacerraf, B.   J. Immunol., 62:97, 1949.
  b. Benacerraf, B., and Kabat, E. A.   J. Immunol., 64:1, 1950.
28. Abell, R. G., and Schenck, H. P.   J. Immunol., 34:195, 1938.
29a. Holley, S. W.   Am. J. Path., 11:937, 1935.
  b. Rich, A. R., and Follis, H. R., Jr.   Bull. Johns Hopkins Hosp., 66:106, 1940.
  c. Aronson, J. D.   J. Exper. Med., 54:387, 1931; J. Immunol., 25:1, 1933.
  d. Rich, A. R., and Lewis, M. R.   Proc. Soc. Exper. Biol. & Med., 25:596, 1927-28.
  e. Moen, J. K., and Swift, H. F.   J. Exper. Med., 64:339, 1936.
  f. Raffel, S., Arnaud, L. E., Dukes, C. D., and Huang, J. E.   J. Exper. Med., 90:53, 1949.
30. Opie, E. L.   J. Immunol., 9:247, 1924.
31. Zinsser, H.   J. Exper. Med., 34:495, 1921.
32a. Chase, M. W.   J. Exper. Med., 86:489, 1947.
  b. ———— in Bacterial and Mycotic Infections of Man, edited by Dubos, R., Philadelphia, J. B. Lippincott Co., 1948.
33. Wells, H. G.   The Chemical Aspects of Immunity, New York, Chemical Catalog Co., 1925.

34. Tomcsik, J.   Proc. Soc. Exper. Biol. & Med., 24:812, 1927.
35. Rosenau, M. J., and Anderson, J. F.   U. S. Pub. Health Service, Hyg. Lab. Bull.,
       No. 29, 1906; No. 45, 1908; No. 50, 1909.
36a. Grove, E. F.   J. Immunol., 23:101, 1932.
  b. Jackson, C.   J. Immunol., 28:225, 1935.
37a. Coca, A. F.   J. Immunol., 4:219, 1919.
  b. Mikulicich, G.   J. Allergy, 22:249, 1951.
  c. Cohen, S. G., Franke, F. R., and Karlson, E. L.   J. Allergy, 22:160, 1951.
38. Manwaring, W. H.   Ztschr. f. Immunitätsforsch. u. exper. Therap., 8:1, 1911.
39. Waters, E. T., and Markowitz, J.   Am. J. Physiol., 130:379, 1940.
40. Code, C. F.   Am. J. Physiol., 127:78, 1939.
41a. Manwaring, W. H., Chilcote, R. C., and Hosepian, V. M.   J.A.M.A., 80:303, 1923.
  b. Schultz, E. W., and Newnan, G.   Proc. Soc. Exper. Biol. & Med., 23:151, 1925.
42a. Kojis, F. G.   Am. J. Dis. Child., 64:93, 313, 1942.
  b. Ratner, B.   Allergy, Anaphylaxis, and Immunotherapy, Baltimore, Williams and
       Wilkins Company, 1943.
43a. Longcope, W. T.   Am. J. M. Sc., 152:625, 1916; Medicine, 22:351, 1943.
  b. Karelitz, S., and Glorig, A.   J. Immunol., 47:121, 1943.
  c. ——— Ann. New York Acad. Sc., 50:705, 1949.
44a. Fleisher, M. S., and Jones, L.   J. Exper. Med., 54:597, 1931.
  b. Kellett, C. G.   J. Path. & Bact., 33:981, 1930.
45. Gerlach, W.   Virchows Arch. f. path. Anat., 247:294, 1923.
46. Hochwald, A., and Rackemann, F. M.   J. Immunol., 53:355, 1946.
47a. Weiser, R. S., Golub, O. J., and Hamre, D. M.   J. Infect. Dis., 68:97, 1941.
  b. McMaster, P. D., and Kruse, H.   J. Exper. Med., 89:583, 1949.
  c. Kopeloff, N., Davidoff, L. M., and Kopeloff, L. M.   J. Immunol., 30:477, 1936.
  d. Code, C. F., and Hester, H. R.   Am. J. Physiol., 127:71, 1939.
  e. King, J. W., and Dreyer, N. B.   Science, 109:568, 1949.
48a. Kabat, E. A., and Landow, H.   J. Immunol., 44:69, 1942.
  b. ——— and Boldt, M. H.   J. Immunol., 48:181, 1944.
49a. Dean, H. R., Williamson, R., and Taylor, G. L.   J. Hyg., 36:570, 1936.
  b. Kellett, C. E.   J. Path. & Bact., 41:479, 1935.
50a. Bailey, G. H., Raffel, S., and Dingle, J. H.   Am. J. Hyg., 25:381, 1937.
  b. ——— and Raffel, S.   J. Immunol., 33:75, 1937.
51. Goodner, K., and Horsfall, F. L., Jr.   J. Immunol., 33:259, 1937.
52. Karsner, H. T., and Ecker, E. E.   J. Infect. Dis., 30:333, 1922.
53. Bronfenbrenner, J.   J. Lab. & Clin. Med., 26:102, 1940.
54a. Weil, R.   J. Med. Res., 27:497, 1913.
  b. ——— and Coca, A. F.   Ztschr. f. Immunitätsforsch. u. exper. Therap., 17:141,
       1913.
55. Dale, H. H., and Kellaway, C. H.   J. Physiol., 54: (Proceedings) 143, 1921.
56a. Morris, M. C.   J. Exper. Med., 64:641, 657, 1936.
  b. Kabat, E. A., Coffin, G. S., and Smith, D. J.   J. Immunol., 56:377, 1947.
57. Bronfenbrenner, J.   J. Allergy, 19:71, 1948.
58. Schultz, W. H.   J. Pharmacol. & Exper. Therap., 1:549, 1910.
59. Freund, J., and Whitney, C. E.   J. Immunol., 15:369, 1928.
60. Grove, E. F.   J. Immunol., 23:125, 1932.
61. Kopeloff, L. M., and Kopeloff, N.   J. Immunol., 36:83, 1939.
62. Warren, S., and Dixon, F. J.   Am. J. M. Sc., 216:136, 1948.
63. Kabat, E. A., and Benacerraf, B.   J. Immunol., 62:97, 1949.
64. Coca, A. F., and Cooke, R. A.   J. Immunol., 8:163, 1923.
65. Cooke, R. A., Editor, Allergy in Theory and Practice, Philadelphia, W. B. Saunders
       Co., 1947, Chapter 13.
66. Hill, L. W.   J. Allergy, 18:60, 181, 1947.
67a. Phillips, J. McI.   J.A.M.A., 78:497, 1922.
  b. Burns, P. W.   J. Am. Vet. M. A., 83:627, 1933.
  c. Pomeroy, B. S.   Cornell Vet., 24:335, 1934.
  d. Wittich, F. W.   J. Allergy, 12:247, 1941.
  e. Moreno, G. R., and Bentolila, L.   Ann. Allergy, 3:1, 1945.
  f. Cortez, J., Brunner, M., and Altman, I.   J. Allergy, 18:305, 1947.

g. Wittich, F. W.   Somatic and Psychiatric Treatment of Asthma, ed. by H. A. Abramson, Baltimore, Williams and Wilkins Co., 1951, Chap. 5.
68. Alexander, H. L., Becke, W. G., and Holmes, J. A.   J. Immunol., 11:175, 1926.
69a. Caulfield, A. H. W., Brown, M. H., and Waters, E. T.   J. Allergy, 7:451, 1936.
  b. Eagle, H., Arbesman, C. E., and Winkenwerder, W.   J. Immunol., 36:425, 1939.
70a. Donnally, H.   J. Immunol., 19:15, 1930.
  b. Cooke, R. A., and Vander Veer, A., Jr.   J. Immunol., 1:201, 1916.
71a. Lewis, P. A., and Loomis, D.   J. Exper. Med., 41:327, 1925; 47:449, 1928.
  b. Lurie, M. B.   Proc. Soc. Exper. Biol. & Med., 39:181, 1938.
72a. Rackemann, F. M., Simon, F. A., Simon, M. G., and Scully, M. A.   J. Allergy, 4:498, 1933.
  b. Kuhns, W. J., Lawrence, H. S., and Pappenheimer, A. M., Jr.   Federation Proc., 10:413, 1951.
  c. Creger, W. P., Choy, S. H., and Rantz, L. A.   J. Immunol., 66:445, 1951.
73. Simon, F. A.   Ann. Int. Med., 12:178, 1938.
74a. Prausnitz, C., and Küstner, H.   Centralbl. f. Bakt., 86:160, 1921.
  b. Heidelberger, M., in Allergy in Theory and Practice, edited by Cooke, R. A., Philadelphia, W. B. Saunders Co., 1947, Chapter 5.
  c. Miller, H., and Campbell, D. H.   Ann. Allergy, 5:236, 1947.
  d. Cavelti, P. A.   J. Allergy, 21:532, 1950.
  e. Kallós, P., and Kallós-Deffner, L.   Internat. Arch. Allergy and Applied Immunol., 2:70, 1951.
75a. Sherman, W. B., Hampton, S. F., and Cooke, R. A.   J. Exper. Med., 72:611, 1940.
  b. Caulfield, A. H. W.   Tr. Am. Clin. & Climatol. A., 1937, p. 1.
76a. Walzer, M., Gray, I., Straus, H. W., and Livingston, S.   J. Immunol., 34:91, 1938.
  b. ———— J. Lab. & Clin. Med., 26:1867, 1941.
77. Loveless, M. H.   J. Immunol., 41:15, 1941.
78. Sherman, W. B., and Stull, A.   J. Allergy, 9:105, 1938.
79a. Caulfield, A. H. W., Brown, M. H., and Waters, E. T.   J. Lab. & Clin. Med., 22:657, 1937.
  b. Winkenwerder, W. L., Eagle, H., and Arbesman, C. E.   J. Immunol., 36:435, 1939.
  c. Weil, A. J., and Reddin, L., Jr.   J. Immunol., 47:345, 1943.
  d. Sherman, W. B., Menzel, A. E. O., and Seebohm, P. M.   J. Exper. Med., 92:191, 1950.
  e. ———— and Coulson, E. J.   Proc. Soc. Exper. Biol. & Med., 77:245, 1951.
80a. Cooke, R. A., and Spain, W. C.   Trans. Assoc. Am. Physicians, 42:330, 1927.
  b. Tuft, L., and Ramsdell, S. G.   J. Immunol., 16:411, 1929.
  c. Sherman, W. D., Cooke, R. A., Crepea, S. B., and Downing, L. M.   J. Allergy, 19:160, 1948.
81a. Rackemann, F. M., and Stevens, A. H.   J. Immunol., 13:389, 1927.
  b. Brunner, N.   J. Allergy, 3:521, 1932; 5:257, 1934.
  c. Davidson, A. G., Baron, B., and Walzer, M.   J. Allergy, 18:359, 1947.
82. Levine, P., and Coca, A. F.   J. Immunol., 11:449, 1926.
83. Cooke, R. A., Barnard, J. H., Hebold, S., and Stull, A.   J. Exper. Med., 62:733, 1935.
84a. Loveless, M. H.   J. Immunol., 47:165, 1943; Federation Proc., 5:250, 1946.
  b. ———— J. Immunol., 38:25, 1940.
85. Cooke, R. A., Loveless, M. H., and Stull, A.   J. Exper. Med., 66:689, 1937.
86. Cohen, M., and Nelson, T.   J. Immunol., 34:63, 1938.
87a. Cooke, R. A.   J. Allergy, 15:212, 1944.
  b. Alexander, H. L., Johnson, M. G., and Bukantz, S. C.   J. Allergy, 19:1, 1948.
88a. Walzer, M.   Ann. New York Acad. Sc., 50:743, 1949.
  b. Tuft, L.   J. Allergy, 9:390, 1938.
89. Rackemann, F. M.   J. Allergy, 15:249, 1944.
90a. Kallós, P., and Pagel, W.   Acta med. Scandinav., 91:292, 1937.
  b. Ratner, B.   Somatic and Psychiatric Treatment of Asthma, ed. by H. A. Abramson, Baltimore, Williams and Wilkins Co., 1951, Chap. 3.
91. Fries, J. H., and Zigmor, J.   Am. J. Dis. Child., 54:1239, 1937.
92. Gruber, G. B.   Virchows Arch. f. path. Anat., 258:441, 1925.
93a. Rich, A. R.   Bull. Johns Hopkins Hosp., 71:123, 1942.

b. ——— and Gregory, J. E.   Bull. Johns Hopkins Hosp., 72:65, 1943.

94a. Klinge, F., and Vaubel, E.   Virchows Arch. f. path. Anat., 281:701, 1931.

b. Rössle, R.   Verhandl. d. deutsch. path. Gesellsch, 26:189, 1931.

95. Clark, E., and Kaplan, B.   Arch. Path., 24:458, 1937.

96a. Gregory, J. E., and Rich, A. R.   Bull. Johns Hopkins Hosp., 78:1, 1946.

b. McKeown, E. F.   J. Path. & Bact., 59:547, 1947.

97a. Swift, H. F.   J.A.M.A., 92:2071, 1929.

b. Coburn, A. F.   The Factor of Infection in the Rheumatic State, Baltimore, Williams and Wilkins Co., 1931.

98. Rantz, L. A., Boisvert, P. J., and Spink, W. W.   Arch. Int. Med., 76:131, 1945.

99. Van Ravenswaay, A. C.   J.A.M.A., 126:486, 1944.

100. Cavelti, P. A.   Arch. Path., 44:13, 1947.

101. Murphy, G. E., and Swift, H. F.   J. Exper. Med., 89:687, 1949.

102a. Sokoloff, L., Wilens, S. L., and Bunim, J. J.   Am. J. Path., 27:157, 1951.

b. Fox, R. A., and Jones, L. R.   Proc. Soc. Exper. Biol. & Med., 55:294, 1944.

c. Hopps, H. C., and Wissler, R. W.   J. Lab. & Clin. Med., 31:939, 1946.

103. Hajos, K.   Ztschr. f. d. ges. exper. Med., 59:383, 389, 1928.

104a. Hills, A. G., Forsham, P. H., and Finch, C. A.   Blood, 3:755, 1948.

b. Spain, D. M., and Thalhimer, W.   Proc. Soc. Exper. Biol. & Med., 76:320, 1951.

105a. Phillips, F. S., Hopkins, F. H., and Freeman, M. L. H.   J. Immunol., 55:289, 1947.

b. Spurr, C. L.   Proc. Soc. Exper. Biol. & Med., 64:259, 1947.

106. Taliaferro, W. H., and Taliaferro, L. G.   J. Infect. Dis., 82:5, 1948.

107. Bukantz, S. C., Dammin, G. V., Wilson, K. S., Johnson, M. C., and Alexander, H. L.   Proc. Soc. Exper. Biol. & Med., 72:21, 1949.

108. Hench, P. S., Kendall, E. C., Slocumb, C. H., and Polley, H. F.   Proc. Staff Meet., Mayo Clin., 24:181, 1949; Arch. Int. Med., 85:545, 1950.

109a. Germuth, F. G., Jr., and Ottinger, B.   Proc. Soc. Exper. Biol. & Med., 74:815, 1950.

b. Fischell, E. E.   Bull. New York Acad. Med., 26:225, 1950.

110a. Berthrong, M., Rich, A. R., and Griffith, P. C.   Bull. Johns Hopkins Hosp., 86:131, 1950.

b. Rich, A. R., Berthrong, M., and Bennett, I. L., Jr.   Bull. Johns Hopkins Hosp., 87:549, 1950.

111a. Finland, M., Kass, E. H., and Engbar, S. H.   Proc. 1st Clinical ACTH Conference, Philadelphia, Blakiston Co., 1950.

b. Mirick, G. S.   J. Clin. Invest., 29:836, 1950.

112a. Leger, J., Leith, W., and Rose, B.   Proc. Soc. Exper. Biol. & Med., 69:465, 1948.

b. Friedlander, S., and Friedlander, A. S.   J. Allergy, 21:303, 1950.

c. Harris, S., and Harris, T. N.   Proc. Soc. Exper. Biol. & Med., 74:186, 1950.

d. Dworetsky, M., Code, C. F., and Higgins, G. M.   Proc. Soc. Exper. Biol. & Med., 75:201, 1950.

e. Malkiel, S.   J. Immunol., 66:379, 1951.

113. Fox, C. L., Jr., Nelson, C. T., and Freeman, E. B.   Federation Proc., 10:408, 1951.

114a. Stollerman, G. H., Rubin, S. J., and Plotz, C. M.   Proc. Soc. Exper. Biol. & Med., 76:261, 1951.

b. Feinberg, S. E., Dannenberg, T. B., and Malkiel, S.   J. Allergy, 22:195, 1951.

c. Cooke, R. A., Sherman, W. B., Menzel, E. O., Chapin, H. B., Howell, C. M., Scott, R. B., Myers, P. A., and Downing, L. M.   J. Allergy, 22:211, 1951.

115. Rose, B.   1st Clinical ACTH Conference, Philadelphia, Blakiston Co., 1950.

116. Germuth, F. G., Jr., Medzel, G. A., Ottinger, B., and Oyama, J.   Proc. Soc. Exper. Biol. & Med., 76:177, 1951.

117a. Moyer, A. W., Jervis, G. A., Black, J., Koprowski, H., and Cox, H. R.   Proc. Soc. Exper. Biol. & Med., 75:387, 1950.

b. Kabat, E. A., Wolf, A., and Bezer, A. E., 1951, Federation Proc., 10:412, 1951.

c. Kallós, P.   Progress in Allergy, 3:1, 1952.

118. Fischel, E. E., Stoerk, H. C., and Bjørneboe, M.   Federation Proc., 10:408, 1951.

119. Soffer, L. J., Shwartzman, G., Schneierson, S. S., and Gabrilove, J. L.   Science, 111:303, 1950.

120. Layton, L. L.   Proc. Soc. Exper. Biol. & Med., 76:596, 1951.

121. Ingle, D. J. J. Clin. Endocrinol., 10:1312, 1950.
122. Selye, H. Ann. Rev. Med., 2:327, 1951.
123. Derick, C. L., Hitchcock, C. H., and Swift, H. F., 1928, J. Clin. Investigation, 5:427, 1928.
124a. Sullivan, C. J., Parker, T. W., and Hibbert, R. W. Proc. Soc. Exper. Biol. & Med., 67:508, 1948.
  b. Smull, K., Wissler, R. W., and Watson, J. M. J. Lab. & Clin. Med., 33:936, 1948.
125. Campbell, B. Science, 108:478, 1948.
126. Good, R. A., Campbell, B., and Good, T. A. Proc. Soc. Exper. Biol. & Med., 72:341, 1949.
127. Swift, H. F. J. Exper. Med., 36:735, 1922.
128a. Homburger, F. Proc. Soc. Exper. Biol. & Med., 61:101, 1946.
  b. Jager, B. V., and Nickerson, M. Am. J. Med., 3:408, 1947.
  c. Rantz, L. A., Boisvert, P. J., and Spink, W. W. Science, 103:352, 1946.
129. Coburn, A. F., and Kapp, E. M. J. Exper. Med., 77:173, 1943.
130a. Forman, C., Seifter, J., and Ehrich, W. E. J. Allergy, 20:273, 1949.
  b. Dammin, G. J., and Bukantz, S. C. J.A.M.A., 139:358, 1949.
  c. Smith, W., and Humphrey, J. H. Brit. J. Exper. Path., 30:560, 1949.
131. Best, C. H., and McHenry, E. W. J. Physiol., 70:349, 1930.
132. ——— and McHenry, E. W. Canad. M. A. J., 43:163, 1940.
133. Cooke, R. A. Allergy in Theory and Practice, Philadelphia, W. B. Saunders Co., 1947, Chapter 1.
134. Fell, N., Rodney, G., and Marshall, D. E. J. Immunol., 47:237, 1943.
135. Feinberg, S. M. J.A.M.A., 132:703, 1946.
136a. Fourneau, E., and Bovet, D. Arch. internat. de pharmacodyn. et de thérap., 46:178, 1933.
  b. Staub, A. M., and Bovet, D. Compt. rend. Soc. de biol., 125:818, 1937.
137. Loew, E. R., MacMillan, R., and Kaiser, M. E. J. Pharmacol. and Exper. Therap., 86:229, 1946.
138. Halpern, B. N. J. Allergy, 18:263, 1947.
139a. Dreisbach, R. H. J. Allergy, 18:397, 1947.
  b. Fischel, E. E. Proc. Soc. Exper. Biol. & Med., 66:537, 1947.
  c. Forman, F., Mertens, E., Graub, M., and Ehrich, W. Proc. Soc. Exper. Biol. & Med., 72:439, 1949.
140. Kyser, F. A., McCarter, J. C., and Stengel, J. J. Lab. & Clin. Med., 32:379, 1947.
141. Doerr, R. Ztschr. f. Hyg. u. Infektionskr., 118:623, 1936.
142. Fox, R. A., and Jones, L. R. Proc. Soc. Exper. Biol. & Med., 55:294, 1944.
143. Moss, J. N., Beiler, J. M., and Martin, G. J. Science, 112:16, 1950.

GENERAL REFERENCES

Dale, H. Brit. M. J., August 1948, p. 281.
Burnet, F. M. M. J. Australia, 1:29, 1948.
Urbach, E., and Gottlieb, P. M. Allergy, New York, Grune and Stratton, 1946.
Ratner, B. Allergy, Anaphylaxis and Immunotherapy, Baltimore, Williams and Wilkins Co., 1943.
Cooke, R. A., and contributors. Allergy in Theory and Practice, Philadelphia, W. B. Saunders Co., 1947.
Rich, A. R. The Pathogenesis of Tuberculosis, Springfield, Ill., Charles C Thomas Co., 1944.

14

DELAYED HYPERSENSITIVITIES

The delayed form of hypersensitivity differs from the immediate in several important respects. Certain of the circumstances and characteristics relating to **induction of the state** as well as to the **nature of the body's reactivity** are strikingly different from those described for the immediate hypersensitivities.

With respect to **induction**, certain conditions are essential for the establishment of delayed hypersensitivity which are not necessary for the immediate. In the case of infectious agents these conditions require the presence in the tissues either of the organism or of certain derivatives of it in addition to the responsible antigen alone. In the case of chemical substances, sensitization must be mediated through the skin, with few exceptions. These requirements are better discussed in relation to the categories of delayed hypersensitivity to be taken up later in this chapter.

With respect to **nature of reactivity**, there are several distinctions to be made.

1. A comparatively lengthy period intervenes in the hypersensitive individual between contact with antigen and the onset of local or systemic effects. No observable reaction occurs for several hours or longer, after which the response becomes progressively more severe, usually reaches a peak at 24 to 72 hours, and may persist for several days.

2. Humoral antibody related to the sensitive state cannot be demonstrated by the transfer of the hypersensitive state to normal recipients. It is a warrantable generalization that the cells of the animal with delayed hypersensitivity are directly vulnerable to antigen without the intermediation of humoral antibody or of any histamine-like substance.

3. There are no specific shock tissues in the nature of smooth muscle, blood vessels and collagen such as are concerned in the immediate reactions. Cells of the body generally are subject to injury by exposure to antigen. In some instances it seems probable that not all cells are so affected; a particular tissue, such as the skin, may alone respond, but again it is not those tissues concerned in immediate hypersensitive responses.

In addition to these differential characteristics which will be remarked upon more fully under mechanisms, the independence of the two forms of response is indicated by the fact that one can be abolished while the other remains intact. Anaphylactic as well as delayed responsiveness may be simultaneously induced by the use of proper antigens and conditions, and it is possible to desensitize to anaphylaxis while leaving delayed hypersensitivity still active (1).

All these differences, and especially the complete lack of relationship of humoral antibody to the delayed allergic state, might suggest some basis other than an immunologic one for this kind of reactivity. Its immunologic essence, however, is indicated by the following considerations (2):

1. An antigenic stimulus is necessary for the induction of the hypersensitive state.

2. In the sensitive subject a reaction occurs only on exposure to the specific inciting antigen.

3. The induction period of a week to 10 days for the establishment of hypersensitivity is of the same order as for other immunologic responses.

4. An anamnestic reaction occurs here as in the case of humoral antibody production. After delayed hypersensitivity has waned, administration of the responsible antigen causes a resurgence after a much shorter interval than was necessary for the original induction.

5. Desensitization can be effected.

DELAYED HYPERSENSITIVITY IN INFECTIOUS PROCESSES. Delayed allergy is a characteristic response of the body in various infections as well as following exposure to certain plants and chemical substances. The hypersensitivity of infection is especially striking in some of the chronic bacterial diseases. Tuberculosis is pre-eminent in this regard in that the sensitive state is not only easily demonstrable by appropriate skin tests with antigenic material, but also because the tissue injury and destruction which ensues from this reactivity play a considerable part in the pathogenesis of the disease. Delayed hypersensitivity is also demonstrable in undulant fever, typhoid fever, tularemia, glanders, chancroid and whooping cough, among the bacterial diseases. Although it is not ordinarily considered in relation to the more acute infectious diseases, this allergic state can be demonstrated following infections with the pneumococcus (3), the streptococcus (4) and other bacteria (5) by means of skin tests with the respective proteins of these organisms. It is perhaps safe to say that a study of any bacterial infection from this standpoint would disclose a very general existence of this form of hypersensitive response (6). Interestingly, in all those cases where the chemical nature of the bacterial component responsible for this reactive state has been revealed, this has been protein. It is difficult to imagine why other antigenic factors in microorganisms do not serve as stimuli for this form of allergic response.

Among the fungal diseases this kind of response appears also to be ubiquitous. The systemic infection caused by *Coccidioides immitis* is accompanied by pronounced delayed reactivity and, as in the case of tuberculosis, the pathogenesis of the progressive disease may be rooted in the destructive effects of the hypersensitive reaction upon tissue cells. Similar reactivity occurs in other systemic fungal diseases such as sporotrichosis, blastomycosis and aspergillosis. This is true as well of the superficial cutaneous infections in which phytid reactions (vesicular dermatitis) may occur in areas at a distance from the actual locus of infection as a hypersensitive manifestation dependent upon constituents of the fungus conveyed by the blood stream (7, 13).

Viral diseases also result in delayed hypersensitivity. A classic instance is that provided by the response of human beings to revaccination with vaccinia virus. There is in this case an accelerated reaction marked by the occurrence of erythematous papules about 24 hours after inoculation; this is in contrast to the slow development of an inflammatory response after three or four days in the newly vaccinated subject (8). In lymphogranuloma venereum (9) a high degree of delayed hypersensitivity develops, and in its more advanced stages this infection is accompanied by considerable tissue destruction. In mumps also recent experimental work in human beings and animals has revealed that delayed reactivity occurs and may serve as a basis for diagnosis of past or current infection (10). There is evidence that a similar allergic state exists as the result of infection with influenza, measles and herpes simplex viruses (11). It seems likely here, as in the bacterial diseases, that continued investigations will reveal a wide-spread occurrence of this form of reactivity, probably in all infections caused by viruses.

The most infamous of the spirochetal diseases, syphilis, induces delayed hypersensitivity in infected individuals (12). Finally, delayed allergy is known to occur in certain diseases of helminthic origin. In many of these infestations the immediate form of hypersensitivity alone seems to become apparent, but in echinococcus disease, for example, the same individual may respond to a skin test with an immediate urticarial reaction and a later indurated delayed type of response. On the other hand, one or the other form of hypersensitivity may be present exclusively (13).

Infectious hypersensitivity is not obviously influenced in its **qualitative** aspects at least by genetic factors. Practically speaking everyone can become sensitized to these agents with sufficient exposure. There are only infrequent exceptions to this, exemplified by Mascher's recent report of 11 patients with tuberculosis, none of whom responded to tests with tuberculin (14). That heritable **quantitative** differences in level of reactivity occur, however, has been appreciated for many years; Negroes, for example, generally develop more intense reactivity to tuberculin than do Caucasians (2). A study from Denmark has recently revealed familial differences in capacity to develop tuberculin sensitivity following BCG vaccination (15). Wide fluctuations in degree of tuberculin reactivity in the same individual from time to time have also long been appreciated (16).

DELAYED HYPERSENSITIVITY IN NONINFECTIOUS PROCESSES. DERMATITIS VENENATA. Sensitization of the delayed type may result from contact with a variety of plants and chemical substances. The induction of sensitivity occurs ordinarily through the skin, and subsequent contact with the inciting agent is followed by skin lesions. In the sensitized individual, the dermatitis resulting from contact may begin to appear within a day, evolving as papular and vesicular lesions with later oozing, crusting and desquamation, all during a period of a week or 10 days (17).

The plant substances most commonly concerned in this form of hypersensitiveness are poison oak, poison ivy, poison sumac, and primrose. Cotton seed may sensitize in a similar fashion; this occurs usually in dock workers who transport the seed. An interesting instance of similar sensitivity is that caused by the laundry marking ink used especially in India and prepared from the nut of the ral tree. Dermatitis may occur on the back of the neck as a result of the marking of shirt collars; this is referred to as dhobie itch. For a long time considered a virus disease, it was recently shown to be the result of sensitization to the plant extract.

Many drugs and chemical substances, including such elements as nickel or mercury, may produce similar contact forms of hypersensitivity. Although sensitization to drugs injected or ingested may take an immediate form, this is very infrequently the case when sensitivity has been incurred through skin contact. Subsequent exposure to the drug by contact, or sometimes by ingestion, then generally results in a dermatitis with the characteristics of the delayed reaction. An interesting example of this is seen following the application of penicillin and other chemotherapeutic and antibiotic agents to the skin and mucous membranes. The incidence of sensitization to penicillin as the result of this form of therapy has been reported to be as high as 10 to 15 per cent. The delayed contact sensitivity which results from topical application of penicillin shows manifestations very similar to those seen in poison oak or ivy dermatitis (18).

The ability of the simpler chemical substances to function as antigenic incitants of the hypersensitive state leads back to the viewpoint, expressed in an earlier chapter, that these may combine with proteins of the host to become complete antigens. This theory is fully discussed by Landsteiner (19) and others (20).

It seems unlikely that a single pattern will suffice to explain all these forms of delayed hypersensitivity in their various details, but certainly all have basic features in common and it is probable that the fundamental issues involved in sensitization to chemical substances and in the hypersensitivity of infection are similar. Evidence for this view will be discussed later.

The question of predisposition to contact sensitization cannot be dealt with so straightforwardly as it can in the case of the infectious hypersensitivities. To some substances everyone can apparently develop contact reactivity; primula extract is one such substance (21). But most other sensitizing agents induce the reactive state only in a proportion of individuals to whom they are applied. The notorious poison ivy, for example, sensitizes about 75 per cent of individuals, and a chemical substance, orthoform, sensitizes 40 per cent (22). An hereditary factor is obvious as in all other biologic phenomena, and has been segregated in guinea pigs by inbreeding, animals of low and high degrees of susceptibility to contact sensitization by chemical substances being established (23). This qualitative distinction between individuals susceptible or entirely insusceptible to contact sensitization by various substances is reminiscent of that seen in the atopic states, but there is no relationship between the two, i.e. contact sensitization may occur in atopic or nonatopic subjects with equal frequency (22). It is not known what constitutional factors determine liability to sensitization, nor why this distinction does not occur with respect to all sensitizing agents. Speculation on this point will be included in the discussion of factors responsible for the establishment of delayed sensitivity.

Manifestations of Delayed Hypersensitive Reactions. In **infectious allergy** responses may occur in a local area of tissue, or systemically, or both. At the site of injection of antigen into the skin, or in a focal lesion where an aggregation of bacteria is present, cells undergo varying degrees of damage depending upon the level of hypersensitivity and the local concentration of antigenic material. The reaction is accompanied by inflammation, which may be violent. Certain diseases, of which tuberculosis is a prime example, may be accompanied by reactions so serious to the integrity of the tissues as to determine to a large extent the pathogenesis of the disease process (2). The tissues involved in a local pulmonary lesion may undergo allergic necrosis and eventually a cavity forms. This enlarges by progressive radial cellular destruction. During this process the erosion of blood vessels and bronchi may permit bacteria and caseous debris to enter the blood stream or a major bronchus. From a bronchus such material may spill into a lower uninfected portion of the lung. When antigen in large quantity is suddenly deposited in a fresh area of sensitized tissue in this way, the intense allergic response takes the form of a tuberculous pneumonia.

Systemic reactions often accompany more severe local reactions, either during the course of infection as described, or as the result of the local injection of too large a diagnostic dose of antigen (tuberculin). Hypersensitive individuals working in laboratories have suffered severe systemic reactions as the result of inhalation of droplets of tuberculin during heat concentration, or of powdered bacillary substance. Such reactions begin three or four hours after contact with the antigen and are marked by fever, malaise, headache, and prostration. If active lesions are present, for instance in the lung, considerable inflammatory activity may occur in such areas. Reactions of this kind induced in experimental animals may be fatal within 8 to 72 hours, but pathologic examination reveals little in the way of specific changes to account for the severity of the symptoms or death.

Not all diseases marked by the occurrence of delayed allergy show such overt effects of antigenic activity upon the progress of the infection. In typhoid fever the rose spots which frequently appear upon the abdominal skin are hypersensitive responses to the local presence of bacilli, but these lesions never progress to necrosis. It may be, however, that the erosions of the intestinal wall in this disease are reflections of allergic tissue destruction. In brucellosis the hypersensitive state is sufficiently marked that a diagnostic skin test is based on its presence, yet descriptions of the pathologic changes in this disease indicate that little if any of its progress can be ascribed to allergic reactions in the tissues.

Plant and chemical **contact allergies** are ordinarily acquired via the skin rather than by a parenteral route. In illustration of this point, the application of penicillin preparations to skin or mucous membranes in general results in contact sensitivity to this drug. In contrast, parenteral injections of penicillin are apt to induce the serum sickness type of sensitivity, with no reactivity to subsequent contact but responsiveness to subsequent injection (24). It should be noted, however, that by employing special procedures the contact form of sensitization can be established by means of parenteral injection of antigens, as will be described in dealing with the factors responsible for these reactive states.

The lesion in contact sensitivity is usually a papular indurated one which later becomes vesicular. Intracutaneous injection of the responsible antigen may produce a lesion similar to the tuberculin reaction, and on the other hand, the tuberculous individual can respond to simple contact with tuberculin with a reaction resembling a patch of poison oak or ivy dermatitis. There is thus much in common between these hypersensitive manifestations, but it is true that in some instances of delayed sensitivity only contact reactions or only intracutaneous reactions can be elicited.

There is some question whether in ordinary contact types of hypersensitivity to plant and chemical substances there is reactivity of tissues other than the epidermis of the skin. It was stated earlier that contact dermatitis appears to be entirely cutaneous in that sensitization must occur through the skin, and subsequent responses are limited to this tissue. However, the first condition in this statement has been proved untenable as will be discussed later, and the second is in need of more adequate investigation by such methods as explanting various visceral tissues, such as the spleen or bone marrow of sensitive animals and human beings, with observations of the reactivity of these cells to the plant and chemical antigens concerned. Cellular reactivity might be found to be more general than is supposed, as is suggested by Crepea and Cooke's success in transferring poison ivy sensitivity, established through skin applications, by the use of splenic cells (29b).

Mechanism of Delayed Hypersensitive Reactions. It was seen in the case of the Arthus reaction that local edema and erythema occur regularly, and that necrosis may eventuate if the reaction is sufficiently intense. Such local injury is due to the fact that the combination of antigen with antibody in the tissues damages blood vessels, and if the vascular damage is of sufficient degree ischemic necrosis ensues. The delayed type of reactivity may be marked by locally occurring cellular injury and death also, but in this case the response appears to result from the destructive activity of the antigen directly upon the sensitized cells with which it comes into contact. Humoral antibody is not concerned; convincing evidence has never come forth that such antibody has any relationship whatever to this reactivity. Further, there has been no demonstration of the occurrence here of an intermediary factor analogous to the H-substance found to be concerned in certain of the immediate forms of hypersensitivity. In line with this the consensus of evidence indicates that the antihistaminic drugs do not influence reactions of the contact or tuberculin type (17, 25) though this opinion is not unanimous (26).

Whether or not cellular antibodies may be involved in delayed reactivity is entirely speculative. It should be noted that though this sensitivity is not transferable by serum, it can be passed to normal recipients by means of cells. This finding was made some years ago by Bail (27) with respect to tuberculosis and has been reaffirmed more recently by Chase and others (28) in relation to the same disease as well as to contact chemical sensitivity (29). Cells of peritoneal exudates, lymph nodes, spleen, and the blood have been employed for this purpose.

The independence of delayed hypersensitivity from humoral antibody and specific shock tissues, and by these tokens its distinction from the immediate forms of allergy, may be demonstrated in several ways. The failure of transfer to normal recipients by means of serum is in itself a partial demonstration. Factors may enter to invalidate this kind of negative evidence, however, since special and perhaps unknown conditions may be necessary for such transfer. This was the situation with regard to the transfer of atopic reactivity before 1921, when Prausnitz and Küstner (30) showed that the humoral substance involved in this instance could be revealed only by carrying it over to normal human skin; in this instance the receptive tissue is restricted. However, other and positive means are available for demonstrating the distinctiveness of delayed hypersensitivity, based upon the objective demonstration of the sensitivity of isolated cells and the independence of this sensitivity from the presence of humoral antibodies or of the particular tissues concerned in immediate responses. Some years ago it was found that the leukocytes of tuberculous animals are subject to injury or necrosis when placed in an environment containing tuberculin (31). Later Rich and Lewis, Aronson and others refined this observation by the use of tissue cultures (32). If a fragment of spleen or bone marrow from a tuberculous animal is grown in culture and exposed to the protein of the bacterium, cellular multiplication and migration is seen to cease after several hours, and subsequently the cells degenerate. Normal tissue growing in the presence of antibody against this protein does not become sensitized, as would a strip of smooth muscle for anaphylactic reactivity. In contrast, when similar cells from animals with immediate hypersensitivity are explanted and subjected to exposure to the responsible antigen, no observable reaction occurs, for in this case the reactive tissues—blood vessels or smooth muscle—are necessary and are of course not provided by the culture explant.

Such experiments have demonstrated then that in delayed hypersensitivity various cells of the body may be sensitive to antigen, that normal cells of the same kind do not become sensitized in the presence of humoral antibodies, and that cells from animals with anaphylactic sensitivity fail to respond to antigen in this same way. These points are illustrated in Figures 42 to 44.

The bone marrow fragment in Figure 42 was obtained from a tuberculous guinea pig and explanted into a plasma medium containing a small amount of tuberculin. After 48 hours most of the cells are seen to be necrotic. The marrow cells portrayed in Figure 43 were obtained from a normal guinea pig and placed into a medium consisting of plasma from a tuberculous animal (containing antiprotein antibodies), and again exposed to tuberculoprotein. The same period of exposure to antigen in this case has left the cells entirely uninjured. In Figure 44 the marrow tissue was derived from an animal with a high level of anaphylactic sensitivity to tuberculoprotein as a consequence of receiving injections of this substance. Again, 48 hours in the presence of the antigen has left these cells entirely unharmed. Similar findings have been made with the tissues of animals sensitized by another bacterium, the streptococcus (33).

Another method which contrasts the same basic characteristics of the delayed and immediate forms of reactivity is provided by the use of the cornea for injection of the test antigen. The cornea, possessing neither blood vessels nor smooth muscle, is not suitable for the demonstration of immediate reactivity even though the test animal be highly sensitized and antibodies in fluid from the limbus bathe this tissue. Once the cornea has been vascularized by the previous application of an irritant, however, a local Arthus reaction can be produced in this tissue. On the other hand, the injection of antigen into the nonvascularized cornea of an animal with delayed hypersensitivity results in injury or destruction of the corneal cells because of their intrinsic capacity to react to the sensitizing substance (34).

Congenital transmission of delayed hypersensitivity of either the infectious or contact type does not take place in man or animals (22, 35). It will be recalled that not all the immediate reactivities are so transmitted either; a notable exception is the atopic state (see page 217). Nor for that matter are all antibodies transferred through the placental tissues (see page 169). This point is therefore not one which is distinctive for the category of hypersensitive states presently being considered.

Desensitization in delayed hypersensitivity can be accomplished, though not so readily as in the case of the anaphylactic state. When anaphylactic and delayed reactivity coexist to the same antigenic substance they may be dissociated by desensitization; the immediate type yields first, leaving delayed reactivity intact. Further persistent treatment with antigen may eventually affect the delayed state also.

Factors Responsible for the Delayed Hypersensitive State. What may the factors be which determine whether the hypersensitive response of an individual partakes of the immediate or delayed character? In the same animal both types of reactivity may coexist to the same antigenic substance but, whereas the immediate form of hypersensitivity is in a sense the basic response to any antigen, the delayed form is found to occur only under more specialized conditions. For consideration of this question we shall take the classic example of delayed reactivity provided by tuberculous infection.

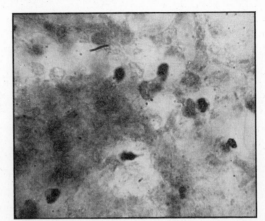

Fig. 42. Bone marrow culture from tuberculous guinea pig in the presence of tuberculin.

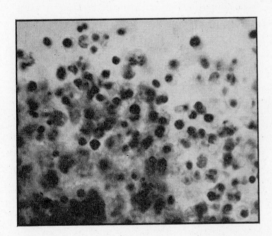

Fig. 43. Bone marrow culture from normal guinea pig in the presence of tuberculous plasma and tuberculin.

Fig. 44. Bone marrow from guinea pig anaphylactically sensitive to tuberculoprotein, in the presence of tuberculin.

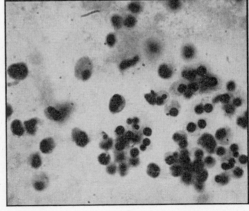
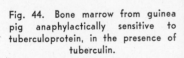

Within two weeks more or less of the entrance of tubercle bacilli into the tissues the body undergoes a change in reactivity to these organisms so that on subsequent contact there occurs an inflammatory response of much greater degree than that which follows the initial lodgment of bacilli in normal tissues. This intensified response is called the Koch phenomenon. If the tissues are sufficiently sensitive and if enough bacilli are reintroduced, cells in the area undergo destruction and eventually the tissue sloughs. The same kind of response occurs also to the bacilli in the primary site once hypersensitivity has been attained, so that in a pulmonary focus, as has been described, necrosis of lung parenchyma may lead eventually to the formation of a cavity. This status of the tissues may be demonstrated by the intracutaneous injection of the **isolated protein** of the bacillus (36), a fact which gives us clear chemical evidence that allergic reactivity in tuberculosis is directed against a single purified component of the organism, and it follows as a basic tenet of immunologic specificity that this same constituent of the bacterial cell must also be responsible for **inducing** the hypersensitive state. This deduction is confounded, however, when one attempts to demonstrate it experimentally by sensitizing animals with isolated protein obtained from the organism. Repeated injection of this substance leads to the formation of humoral antibodies and to the induction of anaphylactic hypersensitivity, but there is no trace of sensitization of the tuberculin type. We are confronted then with the paradoxical situation of knowing the antigenic element of the tubercle bacillus which must cause delayed allergy without being able to reproduce this state by using it as the sensitizing agent. The induction of tuberculin sensitivity has in the past been accomplished in experimental animals only through initiating a tuberculous infection, or by injecting killed bacillary cells in relatively large quantities. Thus, it has appeared that the whole bacterial cell, living or dead, is an essential requirement for the establishment of this hypersensitivity.

In a study of this problem it was observed by the writer and his associates several years ago that if tubercle bacilli were thoroughly extracted with ether, alcohol and chloroform, and these extracted organisms were injected into guinea pigs, they failed to establish tuberculin sensitivity even if employed in very large doses over long periods of time (37). The proteins of the tubercle bacillus are remarkably hardy in standing up to various chemical and physical manipulations, and despite the use of organic solvents, the protein in these defatted cells was found to be antigenically intact, causing the appearance of antibodies as well as of anaphylactic sensitivity in the treated animals. It seemed apparent then that the failure of these defatted cells to provoke the tuberculin type of hypersensitivity was due not to the absence of the provocative (protein) antigen but depended upon the removal of some other ingredient of the cell by the lipoidal solvents. Consequently the extracted lipids were individually mixed with the defatted bacteria and injected into animals. It was found then that the chloroform-soluble substance, a wax-like lipid (38), restored the ability of these bacilli to induce tuberculin reactivity. In this mixture the bacillary bodies themselves acted merely as a source of protein antigen, for it was subsequently found that isolated tuberculoprotein could be employed with the wax to invoke the same reactivity of the tissues. In this combination it became evident that the protein is the responsible antigen, and that the waxy lipid (of which a lipopolysaccharide is the essential component (37c, 39)), possesses some nonantigenic function which causes the animal to respond to the protein along the channel which we know as delayed hypersensitivity. If another protein antigen, such as egg albumin, is substituted for tuberculoprotein, the simultaneous presence of bacillary wax in the tissues will cause hypersensitivity of the delayed type to this substance as well, so that this biological action of the lipid is a general one (34e).

It would be of utmost interest to know whether analagous chemical circumstances might determine the infectious hypersensitivities induced by other microbes and viruses. The writer and his co-workers are carrying on such studies, and at present it appears that a similar situation may exist in the case of a hemolytic streptococcus.

These findings have extended some degree of understanding also to the factors involved in the establishment of the contact reactivity induced by chemical compounds. As was stated earlier, such substances will ordinarily evoke this form of hypersensitivity only through contact with the integument. Parenteral injection of these chemicals induces only the anaphylactic form of hypersensitive responsiveness (17, 19, 22). It has been found, however, that if one such substance, picryl chloride, is injected parenterally into guinea pigs along with the waxy lipid previously described, these animals develop typical contact sensitivity as evidenced by the occurrence of dermatitis venenata on subsequent application of picryl chloride to the skin (1b).

In addition to indicating the importance of this type of lipid derived from an infectious agent in directing the form of the hypersensitive response in the animal body, this experiment suggests the possibility that the spontaneous occurrence of dermatitis venenata to other plant and chemical substances of noninfectious nature may be of necessity mediated through the skin because this tissue perhaps contains a lipid similar in its biological effects to that derived from the tubercle bacillus. Release of such an intracellular lipid as the result of primary irritation of the skin by the causative drug may explain the occurrence of this class of plant and drug sensitivities. Experimental evidence is being sought by the writer that a lipid with such biological properties may indeed occur as a constituent of normal human skin.

It seems evident then that in at least one case a lipoidal constituent of an infectious organism is concerned in the induction of the delayed hypersensitive state in the animal body, and it may be speculated that similar substances present in the cutaneous tissues of the body are perhaps concerned in establishing this type of hypersensitivity to simple chemical substances. The manner in which the lipoidal substance acts is not known. A striking result of the injection of the tubercle bacillary lipid into the tissues is the accumulation of epithelioid and Langhans' cells. Since this histologic response is so marked, it is tempting to attribute to this cellular array some function in the development of the particular form of hypersensitive reactions with which we are concerned. For several reasons, however, such a deduction seems unwarranted. Thus, another lipoidal substance (the phosphatide) derivable from the tubercle bacillus possesses marked histogenic properties of the same kind, yet it fails completely to engender delayed allergic responses to antigenic substances (37). Further, infectious hypersensitivity to various pyogenic bacteria occurs in the absence of such a cellular response. The question of intrinsic mechanism remains to be answered.

SUMMARY

Delayed hypersensitivity represents a category of hypersensitive states which are related to the immediate hypersensitivities in several basic immunologic respects, including dependence upon an antigenic stimulus, the requirement of a latent interval for development of the hypersensitive state, anamnesis when the antigenic stimulus is reapplied after hypersensitivity has waned, specificity of reactivity with respect to the responsible antigenic factor, and amenability to desensitizing procedures. The two categories differ markedly in certain other respects, however, including the circumstances necessary for their induction, and the mechanisms through which reactions occur.

Induction of delayed allergy in the case of the tubercle bacillus requires, in addition to an antigen of this organism, another nonantigenic component of lipoidal nature which determines this type of hypersensitive response. The induction of spontaneous delayed hypersensitivity to noninfectious substances requires that they act through skin or mucous membranes. However, the same lipid effective in determining delayed infectious allergy can also provoke the occurrence of contact sensitivity to simple chemical substances following parenteral injection. This suggests tentatively that the requirement that spontaneous contact sensitization be mediated through the skin is by reason of the skin supplying lipid of similar biological activity to that obtained from the tubercle bacillus.

Delayed reactivity of the body is independent of humoral antibodies, and apparently also of the release of H-substance. Delayed reactivity appears to be a general cellular one, not dependent upon responses of blood vessels or smooth muscle. Reactions of this kind may therefore occur in cultures of explanted cells, or in avascular tissue such as the cornea.

The intrinsic factors in the body which determine that this set of mechanisms come into play rather than, or in addition to, those concerned with immediate hypersensitivity, are not yet appreciated.

BIBLIOGRAPHY

1a. Landsteiner, K., and Chase, M. W. J. Exper. Med., 66:337, 1937.
  b. Raffel, S., and Forney, J. E. J. Exper. Med., 88:485, 1948.
2. Rich, A. R. The Pathogenesis of Tuberculosis, Springfield, Ill., Charles C Thomas Co., 1944.

3a. Tillett, W. S., and Francis, T., Jr. J. Exper. Med., 50:687, 1929; 52:573, 1930; 54:587, 1931.

b. Julianelle, L. A. J. Exper. Med., 51:643, 1930.

4a. Zinsser, H., and Grinnell, F. B. J. Immunol., 10:725, 1925.

b. Mackenzie, G. M., and Hanger, F. M., Jr. J. Immunol., 13:41, 1927.

c. Derick, C. L., and Swift, H. F. J. Exper. Med., 49:615, 1929.

5. Zinsser, H., and Parker, J. T. J. Exper. Med., 37:275, 1923.

6. Kane, L. W. New England J. Med., 232:728, 760, 1945.

7a. Henrici, A. T. Proc. Soc. Exper. Biol. & Med., 41: 349, 1939.

b. Sulzberger, M. B. Ann. New York Acad. Sc., 50:767, 1950.

8. Jenner, E. An Inquiry into the Causes and Effects of the Variolae Vaccinae, London, Sampson Low, 1798.

9. Frei, W. Klin. Whnschr., 4:2148, 1925.

10. Enders, J. F., Cohen, S., and Kane, L. W. J. Exper. Med., 81:119, 1945.

11. Rose, H. M., and Molloy, E. Federation Proc., 6:432, 1947.

12. Rich, A. R., Chesney, A. M., and Turner, T. B. Bull. Johns Hopkins Hosp., 52:179, 1933.

13a. Baer, R. L., and Yanowitz, M. Arch. Dermat. & Syph., 62:491, 1950.

b. Frisch, A. W., Whims, C. D., and Oppenheim, J. M. Am. J. Clin. Path., 17:16, 1947.

14. Mascher, W. Am. Rev. Tuberc., 63:501, 1951.

15. Palmer, C. E., and Meyer, S. N. Pub. Health Rep., 66:259, 1951.

16. Aronson, J. D. Am. Rev. Tuberc., 63:121, 1951.

17. Sulzberger, M. B. J. Allergy, 18:176, 1947.

18a. Markson, L. S. Arch. Dermat. & Syph., 52:384, 1945.

b. Friedlander, S., Watrous, R. M., and Feinberg, S. Arch. Dermat. & Syph., 54:517, 1946.

c. Goldman, L., and Feldman, M. D. J.A.M.A., 138:640, 1948.

19. Landsteiner, K. The Specificity of Serological Reactions, Cambridge, Mass., Harvard University Press, 1945.

20. Gell, P. G. H., Harington, C. R., and Rivers, R. P. Brit. J. Exper. Path., 27:267, 1946.

21. Bloch, B., and Steiner-Wourlisch, A. Arch. f. Dermat. u. Syph., 152:183, 1926.

22. Grolnick, M. Ann. New York Acad. Sc., 50:718, 1949.

23a. Landsteiner, K., and Chase, M. W. Proc. Internat. Cong. Microbiol., 4:772, 1940.

b. Chase, M. W. J. Exper. Med., 73:711, 1941.

24a. Chu., W. C., and Cutting, W. C. Proc. Soc. Exper. Biol. & Med., 63:347, 1946.

b. Peck, S. M., Siegal, S., Glick, A. W., Kurtin, A., and Bergamini, R. J.A.M.A., 138:631, 1948.

25a. Kreis, B. Ann. Inst. Pasteur, 72:308, 1946.

b. Birkeland, J. N., and Cornfeld, L. J. Bact., 54:82, 1947.

c. Friedman, E., and Silverman, I. Am. Rev. Tuberc., 61:442, 1950.

d. Hunter, D., Hude, L., and Davis, J. D. Am. Rev. Tuberc., 62:525, 1950.

e. Weiser, R. S., Evans, E., and St. Vincent, L. Proc. Soc. Exper. Biol. & Med., 73:303, 1950.

26a. Mayer, R. L. Ann. Allergy, 5:113, 1947.

b. Henderson, A. R. Am. Rev. Tuberc., 60:811, 1949.

c. Criep, L. H., Levine, M. I., and Aaron, T. H. Am. Rev. Tuberc., 59:701, 1949.

d. Graub, M., and Barrist, E. M. Am. Rev. Tuberc., 61:735, 1950.

27. Bail, O. Ztschr. Immunitätsforsch. u. exper. Therap., 4:470, 1910.

28a. Chase, M. W. Proc. Soc. Exper. Biol. & Med., 59:134, 1945.

b. Kirchheimer, W. F., and Weiser, R. S. Proc. Soc. Exper. Biol. & Med., 66:166, 1947.

c. Cummings, M. M., Hoyt, M., and Gottshall, R. Y. Pub. Health Rep., 62:994, 1947.

d. Laurence, H. S. Proc. Soc. Exper. Biol. & Med., 71:516, 1949.

e. Metaxas-Bühler, M. Internat. Arch. Allergy and Applied Immunol., 1:325, 1951.

29a. Landsteiner, K., and Chase, M. W. Proc. Soc. Exper. Biol. & Med., 49:688,1942.

b. Crepea, S. B., and Cooke, R. A. J. Allergy, 19:353, 1948.

30. Prausnitz, C., and Küstner, H. Centralbl. f. Bakt., 86:160, 1921.

31a. Holst, P. M.   Tubercle, 3:337, 1922.
   b. Stewart, F. W., Long, P. H., and Bradley, J. I.   Am. J. Path., 2:47, 1926.
32a. Rich, A. R., and Lewis, M. R.   Bull. Johns Hopkins Hosp., 50:115, 1932.
   b. Aronson, J. D.   J. Immunol., 25:1, 1933.
   c. Moen, J. K., and Swift, H. F.   J. Exper. Med., 64:339, 1936.
   d. Heilman, D. H., Feldman, W. H., and Mann, F. C.   Am. Rev. Tuberc., 50:344, 1944.
33. Moen, J. K.   J. Exper. Med., 64:355, 1936.
34a. Derick, C. L., and Swift, H. F.   J. Exper. Med., 49:615, 1929.
   b. Julianelle, L. A.   J. Exper. Med., 51:633, 643, 1930.
   c. Holley, S. W.   Am. J. Path., 11:937, 1935.
   d. Rich, A. R., and Follis, H. R., Jr.   Bull. Johns Hopkins Hosp., 66:106, 1940.
   e. Raffel, S., Arnaud, L. E., Dukes, C. D., and Huang, J. S.   J. Exper. Med., 90:53, 1949.
35. Kile, R. L., and Pepple, A. W.   J. Invest. Dermat., 1:59, 1938.
36a. Mueller, J. H.   J. Exper. Med., 43:1, 1926.
   b. Seibert, F. B., and Munday, B.   Am. Rev. Tuberc., 25:724, 1932.
   c. ——— Science, 63:619, 1926.
37a. Raffel, S.   Am. Rev. Tuberc., 54:564, 1946.
   b. ——— J. Infect. Dis., 82:267, 1948.
   c. ——— Experientia, 6:410, 1950.
38a. Crowder, J. A., Stodola, F. H., Pangborn, M. C., and Anderson, R. J.   J. Am. Chem. Soc., 58:636, 1936.
   b. Anderson, R. J.   J. Biol. Chem., 74:525, 1927; 83:505, 1929.
39. Choucroun, N.   Compt. rend. Acad. d. sc., 226:1477, 1948.

GENERAL REFERENCES

Sulzberger, M. B.   Dermatologic Allergy, Springfield, Ill., Charles C Thomas Co., 1940.
Cooke, R. A., and others.   Allergy in Theory and Practice, Philadelphia, W. B. Saunders Co., 1947.
Ratner, B.   Allergy, Anaphylaxis, and Immunotherapy, Baltimore, Williams and Wilkins Co., 1943.

15

RELATION OF HYPERSENSITIVITY TO IMMUNITY

We have already discussed in Chapter 10 the question of the protective value to the body of the allergic reaction in respect to infectious agents. A more elaborate consideration seems warranted now that the hypersensitive states have been considered in some detail. The question has remained a vexing one for half a century because of the difficulty of dissociating for individual assessment all the responses to an infectious microbe of which the body is capable.

It is often stated by those who believe the allergic reaction to be part of the defense mechanism that protection is afforded against invasion at the expense of local tissue damage. Such statements attempt to bridge the seeming paradox that this reaction which is on the one hand protective is on the other injurious. There is actually no paradox involved here so far as immunologic mechanisms are concerned, for we have seen that the reaction of antibody with antigen of the microbe may impede its progress as a pathogen (by agglutination, bacteriolysis, opsonization, virus neutralization); this is one aspect of an immunologic response. A second aspect may follow in which the tissues of the host are influenced by the result of the primary reaction, because of the liberation of an intoxicating substance such as histamine (a hypersensitive reaction of the immediate type) or possibly as the direct consequence of exposure of sensitized cells to antigen of the infectious agent (a delayed type of reaction).

There is then no theoretical objection to the viewpoint that the hypersensitive reaction may be protective while at the same time resulting in damage to host tissues, and we can proceed to examine the possibility that this may be the case.

If the hypersensitive reaction is protective against pathogenic organisms, on what basis could it serve the body in this respect? Two possible premises suggest themselves. One may be the fact of antibody-antigen union itself, since as we have seen the same antibody which inhibits the progress of a microbe in the tissues could be responsible for a hypersensitive reaction. The protective activity and the allergic reaction would then be parts of the same immunologic entity. A second possibility is nonspecific; that the hypersensitive reaction is followed by considerable local inflammation, and this might effectively localize and cause the destruction of foreign agents in the tissues. We can evaluate available evidence to find whether either of these possibilities is of actual consequence in acquired resistance to infection.

1. The possibility that protection is afforded by the same antibody-antigen combination which results in the hypersensitive reaction. A logical consideration of this point requires a return to the fundamental consideration that every infectious agent is a bundle of antigenic substances, all of them potential or actual stimulants of immunologic responses. When we deal with those instances among the bacteria where the evidence is sufficient for judgment, we know that one particular antibody directed against a single antigen in the organism constitutes the effective protective response. This is true of the capsular polysaccharide of the pneumococcus, of the capsular antigens of the hemolytic streptococci, and of the "Boivin complexes" of the enteric bacilli. Now it is necessary to inquire whether in any of these cases the immunologic response against these particular antigens of **the bacterial cell** is also involved in producing allergic reactions. In the case of the pneumococcus, for example, two distinct hypersensitive states may be demonstrated as the result of infection or vaccination, although neither is of importance to the pathogenesis of the infection caused by this organism. One hypersensitivity is of the immediate Arthus type and is directed against the capsular polysaccharide; a response may be elicited by injection of the specific polysaccharide into the skin (1). In this case it will be noted that the same antigen is involved in the induction of hypersensitivity as well as protective antibodies. In this instance therefore the antigen-antibody reaction which is protective may give rise also to a hypersensitive reaction (2). However, this is not the allergic reaction characteristically associated with either this or other infectious agents. It is the second type, the **delayed infectious** hypersensitive response, which has been called into question as affording protection to the body. This delayed allergic state is engendered by the nucleoprotein of the organism (1) and is not concerned in resistance to the pneumococcus since antibodies directed against the capsular polysaccharide constitute practically the whole story of immunity to this bacterium. This fact may be confirmed by the passive transfer of antipolysaccharide immune body to normal animals; the protection thereby conferred is entirely independent of any immunologic responsiveness to the protein. It is thus evident that in the case of this bacterium, of which the antigenic components and the immune responses are well known, the delayed hypersensitive reaction plays no part in the mechanism of acquired immunity.

If we turn to an infectious process in which the hypersensitive state is more striking, the best example is provided by tuberculosis. This disease has long been considered an instance in which the allergic status of the tissues may be important in resistance to subsequent reinfection (3). The introduction of bacilli into the skin of a previously infected subject results in allergic necrosis and subsequent sloughing of the area—the Koch phenomenon. Spectacular though this casting out of offending organisms is, it does not seem to be a basic feature of the resistance acquired against the tubercle bacillus as is evident from the following considerations. First, it is known that the protein of this microbe is responsible for the Koch type of hypersensitivity. As was discussed in the preceding chapter, purified protein of the organism may be employed with a nonantigenic lipoidal factor to induce this hypersensitive state in experimental animals. Such animals are found to be without resistance to subsequent test infection (4). Second, when animals have been vaccinated with BCG they acquire both resistance and hypersensitivity to the tubercle bacillus. Protracted injections of tuberculin can eventually abolish hypersensitivity, but such desensitized animals retain their acquired resistance (5). Thus, although we suffer the disadvantage of ignorance concerning the factor which actually is responsible for inducing resistance to this bacillus, we know that the antigen which causes hypersensitiveness is not responsible for it. This particular immunologic response seems to have no power whatever to interfere with the destiny of the tubercle bacillus in the tissues of the host. The allergic reactivity and the resistance which follow tuberculous infection, or vaccination with an attenuated organism such as BCG, are usually parallel but they are not identical phenomena (6).

2. The possible protective activity of the intensified inflammation consequent to the allergic reaction. This aspect of the question has been discussed to some extent in Chapter 2 with regard to the inflammatory reaction as an expression of native immunity. As the result of any local hypersensitive reaction, whether of the immediate or the delayed type, there occurs an inflammatory response which is more intense than that which would occur in normal tissues exposed to the same exciting agent.

The question is whether such exaggerated inflammatory responses can per se restrict the spread of infectious agents better than could a lesser degree of inflammation in the tissues of a host exposed to the agent for the first time. If the inflammation of re-exposure (i.e. allergic inflammation) does possess an exacerbated localizing potential then it should be considered a mechanism of acquired immunity, regardless of what antigen of the microbe is concerned in inducing this response.

It should first be reiterated that though the inflammatory reaction is generally helpful to the body in impeding the spread of microbes through the tissues, this is not necessarily the case. One of the protective attributes of inflammation is the rapid accumulation of phagocytic cells. Some microbes are not destroyed by these cells, however; they may reside in apparent harmony with the cell for long periods during which they can multiply and be transported to far areas of the body, there to set up foci of infection. In general, however, we know that inflammation is protective for the reasons which have been outlined in Chapter 2.

Granting this fact, is there any evidence that an intensified inflammation provides amplified protection which might account for acquired immunity? This has been considered to be the case by workers concerned especially with the basis for acquired resistance in tuberculosis (3). Careful pathologic studies, however, have failed to substantiate this viewpoint in the case of either the tubercle bacillus or other microorganisms. Thus, several workers have found that the introduction of *Pasteurella cuniculicida,* pneumococci and other bacteria into areas where exaggerated inflammatory reactions have then been induced, in hosts without immunity to these organisms, actually led to a more rapid spread than was the case in normal animals. In the first place, the spread of bacteria begins before even the accelerated inflammatory reaction can become mobilized, and secondly, the sweep of fluids through the tissues during the course of an intense reaction can spread bacteria with it (6a, 7). Thus, the violent inflammation which may attend the allergic reaction can vitiate the benefits which might be supplied by a milder response in non-hypersensitive tissues.

In résumé, the hypersensitive reaction could be of aid to the body in resisting an infectious agent if the specific antibody responsible for the allergic response were also the antibody effective in thwarting the progress of the organism, or if the intense inflammation occasioned by the hypersensitive reaction possessed increased powers to isolate and kill the agent at the portal in the tissues, or both.

The first possibility has not been substantiated in any instance among the bacterial diseases on which sufficient information exists to permit an opinion. The antibodies known to be associated with protection against such agents as the pneumococcus and the hemolytic streptococcus are able to give rise to the Arthus type of response following combination with antigen in the tissues, but this immediate form of hypersensitive reactivity is not the allergy of infection which has been regarded as the protective one. The latter delayed type of responsiveness is, in all cases so far investigated, an antiprotein response, and is not synonymous with the acquired protective reaction. This is not to say that such a possibility is precluded, since the considerations which have been dealt with must be worked out individually for each infectious process.

The second possibility does not seem warranted because the protective properties of the intense inflammatory response which follows the hypersensitive reaction is not more localizing, and may be less so, than the milder inflammation provoked by the same antigenic stimulus in normal tissues. (For a contrary opinion, see Menkin and Opie [8].)

At the present time, therefore, there exists no basis for regarding the hypersensitive reaction as part of the mechanism of resistance to infectious disease. On the contrary, it must be assessed as a liability in view of the damage which it may inflict upon the tissues of the host.

BIBLIOGRAPHY

1. Tillett, W. S., and Francis, T., Jr.   J. Exper. Med., 50:687, 1929.
2. Opie, E. L.   J. Immunol., 17:329, 1929.
3a. Krause, A. K.   Am. Rev. Tuberc., 14:271, 1926.
 b. Willis, H. S.   Am. Rev. Tuberc., 17:240, 1928.
4. Raffel, S.   J. Infect. Dis., 82:267, 1948; Experientia, 6:410, 1950.
5a. Rothschild, H., Friedenwald, J. S., and Bernstein, C.   Bull. Johns Hopkins Hosp., 54:232, 1934.

b. Willis, H. S., and Woodruff, C. E.   Am. J. Path., 14:337, 1938.

c. ———— Woodruff, C. E., Kelly, R. G., and Voldrich, M.   Am. Rev. Tuberc., 38:10, 1938.

6a. Rich, A. R.   Physiol. Rev., 21:70, 1941.

b. ———— The Pathogenesis of Tuberculosis, Springfield, Ill., Charles C Thomas Co., 1944.

7a. Hanger, F. M.   J. Exper. Med., 52:485, 1930.

b. Cannon, P. R., and Hartley, G., Jr.   Am. J. Path., 14:87, 1938.

c. ———— Physiol. Rev., 20:89, 1940.

d. Lurie, M. B.   J. Exper. Med., 63:923, 1936.

8a. Menkin, V.   Physiol. Rev., 18:366, 1938.

b. Opie, E. L.   Medicine, 15:489, 1936.

16

OTHER HYPERSENSITIVE AND HYPERSENSITIVE-LIKE STATES

The purposes of this chapter are several. First, to take up in greater detail hypersensitivity to drugs and foods in order to account for certain peculiarities which could not be adequately described in preceding chapters concerned with the basic aspects of the hypersensitive states. Second, to discuss idiosyncrasies to cold, light and other physical factors which are termed physical allergies. And finally, to describe certain syndromes producible in man and experimental animals which resemble hypersensitive reactions though they are not. These include the Shwartzman-Sanarelli phenomenon and anaphylactoid shock.

Drug Hypersensitivities. As has been said before, hypersensitivity to drugs and chemicals may be of immediate or delayed type. In the former case, induction generally comes about as the result of ingestion, injection, or inhalation of antigen; occasionally skin contact may also cause it. The manifestations of this hypersensitivity include respiratory difficulties, urticaria and rashes as well as periarteritis nodosa, lupus erythematosus and probably other systemic collagen diseases.

Delayed reactivity usually results from superficial cutaneous contact with drugs and chemicals, or from intradermal injection, i.e. the sensitization is characteristically mediated through the skin. Infrequently, however, it appears that deeper injection or ingestion may result in this kind of reactivity (1, 2). It is evident that these instances may also be due to skin contact, for deep injections may allow seepage into the skin and taking drugs by mouth requires preliminary handling. The manifestation of contact sensitivity consists of dermatitis upon subsequent exposure of the skin to the chemical involved, although the allergen may also affect the skin from within, i.e. if sensitization to a drug is acquired through contact, subsequent ingestion may precipitate typical contact dermatitis. Cooke (3) describes the example of a patient who became sensitized to mercury through handling it and subsequently developed dermatitis from ingestion of mercury-containing drugs.

Some of these conditions for induction of sensitivity may result in the simultaneous development of both immediate and delayed reactivity. Most often, however, one or the other type alone arises from the exposure which is most propitious for the induction of that particular type.

The range of chemical substances which may incite hypersensitivity is wide, including metals such as mercury and nickel, simple chemicals such as formaldehyde, and such drugs as quinine, arsenicals, sulfonamides and antibiotics. Clearly these things are not antigens, but it has been demonstrated repeatedly that many simple substances can readily become conjugated with proteins to function as antigens (4). Whether all the simple substances capable of sensitizing are able to form conjugates of this kind in the body is questionable, but evidence from human beings and animals suggests that some simple modification—perhaps only adsorption to protein—may explain the acquisition of antigenicity and the peculiarities in elicitation of skin reactions which are to be discussed.

These paragraphs have so far been a recapitulation of basic points developed in preceding chapters. The peculiar problems in drug hypersensitivity which justify further elaboration are these:

1. In the **immediate** hypersensitive states caused by drugs the elicitation of direct skin reactions and the demonstration of circulating antibodies by passive transfer are both usually negative, in contrast to the situation with respect to ordinary antigenic substances.

2. Contact **delayed** sensitivity is practically always induced by simpler chemical substances; rarely by complete antigens such as proteins.

3. In contact **delayed** hypersensitivity caused by drugs skin reactivity is sometimes not demonstrable by the application of the offending substance to the skin (patch test), even though the reactive state is one in which the skin is largely or perhaps exclusively involved.

4. Certain of the manifestations of hypersensitivity to drugs do not fall into the usual category of hypersensitive responses, and are therefore still difficult to assess. Gastrointestinal disturbances unaccompanied by any other more familiar sign or symptom, and granulocytopenia, are among these manifestations.

Possible answers to these special questions raised by drug hypersensitivities are discussed in the following paragraphs.

1. The failure of direct skin tests and passive serum transfer in immediate hypersensitive reactivity to drugs. It has been known for many years that direct skin reactions as well as passive transfer tests almost always fail in the drug hypersensitivities of human beings. It seems evident from reported exceptions to this rule, however, that some rational explanation should be at hand to account for the failure. Direct skin reactions of the wheal and erythema type have been seen in patients sensitive to salvarsan, formaldehyde, phthalic anhydride, chloramin-T, sulfathiazole and sulfadiazine, and transferable antibodies have been demonstrable also in some of these instances (5).

Bronfenbrenner (6) believes that the reason for the paucity of positive reactions rests in the incapacity of most of these simple haptens to react with the antibody which has been formed in response to the chemical conjugated with protein. Several considerations support this idea: (*a*) in patients with urticarial sensitivity to penicillin, Peck and co-workers (7) found no positive immediate intradermal tests to the antibiotic, but 40 per cent of these subjects showed reactions at 48 hours. This suggests as one possibility that the penicillin must have an opportunity to combine with a protein constituent before the reaction with antibody can develop. (*b*) More directly, Oriel (8) has shown in a patient with sensitivity to aspirin that this drug in itself would not elicit a skin reaction, while an aspirin proteose complex isolated from the patient's urine successfully induced such a response, and Leftwich (9) has made analogous observations with sulfonamides. Chase (10) has amply verified this kind of evidence in guinea pigs. Animals were sensitized by repeated intradermal injections of various chemical substances and later tested directly or by the passive transfer of serum to normal recipient animals, using for this purpose the chemical substance itself or a conjugate with protein. In some instances the simple chemicals themselves were entirely effective in eliciting immediate skin reactions. However, one substance, picryl chloride, caused reactions which required one to three hours for their development, and another chemical, 2:4 dinitrochlorobenzene, elicited virtually no response in sensitized animals or in recipients of the serum of such animals—after 10 hours only a slight transient edema became visible. In both these cases the use of protein conjugates for the tests resulted in prompt skin reactions. Chase concludes that the detection of early-type reactivity in human beings may also depend upon the nature of the chemical allergen; if this is poorly reactive, a preformed conjugate could yield success.

As regards the infrequency of transfers of drug sensitivity with the sera of hypersensitive individuals, the same factor of a satisfactory test antigen is obviously of great importance in determining a positive result. An additional factor is suggested by Chase's very general success in transferring sensitivity from guinea pigs which had been repeatedly injected with the chemical substances under study. It seems probable that in human beings also sera obtained from subjects repeatedly exposed to antigen should be generally effective in passive sensitization. Exposure to drugs and chemicals, however, is apt to be more restricted than exposure to such environmental allergens as house dust or pollens, and this may explain the general absence of detectable antibodies in drug hypersensitivity.

These observations and experiments clarify a good deal, but whether they satisfy fully the question originally posed is uncertain. Some observations remain unexplained. Thus, Rosen (11) observed in a subject sensitive to streptomycin an immediate systemic reaction coming on two minutes after an intradermal test injection of the drug, with wheezing, pruritus and collapse, in the absence of a response at the test site. In this case it is apparent that the injected drug was immediately active as an antigen systematically, yet it failed to stimulate a local skin response.

2. The restriction of induction of contact delayed hypersensitivity to nonantigenic substances. Oddly enough, contact reactivity almost without exception develops in response to simple chemical substances or to oily derivatives of plant and animal origin. Contact sensitization to domestic animals, for example, is found to be directed toward substances extractable by organic

solvents from the dander and hair rather than to the proteins from these sources. There are certainly ample opportunities for contact of the skin with all manner of proteinaceous substances in the environment, yet sensitization of this kind rarely develops.

The fact that the initially nonantigenic substances to which contact sensitivity occurs can become antigenic by combining with body proteins affords an explanation of their capacity to sensitize. It does not, however, explain why **only such substances** sensitize. Straus and Coca (12) have emphasized this point as one which requires clarification.

A suggested explanation for which experimental evidence is not yet available seems warranted by the following considerations:

(a) Simple substances can sensitize by skin contact.

(b) Simple chemical substances rarely induce contact sensitivity if introduced parenterally beyond the skin.

(c) Complete antigens rarely induce contact sensitivity by way of the skin.

(d) Complete antigens and simple substances may both, under special conditions, cause the development of contact reactivity if injected parenterally beyond the skin. We know that in tuberculosis of man and the guinea pig sensitivity to tuberculoprotein can be demonstrated by the superficial application of this substance as a patch test. Landsteiner and Chase (13a) have shown that other substances can induce contact reactivity following deep parenteral injection **provided that dead tubercle bacilli are simultaneously injected.** The writer has found that a particular lipoidal factor from the bacillus is responsible for this effect (13b).

(e) It appears from this chain of thought that the capacity to induce contact reactivity through skin exposure may depend upon the fact that this tissue supplies a lipoidal substance analogous in its activity to that derived from the tubercle bacillus. Nonantigenic substances may then be proficient in causing sensitivity because they must combine with a constituent of the skin in order to become antigenic, and in this process there may be released from cutaneous cells a lipoidal substance with the requisite characteristics. Complete antigens do not combine with a carrier, hence do not set in motion the events which release such a lipid.

3. The failure of patch tests to reveal the presence of contact reactivity to chemical substances. Although in general cutaneous contact hypersensitivity is readily demonstrable through the application of the responsible agent as a patch test, one finds recorded instances of failures of this procedure. One such description, for example, relates the occurrence of dermatitis following repeated applications of sulfathiazole powder to the ears. Subsequent **oral** administration of the drug resulted in severe dermatitis of the ears and later of other areas of the body, but patch tests were negative (14). Other similar incidents have been described (15) though these are not frequent (16).

The reasons for such failures of skin reactions are not known. Epstein (17) believes that contact sensitivity may be of two kinds; one in which the epidermis alone becomes reactive, and in this case patch tests are positive; the other a sensitivity of the cutis in which the epidermis takes no part. In the latter case contact tests are negative while intradermally injected allergens reveal the sensitivity. It was mentioned in Chapter 14 that contact reactivity is generally considered to be limited to the skin, though it seems questionable whether adequate study has been made of the possible reactivity of other tissues and cells. Epstein's viewpoint delimits this consideration even further. Even if it proves to be correct, however, it explains what happens, but not why or how these variations in reactivity occur.

4. The occurrence of unusual manifestations of hypersensitivity to drugs and chemicals. A variety of clinical affections have been attributed to drug idiosyncrasy, but as Dragstedt (18) points out many of these untoward effects betoken toxicity rather than hypersensitivity, even though this may not occur in every instance in which the drug is administered. Sometimes the drug may prove toxic because of a deficiency in the body of another substance which would ordinarily inhibit this activity. Dragstedt quotes observations by Müller of cases of polyneuritis caused by sulfonamides in which damage to nervous tissue by these drugs was thought to depend upon thiamine deficiency or other predisposing factors.

Granulocytopenia appears to be one of the unusual clinical manifestations of hypersensitivity to any of a variety of drugs of which examples are the sulfonamides, thiouracil and aminopyrine. Gastrointestinal disturbances also are often included among possible hypersensitive manifestations of drug and chemical hypersensitivity. Whether these are hypersensitive responses in the immunologic sense is difficult to ascertain, but the frequent concomitance of cutaneous edema or hives lends to these abdominal disturbances an authenticity which is otherwise difficult to establish (2).

Food Hypersensitivities. Food substances can account for atopic hypersensitivity manifested by the occurrence of asthma, rhinitis and urticaria. Asthma in infants and children is thought by some allergists to be caused principally by foods (19). Others believe that this is not often the case (2), but whatever the frequency no one doubts its occurrence. Cooke cites the example of a violent attack of asthma resulting from the handling of an unbroken egg (2).

Several questions arise in the consideration of hypersensitivity to foods. The first concerns the basis for the occurrence of dermatitis of the so-called flexural type in children. A second question is the same as one which was discussed in relation to drug hypersensitivity, namely, a rather frequent failure of skin reactivity to foods which appear to be etiologically related to clinical manifestations of allergy. The third question is again a repetition of one considered in relation to chemicals and drugs—the possibility that unusual clinical manifestations of hypersensitivity may occur.

1. Flexural dermatitis involving the cubital and popliteal spaces and the face and neck is generally included among the atopic syndromes, with eggs and milk the responsible allergens in many children. As has been mentioned before, Cooke (2) disagrees with this viewpoint because in his experience the

children who respond to such allergens with skin wheals reveal no exacerbation of their eczema following ingestion of the foods in question. He thinks therefore that the atopic reactivity to foods is a coincidental circumstance in children who have also a **delayed contact-type** of hypersensitivity to some other substance, frequently a drug or an antibiotic agent. The burden of proof would seem to lie with the proponents of this viewpoint, for we know that reactivity of the immediate type can result in chronic vascular lesions (e.g. periarteritis nodosa, Chapter 13) and this type of dermatitis may be in the same category of responses. It would be curious indeed if this dermatitis should occur in persons who merely by coincidence reveal urticarial reactivity to skin tests with foods and other environmental agents.

2. The second question appears to warrant the same answer that was made in the discussion of drug sensitivities. Instances of failure of skin reactions in food hypersensitivity are much less frequent than in the case of allergies to chemical substances. Where such failures occur, however, the possibility suggests itself here also that the original food substance is incapable of evoking a test reaction because a derivative of it is actually the sensitizing agent. Cooke provides as an illustration of this the case of a patient whose sensitivity to ingested milk was manifested by asthma, abdominal pain, nausea and diarrhea. The fact that these events began about two hours after ingestion intimated the necessity for some alteration in the food to provide the active antigen. This inference was borne out by skin tests which were negative to milk itself, but positive to the proteoses of whey (2).

3. The presumptive unusual manifestations of hypersensitivity to foods include gastrointestinal disturbances (abdominal pain, nausea, vomiting and diarrhea). These were mentioned also as possible consequences of hypersensitivity to drugs, but much more frequently such symptoms are associated with foods. There are many shades of opinion on this matter among clinical allergists. Some think that the relationship between gastrointestinal symptoms and allergy is a common one, others believe this to be unusual, and still others follow a middle course. The difficulty in evaluating the question is emphasized in a recent editorial by Lowell (20). He points out to begin with the danger of too readily ascribing physical and psychic troubles to foods, and once this relationship has been established, the difficulty in proving that the basis for these disturbances is a hypersensitive one. To gather evidence on the first point he recommends stringently controlled observations involving the employment of foods in disguised forms to evoke the manifestations complained of. If a clear-cut cause and effect relationship can be established, then one should proceed with immunologic technics to prove the allergic nature of the relationship.

The first of these conditions has been carefully observed in certain studies in which radiologic evidence of hyper- or hypotonicity and hypermotility of the small intestine, and sometimes delayed gastric emptying, have been seen to follow the ingestion of specific foods (21). The results of such studies have not always been definitive, however, for patients have been observed to show such changes before the suspected food was given (21b). Since such cause and effect evidence is not clear as yet, and since even less is known about the immunologic status of patients with these gastrointestinal manifestations, the question of the occurrence of gastrointestinal allergy must for the present remain moot.

Another line of thought in the matter of hypersensitive manifestations caused by foods is even further removed from conventional concepts of hypersensitive responses. Coca has described a state which he terms familial nonreaginic allergy (22). This is considered to consist of a hypersensitivity to foods occurring upon an evident hereditary basis as do the atopic sensitivities. In nonreaginic allergy, however, no antibody mediation is demonstrable either by direct skin tests or by the Prausnitz-Küstner reaction. The constant characteristic by which this state is said to be recognizable is acceleration of the pulse after the provocative food has been ingested. The manifestations listed for this kind of hypersensitivity are protean, including, in addition to the conventional asthma and urticaria, such symptoms and signs as anginal pains, heartburn, fatigue and petit mal. In the absence, by definition, of an immunologic basis for study, it is difficult to assess these observations from the standpoint of immunologic hypersensitivity. This subject has been discussed by Meyer (23).

Physical "Allergy." An interesting and puzzling sequence of events occurs in certain individuals following exposure to various physical factors such as cold, heat, sunlight or mechanical irritation. A common manifestation is urticaria of the exposed part, or angioedema. Systemic effects may accompany this, with headache, fever, tachycardia, fall in blood pressure and collapse. No attempt will be made here to deal with the responses to each of the physical factors individually; instead, the possible general mechanisms of their occurrence will be considered. We may eventually find that this kind of treatment is not warranted by the facts, but facts are scarce now and the speculations which seem to be applicable are of general nature.

The kinds of mechanisms which may explain physical "allergy" seem to fall into two categories: (1) the physical agent directly activates a response in a suitable subject which manifests itself in the signs and symptoms just enumerated, or (2) the response is in some way mediated through an immunologic mechanism.

1. As for the first possibility, a simple explanation for many instances of sensitivity may be embodied in Lewis's (24) concept of the triple response to injurious agents (see Chapter 13). This supposes that histamine or H-substance is released from cells by the irritative action of mechanical factors, such as scratching the skin. In support of this concept Horton (25) has found that exposure to cold in sensitive individuals is evidenced by effects upon blood vessels, gastric secretion and blood pressure characteristic of histamine. Rose (26a) has studied the histamine content of the blood in 15 cases of reactivity to cold, heat, light and mechanical irritation (dermographism), and found increases above the normal in seven of these.

The fact that histamine may be responsible for the manifestations of physical hypersensitivity does not mean of course that the eventual mechanism of its release may not be an immunologic one for, as discussed in Chapter 13, the antigen-antibody reaction occurring in vivo is also thought to release histamine. There is at this time no conclusive proof that the manifestations of sensitivity are the result of a direct release of histamine subsequent to exposure to the physical factor involved, but the possibility that this happens in some instances seems a logical one. In this connection it is interesting to note that not all cutaneous reactions to cold are of the urticarial histamine type. Delayed reactions of the tuberculin type have been seen to occur in various patients about 24 hours after a two minute application of ice to the skin. This was found in about 10 per cent of normal individuals, and in half or more of patients with asthma, tuberculosis or diabetes; it was especially severe in the tuberculous subjects. The meaning of this is not clear (26b).

Another nonimmunologic explanation for the occurrence of sensitive manifestations applies to the restricted instance of reactivity to light. Certain chemical substances, if ingested or injected, or derived from endogenous sources, lead to sensitivity to light. Hematoporphyrin is well known in this respect. This may derive from hemoglobin under such circumstances as hepatic dysfunction or lead poisoning. Sulfanilamide has been reported to cause photosensitivity also. Sometimes also superficial contact of the skin with plants may sensitize it so that a dermititis occurs upon subsequent exposure to light. This subject is discussed in more detail by Harkavy (27), Walzer (28) and Bronfenbrenner (6).

2. The possibility that an immunologic mechanism may mediate reactivity to physical factors can be rationalized in several ways. The supposition that antibodies may be involved in such reactivity stems from the finding that in certain instances individuals sensitive to any of the physical factors mentioned may transfer this sensitivity to the skin of normal recipients by means of serum (27). This happens relatively infrequently, but certain well studied instances, such as that of Sherman and Seebohm's (29) case of cold sensitivity, leave little doubt that it does occur. The question is, to what antigenic factor are such antibodies produced? The possibilities seem to be these:

(a) Antibodies are directed against the physical factor itself. This idea has neither theoretic nor factual support in its favor.

(b) Antibodies are directed against a tissue constituent, and the reaction between them occurs under the conditions imposed by the physical factor involved. The best example of this possibility is provided by the occurrence of cold agglutinins or hemolysins which react with the subject's own erythrocytes at low temperature, as in some cases of syphilis (30a). (See also Chapter 31.) The frequent occurrence of cold hemagglutinins in people with atypical pneumonia should afford an opportunity to determine whether cutaneous reactivity to cold is frequent in this disease; this point has not been investigated, to the writer's knowledge. Apparently the intravascular breakdown of erythrocytes can follow chilling in such patients, however (30b).

Cold reacting antibodies to antigens other than those of the red cells is also a possibility. In the case of sensitivity to cold studied by Sherman and Seebohm (29) the passively transferable antibody was not absorbed from the serum by type O red cells in the cold, but finely divided normal human skin successfully removed the transferable factor at low temperature.

(c) Antibodies are directed against an autoantigen which is produced in the body by the action of the physical factor. A normal cellular constituent, in other words, may be so altered chemically by cold, heat, trauma or light as to function as a foreign antigenic substance in the body, stimulating the formation of antibodies. Whenever the same physical factor again acts upon the tissues to release more of the same antigen, a reaction occurs with the previously manufactured antibody to result in the clinical manifestations of physical "allergy."

This viewpoint has indirect evidence to recommend it as a possibility, but there is more question of its probability. The work of Rivers and Schwentker (31a) and much subsequent additional information has shown that nervous tissue altered by aseptic autolysis or by infection with vaccinia virus can function as an antigen in the animal species from which it derives. Other examples of altered antigenicity of tissues (6) have been recorded (see Chapter 31). Whether the physical factors under discussion here are able to accomplish such changes in living tissue is not yet certain, but Karady (31b) has presented affirmative data for guinea pigs. There is not yet definitive evidence that this may be a mechanism responsible for spontaneous physical "allergic" reactions.

(d) Finally, the possibility exists that the sensitization in these instances of physical "allergy" is of a conventional type, e.g. to a food or inhalant, and that the superimposition of the physical factor brings forth the manifestations of a true hypersensitive reaction. It has been described that desensitization to the underlying hypersensitivity has, in some patients, eliminated reactivity to the physical factor (32). Undoubtedly some instances of apparent sensitivity to physical factors are explainable on this basis.

Hypersensitive-like Reactions. Under certain conditions animals may manifest lesions or systemic syndromes which simulate hypersensitivity, but which are mechanistically unrelated to it. Some of the more interesting instances will be discussed here.

1. SHWARTZMAN-SANARELLI PHENOMENON. Some years ago Sanarelli (33) observed striking intestinal reactions during an investigation dealing with the reproduction in animals of various intestinal diseases commonly observed in man. He found that rabbits injected with a sublethal dose of cholera vibrios and later reinjected with a small number of colon bacilli, died. Death could be attributed to neither of these inocula in themselves. Autopsy revealed necrosis of the intestinal mucosa (where cholera vibrios had localized), a condition to which Sanarelli applied the term hemorrhagic allergy.

As a result of repeated observations of this kind Sanarelli concluded that many of the acute abdominal crises which occur in human beings, such as acute appendicitis or acute hemorrhagic pancreatitis, might be interpreted on a common basis, to wit, that as the result of chronic or subacute inflammation the tissue acquires a sensitivity to the causative organisms, and when the latter enter the blood stream the locally affected tissue undergoes destruction.

Shwartzman (34) as well as Hanger (35) rediscovered this kind of reaction in 1928, and Shwartzman's extensive investigations have revealed that although Sanarelli's factual observations are acceptable his concept of allergic reactivity was wrong. Shwartzman found that intense hemorrhagic and necrotic skin reactions could be induced in the skin of rabbits under the following conditions. The filtrate of a young agar culture washing of *Salmonella typhosa,* or any one of a variety of other organisms, is first injected intradermally. Nothing much happens as a result of this initial or **preparatory** injection. If now 24 hours later a small amount of the filtrate is injected intravenously a marked change occurs in the initial skin site within the next two to four hours. This area assumes a purplish congested appearance, then quickly undergoes hemorrhagic necrosis, the reaction reaching its height at about five hours after the intravenous injection. Histologically the lesion shows thrombosis, disruption of blood vessels and hemorrhage. The intravenous injection is termed the **provocative** dose.

With the proper strains of organisms, amounts of material may be employed to provoke this reaction which in themselves, injected into the skin or intravenously, are entirely nontoxic. The criticism that the intradermal inoculation serves only to create an area of mild inflammation so that the intravenously injected material is concentrated in this area with destructive results has been shown to be irrelevant, since the skin cannot be prepared by the use of substances, such as xylene, with marked ability to evoke inflammation (34).

The essential conditions for the establishment of the reaction indicate that it is not of hypersensitive nature:

(a) The provocative injection must be given intravascularly.

(b) The provocative injection must follow within a limited interval of time after the preparatory injection. Generally, the second dose is ineffective if given earlier than 8 hours or later than 32 hours after the first.

(c) Bacterial and other substances may induce reactivity and elicit the reaction. There is no antigenic specificity involved, however; one filtrate may be employed for preparation and another antigenically unrelated material may be used for the provocative dose. Furthermore, it has been shown that nonantigenic substances such as agar or starch solutions may be employed for the intravenous injection after proper skin preparation has been effected (36).

These conditions distinguish the Shwartzman-Sanarelli reaction from local allergic reactions of either the Arthus or delayed types on several counts. In the first place, reinjection of material into the same site as employed for the preparatory dose is not effective. Secondly, the time interval between injections is not in the range of any of the known immunologic responses; the "sensitization" comes on too early and vanishes too promptly. And finally, there is no evidence here of immunologic specificity.

Apitz (37) has described a generalized reaction resulting from successive injections of bacterial filtrate intravenously at 24-hour intervals. The kidneys, lungs, liver and heart revealed diffuse vascular and degenerative changes. It was further shown by Shwartzman (34) that spontaneous preparation of a tissue may occur under certain conditions so that only one intravenous injection is necessary to produce the characteristic hemorrhagic necrosis. This is observed, for example, in the transplantable tumors of laboratory animals. The possibility that similar circumstances may occur under a variety of conditions in human beings is evident, but there has thus far been little success in defining this conclusively. One provocative suggestion has been made by Rich (38) with regard to the flareup of focal pulmonary lesions of tuberculosis which occurs after the injection of tuberculin. This may be a Shwartzman effect in tissue prepared by the existing infection. Others (39) have described the occurrence of hemorrhagic necrotic skin lesions in patients with sinus infections (equivalent to the provocative dose) who were injected into the skin with bacterial vaccine or toxin or pollen-antibody mixture (equivalent to the preparatory doses).

An adequate explanation of the mechanism underlying this reaction has not yet been made. Shwartzman (34) suggests that the preparatory injection induces a "vulnerability" of the tissues—some functional disturbance in the cells—which makes them susceptible to severe damage provided the "toxic" factor is present in the circulation. In view of the fact that the "toxic" factor may be starch or agar, its activity evidently does not fall within the ordinary definition of toxicity. More recently Stetson and co-workers (40) have reported that the vulnerability of tissues occasioned by the preparatory injection consists in increased lactic acid formation brought about by the polymorphonuclear cells in the local area. They believe that this may injure the endothelium of the small vessels in the area so that following the provocative injection masses of platelets and granulocytes adhere to the walls, interrupt the blood flow, and thus bring about ischemic necrosis. More evidence for this viewpoint will be needed before it can be considered as established.

2. ANAPHYLACTOID REACTIONS. The injection of a variety of substances into the body may result in acute symptoms of shock which resemble the anaphylactic syndrome. In some instances the mechanisms underlying this kind of primary shock may be the same as those underlying anaphylaxis, i.e. the liberation of histamine from tissues. In other cases a direct toxic activity of the injected agent appears to cause the pathologic alterations and symptoms, and though the latter closely resemble anaphylaxis the former are apt to differ. Thus, the emphysema characteristic of anaphylaxis is usually absent; instead there often occurs peribronchial edema, thrombosis, embolism, and hemorrhage. The occurrence and extent of these changes varies with different agents.

Among the substances which induce a syndrome closely related to anaphylaxis in the nonsensitive animal are snake and bee venoms; these liberate histamine and "slow reacting substance" from the tissues, possibly because of their content of lysolecithin-like enzymes (41), and perhaps also of proteolytic enzymes, since trypsin causes histamine release also (42). These reactions to venoms have been employed for the study of anaphylactic mechanisms, as described in Chapter 13.

The substances which may directly affect the lungs of guinea pigs to produce pulmonary symptoms are manifold. A list provided by the studies of Hanzlik and Karsner (43) includes acetic acid, India ink, colloidal iron, beef and horse lung extract, sodium citrate, tragacanth—in short, substances belonging to many chemical categories, all sharing the ability to cause profound alterations in the lung, as well as in other tissues and organs. With most of these substances the emphysema characteristic of anaphylaxis is usually absent; instead there often occurs peribronchial edema, thrombosis, embolism and hemorrhage. The occurrence and extent of these changes vary with different agents. Anaphylactoid shock may be confused with anaphylaxis unless adequate control studies are made.

3. PRIMARY (HETEROPHILE) SHOCK. An instance of acute shock associated with an antigen-antibody reaction, but differing in some respects from anaphylaxis, is that which occurs following the intravenous injection of a Forssman antibody-containing serum (see Chapter 31) into a normal guinea pig (44). In this case the antigen concerned in the reaction is a part of the animal's own protoplasm, and an antibody against this is introduced. This has been referred to as reversed passive anaphylaxis, but there is some doubt that the mechanism of shock here is the same as that in anaphylaxis. The effects occasioned by Forssman antibody seem to depend upon direct injury to cells containing antigen. Though pulmonary symptoms constitute the major feature of this reaction following intravenous injection of the serum, there is massive edema with frothing at the nose, and extensive lung hemorrhage, but comparatively little emphysema. Redfern, among others, has found that the capillary endothelium is probably the main point of attack in this syndrome (45). If antibody is injected into the carotid artery the resultant disturbances and lesions are neurologic, while the anaphylactoid manifestations are minimal or absent (46).

BIBLIOGRAPHY

1. Sulzberger, M. B. J. Allergy, 18:176, 1947.
2. Cooke, R. A. Allergy in Theory and Practice, Philadelphia, W. B. Saunders Co., 1947.
3. ——— J. Allergy, 15:203, 1944.
4a. Landsteiner, K., and Jacobs, J. J. Exper. Med., 64:625, 1930.
 b. Rosenthal, S. R. J. Immunol., 34:251, 1938.
 c. Gell, P. G. H., Harington, C. R., and Michel, R. Brit. J. Exper. Path., 29:578, 1948.
 d. Landsteiner, K. The Specificity of Serological Reactions, Cambridge, Mass., Harvard University Press, 1945.
5a. Kern, R. A. J. Allergy, 10:164, 1939.
 b. Feinberg, S., and Watrous, R. J. Allergy, 16:209, 1945.

c. Sherman, W. B., and Cooke, R. A.   Am. J. Med., 2:588, 1947.
d. Chase, M. W.   Bacterial and Mycotic Infections of Man, ed. by R. J. Dubos. Philadelphia, J. B. Lippincott Co., 1948, Chapter 6.
e. Walzer, M.   Ann. New York Acad. Sc., 50:743, 1949.
6. Bronfenbrenner, J.   J. Allergy, 14:105, 1943.
7. Peck, S. M., Siegal, S., Glick, A. W., Kurtin, A., and Bergamini, R.   J.A.M.A., 138:631, 1948.
8. Oriel, C.   Proc. Roy. Soc. Med., 24:1171, 1931.
9. Leftwich, W. B.   Bull. Johns Hopkins Hosp., 74:26, 1944.
10. Chase, M. W.   J. Exper. Med., 86:489, 1947.
11. Rosen, F. L.   J.A.M.A., 137:1128, 1948.
12. Straus, H. W., and Coca, A. F.   J. Immunol., 33:215, 1937.
13a. Landsteiner, K., and Chase, M. W.   J. Exper. Med., 73:431, 1941.
  b. Raffel, S., and Forney, J. E.   J. Exper. Med., 88:485, 1948.
14. Sams, W. M., and Capland, L.   Arch. Dermat. and Syph., 44:226, 1941.
15. Miller, J. L.   Arch. Dermat. & Syph., 43:379, 1942.
16. Weiner, A. L.   J.A.M.A., 121:411, 1943.
17a. Epstein, S., and Pinkus, H.   Ann. Allergy, 4:186, 1946.
  b. ——— Ann. Allergy, 4:438, 1946.
18. Dragstedt, C. A.   J.A.M.A., 135:133, 1947.
19. Rowe, A. H., and Rowe, A., Jr.   California, Med., 69:2, 1948.
20. Lowell, F. C.   J. Allergy, 21:563, 1950.
21a. Tallant, E. J., O'Neill, H. A., Urbach, F., and Price, A. H.   Amer. J. Digest. Dis., 16:140, 1949.
  b. Lepore, M. J., Collins, L. C., and Sherman, W. B.   J. Allergy, 22:146, 1951.
22. Coca, A. F.   Familial Non-Reaginic Allergy, Springfield, Ill., Charles C Thomas Co., 1943.
23. Meyer, M. G.   Ann. New York Acad. Sc., 50:773, 1949.
24. Lewis, T.   The Blood Vessels of the Human Skin and Their Responses, London, Shaw and Sons, Ltd., 1947.
25. Horton, B. T., Brown, G. E., and Roth, G. M.   J.A.M.A., 107:1263, 1936.
26a. Rose, B.   J. Allergy, 12:357, 1941.
  b. Saier, M. H., Van Deventer, W. C., and Barnett, G. D.   Proc. Soc. Exper. Biol. & Med., 29:936, 1931-32.
27. Harkavy, J.   Allergy in Theory and Practice, ed. by R. A. Cooke, Philadelphia, W. B. Saunders Co., 1947, Chapter 30.
28. Walzer, M.   J. Allergy, 9:64, 1937.
29. Sherman, W. B., and Seebohm, P. M.   J. Allergy, 21:414, 1950.
30a. Harris, K. E., Lewis, T., and Vaughan, J. M.   Heart, 14:305, 1929.
  b. Neely, F. L., Baria, W. H., Smith, E., and Stone, C. F., Jr.   L. Lab. & Clin. Med., 37:382, 1951.
31a. Rivers, T. M., and Schwentker, F. F.   J. Exper. Med., 61:689, 1935.
  b. Karady, S.   J. Immunol., 37:457, 1939.
32. Duke, W. F.   Asthma, Hay Fever, Urticaria and Allied Manifestations of Allergy, St. Louis, C. V. Mosby Co., 1935.
33. Sanarelli, G.   Ann. Inst. Pasteur, 38:11, 1924.
34. Shwartzman, G.   Phenomenon of Local Tissue Reactivity, New York, Paul B. Hoeber, Inc., 1937.
35. Hanger, F. M.   Proc. Soc. Exper. Biol. & Med., 25:775, 1928.
36a. Sickles, G. M.   Annual Report of the Division of Laboratories and Research, New York State Dept. of Health, 1934, p. 8.
  b. Freund, J., and Hosmer, E. P.   J. Immunol., 29:279, 1935.
37. Apitz, K.   J. Immunol., 29:255, 1935.
38. Rich, A. R.   The Pathogenesis of Tuberculosis, Springfield, Ill., Charles C Thomas Co., 1944.
39. Harkavy, J., and Romanoff, A.   J. Allergy, 10:566, 1939.
40a. Thomas, L., and Stetson, C. A., Jr.   J. Exper. Med., 89:461, 1949.
  b. Stetson, C. A., Jr., and Good, R. A.   J. Exper. Med., 93:49, 1951.
  c. ——— J. Exper. Med., 93:489, 1951.

41. Feldberg, W., Holden, H. F., and Kellaway, C. H.   J. Physiol., 94:232, 1938.
42. Roche e Silva, M.   J. Allergy, 15:399, 1944.
43. Hanzlik, P. J., and Karsner, H. T.   J. Pharmacol. & Exper. Therap., 23:173, 1924.
44. Bull, C. G.   The Newer Knowledge of Bacteriology and Immunology, ed. by E. O.
       Jordan and I. S. Falk, Chicago, University of Chicago Press, 1928, Chapter 53.
45. Redfern, W. W.   Am. J. Hyg., 6:276, 1926.
46a. Forssman, J.   Biochem. Ztschr., 110:164, 1920.
  b. Jervis, G. A.   Arch. Path., 35:560, 1943.

17

ANALYSIS OF IMMUNOLOGIC MECHANISMS
OF ACQUIRED IMMUNITY

Neither active nor passive immunization procedures have fulfilled the promise held out by the startling developments of the closing years of the past century. In 1880 it might have been a fair assumption from Pasteur's experiments with vaccination against anthrax, rabies and chicken cholera, and from von Behring's dramatic revelation of the lifesaving powers of diphtheria antitoxin, that infectious diseases were at a last stand; that by a simple process of extension of the principles of active and passive immunization the prevention or cure of all microbic diseases might be accomplished. This hope was soon disappointed and there ensued a long period during which immunologic studies added few practical benefits to the struggle against infectious diseases. During this time however some of the reasons for failure were uncovered: mutation of bacteria in culture with loss of essential immunizing antigens, degradation of antigens as the result of the physical or chemical manipulations involved in preparing vaccines and the possible inability of humoral antibodies to attack intracellularly located agents, and other points which are more fully discussed in Chapter 9. As a result of the accumulation of such information the long lean period has been succeeded, in the past 10 or 15 years, by a considerable reactivation, and the list of infections which may now be prevented or modified by vaccination has attained a quite respectable length.

There remain still many opportunities to expand this list and to better some of the procedures already available. Whatever welcome additions to chemotherapeutic and antibiotic weapons the future may yield, prevention rather than therapy remains the desirable goal. The rational approach to this goal lies in an understanding of the mechanics through which the body is able to acquire and to implement immunity. We are by now well acquainted with one such mechanism in which the formation of humoral antibodies is the key event. Possibly this is the only expression of acquired resistance available to the animal body, but certain glimmerings of knowledge make this seem doubtful, and if any chinks of light seem to come from other directions they should be followed. There seems no better way to seek out these possible new directions than by undertaking an analysis of what is presently known or thought about the workings of immunity in individual infectious diseases, and to this end the succeeding twelve chapters are devoted.

Our main concepts of the workings of acquired immunity have not changed in their general outlines during the past half century or more. The over-all picture of this process is a simple one; it depicts the offending organism as possessed of some power to overcome the native defenses of the body and this ability gives the microbe its virulence (see Chapter 3). The host on the other hand can acquire a special property (antibody) which neutralizes these virulence properties and puts the microbe back at the mercy of the body's defenses (chiefly phagocytic cells). This simplified viewpoint infers that the virulence property of the organism is the stimulator of acquired resistance, since the instrument of the latter is directed against this property.

The first of the succeeding chapters deals with a host-parasite relationship which seems to fit the virulence (antigen)-antivirulence (antibody) concept quite well. But in many other infections it has not been possible as yet to correlate the presence of antibodies against a virulence factor, or in fact against any constituent of the offending microbe, with the immune state. There may be several reasons for this: the virulence factor may not be an antigenic constituent of the cell at all (see Chapter 3) and therefore there can be no antibody directed against it; or antibodies against an antigenic virulence factor are unable to stem its activity, or cannot get at it because the microbe is inaccessibly situated. Some other mechanism may then function as the mediator of resistance in place of antibody, as discussed in Chapter 10. The difficulties in assessing the relationship of antibody to resistance in any particular case have been described in general terms in Chapter 9.

The discussions of individual infectious diseases in the chapters which follow will undertake to examine the viewpoint of antibody vs. virulence immunity in each case by marshalling evidence on these points: (*a*) what is the protection-inducing factor in the organism being considered; (*b*) is it also the factor chiefly responsible for virulence; and (*c*) does resistance function through a negation of this virulence factor, or does it work in some other way. The general possibilities which may eventuate are shown in the following chart:

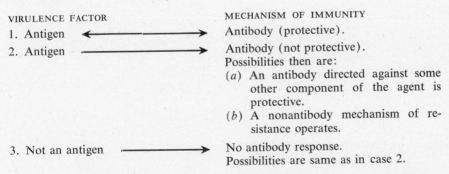

VIRULENCE FACTOR   MECHANISM OF IMMUNITY

1. Antigen ⟷ Antibody (protective).

2. Antigen ⟶ Antibody (not protective).
Possibilities then are:
(*a*) An antibody directed against some other component of the agent is protective.
(*b*) A nonantibody mechanism of resistance operates.

3. Not an antigen ⟶ No antibody response.
Possibilities are same as in case 2.

The 12 diseases to be discussed are arranged in a sequence which is intended to illustrate these possibilities. The first six are primarily bacterial diseases. The first of these, pneumococcal infection, exemplifies a host-parasite relationship in which an antibody response to the chief determinant of virulence, a capsular antigen, is the central mechanism of acquired resistance (case 1 in the chart). The second infection, anthrax, appears to represent an instance in which the antibody-virulence factor relationship does not explain acquired immunity; this may then fall into the second category in the chart. In the four succeeding cases, plague, cholera, bacillary dysentery and tuberculosis, the possibilities still permit considerable discussion.

Following these there are described three bacterial toxic diseases: botulism, diphtheria and gas gangrene. In these cases we deal with the relationships of diffusible microbial poisons to virulence and host immunity.

Finally, three instances of viral disease are sampled, and again the possibilities of antibody or some other mechanism of immunity are discussed in the light of the basic evidence currently at hand.

18

PNEUMOCOCCAL DISEASE

The immunologic relationship between the pneumococcus and its host has probably been the most thoroughly studied of any infectious system. This relationship is a straightforward one in laboratory hosts; it is a simple matter to demonstrate acquired immunity to this organism in properly vaccinated animals, to transfer this property to normal animals by means of serum, and with proper methods to disclose the nature of the protective endowment. Whether an equally precise relationship exists in the case of the human being has been questioned because reinfections with serologically homologous types of the organism occur not infrequently (1). However, there is evidence that vaccination of animals as well as man is of value in preventing disease only for brief periods (2) so that one may assume, unless more evidence to the contrary becomes available, that resistance is acquired by man in the same way as it is by rabbits, and that in both cases it is short-lived (3).

Protection-Inducing Factor. There is no question but that the essential immunizing factor of the pneumococcus is the polysaccharide of its capsule. This carbohydrate, referred to as soluble specific substance (SSS), is one of several identified antigens of the pneumococcal cell. It comprises the outermost layer of material, and is of course microscopically visible. Other known cellular antigens include a carbohydrate of the soma of the cell, called C substance; nucleoprotein; a protein which appears to vary in its antigenic properties in different strains (4); and Forssman antigen. The C substance, the nucleoprotein and the Forssman antigen are antigenically the same in all pneumococci, although the last-named substance does not occur in all strains (5). The SSS, however, differs chemically and antigenically in different strains, and the pneumococci as a group have been subdivided on this basis into 75 serologically distinct types, and probably more exist.

Although antigenic heterogeneity among pneumococcal strains was already recognized in the last century by French workers (3a, 6), the chemical basis for this individuality was not appreciated until Heidelberger and Avery (7) clarified the carbohydrate character of the capsular substances. A good deal can be tabulated now about the chemical and physical characteristics of many of these polymerized polysaccharides (6, 8).

The frequency with which various types of pneumococci cause disease in human beings as well as other interesting questions which we must forego here are discussed in textbooks dealing with medical bacteriology, medicine and public health. For our ends we shall inquire into the nature of the evidence that the type specific substances are related to the appearance of acquired resistance in vaccinated or previously infected hosts. Such evidence falls along the following four lines.

1. Acquired immunity results from the presence of encapsulated organisms in the body. Pneumococci in common with many other bacteria can exist in a genetically modified form without the surface antigen. In cultures this variation may occur spontaneously, a dissociation of encapsulated from unencapsulated cocci becoming visible to the unaided eye because of a difference in colonial morphology. Colonies of capsulated organisms look smooth and are called S colonies; unencapsulated variants grow as rough, or R colonies. This dissociation may be magnified, so to speak, by the addition of anticapsular antibodies to the medium, for this suppresses the S forms and permits the development of the R. The same change may occur in vaccinated animals and in patients recovering from pneumococcal infection (9). R forms may also revert to the encapsulated variety.

The administration of a vaccine comprised of encapsulated pneumococci induces a high degree of acquired immunity in animals, while the employment of R organisms is almost useless for this purpose. Some qualification of this statement is necessary, since there is evidence that a degree of resistance may be induced by the C carbohydrate of nonencapsulated strains (10). This resistance however is trivial relative to that invoked by encapsulated microbes.

This kind of evidence in itself strongly suggests that the capsular antigen is the essential immunizing factor of the pneumococcus. It does not prove the point, since it remains possible that some other property essential for inducing immunity may be lost coincidentally with the capsule. More specific implications, however, are not difficult to find, as outlined below.

2. Acquired immunity is type specific. An animal vaccinated with pneumococci of a particular type develops an immunity directed against organisms of this type alone. Possible exceptions to this may occur in those instances where an antigenic relationship exists between the SSS of two types, as between II and V, and III and VIII. In these cases there is probably some cross-protection (11). This fact only bulwarks the viewpoint that the capsular polysaccharide is the chief incitant of immunity, since it sharply defines the correlation of resistance with the antibody response to capsular antigen.

Evidence for the specificity of acquired resistance has come also from therapeutic experiences in human beings. This was recognized as the primary consideration in treating pneumococcal pneumonia with horse and rabbit antisera in the pre-antibiotic days. A prognostic skin test introduced by Tillet and Francis (12) depended upon the intradermal injection of SSS of the pneumococcal type known to be causing disease. The occurrence of a positive skin reaction usually denoted a favorable outcome, and this specific reaction was shown to depend upon the emergence in the patient of an adequate level of humoral antibody against the capsule of the infecting organism

(13). Earlier studies also had indicated the importance of a positive type-specific antibody balance in recovery from pneumonia (14).

3. Resistance can be passively transferred to normal animals by serum containing anti-SSS antibodies alone. If an antiserum obtained after vaccination with encapsulated organisms is deprived of all antibodies except those directed against the SSS by absorption with unencapsulated bacteria, the serum is found to retain its ability to convey specific resistance. On the other hand, if these antibodies are removed by absorption with purified SSS the protective property of the serum is greatly diminished (15, 16).

4. Vaccination with purified capsular polysaccharide induces resistance against infection with the pneumococcus of homologous type. Earlier preparations of type I SSS failed to induce resistance because the treatment with strong alkali employed in the isolation procedure destroyed a labile acetyl group and impaired antigenicity. Gentler chemical methods however yielded products which are antigenic per se in mice and human beings (see Chapter 4). Vaccination with these substances protects mice against the homologous organisms (16), and it probably does the same for human beings, as will be discussed in the last section of this chapter.

Available evidence then shows us that pneumococci without capsules do not invoke significant resistance, that encapsulated organisms incite resistance which is highly specific and that this type specificity is determined by the antigenic structure of the capsule, that anticapsular antibodies alone can convey passive protection, and finally that vaccination with purified capsular antigen immunizes animals, and probably man as well, against subsequent infection by the homologous organism. This evidence leaves us no cause to doubt the importance of capsular polysaccharide in determining immunity to the pneumococcus. Certain questions of quantitative import concerning the lack of parallelism between antibody levels and immunity will be considered in the discussion of the mechanisms of resistance, but these do not interfere with the central conclusion to which the evidence leads us.

Relation Between the Protection-Inducing Factor and Virulence. The possible bases for the virulence of the pneumococcus have been discussed in Chapter 3 in a more general context. At the present time the processes of virulence cannot be completely described for any of the infectious agents, and in the case of the pneumococcus, as of other microbes, there are doubtless multiple factors which account for the ability to cause disease. There is some evidence for example that a spreading factor may contribute to virulence ([17], see Chapter 3). Whatever the influence of this and other possible factors, the *sine qua non* of pathogenicity in the case of the pneumococcus is the possession of a capsule, for without it the organism is virtually impotent in this respect. In substantiation of this point it has been demonstrated that the addition of capsular substance to pneumococci of slight virulence can cause them to become highly pathogenic for the mouse and rabbit (18). As pointed out in Chapter 3, the capsule in itself does not assure virulence of pneumococci or of other bacteria in which a similar relationship of capsule to virulence exists. Other factors must also be of importance in determining disease-producing capacities.

The activity of the capsule as a determinant of virulence seems to depend mainly upon a peculiar ability to prevent leukocytes from engulfing the organism. Rough pneumococci are readily taken up by phagocytes and destroyed, whereas smooth forms are ingested only to a limited extent by the phagocytes of normal susceptible animals ([19], see Chapter 3).

Mechanism of Acquired Resistance. We see that the factor of the pneumococcus which is most important in inducing acquired resistance is the same as that which is mainly responsible for the virulence of this bacterium. It follows that immunity must be expressed through an action of the immunized subject against the virulence factor. This is accomplished by the elaboration of an antibody against the SSS which causes agglutination (i.e. localization) of organisms in the tissues and, more important, permits phagocytosis to proceed as it would in the normal host against an unencapsulated bacterium. The evidence that this takes place is supplied by experiments which show that anticapsular antibody accomplishes the destruction of pneumococci in vivo in the presence of phagocytic cells. On the other hand, neither phagocytes alone nor antibody in the absence of phagocytes (depleted through bone marrow injury) is effective (20).

The importance of anti-SSS antibody to acquired immunity and the fact that the water-soluble capsular antigen may reach high concentrations in the body fluids of infected subjects brings up an interesting facet of the struggle between parasite and host in pneumococcal disease. In cases of type III pneumococcal lobar pneumonia the concentration of polysaccharide in the sputum may reach 10 per cent (21), and it is found free in the blood of over 25 per cent of patients (22). This dissolved antigen by combining with circulating antibody may shield the microbes themselves from such combination, and thus from subsequent phagocytosis (15, 23). The type III organism appears to be the worst offender in this respect because its capsule is especially large and the antigen is relatively a poor one; consequently the dissolution of these cocci in the body would set free a large amount of antibody-neutralizing substance to combine with the small amount of antibody which the host is able to form. This may account in part for the high fatality rate of untreated pneumonia caused by this pneumococcal type; the 45 to 60 per cent mortality is higher than that occasioned by any of the other types of this organism.

It was mentioned earlier that there is often a failure of quantitative correlation between the serologic behavior of an antiserum in agglutinating pneumococci or precipitating SSS in the test tube and its protective ability in vivo (24). Thus, sera from vaccinated animals which fail in serologic tests may yet protect against challenge infection. Although this might seem to imply a contradiction to the importance attributed to anticapsular antibody in resistance, skepticism is not actually warranted on this account. In the first place, antibody which is incapable of agglutinating organisms can often be shown, by various technics, to attach to their surfaces, and this in itself may be sufficient to permit phagocytosis. The divergence possible between the precipitative and protective activities of antibody has been clearly set forth by the work of Goodner and Horsfall (25) with horse antipneumococcus serum. As described in an earlier chapter, the antibody produced against any single antigen is not necessarily homogeneous in either serologic or physico-chemical characteristics. It is not surprising therefore that Goodner and Horsfall were able to separate antibodies with varying flocculative capacities for SSS from single specimens of serum. It is unexpected however that that portion of the antibody showing only moderate precipitating activity in vitro was found to be greatest in protective capacity in vivo. Why this should be so is not clear, but its existence as fact helps to account for the observations of quantitative divergence of the serologic capacities of an animal's serum from its ability to resist challenge infection. A further insight into the lack of serologic-protective correlation is provided by the demonstration that very small concentrations of circulating antibody suffice for protection (26).

Practical Procedures for Vaccination. Effective prophylaxis for pneumococcic pneumonia has been sought for the past half century (3a), and for some years it has been within reach, but despite the fact that the pneumococcus is a leading cause of infectious morbidity, there has been no move toward a wide adoption of vaccination in areas and during seasons of greatest prevalence. Perhaps this is due in part to the brevity of acquired immunity, which extends probably for not more than a few months (1, 2). Yet with no better promise in this respect a good deal more energy has been devoted in recent years to vaccination against another respiratory disease, that caused by influenza virus.

Early work with pneumococcal vaccines was often poorly controlled and consequently difficult of interpretation; nevertheless there was evidence from such experiences as those of Lister in human beings that the use of vaccines of killed pneumococci of the types most likely to cause disease had definite merit (3a, 27). Beginning in 1935 Felton (28) and his co-workers obtained good results with isolated capsular polysaccharides, and such observations have been extended by others. A well controlled experiment carried out in an Army camp in 1945 with subcutaneously injected polysaccharides of types I, II, V and VII was followed, after one injection, by the cessation of pneumonia caused by pneumococci of these types two weeks later. In the control unvaccinated group pneumonia continued to occur, but even here the incidence of disease was lowered because the chain of infection was interfered with by the reduction of carriers. Immunity appeared to persist for about six months. Emphasizing the importance of these observations was the fact that pneumonia caused by pneumococcal types not represented in the vaccine continued to occur with usual frequency in both vaccinated and control groups (29).

BIBLIOGRAPHY

1. Strauss, E., and Finland, M.   Ann. Int. Med., 16:17, 1942.
2. Stillman, E. G., and Goodner, K.   J. Exper. Med., 58:195, 1933.
3a. White, B.   The Biology of Pneumococcus, New York, The Commonwealth Fund, 1938.
 b. Heffron, R., Pneumonia, with Special Reference to Pneumococcus Lobar Pneumonia, New York, The Commonwealth Fund, 1937.
4. Austrian, R., and MacLeod, C. M.   J. Exper. Med., 89:439, 1949.
5. Bailey, G. H., and Shorb, M. S.   Am. J. Hyg., 13:831, 1931.
6. Burger, M.   Bacterial Polysaccharides, Springfield, Ill., Charles C Thomas Co., 1950.
7. Heidelberger, M., and Avery, O. T.   J. Exper. Med., 38:73, 1923.
8. Kabat, E. A., and Mayer, M. M.   Experimental Immunochemistry, Springfield, Ill., Charles C Thomas Co., 1948.
9. Wadsworth, A. B., and Sickles, G. M.   J. Exper. Med., 45:787, 1927.
10a. Tillett, W. S.   J. Exper. Med., 48:791, 1928.
  b. Felton, L. D.   J. Immunol., 27:379, 1934.
  c. Enders, J. F., Wu, C-J., and Shaffer, M. F.   J. Exper. Med., 64:425, 1936.
  d. Dubos, R. J.   J. Exper. Med., 67:799, 1938.
  e. Day, H. B.   J. Hyg., 42:532, 1942.
11. Finland, M., and Winkler, A. W.   J. Clin. Investigation, 13:79, 97, 1934.
12. Tillett, W. S., and Francis, T., Jr.   J. Exper. Med., 50:687, 1929.
13. Wood, W. B., Jr.   J. Clin. Investigation, 19:95, 105, 1940.
14. Blake, F. G.   Arch. Int. Med., 21:779, 1918.
15. Enders, F., and Wu, C-J.   J. Exper. Med., 60:127, 1934.
16. Avery, O. T., and Goebel, W. F.   J. Exper. Med., 58:731, 1933.
17a. Goodner, K.   J. Exper. Med., 58:153, 1933.
  b. Humphrey, J. H.   J. Path. & Bact., 56:273, 1944.
  c. Thompson, R. T.   J. Lab. & Clin. Med., 33:919, 1948.
18a. Felton, L. D., and Bailey, G. H.   J. Infect. Dis., 38:131, 1926.
  b. Sia, R. H. P., and Zia, S. H.   Proc. Soc. Exper. Biol. & Med., 29:791, 1932.
19. Smith, M. R., Perry, W. D., Berry, J. W., and Wood, W. B., Jr.   J. Immunol., 67:71, 1951.
20. Rich, A. R., and McKee, C. M.   Bull. Johns Hopkins Hosp., 54:277, 1934. 76:497, 1942.
21. Tripp, J. T., Frisch, A. W., Barrett, C. D., Jr., and Pidgeon, B. E.   J. Exper. Med.,
22. Bukantz, S. C., DeGara, P. F., and Bullowa, J. G. M.   Arch. Int. Med., 69:191, 1942.
23a. Sia, R. H. P.   J. Exper. Med., 43:633, 1926.
  b. Sickles, G. M.   J. Immunol., 14:329, 1927.
  c. Cole, R. I.   J. Exper. Med., 26:453, 1917.
  d. Downie, A. W.   J. Path. & Bact., 45:149, 1937.
24a. Stillman, E. G.   J. Exper. Med., 51:721, 1930.
  b. Robertson, O. H.   J. Exper. Med., 66:705, 1937.
25. Goodner, K., and Horsfall, F. L., Jr.   J. Exper. Med., 66:413, 425, 437, 1937.
26. Walsh, T. E., and Cannon, P. R.   J. Immunol., 31:331, 1936.
27. Lister, F. S., and Ordman, D.   Rep. S. African Inst. Med. Res., 7:1, 1935.
28. Skwurzel, G. M., Simmons, J. S., Dublin, L. I., and Felton, L. D.   Pub. Health Rep., 53:1877, 1938.
29. MacLeod, C. M., Hodges, R. G., Heidelberger, M., and Bernhard, W. G.   J. Exper. Med., 82:445, 1945.

19

ANTHRAX

Bacillus anthracis is a member of the aerobic spore-forming bacilli, the only one of this group with pathogenic properties. Anthrax is an infrequent disease of human beings or animals in these times, but the host-parasite relationship in this infection is of considerable interest because it provides the student of infectious disease with the only clear indication so far available that the immunologic pattern of acquired resistance need not necessarily follow the classic model described in the preceding chapter. Pneumococcal immunity is so rational mechanistically that there is a natural tendency to try to fit immunologic information about other diseases into the same mold. In many cases such information cannot be squeezed into the mold even by manipulating facts and suppositions, and we are left wondering. It is thus refreshing to find specific immunochemical evidence for another possible channel for thought about the questions which the study of immunity poses.

Protection-Inducing Factor. Pasteur in 1881 first demonstrated the immunizing ability of living anthrax bacilli attenuated by heat; his spectacular public exhibition at Pouilly-le-Fort comprised part of this demonstration. Bail (1) in 1904 showed that the bacteria-free edema fluid from anthrax lesions could actively immunize animals. When Tomcsik and his co-workers (2) in the early thirties of this century undertook an extensive investigation of the antigenic structure of the anthrax bacillus and its possible relationship to acquired resistance, it seemed a perfectly logical expectation that the findings would prove entirely analagous to those already uncovered for the pneumococcus, embracing the occurrence of a capsule on the virulent organism, the production by the vaccinated animal of an antibody against this capsule, and as a consequence of this antibody, the attainment of a marked degree of acquired immunity.

The reasons for such an expectation were these: first, the virulent anthrax bacillus possesses a well defined capsule when growing in the tissues or under the proper circumstances in culture, while the entirely avirulent organism never shows this. Second, Preisz (3) had already described a close relationship of capsule formation in vivo to the virulence of the bacillus. And now Tomcsik and Szongott (2a) isolated this capsular antigen and showed it to possess marked serologic activity, and were able to produce good concentrations of antibodies against it in rabbits with a vaccine of killed encapsulated bacilli.

It remained, to complete the analogy with the pneumococcus, to demonstrate the efficacy of the anticapsular antibodies in protection against the bacillus, and at this point the analogy faltered. In rabbits actively or passively provided with anticapsular antibody in large quantity there was little evidence of protection against infection. In guinea pigs passive immunity tests were even less rewarding, and as a result of their careful studies these authors pointed out that something was amiss in the correlation of this immunity relationship with that of the pneumococcus (2b).

More recent work in the United States and England has clarified this situation further. Cromartie and his co-workers (4a, 4b) first confirmed Bail's (1) early observations of the immunizing efficacy of the filtrates of infected tissue fluids as had other investigators in the intervening years. By electrophoretic analysis it was then demonstrated that the immunizing substance for rabbits and sheep is present in the globulin components of the infected tissue extract. It was further shown that this immunizing factor is electrophoretically distinct from the capsular material; it is a heat-labile substance which is destroyed by trypsin (4b, 4c). It may be produced in artificial medium but only in the presence of body fluids which supply two essential ingredients —albumin (or a substance associated with it) and a dialyzable salt replaceable by sodium bicarbonate (5). The synthesis by the organism of the protection-inducing factor in such a culture medium is **entirely independent of the capsulation of the bacilli,** nor does the factor at any time occur as a constituent of the organism itself, even at the period when its concentration in the medium is at a peak (5a). Thus, an immunizing factor not entirely defined in character but evidently not a part of the bacterial cell itself is produced by the anthrax bacillus growing in the tissues or in medium containing tissue fluid.

The next question concerns the antigenic qualities of this factor in relation to the induction of acquired resistance. Despite pointed attempts there has not yet been produced any evidence whatever that the substance is an antigen, or that the resistance which it induces depends upon the production of antibodies. Gladstone's culture factor, as well as lesion extracts, may induce solid resistance in rabbits without giving rise to an antibody detectable either by delicate in vitro tests or by the ability of the serum or of extracts of spleen and other antibody-producing tissues to transfer resistance passively. Continued vaccination does eventuate in a transferable protective activity of the serum (4b, 5a, 5e), but this activity cannot be absorbed from the serum, or neutralized, by the immunizing substance present in cultures or in lesions, nor by the living encapsulated bacillus itself. It seems difficult to avoid the tentative conclusion then that the protection-inducing substance is not an antigen, and that whatever the nature of the protective factor which it activates in the animal body, this does not fit our definition of antibody.

In summary then, a good deal of evidence accumulated over more than half a century has revealed that the relationship of the anthrax bacillus to acquired resistance in the rabbit and sheep does not fulfill the expectations which a superficial appraisal would certainly suggest. In the first place, a well-defined capsule which is related to virulence, and which has good antigenic qualities, fails to immunize against infection. Second, the factor which does immunize is apparently not a constituent of the bacillary cell at all, but a diffusible product of metabolism. And finally, the immunity response which this factor engenders, although it may become demonstrable in the serum, does not fulfill even the elementary requirement (i.e. absorption or neutralization by the factor inducing it) which would include it in our definition of an antibody.

These findings do not complete the immunologic history of anthrax resistance. Tomcsik and Ivanovics (2b) in the work described earlier did not limit their studies to the rabbits and guinea pigs in which anticapsular antibody failed to provide immunity to infection. In mice they found that this antibody did confer solid passive resistance. Of these results there can be no doubt; the authors found that sera containing anticapsular antibody alone provided protection, that absorption of these sera with purified capsular antigen removed the protective property, and that the injection of capsular substance into passively immunized mice abolished resistance by neutralizing the antibody. Further, it was shown that antibodies against other bacillary antigens were useless for protection (5g, 5h).

How can we explain this discrepancy in immunologic mechanisms as between different species of hosts? We must depart again from a natural assumption, in this case that the immunity relationships uncovered in one species of animal for a particular infectious agent extends to other species as well. There is available a well defined instance, that of acquired resistance to *Pasteurella pestis,* which reveals that two different immunizing factors in this organism account for the induction of resistance in two animal species, the guinea pig and the mouse ([6], see Chapter 20). We may tentatively infer that an analogous situation exists in the case of the anthrax bacillus. In the mouse the situation is similar to that seen with the pneumococcus, i.e. the capsular antigen which is concerned with bacillary virulence is also the immunizing substance in this animal, and antibodies against it are synonymous with acquired resistance. In other animals (the rabbit, sheep and guinea pig) the immunologic picture is a different one, as just described. What the situation may be in man remains still an open question.

Relation Between the Protection-Inducing Factor and Virulence of the Anthrax Bacillus. It was mentioned before that the virulent anthrax bacillus produces a well defined capsule when it grows in the tissues. Although this organism grows readily in ordinary media in vitro, it fails to produce the capsule except under special conditions; i.e. the presence of serum in the medium, or of an increased concentration of CO_2 in the atmosphere. Oddly enough, attenuated bacilli frequently produce the capsule in ordinary media as well as in the tissues, while totally avirulent organisms fail to produce it under any circumstances. This relationship is shown in Figure 45, in which the diagrams to the left in each column depict the colony forms, those to the right the bacilli. The intermediate or mucoid form may be at various levels of attenuation, and does not always produce capsules on ordinary medium. The essential features for our consideration here however are these: virulent forms **always produce** capsules in the tissues (or under in vitro conditions approximating the tissue environment) whereas totally avirulent bacilli **never do so** (7).

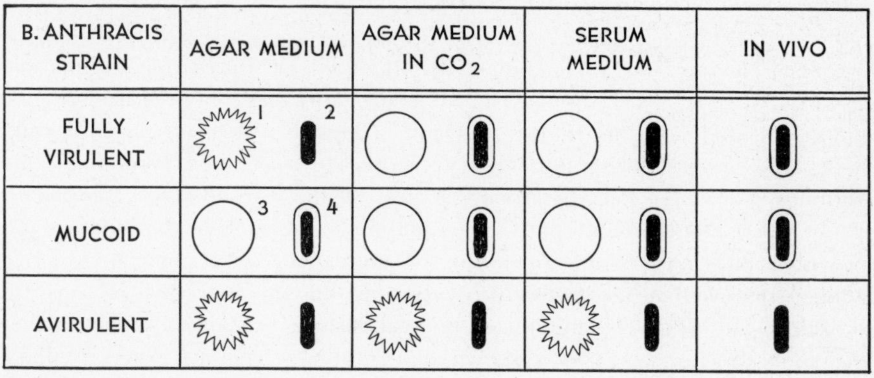

B. ANTHRACIS STRAIN	AGAR MEDIUM	AGAR MEDIUM IN CO_2	SERUM MEDIUM	IN VIVO
FULLY VIRULENT	1 2			
MUCOID	3 4			
AVIRULENT				

Fig. 45. Relation of capsule formation to environment in B. anthracis. 1, rough colony. 2, "rough" bacillus. 3, smooth colony. 4, "smooth" bacillus.

Bail and Weil (8) long ago described the existence of an "aggressin" in extracts of anthrax lesions—a substance which appeared to aid in the establishment of infection in the normal host. This substance was not well defined by Bail's work, since the extracts were not filtered free of bacterial cells. However, other early workers (3, 9) demonstrated a parallelism between virulence and the formation of capsules in vivo. More recent studies have provided a great deal of information about the nature and activity of the capsular material. Chemically the substance has been found to be proteinaceous (2a, 10) and is now known to be a polypeptide made up of 50 to 100 d (−) glutamic acid units (11). As to its activity as a factor in virulence, recent work by Watson and others (4b, 4c) has provided us with considerable information. These investigators (cf. Bail and Weil) have isolated a material from anthrax lesion filtrates which bears a close relationship to capsular polypeptide in its chemical and electrophoretic properties, though it diverges to some extent in its biologic activities. Injection of this substance intracutaneously into rabbits causes local changes very similar to those resulting from the injection of anthrax spores, including edema, fragmentation of collagen, hemorrhage and moderate cellular infiltration. Perhaps more to the point with respect to its influence in establishing the anthrax bacillus as an agent of infection in the tissues, this substance completely neutralizes the activity of an **anthracidal factor present in the tissues of normal animals.** In this important respect the lesion filtrate factor and the capsular substance isolated from bacillary cells were found to be of comparable activity.

It seems very likely then that the capsular polypeptide of the anthrax bacillus functions as a virulence factor by vitiating a bactericidal property possessed by normal tissues, and in this sense it may be the element which Bail described as "aggressin" half a century ago. Whether this last possibility is true requires specific study, because there has been no pointed evidence since Bail's reports that the lesion extract material will serve to convert a sublethal dose of anthrax bacilli into a lethal one.

We may conclude then that so far as the rabbit, guinea pig and sheep are concerned, the factor responsible for inducing resistance is entirely distinct from the substance (the capsular antigen) associated with the virulence of the bacillus, as shown by:

1. the failure of the antigenic capsular substance to induce effective resistance;

2. the failure of anticapsular antibody to transfer resistance passively;

3. the failure of capsular material to absorb the protective substances from the serum of immune animals; and

4. the chemical and biologic demonstration that another substance, distinct from the capsular polypeptide, is responsible for inducing immunity in these species.

In the case of the mouse on the other hand there is reason to believe that the virulence factor and the immunizing substance of the bacillus are identical, both being the capsular antigen.

Mechanism of Acquired Resistance to Anthrax Infection. The mechanisms through which acquired resistance may function in the rabbit group of hosts is not entirely clear, although intensive investigation of this point has been made by Cromartie and his colleagues (4a, 12). We might best approach the question by considering first what takes place in the normal rabbit injected with anthrax spores (12). During the first four hours germination and proliferation of bacilli proceeds rapidly, and local damage to tissues with an inflammatory response occurs. Progressive multiplication of capsulated bacilli continues until the death of the host, and during the entire process only few leukocytes venture into the damaged areas.

If next we consider the situation similarly studied in species of animals natively insusceptible to anthrax (the dog and swine), the picture unfolds differently. Here, a firm cutaneous nodule develops at the site of injection of spores. During the early hours after injection there occurs, as in susceptible hosts, germination of spores and a gradual increase in numbers of capsulated organisms. At 12 hours, however, a radical change occurs; the capsules disappear and the bacillary bodies stain unevenly. The organisms at this time are undergoing obvious deterioration, and this process is extracellular; the large numbers of leukocytes which have meanwhile collected about the foci of bacteria partake of them only occasionally, insignificantly so far as accounting for their destruction is concerned.

Turning now to the sequence of events in rabbits with acquired resistance to the bacillus the picture is found to be precisely the same as that seen in the natively insusceptible host, i.e. an initial multiplication of bacilli and, at about 12 hours after injection of the infective dose, a widespread loss of capsules and disintegration of bacterial bodies without the intervention of phagocytosis (4a). What kind of acquired mechanism may be responsible for this? We have no definite knowledge of a similar pattern of acquired immunity in other diseases; our well known models all depend, for the eventual destruction of bacteria, either upon the activity of lytic antibody and complement in the case of a limited group of gram-negative bacilli, or more generally upon phagocytosis and intracellular destruction. Some other mechanism appears to be at work here. Cromartie and his associates (4a) suggest that the fundamental process of acquired resistance is the same as that of native resistance in the insusceptible host, and that this consists primarily of an interference with the formation of capsular substance, since the disappearance of this appears to precede the disintegration of the bacterial bodies. Ascoli (13) suggested many years ago that the acquired resistance factor in anthrax may be antiblastic, or inhibitory to bacterial reproduction. If this is so, the effect does not become apparent for some hours since, as described, bacilli introduced into immunized hosts multiply for a time before destruction occurs.

If we assume that the factor which leads to the destruction of bacilli in the susceptible host with acquired resistance is the same as that active in the natively insusceptible host, our next question concerns the nature of this factor. It has been known for some time that an anthracidal substance exists in the tissues of normal animals. This material has been isolated and partially characterized chemically; it is a basic polypeptide with high lysine content, and is obtainable from leukocytes and other cells and tissues (14). This isolated substance is active in the destruction of *B. anthracis* in vitro, and may even act as a chemotherapeutic agent for anthrax infection in vivo. It is destructive for other species of bacteria also (15). It appears to be responsible for the inhibition of capsule formation which takes place in insusceptible animals. This substance is in turn counteracted by the capsular antigen (virulence factor) of the anthrax bacillus. Presumably then the insusceptible host possesses a sufficient level of the anthracidal factor to eliminate bacilli despite the neutralizing tendency of the capsular antigen, while the susceptible host either lacks a sufficient concentration or the ability to mobilize this substance for effective action.

It is difficult to conceive how this mechanism of native resistance in the insusceptible animal may take part also in the susceptible host with acquired resistance. We can only speculate that the susceptible animal may have less of this substance than the natively resistant, or that it is not so readily freed from the cells and made available for action, and that the process of immunization in some way results in a greater ability of the animal to make use of the factor, either by increasing its quantity or by mobilizing that already present in the tissues. On the other hand the anthracidal substance may have no role in acquired immunity at all; the entire process may depend upon some acquired ability of the host the nature of which still eludes us.

SUMMARY

The evidence at hand suggests rather clearly that acquired immunity to anthrax may be implemented in at least two different ways, depending upon the responding host. These are diagrammatically illustrated in Figure 46. In the rabbit, sheep and guinea pig the pathways of immunity can be sketched only tentatively, but the factual information now available is sufficient to reveal their uniqueness. The traditionally accepted identity between virulence

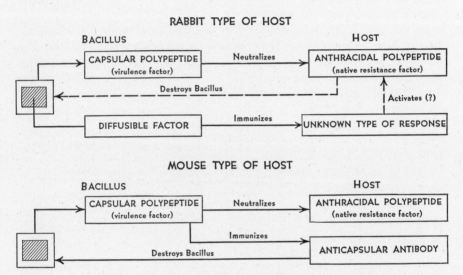

Fig. 46. Diagrammatic representation of probable relationships between bacillary factors (virulence and immunizing) and acquired resistance in hosts of rabbit and mouse types.

factor (the capsular antigen) and the immunizing substance of certain pathogenic microbes does not hold true in this instance. The protective response of the host is not directed against the capsular antigen, and furthermore it does not partake of the characteristics of antibody either in respect to its behavior as a serum constituent (absorbability or neutralizability by the substance which induced it) or its mode of action against the bacilli of challenge infection. The nature of this mechanism of protection can only be tentatively speculated upon now, as is done in the diagram. In the mouse on the other hand the mechanism of acquired resistance hinges upon the activity of anticapsular antibody. Whether this terminates infection by increasing the susceptibility of bacilli to phagocytosis, or whether by combining with capsular antigen it permits the anthracidal polypeptide of the tissues to become effective, is not known.

Which, if either, of these mechanisms may pertain to acquired immunity in man remains to be answered.

Practical Procedures for Vaccination. Pasteur's vaccinating procedure (16) is still employed for the immunization of livestock. For this purpose two vaccines are used, both attenuated but in varying degree by cultivation at 42° C. The first vaccine lacks virulence for rabbits and guinea pigs, but is virulent for mice, while the second lacks virulence only for rabbits. Of the first vaccine 0.1 ml. (for sheep) or 0.25 ml. (for cattle) of a 48 hour culture is injected subcutaneously. The same amounts and routes are employed with the second vaccine 12 days later.

Spores of avirulent bacilli may be more effective as a vaccine (17). It has been suggested also that lesion edema fluid may be useful for immunization (18).

In the case of all these vaccines the practical procedures for immunization are seen to coincide with the fundamental considerations discussed in respect to the induction of acquired resistance in hosts of the rabbit type. Thus, empirical experience has ruled out the use of killed encapsulated bacilli, whereas living attenuated or avirulent organisms have been observed to possess merit.

BIBLIOGRAPHY

1. Bail, O.   Centralbl. f. Bakt., I, Orig., 36:266, 1904.
2a. Tomcsik, J., and Szongott, H.   Ztschr. Immunitätsforsch. u. exper. Therap., 77:86, 1933.
   b. ———— and Ivanovics, G.   Ztschr. Immunitätsforsch. u. exper. Therap., 94:28, 1938.
3. Preisz, H.   Centralbl. f. Bakt., I, Orig., 49:341, 1909.
4a. Cromartie, W. J., Watson, D. W., Bloom, W. L., and Heckly, R. J.   J. Infect. Dis., 80:14, 1947.
   b. Watson, D. W., Cromartie, W. J., Bloom, W. L., Kegeles, G., and Heckly, R. J.   J. Infect. Dis., 80:28, 1947.
   c. ———— Cromartie, W. J., Bloom, W. L., Heckly, R. J., McGhee, W. J., and Weissman, N.   J. Infect. Dis., 80:121, 1947.
5a. Gladstone, G. P.   Brit. J. Exper. Path., 27:394, 1946.
   b. Schilling, S. F.   J. Am. Vet. M. A., 72:300, 1927.
   c. White, P. B.   Brit. J. Exper. Path., 27:356, 1946.
   d. Heckly, R. J., and Goldwasser, E.   J. Infect. Dis., 84:92, 1949.
   e. Gladstone, G. P.   Brit. J. Exper. Path., 29:379, 1948.
   f. Wright, G. G., Hedberg, M. A., and Feinberg, R. J.   J. Exper. Med., 93:523, 1951.
   g. Pochon, J.   Rev. Immunol., 4:457, 1938.
   h. Staub, A. M., and Grabar, P.   Ann. Inst. Pasteur, 73:1, 1947.
6a. Meyer, K. F.   Ann. New York Acad. Sc., 48:429, 1947.
   b. Baker, E. E., Sommer, H., Foster, L. E., Meyer, E., and Meyer, K. F.   Proc. Soc. Exper. Biol. & Med., 64:139, 1947.
   c. Meyer, K. F.   J. Immunol., 64:139, 1950.
7. Tomcsik, J.   Schweiz. Ztschr. f. Path. u. Bakt., 12:489, 1949.
8. Bail, O., and Weil, E.   Arch. Hyg., 73:218, 1911.
9. Gruber, M., and Futaki, K.   München. med. Wchnschr., 54:249, 1907.
10. Tomcsik, J., and Szongott, A.   Ztschr. f. Immunitätsforsch. u. exper. Therap., 76:214, 1932.
11a. Ivanovics, G., and Erdös, L.   Ztschr. f. Immunitätsforsch. u. exper. Therap., 90:5, 1937.
   b. ———— and Bruckner, V.   Ztschr. f. Immunitätsforsch. u. exper. Therap., 90:304, 1937.

c. Tomcsik, J., and Ivanovics, G.   Ztschr. f. Immunitätsforsch. u. exper. Therap., 93:196, 1938.

d. Hamby, W. E., and Ryden, H. N.   Biochem. J., 40:297, 1946.

12. Cromartie, W. J., Bloom, W. L., and Watson, D. W.   J. Infect. Dis., 80:1, 1947.

13. Ascoli, A.   Ztschr. f. physiol. Chem., 48:315, 1906; Centralbl. f. Bakt., 46:178, 1906.

14. Bloom, W. L., Watson, D. W., Cromartie, W. J., and Freed, M.   J. Infect. Dis., 80:41, 1947.

15. ――― and Blake, F. G.   J. Infect. Dis., 83:116, 1948.

16. Pasteur, L., Chamberland, C. E., and Roux, E.   Compt. rend. Acad. d. sc., 92:1378, 1881.

17. Gochenour, W. S., Schoening, H. W., Stein, C. D., and Mohler, W. M.   U. S. Dept. Agricult. Tech. Bull., 468, 1935.

18. Salsbery, C. E.   J. Am. Vet. M. A., 70:359, 1926-27.

20

PLAGUE

The recurrent epidemicity of plague in India and other parts of Asia has made this disease one of particular interest to students of immunity, for a practical solution of the disease problem would be greatly abetted by a dependable prophylactic agent. Theoretically perhaps an easier solution might be offered by rodent control measures, but economic factors have so far prevented their effective application. Vaccination has been used since Haffkine's preparation was introduced in 1897 (1). Thirty-five years later, after millions of doses had been dispensed and much study had been devoted to the subject, Sokhey (2) reviewed the questions still to be answered about the preparation and use of this vaccine. The list embraced practically every item pertinent to the intelligent use of an immunizing agent, viz., whether there are antigenic differences between strains of *Pasteurella pestis,* whether freshly isolated and virulent strains might be more suitable for the preparation of vaccine than laboratory strains, whether avirulent living or killed organisms could be used, what might be the optimal medium and conditions for cultivation of the microbes for vaccine preparation, and what might be the most favorable method for killing the bacteria so as to retain maximal immunizing potency. The fact that these questions had for so long remained unanswered suggests the difficulties that can be encountered in trying to solve the apparently straightforward question as to whether a vaccine can or cannot induce immunity. Since the time of Sokhey's audit a good deal has been learned about this problem and the nature of the information described in succeeding paragraphs will intimate why it was so long in coming.

The essential prologue to any discussion of the mechanics of acquired immunity is establishment of the basic premise that specific resistance is induced by the agent in question. In the case of *Pasteurella pestis* in the human host the evaluation of this point has been complicated by conflicting statements as to the quantitative aspects of resistance. Meyer (3) believes that postinfection immunity is only relative and temporary, lasting perhaps six or eight months, while other students of the disease consider it to be enduring (4, 5). Qualitatively however all are agreed that immunity follows the infection in man and in animals as well.

Protection-Inducing Factors. It is now established that the plague bacillus illustrates the possibility that different components of a microbial cell can be responsible for the immunization of different species of animals. This interesting fact of course complicates the development of our immunologic story, and from the practical standpoint brings up very obvious questions about the proper composition of a vaccine for use in human beings.

The background for this disclosure of the multiple immunizing capacities of the plague bacillus begins with a description of its antigenic constitution. Some years ago Rowland (6) demonstrated the presence of a gelatinous envelope about plague bacilli cultivated at 37° C. This was later affirmed by Schütze (7) who also verified older findings that the envelope is absent from all cultures grown at 20° C., is present to a slight degree about virulent organisms cultivated at 26° C., and occurs in all virulent as well as many avirulent strains grown at 37° C. (8). Rowland called this structure an envelope rather than a capsule because it lacked a limiting membrane and failed to take strains. He considered it to be an exudate in which the chains of bacilli are embedded. Etinger-Tulczynska (9) has later characterized bacterial envelopes or slimes as cellular secretions in distinction to the capsule which is part of the cell itself. Schütze (7) determined that this envelope substance is a heat-labile antigen, one of two main antigenic components of the organism. The other antigen, contained in the bacillary body itself, is relatively heat stabile. Both antigens induce antibodies which agglutinate the organism, in one case when it is surrounded by envelope, in the other case when it is uncoated.

More recently Baker and his associates (10a) have been able to furnish some chemical definition for these antigens. The envelope substance readily dissolves in normal saline and separates into three fractions on addition of increasing concentrations of ammonium sulphate. The first two fractions to precipitate are, respectively, a carbohydrate-protein and a protein. These substances are very much alike antigenically and are nontoxic for mice; the authors believe that the second may represent a degradation product of the first. The third fraction is also a protein and is highly toxic for mice, but its immunogenic features are not yet known. Amies (10b) has in part confirmed these findings.

The bacillary cell antigen is water insoluble, but it is as yet little-known chemically and is referred to simply as the somatic antigen (7, 11). There do not appear to be antigenic differences among strains of this bacillus, nor morphologic differences in colonial characteristics (5, 8, 12-15).

ANTIGENS RESPONSIBLE FOR THE IMMUNIZATION OF DIFFERENT SPECIES OF HOSTS. Some perception of the possibility that different bacillary substances might induce protection in different species of animals has existed for many years. In 1912 Rowland (16) had already observed that different strains of *P. pestis* could more effectively immunize either mice or guinea pigs, and later experiences suggested that the envelope substance is more concerned in the protective vaccination of the mouse, rat and monkey, while the bacterial cell itself is of prime importance in the guinea pig (12, 13, 15, 17-21).

This evidence has not been entirely straightforward, in part because it is so easy to multiply variables in experiments with this organism. For example, growth at low temperatures, at which the bacilli multiply most rapidly, results in bacteria without envelopes, and the heat-killing of enveloped organisms which have been cultivated at 37° C. is very likely to destroy the envelope. One must know therefore the details of preparation in order to be able to assess the probable antigenic content of a vaccine, and this kind of information is not always made clear in published reports. Aside from this source of confusion, Schütze (12) has found that while the envelope is of utmost importance for immunization of the rat, it is only partially effective in the mouse, and some factor in addition to the envelope may be necessary for the induction of the maximal immunity of which this animal is capable. This possibility had also emerged from the earlier studies of Rowland (6).

The recent immunologic work of Meyer and his associates with the chemically defined fractions previously described has dispelled much of the fog of detail through the use of these isolated substances for vaccination. In these experiments it was found that the water-soluble envelope antigen (fractions 1 and 2) in itself induces resistance in mice and rats as well as do whole enveloped bacilli. In these animals the water-insoluble somatic substance is without value for immunization. In the guinea pig the converse is true; only the cellular residue is capable of establishing immunity (3, 10a, 21). These findings thus epitomize the accumulated observations of a number of earlier investigators and leave little doubt of the essential validity of the conclusion that different bacillary factors account for acquired immunity in different species of animals.

We turn now to the possible nature of the immunizing activity of each of these bacterial factors; whether they owe their protection-inducing abilities to their properties as antigens or whether they may influence the body in some other way to become resistant to infection.

The envelope substance almost certainly immunizes by virtue of its antigenicity. It induces the formation of antibodies which precipitate with it in the test tube, and agglutinate enveloped bacterial cells, and an antiserum containing these antibodies can confer passive protection upon normal animals (10b, 18, 20, 21). In order to bring the evidence for this antigen-antibody relationship in protection to an unqualified conclusion it would be desirable to test whether absorption of an antiserum with envelope antigen removes its protective along with its serologic properties, for our knowledge of anthrax immunity (Chapter 19) reveals that a humoral resistance factor may not show the usual attributes of antibody. In the present instance, however, even without this final evidence it seems virtually certain that the anti-envelope antibody functions as the instrument of immunity.

The somatic immunizing factor can be characterized only vaguely; it is a water-insoluble property of nonenveloped bacilli which induces resistance in guinea pigs. It was mentioned before that serologic variation among strains of P. pestis has not been found to occur; this indicates a homogeneity of antigenic composition of the cell bodies of these organisms. However, not all strains of the bacillus possess the somatic immunizing factor for guinea pigs

(5, 18). This suggests that the immunizing factor may not be an antigen, for if it were its absence from certain strains should have been observed in the antigenic analyses. It would be of importance to the clarification of this point to determine whether the antibodies produced against the somatic antigen described by Schütze (7) have any relationship to the guinea pig immunizing factor.

The immunizing substance is frequently lacking in killed bacillary vaccines while it is much more regularly supplied (22, 23) by living avirulent organisms (with the exceptions just discussed). One possible explanation for this fact is that in vaccines of nonviable bacilli the immunizing substance is destroyed by the manipulations required for killing the cells; another is that avirulent bacilli may proliferate in vivo to supply more of the substance than can be provided by the fixed mass of bacteria injected as killed vaccine. One must keep in mind also the possibility that the immunizing factor may not be a fixed cellular constituent but rather a product of the metabolism of the living bacterium (24). Thus, we cannot be certain at the present time that the somatic immunizing factor is either an antigen or a chemical structure of the cell body.

In summary, a rather well defined antigenic envelope of the plague bacillus induces protective resistance in mice, rats and monkeys. This antigen is produced by virulent and many avirulent bacilli growing at body temperature. Another factor, associated with the bacterial body, is responsible for inducing immunity in guinea pigs. The characterization of this substance is still very meagre; its possible antigenicity has not been established, and there is as yet no clear evidence as to whether the resistance which it induces is based upon the stimulation of antibody formation.

Relationship of Virulence to the Protection-Inducing Factors. The plague bacillus causes marked pathologic alterations owing to toxicity associated with the cell body (5, 10a, 14). The toxin or toxins affect vascular endothelium; as a consequence hemorrhages and tissue necrosis occur. It injures also heart muscle and the adrenals (21, 25). These serious derangements however are secondary effects of pestis infection; they do not explain the virulence of the bacillus in terms of its initial ability to become established in the tissues. The toxicity in fact is a property of avirulent as well as virulent bacilli (17).

A search for the factors which may determine the initiation of infection reveals that in both the normal mouse and guinea pig avirulent as well as virulent bacilli can invade the visceral organs from a cutaneous focus. The avirulent bacilli may persist for perhaps a week (12, 17, 21). Only scant phagocytosis of both kinds of bacilli occurs during this interval. It seems probable that the envelope antigen discourages phagocytosis as do the capsules of certain other bacteria; it may be recalled that many avirulent strains of plague bacilli growing at body temperature form envelopes. By this token it is apparent that inhibition of phagocytosis alone cannot account for virulence for if it did we should expect all enveloped forms to set up infection (21, 26). Some additional vital factor must take part in determining the relative destinies of these two kinds of bacilli in the tissues; perhaps this resides in their relative abilities to utilize the host environment for their metabolic needs (27). Suggestive of this possibility is the observation of distinct differences in one enzyme activity between strains virulent and avirulent for the mouse. The former are uniformly better catalase producers than the latter (28). Perhaps suggestive of the same possibility is the fact that toward the end of an epizootic relatively avirulent strains of bacilli are often isolated from affected animals, but these are antigenically and colonially identical with virulent strains (29). Such strains have apparently lost an endowment which is not a fixed morphologic or antigenic property of the cell.

In the mouse-rat-monkey group of animals then the immunizing factor of the bacillus (envelope antigen) is probably related to virulence, but other factors of unknown nature, possibly metabolic, are also of great importance in its determination. Qualitatively at least this situation resembles that seen in the case of the pneumococcus-host relationship (Chapter 18).

For the case of the guinea pig conjecture must be more restricted since we have so little knowledge of the nature of the bacillary factor which immunizes this animal. Old work of Kolle and others (30) has shown that bacilli avirulent for the rat may be virulent for guinea pigs, implying that some other bacterial property occasions virulence for the latter species, but what this may be is not known. It is possible that here also the envelope antigen may be of importance, for it was pointed out before that enveloped organisms are not well phagocytized in the normal guinea pig. Again in conjunction with this there may be a metabolic trait which favors survival in the tissues of this host.

If the envelope proves to be concerned in virulence for the guinea pig, in this case it can have no relation to the immunizing factor for this animal since the envelope does not induce resistance in this species.

Mechanism of Acquired Resistance. Since the immunizing properties of the plague bacillus differ for the mouse and the guinea pig types of host, the possible mechanisms of resistance will be discussed separately for these two cases.

In the mouse, rat and monkey, as has been described, specific resistance may be invoked by administration of envelope antigen, and this substance appears also to be related to the virulence of the parasite. It seems well established furthermore that acquired immunity is effected through the action of antibodies upon this antigen, for in the tissues of vaccinated animals virulent bacilli are fixed at the site of injection by agglutination and are then intensively phagocytized (20, 21, 26). There is no evidence that the increased phagocytosis can occur independently of the serum antibody, i.e. that the phagocytes of the immunized animal themselves have any increased capacity to phagocytize these bacilli or to destroy them after ingestion (21, 31). This situation is then an analogue of that obtaining in the host immune to the pneumococcus.

It has been suggested that the immune body fluids alone may have some inhibitory effect upon plague bacilli, but it is not entirely clear that this is the case (16, 31, 32).

The mechanism of acquired immunity in the guinea pig is more difficult to assess. Since the surface envelope substance is not the immunizing factor in this case one would not expect to find increased phagocytosis in the immunized guinea pig, for we ordinarily consider opsonization to depend upon an alteration of the surface antigen of a microbe by an antibody directed against it. Nonetheless recent experiments indicate that intense phagocytosis does take place in this animal (21, 31, 33). We have thus to attempt to correlate two pieces of information which seem to be at odds—that a somatic factor of the microbe induces immunity, but that the expression of this immunity is through an increased phagocytosis of enveloped cells. Confirmation of this interesting possibility would be of great interest to students of immunity.

SUMMARY

The immunologic relationship between the plague bacillus and the monkey, rat and mouse group of hosts appears to be similar in its main outlines to that described for the pneumococcus. A surface antigenic factor induces specific resistance and in part at least accounts for the virulence of the microbe. Acquired immunity is mediated through the agglomeration of bacilli in the tissues and opsonization. The organisms are then destroyed by phagocytes.

In the guinea pig the relationship is obviously not the same, but beyond this the situation is difficult to define. It seems well established that a different bacillary factor induces resistance in this animal. The nature of this factor is still unknown; neither can we describe its relevancy to the virulence of the bacterium for this host, nor to the mechanism of resistance, which is described as dependent upon an intensified phagocytosis of bacilli.

Vaccination Procedures. The vaccine originally prepared by Haffkine in 1897 (1) consisted of bacilli cultivated for six weeks at about 27° C., killed by heat and phenolized. Reference to the preceding discussions of the immunizing factors of this bacillus will make it apparent that this mode of preparation bodes ill for the immunizing efficacy of the vaccine for either the monkey-rat-mouse group of animals or for the guinea pig. Cultivation at low temperature results in the development of little or none of the envelope antigen necessary for immunization of the former, and heat and phenol may destroy the efficacy of the somatic substance necessary for immunization of the latter. If the immunologic responsiveness of man is like that of either of these animal types, Haffkine's original vaccine might be expected to be entirely disappointing.

The technic of vaccine preparation in the Haffkine Institute has been modified from time to time so that by 1939 the temperature of cultivation had been raised to 37° C., at which envelope forms, and the heat treatment had been reduced from one hour at 70° C. to 15 minutes at 60° to 64° C. (2). A statistical study carried out by Taylor (34) indicated that this vaccine had prophylactic value for human beings.

During World War II the U. S. Army employed formalin-killed bacilli in doses of one to two billion for each injection, repeated three times. Meyer (3) found that human beings and animals who had received this vaccine, as well as others prepared by the use of other chemical and physical bactericides, produced antibodies which were passively protective for mice. Larger doses of bacilli (8 to 12 billion per dose) and the addition to the bacterial suspension of an adjuvant such as alum provided the most favorable results. It should be appreciated that the measure of effective immunization employed here is an inferential one; the ability of serum to protect mice is not necessarily an index of a similar ability to protect the individual who supplied it, unless the human being depends upon the same mechanism of resistance (anti-envelope antibody) as does the mouse. This we do not know.

During the past two decades interest in some countries has turned to the use of vaccines made up of living avirulent bacilli (3). Otten (35), Girard and Robic (36) and Pirie and Grasset (37) have published reports of several million human vaccinations with suspensions of viable bacilli possessing large envelopes, and with a marked capacity to immunize both mice and guinea pigs. No reversions to virulence of such strains have been reported, and since living organisms provide a means for attaining a large mass of antigen (or other immunizing factors) and a prolonged stimulus in the body, this kind of vaccine appears to be a most promising one for the protection of human beings. The same may be said for the use of isolated envelope substance (38).

Until we know which immunizing factor of the plague bacillus induces resistance in human beings it will be of importance to employ strains which are effective in inducing immunity both in guinea pigs and mice (39).

BIBLIOGRAPHY

1a. Haffkine, W. N.   Brit. M. J., 1:1461, 1897.
  b. ———— Indian M. Gaz., Orig., 32:201, 1897.
2. Sokhey, S. S.   Indian J. M. Research, 27:313, 1939.
3. Meyer, K. F.   Ann. New York Acad. Sc., 48:429, 1947.
4. Maxcy, K. F.   Rosenau's Preventive Medicine and Hygiene, New York, Appleton-Century-Crofts, Inc., 1951.
5. Jawetz, E., and Meyer, K. F.   J. Infect. Dis., 73:124, 1943.
6. Rowland, S.   J. Hyg., Plague Suppl. 3, 13:418, 1913-14.
7. Schütze, H.   Brit. J. Exper. Path., 13:284, 1932.
8. Wats, R. C., Wagle, P. M., and Puduval, T. K.   Indian J. M. Research, 27:373, 1939.
9. Etinger-Tulczynska, R.   Ztschr. f. Hyg. u. Infektionskr., 114:769, 1933.
10a. Baker, E. E., Sommer, H., Foster, L. E., Meyer, E., and Meyer, K. F.   Proc. Soc. Exper. Biol. & Med., 64:139, 1947.
  b. Amies, C. R.   Brit. J. Exper. Path., 32:259, 1951.
11. Schütze, H.   Brit. J. Exper. Path., 13:289, 1932.
12. ———— Brit. J. Exper. Path., 20:235, 1939.
13. Bhatnagar, S. S.   Indian J. M. Research, 28:1, 1940.
14. ———— Indian J. M. Research, 28:17, 1940.

15. Otten, L.   Indian J. M. Research, 24:730, 1936.
16. Rowland, S.   J. Hyg., Plague Suppl. 2, 12:358, 1912.
17. Jawetz, E., and Meyer, K. F.   J. Infect. Dis., 74:1, 1944.
18. Schütze, H.   Brit. J. Exper. Path., 15:200, 1934.
19. ——— Brit. J. Exper. Path., 13:293, 1932.
20. Bhatnagar, S. S., and Shrivastava, D. L.   J. Hyg., 44:307, 1946.
21. Meyer, K. F.   J. Immunol., 64:139, 1950.
22. Strong, R. P.   Philippine J. Sc., 1:181, 1906.
23. ——— Philippine J. Sc., 28:155, 1907.
24. ——— J. M. Research, 13:325, 1908.
25. Wayson, N. E., and McMahon, M. C.   J. Lab. & Clin. Med., 31:323, 1946.
26. Meyer, K. F., Hoessly, G. F., and Larson, A.   Science, 108:681, 1948.
27. Jawetz, E., and Meyer, K. F.   Am. J. Path., 20:457, 1944.
28. Rockenmacher, M.   Proc. Soc. Exper. Biol. & Med., 71:99, 1949.
29. Smith, D. T., and Conant, N. F.   Zinsser's Textbook of Bacteriology, 10th ed.,
       New York, Appleton-Century-Crofts, Inc., 1952.
30. Kolle, W., Hetsch, H., and Otto, R.   Ztschr. f. Hyg. u. Infektionskr., 48:368, 1904.
31. Jawetz, E., and Meyer, K. F.   J. Immunol., 49:15, 1944.
32. Rowland, S.   J. Hyg., Plague Suppl. 2, 12:1, 30, 1912.
33. Jawetz, E., and Meyer, K. F.   J. Immunol., 49:1, 1944.
34. Taylor, J.   Indian M. Research Mem., No. 27, p. 3, 1933.
35. Otten, L.   Med. v. d. Dienst. d. volksges. in Ned. Ind., 30:61, 1941
36. Girard, G., and Robic, J.   Bull. Soc. path. exot., 35:42, 1942.
37. Pirie, J. H. H., and Grasset, E.   South African M. J., 12:294, 1938.
38. Meyer, K. F., and Foster, L. E.   Stanford M. Bull., 6:75, 1948.
39. Bulloch, W.   A System of Bacteriology in Relation to Medicine, London, His
       Majesty's Stationery Office, 3:137, 1929.

21

CHOLERA

This acute intestinal disease, like plague, is continuously present in south-east Asia, particularly in India and part of China, occasionally spreading in epidemic form to contiguous territories such as Egypt, where a major visitation took place in 1947 and 1948. Again as in the case of plague the sanitary measures required to wipe out this water-borne disease are well enough understood, but they are difficult to apply in those parts of the world where the disease prevails.

Whether a significant degree of immunity is acquired to this intestinal infection is open to some question. The disease occurs only in the human being. It is thought that second attacks are uncommon for at least a few years following an initial bout. The closest approach to an experimental model of the disease was devised by Koch (1) who introduced vibrios directly into the duodenum of guinea pigs, or administered them orally following liberal doses of alkali and opium. Such prepared animals retain the vibrios in the intestinal tract for several days, and after recovery from nonlethal doses of the microbes show an altered receptivity to second infection (2).

Despite the superficial character of this infection, some specific resistance thus appears to be developed against it in animals and man (3).

Protection-Inducing Factors. The cholera vibrio possesses, in its smooth form, a heat-stable somatic (O) antigen which may vary among strains and seems to depend for its serologic specificity upon a polysaccharide component (4, 5, 6). There are additional antigens of the body of the organism as well as of the flagellum; these latter seem to take no part in the induction of resistance (7).

The possible role of the O antigen in invoking immunity in mice has been studied most recently by Burrows and his associates (7). This method of study in an unnatural host is made possible by challenging animals with bacteria suspended in mucin and injected into the peritoneal cavity (8). Heat-killed organisms induced resistance as measured both by active and passive protection tests, but it was not clear in Burrow's experiments that the somatic antigen alone accounted for this. Antisomatic antibodies were produced, but after antisera had been absorbed with the somatic antigen they still retained protective ability. Thus, whatever the immunizing ability of somatic antigen there appears to be some other protection-inducing bacillary factor unrelated to it.

The possible identities of such additional factors is suggested by studies of the cytoplasmic toxins of the microbe. A substance of phospholipid nature has been isolated from *Vibrio comma* by Burrows and co-workers (9, 10). This substance increases the permeability of intestinal tissue to the passage of fluids. In vaccinated animals it induces antibodies which neither agglutinate the bacterium nor neutralize the toxic substance itself, but convey protection to mice against the intraperitoneal type of infection just described. It is possible that this response represents the protective factor unabsorbed from antisera by somatic antigen, though the point requires clarification. Another toxic constituent of this bacterium has been described by Burnet and Stone (11) as present in culture filtrates. This causes shredding of intestinal epithelium. It is also an antigenic substance, and antisera may be developed against it by vaccination of rabbits and human beings with killed bacilli (12, 13); such antisera neutralize the toxicity of the substance. The possible relationship of these antibodies to protection has not yet been studied.

We have some information then about three factors of the cholera vibrio which may take part in inducing resistance to this bacterium. Against one of these factors—the somatic antigen—agglutinating and lytic antibody is produced. Against the second—a lipoidal toxic substance—a serologically undetectable but protective humoral factor is elaborated. (It should be noted that the antigenicity of lipoidal substances as a class is still a doubtful issue. See Chapter 4.) Against the third factor, also a toxin, neutralizing antibodies are formed. If we could be certain of all these points they would adequately account for acquired immunity to the disease, but the study has its complexities and more investigations will be required before these data can be accepted as factual.

Relation Between Protection-Inducing and Virulence Factors. Cholera in man is a most superficial bacterial infection, the vibrios remaining so well confined to the lumen of the intestine that they rarely penetrate the submucosa or appear in the blood stream. The essence of this disease apparently is due to local injury of the intestinal wall effected by bacterial somatic toxin; as a consequence of this salts and fluid are lost to the body. The great import of this local alteration to the affected host is reflected in the efficacy of simple parenteral replacement of water and salts in modifying the course and outcome of the disease. Reimann (14) states that the mortality may be reduced from the usual 50 to 70 per cent level to 5 per cent simply by providing saline infusions.

The superficial nature of this infection—the fact that it does not gain a foothold in the tissues—makes it seem unnecessary to seek an aggressive factor, such as the surface O antigen, to account for the establishment of this bacterium in the host, as may be the case for example with the *salmonellas* (15). The ability of a vibrio to produce cholera would seem to depend upon its capacity to derange the intestinal surface through its toxicity. Some evidence is at hand to incriminate the intoxicating properties of strains of the organism in this respect.

Somatic toxins of *V. comma* have been variously characterized since Roux in 1896 reported that such substances diffused through collodion membranes (16). Some years later a toxic protein and a glyco-lipid of the Boivin type were described as accounting for the endotoxicity of the organism (17) but these observations have not been brought to a satisfying conclusion. The best known of the so-far described toxic factors from the standpoint of relationship to virulence have been the two endotoxins mentioned in preceding paragraphs, the lipoidal substance of Burrows (18) and the mucinase of Burnet and Stone (11). The lipid toxin was found to decrease in amount in strains of organisms which were waning also in their ability to produce enteric infections in guinea pigs (9, 10), a parallelism which suggests some significance in disease production. The activity of this toxin is to cause a considerable increase in the permeability of intestinal strips to fluids in vitro (10), again a strong intimation of a close relationship to one of the characteristic occurrences in the disease itself.

The second toxic factor acts also upon the guinea pig intestine. When a section of ileum is exposed to this substance in vitro the epithelium shreds and flakes much as does the lining of the human intestine in cholera to result in the rice-water appearance of the stool.

Both of these toxins appear to be part of the total cytoplasmic poison of *V. comma.* Whether they are related to each other is not known, but both seem to relate very suggestively to the essential events distinctive of cholera as a disease of human beings.

In résumé, two cytoplasmic toxins which are probably concerned in the pathogenic activity of the cholera vibrio may also be responsible for the induction of specific resistance to this organism. On the other hand the somatic antigen appears to have some connection with the immunizing capacity of the organism, but it cannot be assigned a role in virulence.

We must remain content for the present to regard the cholera vibrio as a probable but still incompletely understood example of a bacterium which owes the major features of its virulence to the same substances which are in part responsible for inducing specific protection in the host.

Mechanisms of Acquired Resistance. As pointed out earlier, it is possible to establish enteric infection in the guinea pig which has been pretreated with alkali and opium. Burrows believes that this is a true infection as attested by proliferation of organisms over a period of several days and the shredding of intestinal epithelium, though little or no diarrhea occurs (18). This experimental model of the human disease permits the study of specific resistance mechanisms which we hope may bear upon these processes in the human being also.

First we have for consideration several antibody responses which may be related to immunity. These antibodies—to somatic O antigen, to lipid endotoxin, and to the shredding factor—may themselves be related, but since we cannot be certain of this now they will be discussed as individual entities.

The anti-O antibody is apparently directed against a polysaccharide-

containing antigen of the smooth vibrio. This is the antibody which agglutinates the organisms and causes their lysis in the presence of complement,
for both of these activities may be negated by the addition of O antigen to
antisera (19). Lysis of *V. comma* constitutes the classic example of this particular activity of antibody upon bacterial cells; Pfeiffer (20) pointed out in
the last century that antibody and complement effectively destroy vibrios
injected intraperitoneally into actively or passively immunized guinea pigs.
It is said that the sera of most human beings convalescent from cholera are
capable of lysis (3). Further, it is recognized that during recovery from this
disease the bacteriologic process usually stops abruptly; within a few days
the excretion of vibrios ceases entirely, unlike the situation which often obtains in salmonellosis or in bacillary dysentery. This might suggest the lysis
of bacteria as a final thrust on the part of the host immunized by his infection
(though the advent of bacteriophage, which seems to occur frequently in
this disease, may determine this end result as well as lytic antibody).

Despite these logical bits of information converging to favor the view
that the anti-O lytic response may account for resistance to cholera vibrios,
there are at least two obstacles to the final acceptance of such a conclusion.
The first is the finding by Burrows (7) mentioned earlier, that sera deprived
of this antibody through absorption nevertheless retain protective powers.
The second is the question whether these antibodies which are so spectacu-
larly efficient in the peritoneal cavities of guinea pigs can be brought to bear
upon the organism in its intestinal locale in the spontaneously infected human
subject. If antibody can reach and act in this site, is complement also available and active in the enteric contents?

The first of these questions may perhaps be answered by a discussion of
a second antibody response, that against the lipoidal endotoxin. Though this
antibody does not neutralize the characteristic toxic activity of the antigen
which stimulates it, it nonetheless appears to protect mice against the organism itself (9, 10). This observation is remarkable on two counts; because it
implicates a lipid as an inducer of antibody whereas antigenicity is not clearly
a property of this class of substances, and because it implies a protective
activity of this antibody in the absence of a demonstrable neutralization of
the toxic activity of the substance which induces it. If these points are veri-
fiable however, the antilipoidal response may prove to be the protective humoral substance which Burrows found in antisera after adsorption of anti-O
antibody. In what way it may act upon the microbe is still a mystery.

The final protective antibody possibility is that against the mucinase factor
of Burnet and Stone (11). This antibody directly neutralizes the epithelial-
shredding activity of filtrates of *V. comma* in vitro (12, 13); presumably it
may also do this in vivo, though actual protection tests have apparently not
been carried out.

We return now to the crux of the entire question of antibodies as a mechanism of immunity in cholera—whether they can appear and function in the
intestinal content. In his experiments with guinea pigs, Burrows (2) observed

an altered receptivity to a second administration of vibrios which was indicated by resistance to several lethal doses and by a sharp reduction in the number of bacteria recoverable from the feces soon after their ingestion. It was found then that agglutinating antibody was present in the feces following the first exposure to organisms, whether this was through ingestion or parenteral introduction of killed vaccine. This antibody was specific in its agglutinating activity, was absorbed by vibrios, and was protective in mice; presumably it was anti-O substance. The presence in human feces of antibodies against dysentery bacilli had been described some time earlier by Davies (21). Burrows calls this "coproantibody" and regards it as a secretion of the intestine rather than a simple result of inflammatory exudation (22). There is evidence to support this viewpoint, including such findings as those of Barksdale and Ghoda (23) that in human beings with bacillary dysentery caused by Sonne or Flexner organisms the sera and feces show differences in the specificity of agglutinin content. Thus, in all cases of Sonne infection studied the serum reacted only with phase I antigen while fecal extracts showed both phase I and II agglutinins. Similar qualitative differences were noted in respect to the Flexner bacilli. Generally, antibodies appeared earlier in the feces than in the serum.

The importance of intestinal antibody to resistance of guinea pigs to cholera infection is suggested by Burrows' observation (18) that unless this was present at the time of reinfection there was no altered receptivity to the vibrios. The presence of coproantibody could be demonstrated in guinea pigs for about 30 days following a primary infection; in vaccinated human beings it persists for about three months.

The information so far available does not clarify the kinds of antivibrio substances which may appear in the intestinal content. Whether it is entirely antisomatic antibody, or whether antiendotoxic antibodies may also materialize here, remains to be clarified. Nor do we know as yet whether complement is also present to permit the anti-O substance to cause lysis of the microbes. But it seems that the principle is established that antibody does manifest itself in the enteric lumen in response to intestinal microbes.

Before closing this discussion of mechanism of resistance to cholera we might inquire whether any other mechanism than antibody may be implicated in this. Tentative evidence for this possibility again comes from studies of Burrows (9, 10) with guinea pigs vaccinated against the lipoidal endotoxin. As stated earlier, antibody against this factor will combine with it, but will not neutralize its ability to affect the permeability of intestinal strips. Further, if intestinal strips from normal animals are soaked in such antilipoidal sera they do not gain the ability to resist the action of the toxin. Yet when such strips are obtained from actively vaccinated animals they are found to be resistant to this effect of the endotoxin (24). Burrows suggests the presence of antibodies within the macrophages of the intestinal wall to account for this, but if antibodies supplied in profusion from outside are unable to divert the endotoxin it is difficult to see why they would be more effective when they are bottled up inside macrophages. This effect is more easily understood if we assume that vaccination induces some alteration in the intestinal tissue which influences its capacity to permit the passage of fluids. Such an effect in response to an antigenic stimulus is without precedent, and it would be of utmost interest to have such studies confirmed and extended.

SUMMARY

So far as we know now, the constituents of *V. comma* which may induce specific resistance are three: a somatic polysaccharide-containing antigen of the colonially smooth bacterium, a lipoidal endotoxin, and an endotoxin with the enzymatic properties of mucinase. From the mechanistic standpoint, it seems unlikely that the somatic antigen has anything to do with the virulence of the organism, for it is difficult to conceive how a microbe which fails to invade the tissues of the host could profit by the properties usually associated with O antigen (e.g. discouraging phagocytosis) to establish itself as a pathogenic agent. The nature of cholera makes it seem likely that the endotoxins of the organism may account for its pathogenic activities. The two endotoxic factors which have been discussed apparently explain the outstanding features of the disease: loss of fluids through the intestines, and shredding of the intestinal mucosa. Thus, it seems likely that two of the three factors tentatively proposed as inducers of specific resistance to cholera are also factors which lend virulence to the causative organism.

Acquired immunity to the vibrio seems to be implemented in part by the occurrence of antibodies against these various factors. The possible functions of these antibodies in protection have been discussed; the manner in which they may arrive in the intestinal lumen is thought to be through a process of secretion by the intestine itself. In addition to the antibodies, there is some evidence to suggest that the intestinal wall may become altered by immunization so that it no longer responds to the lipoidal endotoxin of the vibrio with increased permeability to fluids.

These possible mechanisms embrace two essential protective effects; the first, a defense against the damaging endotoxins derived from bacterial bodies; the second, an antibacterial activity suggested by the abrupt disappearance of vibrios from the feces of patients within a short time after the termination of the disease (3).

Much of the information dealt with here requires confirmation and extension before this diagrammatic representation of relationships can be considered more than tentative.

Practical Procedures for Vaccination. Apparently any one of a variety of procedures for producing a nonviable vaccine is equally satisfactory for prophylactic purposes in man, as judged by antibody responses and passive protection tests (12). The assessment of the value of these vaccines in terms of protection of the individuals vaccinated is much more dubious, but as mentioned before, a recent opinion based upon available statistics favors the viewpoint that some degree of effective protection is established in vaccinated populations (3).

Whatever the method of vaccine preparation large numbers of bacilli are employed, usually 8,000 to 10,000 million organisms per milliliter. One currently employed vaccine (25) consists of agar cultures killed by heat and preserved with 0.5 per cent phenol. An initial dose of 0.5 ml. is followed by a second dose of 1.0 ml., 7 to 10 days later. Booster injections of 1 ml. are recommended at six month intervals. The epidemiologic opinion which dictates this frequent revaccination coincides with Burrows' (18) observations of the brief persistence of coproantibody following immunization.

BIBLIOGRAPHY

1. Koch, R. Deutsche med. Wchnschr., No. 37A:1, 1885.
2. Burrows, W., Elliott, M. E., and Havens, I. J. Infect. Dis., 81:261, 1947.
3. ——— Mather, A. N., Elliott, M. E., and Wagner, S. M. J. Infect. Dis., 79:159, 1946.
4a. Yang, Y. N., and White, P. B. J. Path. & Bact., 38:187, 1934.
 b. White, P. B. J. Path. & Bact., 41:567, 1935.
 c. ——— Brit. J. Exper. Path., 17:229, 1936.
5. Linton, R. W. Bact. Rev., 4:261, 1940.
6. Burrows, W., Mather, A. N., McGann, V. G., and Wagner, S. M. J. Infect. Dis., 79:168, 1946.
7. ——— Mather, A. N., Elliott, M. E., and Havens, I. J. Infect. Dis., 81:157, 1947.
8. Griffitts, J. J. U. S. Pub. Health Rep., 57:707, 1942.
9. Burrows, W., Mather, A. N., Wagner, S. M., and McGann, V. G. Proc. Soc. Exper. Biol. & Med., 57:308, 1944.
10. ——— Proc. Soc. Exper. Biol. & Med., 57:306, 1944.
11. Burnet, F. M., and Stone, J. D. Australian J. Exper. Biol. & M. Sc., 25:219, 1947.
12. Singer, E., Wei, S. H., and Hoa, S. H. J. Immunol., 59:341, 1948.
13. ——— Wei, S. H., and Hoa, S. H. J. Immunol., 60:181, 1948.
14. Reimann, H. A., Chang, G. C. T., Chu. L. W., Liu, P. Y., and Ou, Y. Am. J. Trop. Med., 26:631, 1946.
15. Boivin, A. Ann. Inst. Pasteur, 67:377, 1941.
16. Metchnikoff, E., Roux, E., and Salimbeni, G. Ann. Inst. Pasteur, 10:257, 1896.
17a. Gallut, J. Ann. Inst. Pasteur, 69:123, 1943.
 b. Grabar, P., and Gallut, J. Ann. Inst. Pasteur, 71:321, 1945.
18. Burrows, W., Elliott, M. E., and Havens, I. J. Infect. Dis., 81:261, 1947.
19. Linton, R. W., and Shravastava, D. L. Proc. Soc. Exper. Biol. & Med., 31:406, 1933.
20. Pfeiffer, R. Ztschr. f. Hyg. u. Infektionskr., 18:1, 1894; 19:75, 1895; 20:198, 1895.
21. Davies, A. Lancet, 2:1009, 1922.
22. Koshland, M. E., and Burrows, W. J. Immunol., 65:93, 1950.
23. Barksdale, W. L., and Ghoda, A. J. Immunol., 66:395, 1951.
24. Burrows, W., Wagner, S. M., and Mather, A. N. Proc. Soc. Exper. Biol. & Med., 57:311, 1944.
25. Parish, H. J. Bacterial and Virus Diseases, Antisera, Toxoids, Vaccines and Tuberculins in Prophylaxis and Treatment, Baltimore, Williams and Wilkins Co., 1948.

22

BACILLARY DYSENTERY

Surveys carried out in the United States over a period of years have revealed that most severe acute diarrheal disease is caused by *Shigella,* and for every ill person there are 8 to 10 who carry the organism without symptoms. The distribution of infection fluctuates widely even in neighboring areas, dependent largely upon the hygienic mores of the population group studied. In a recent study, for example, only two isolations of a *Shigella* were made from 5,000 fecal samples cultured in New York City, while in areas of Georgia, New Mexico, and California the infection rate ran as high as 20 per cent (1). As is well known, dysentery may become a much more prominent and very debilitating disease among military personnel under war conditions, or even in barracks or aboard ship (2).

In this country the most frequent infecting agent is *Sh. paradysenteriae,* with *Sh. sonnei* second in importance. The type species and the most violent disease producer is *Sh. dysenteriae,* but this is only infrequently found in this part of the world. Other pathogenic species, also not commonly found here, are *Sh. ambigua* and the para-Shiga group (3).

Like cholera, bacillary dysentery occurs spontaneously only in man, though under the forced draft of large doses of organisms or of folic acid deficiency monkeys may be infected (4). As with the other diseases which have been discussed, the question arises here whether significant immunity can be acquired by man through infection or vaccination. The answer to this is complicated by the fact of heterogeneity of the somatic antigen of the commonest infecting species, *Sh. paradysenteriae,* for if this antigen is responsible for the induction of immunity, then obviously the matter of antigenic type is of utmost importance in assessing the occurrence of resistance to second or subsequent attacks. Hardy and Watt (5) have weighed this factor in a study of the disease in institutional inmates and found that clinical infection provides a degree of protection against subsequent clinical attacks by a homologous strain of *Shigella* but, strangely enough, little resistance against subclinical infection with such a strain. No cross protection was found at all. The epidemiologic pattern of the disease in different age groups of the population also suggests the acquisition of specific immunity with increasing opportunities for exposure (1).

Protection-Inducing Factors. Evidence is at hand that two kinds of bacillary substances may act as potential instigators of immunity. Two of the

311

species, *Sh. dysenteriae* and *Sh. ambigua,* upon autolysis, release antigenic toxins. Though these are not, strictly speaking, exotoxins they are usually described by this term because their poisonous properties are readily neutralized by antibody, and because they are relatively heat labile. A second substance occurs as a component of all shigellae, though with different antigenic specificities in different species and in types within species. This is a somatic (O) antigen of Boivin type, a toxic substance of a class which occurs generally in the colonially smooth forms of enteric bacilli (6). The toxicities of these antigenic substances are not appreciably neutralized by specific antibodies and they are heat stable, hence the appellation endotoxin is applied to them.

SHIGA EXOTOXIN. Of the two exotoxins which have been described in the literature, little information is available concerning that of *Sh. ambigua.* This discussion, therefore, will be concerned with the toxin of *Sh. dysenteriae* (7). This is a protein constituent of colonially rough as well as smooth forms of the bacillus and is released upon autolysis or disruption of cells (8). The toxin is produced in largest quantity under highly aerobic conditions in a medium free of inorganic iron (9), and it has been purified (9, 10, 11). Treatment with formalin converts it to a toxoid which can excite the formation of antitoxin in man and animals (10, 12), but which induces no antibody visibly active upon the bacillus itself (10).

There is some issue concerning the breadth of protection conferred by vaccination with toxoid. It is generally agreed that toxoid-treated animals become resistant to the effects of the toxin itself (2, 9, 13), but in addition some investigators have reported an immunity to the bacilli; (9, 13b, 13d); this point is not settled (2, 13a). Unfortunately for the clarification of this issue, toxin has in some instances been prepared from S forms of bacilli (13b, 13d), so that somatic antigen may have been included in the preparations employed for vaccination. Dubos and Geiger (9) obtained toxin from rough organisms, thus precluding the presence of O antigen, and found the derived toxoid to activate resistance in mice not only against the toxin and virulent Shiga bacilli, but against *Sh. paradysenteriae* and *Sh. sonnei* as well. Since the latter species possess no exotoxin and, as will be described later, are unlike the Shiga bacillus with respect to the somatic antigen, it is difficult to account for this cross protection.

Boroff (14) disagrees with the entire concept of an exotoxin in *Sh. dysenteriae.* He believes that the microbe possesses but one toxic factor, the somatic antigen, which is present in S and R forms but which is complete and hence antigenic only in the former, and that this may immunize animals to the toxin (i.e. the endotoxin) as well as to the bacillus. This viewpoint needs verification.

SOMATIC ANTIGENS. The O antigens of smooth phase shigellae are complexes of polysaccharide, phospholipid and protein. The somatic antigen of *Sh. dysenteriae* is homogeneous as is that of *Sh. ambigua,* but two antigenic types as well as phase variations of *Sh. sonnei* are known, and *Sh. paradysenteriae* is considerably more heterogeneous than this. The antigenic classification of types of this organism has not been settled (2, 15, 16), but the extent of antigenic heterogeneity is indicated by one system of classification which proposes 19 serologic types in *Sh. paradysenteriae* (16, 17).

These somatic antigenic complexes are readily extractable from the bacterial cells by a variety of chemical methods (6c, 18). The polysaccharide component determines the antigenic specificity of the complex (19, 20) and in itself can elicit antibodies in man and the mouse (18e). Injection of these complexes into animals and human beings evokes agglutinins for the bacterial cells, and such antisera confer protection upon mice against the homologous virulent bacilli (13d, 16, 18e, 19, 20, 21). Further, it has been demonstrated that an isolated O antigen may absorb from the serum of rabbits vaccinated with formol-killed bacilli 97 per cent of its precipitative (and agglutinative) antibody and 95 per cent of its mouse protective properties, and that the polysaccharide portion of the complex alone can remove 90 per cent and 77 per cent, respectively, of these activities (20). It seems quite evident, therefore, that a major part of the antibacillary protective antibodies induced in man or animals by killed *Sh. paradysenteriae* must be attributed to the activity of the somatic antigen in the body. The judgment of the protective properties of these antibodies, however, is based upon passive transfer to mice, a species which is not susceptible to natural infection with these organisms. As in the case of *Vibrio comma,* here also challenge organisms are mixed with mucin and injected into the peritoneal cavities of the test animals. Unprotected mice die of intoxication caused by the progressive multiplication of bacilli in this locale while animals given antibodies are able to destroy the organisms and survive. Whether this kind of experiment portrays the mechanism of resistance in man to an enteric infection is a question which will be discussed later; the evidence from such experiments does reveal, however, that antibodies with antibacterial activity are induced by this specific constituent of the bacillary cell.

Despite this evidence for the probable identity of agglutinating and protective antibody as a response to somatic antigen, some studies with the sera of vaccinated animals and human beings (22) and with human convalescent sera (23) have failed to verify this parallelism. In some instances the agglutinating activity is not consistent with the protective value of a serum; in other cases agglutinins may be entirely undemonstrable while the serum is protective for mice. These irregularities may be explainable in several ways, as discussed in relation to similar findings with antipneumococcal serum (see Chapter 18) and in a more general sense in Chapter 9. Thus one portion of antibody isolated from a serum and found to be active in agglutination may not necessarily be as effective in protection as another fraction of antibody from the same serum which is poorer in in vitro serologic activity. Or a serum may contain univalent antibody which is entirely devoid of agglutinating ability but is nonetheless able to combine with antigen and to effect the changes (e.g. opsonization) which suffice to give it a protective quality in vivo. In this connection Morgan and Schütze (24) studied sera from individuals vaccinated with *Sh. dysenteriae* and applied to these the "developing" technic of Coombs (see Chapter 8). The agglutinating titers of these sera were in some instances amplified 18-fold over those obtained by the conventional titration procedure, a finding which implies the presence in these sera of a good deal of nonagglutinating antibody.

In summary, there appear to be two kinds of potential protection-inciting factors in the shigellae. In the case of *Sh. dysenteriae* (and perhaps also of *Sh. ambigua*) the proteinaceous exotoxin is one of these factors. It induces antitoxins and perhaps immunity against the bacilli themselves. The second factor occurs in all species of shigellae; this is the somatic or O antigen (endotoxin). The ability of the O antigens to engender resistance demonstrable by passive tests in animals is high; whether they may also induce appreciable protection against the spontaneous disease in man will be discussed later.

Relation Between Protection-Inducing Factors and Virulence. It is difficult to know how to judge the virulence characteristics of the dysentery bacilli. The nature of the infection occasioned in man by these organisms stands midway between that produced by the cholera vibrio and the typhoid bacillus. Cholera, as discussed in the preceding chapter, is a disease in which the relationship of the etiologic agent to the host's tissues is of a most superficial kind. The organisms remain virtually outside the body, in the intestinal lumen; it is the cytoplasmic toxin of disintegrating vibrios which appears to account for the disease. For this organism there seems, therefore, no reason to postulate a mechanism which might permit vibrios to establish themselves in the host's tissues; hence the virulence of *V. comma* was discussed from the standpoint of its capacity to alter the normal functioning of the intestinal structure. In the case of the typhoid bacillus the disease is also primarily an intestinal one, but this bacterium has an obvious relationship to the tissues of the host. It enters the blood stream and subsequently establishes itself not only in intestinal tissue but in other organs as well. The dysentery bacilli are neither as superficial as the *V. comma* nor as ubiquitous as *S. typhosa*. These microbes remain confined to the wall of the large bowel and occasionally of the terminal ileum. Inflammation of the mucosa may be followed by necrosis and ulceration, and on the floors of the ulcers dysentery bacilli are frequently found in large numbers. Sometimes the bacilli may reach mesenteric lymph nodes, but they do not invade the blood stream nor set up in distant tissues or organs.

It seems likely that in pathogenic characteristics this organism should be regarded as more akin to the cholera than the typhoid agent. If this is true then again we are not concerned with mechanisms which may explain the ability of the organism to proliferate in the tissues; the alterations brought about in the affected host do not depend upon this, but rather upon injury to the intestinal wall caused by the toxic constituents of microbes which remain aloof from the tissues. Adopting this premise we shall discuss the virulence of the shigellae from the standpoint of how they bring about intestinal damage. There is evidence that both factors described as possible protection-inducing substances may be related to the pathogenesis of dysentery.

Shigella dysenteriae causes a disease with a higher mortality potential than do the other members of the genus, and this is generally ascribed to its possession of exotoxin. In the rabbit this toxin induces paralysis and other nervous system manifestations, but such phenomena occur infrequently in man with Shiga dysentery. Infants may develop convulsions and nuchal rigidity more frequently than do adults, but this may come about under other circumstances than infection with *Sh. dysenteriae* and is probably not a specific effect of the toxin in question. More related to the intestinal disease of human beings are the changes induced in rabbits and monkeys following intracutaneous or intravenous injection of the toxin, consisting of hemorrhagic patches in the intestinal mucosa as well as focal hemorrhages in other tissues (13a, 25). These changes appear to result only from hematogenous transport of the toxin, for if this is given orally to normal monkeys there is not sufficient absorption to produce these effects (25). Perhaps, however, if the mucosa has been already damaged by other bacillary constituents in the course of an infection, this toxin may exert a direct local effect upon the vascular system of the bowel wall. Some observations of the activity of this toxin in human beings have been described by Dubos and Geiger (9). Laboratory workers who had accidentally inhaled powdered exotoxin developed fever, headache, nausea, and diarrhea.

It is of interest that this toxin may be produced by rough as well as smooth forms of *Sh. dysenteriae*. So far as this pathogenic activity is concerned, therefore, it is not necessarily a property of those bacteria to which, from the standpoint of colonial structure, we ordinarily ascribe pathogenic powers. But as will be discussed in succeeding paragraphs, the S form of the bacillus may bring about other changes in the host without which the exotoxin may not be effective.

The somatic (O) antigens which all colonially smooth shigellae possess have properties which might account for the establishment of dysentery bacilli in the tissues, including a repellent effect against phagocytic cells (26) and the induction of leukopenia (19). As said before, however, there is little reason to believe that such aggressive activities are necessary to account for the ability of dysentery organisms to cause disease. More to the point are the damaging effects of these substances upon the intestinal tissues directly. Following parenteral injection in various experimental animals they cause pronounced enteritis marked by intense vascular congestion and sometimes petechiae (13a, 27). Along with this they occasion a general nonspecific intoxication with fever and malaise. In the case of this substance there is again reason to ascribe some aspects of the disease process to an isolable factor of the organism. Oddly enough, however, the ordinarily nonpathogenic enteric bacillus *E. coli* possesses an O antigen with similar properties (27). It is apparent from this fact that the toxicity of the somatic antigen is not in itself sufficient to account for the local pathologic alterations caused by these organisms, but we are so far ignorant of what other factors may be responsible.

In summary, the exotoxin of *Sh. dysenteriae* and the somatic antigens of shigellae generally appear to be capable of instigating protective antibodies in vaccinated or infected hosts demonstrable by animal tests, and these same factors seem to have a part in the pathogenesis of bacillary dysentery. However, other unknown factors are doubtless also concerned in the pathogenic activities of these bacilli.

Mechanisms of Acquired Resistance. As determined by the mouse protection test, acquired resistance to the shigellae appears to be directed, via antibodies, against those components which we have considered to be virulence factors of the organisms. The difficulty comes in interpreting this evidence gleaned from a forced intraperitoneal or intracerebral infection in an unnatural host in relation to immunity processes in the human being. Watt and De Capito (28) in a study of human dysentery could find no correlation between the presence or absence of humoral antibodies and the occurrence of subsequent infection. Several interpretations may be put upon these findings. One is that antibodies have no part in the specific immunity of man to dysentery. This negative viewpoint seems unjustified if we recall that the immunity observed in institutional inmates by Hardy and Watt (5) followed the lines of antigenic type specificity, a fact strongly suggestive of a role of antibodies in the process. A second is that antibody activities determined by serologic test do not necessarily reflect antibacterial efficacy, as discussed earlier in this chapter. A third, and perhaps most likely interpretation, takes into account the observations of coproantibody described in respect to cholera (see Chapter 21). It appears, surprisingly enough, that the antibodies which materialize in the intestinal lumen may have little relevancy to those appearing in the blood stream, either from the standpoint of kind or of time of appearance and disappearance. Several studies have elaborated this viewpoint. Thus, Barksdale and Ghoda (29) found in patients with dysentery caused by *Sh. paradysenteriae* or *Sh. sonnei* an earlier appearance of antibodies in the feces than in the blood, and qualitative differences in the kind of antibodies in these locales, i.e. the occurrence of antibodies to phase I and II Sonne antigens in the feces and of phase I antibodies alone in the serum.

If antibodies do appear preferentially in the gut of infected or vaccinated (30) individuals, what protective activity may be expected of them?

We may surmise that if the Shiga antitoxin appears in this location it can directly neutralize the toxin of *Sh. dysenteriae,* but the author is unaware of efforts to detect this antibody in the intestinal contents.

Antisomatic antibodies have been reported to exist here (29, 30). These do not neutralize the poisonous properties of the O antigen which, like other endotoxins, is not appreciably influenced in this respect by combination with antibody. A possible explanation for this lack of neutralizability may be found in the fact that while the toxicity of the O complex seems to reside in its protein portion (19, 31), its antigenicity is determined by the polysaccharide component. It would seem then that anti-O antibody simply fails to combine with the poisonous portion of the complex.

We must then discount a direct somatic toxin-neutralizing ability of this antibody, but there is another activity through which this antibody may possibly interfere with the intoxicating property of the organism. Combination with bacilli may lead to their early elimination by phagocytes before sufficient bacterial substance can accumulate to cause injury to the intestinal wall. If this is a true picture of events, we should regard this activity of anti-O antibody as only variably decisive, for the carrier rate following attacks of dysentery, though not so high as after typhoid fever, is considerably higher than that following cholera. Hardy and Watt (5) have found that about 80 per cent of individuals retain dysentery bacilli for an average period of 34 days following recovery. Possibly this may be because the antibody-complement lytic mechanism is very effective in the destruction of *V. comma*, but is of less, if any, significance in the case of the shigellae.

The broad protection reported (9) to follow vaccination of mice with *Sh. dysenteriae* exotoxin alone, effective against other species and demonstrable by a greatly enhanced bactericidal activity of these sera upon the various shigellae in vitro, cannot be adequately discussed from the standpoint of resistance mechanisms at this time. If antibody is concerned here it is difficult to reconcile the absence of specificity of action with the facts presently known to us. Some other explanation may have to be sought for the cross protection suggested by these experiments.

To summarize, one is able to rationalize the specific immunity of man to bacillary dysentery on the basis of enteric antibody responses to the specific somatic antigens, probably acting in the main through opsonization of the microbes. In the case of the exotoxic species, neutralizing antitoxins may be an additional response of potential protective merit. The net effect of these antibody activities would be to eliminate the toxic factors of these organisms which in part at least account for their pathogenic action. So far as we can judge now, the relationship between parasite and host in this disease seems again to exemplify a situation in which pathogenic and protection-inducing factors are synonymous, with specific resistance directed against these factors through the medium of antibodies. More detailed information may alter this viewpoint, for it is far from being an unqualified one.

Vaccination Procedures. The eventual emergence of a satisfactory vaccine for the control of bacillary dysentery will depend upon several considerations including (a) a satisfactory amalgam of antigens to cover the most frequent etiologic species and types, (b) the reduction of the toxicity of the O antigens, and (c) the demonstration that these vaccines can afford protection against enteric disease in man. Some information is available on each of these points.

(A) BROAD ANTIGENIC PROPERTIES. The most encouraging lead with regard to breadth of protection is provided by the work just described with Shiga toxoid (9). Less inclusive, but promising, has been the use by Perlman, Binkley, and Goebel (18e) of the somatic antigen of *Sh. paradysenteriae* type V (antigenic classification of Andrewes and Inman). In human beings this evokes antibodies cross reacting with type Z organisms, and as pointed out by these workers, the V, Z, VZ and Y types are closely related serologically. They suggest that a mixed vaccine containing types V and W of *Sh. paradysenteriae, Shigella* sp. Newcastle, and *Sh. sonnei* would anticipate the greatest number of enteric infections in this country.

(B) DETOXIFICATION. The detoxification of Shiga exotoxin may be accomplished by formalinization or by ultraviolet irradiation (9, 12, 13b). Toxicity for man, however, is not entirely eliminated by either method.

There is more difficulty in the attempt to reduce the toxicity of isolated somatic antigens or of the whole bacillary vaccines of which they are a part. Halbert (32) has employed both these preparations in saline-in-oil emulsions (see description of adjuvants in Chapter 6) and found a considerable reduction of toxicity along with enhancement and prolongation of antibody responses in animals. However, later work with similar vaccines in human beings has proved disappointing in respect to inducing humoral agglutinating and mouse protective properties (33). The authors' suggestion that too few organisms may have been employed (1.2 billion) finds support in another study (22) in which the total vaccinating doses employed in children ranged between 15 and 30 billion organisms by the subcutaneous route; here appreciable agglutinative and mouse protective responses occurred. It appears that adequate *Sh. paradysenteriae* vaccines will necessarily contain large concentrations of bacilli. Vaccination by the intravenous route results in a considerable response to relatively small amounts of vaccine (10 million organisms total), but the severe systemic reactions evoked puts this procedure outside the pale of practicality.

Ultraviolet irradiation has been suggested for the detoxification of somatic antigens. Goebel and co-workers (18f) have concluded that the reduction of toxicity is so closely paralleled by loss of antigenicity as to make this an unpromising approach, but others (34) have been more optimistic about this method.

It has been reported that acetylation of the O antigen of *Sh. dysenteriae* with acetic anhydride brings about a 60-fold reduction of toxicity for mice and rabbits with retention of ability to induce protection, but not agglutinins (35). A variety of other chemical procedures has been employed with varying degrees of success (18f). The problem of securing a favorable antigenicity/toxicity ratio is still an open one, though probably not far from a conclusion sufficiently favorable to permit the practice of routine vaccination in human beings where this is indicated.

(C) PROTECTION OF MAN. Thus far there is no settled conviction about the usefulness of vaccines in man; reports of their efficacy run the gamut from high optimism to disappointment (2). Shaughnessy (36) has described a well-controlled human experiment wherein 53 adults were immunized with heat- or ultraviolet-killed organisms of mixed types of *Sh. paradysenteriae,* and were subsequently challenged by the oral administration of living bacilli of one of the types represented in the vaccine. Clinical dysentery occurred as extensively in the vaccinated subjects as in a control group of 30 unvaccinated individuals; the incidence of disease was over 60 per cent. This kind of controlled experiment in human subjects cannot often be carried out; it is, therefore, unfortunate that the results obtained are so apparently discouraging. There are good reasons for repetition of such an experiment, however: first, the total dose of vaccine employed contained 2 billion organisms of the type subsequently employed to test resistance, and as indicated by later data (22, 33) this is probably insufficient for the proper immunization of human beings, and second, the immunizing strain against which the challenge infection was made was highly virulent for mice but, as later found, not for man, and homologous virulence may be an essential characteristic for a successful vaccine. Other suggestions for improvement in experimental conditions, such as wider spacing of immunizing injections, were made by the investigators themselves.

BIBLIOGRAPHY

1. Watt, J.   Shigellosis, in Rosenau, Preventive Medicine and Hygiene, ed. by K. F. Maxcy, New York, Appleton-Century-Crofts, Inc., 1951.
2a. Weil, A. J.   J. Immunol., 55:363, 1947.
  b. —— Ann. Rev. Microbiol., 1:309, 1947.
3. Felsen, J.   Bacillary Dysentery, Colitis and Enteritis, Philadelphia, W. B. Saunders Co., 1945.
4. Dack, G. M., and Petran, E.   J. Infect. Dis., 55:1, 1934.
5. Hardy, A. V., and Watt, J.   J.A.M.A., 124:1173, 1944.
6a. Boivin, A., and Mesrobeanu, L.   Compt. rend. Soc. de biol., 112:76, 1933.
  b. —— Mesrobeanu, I., and Mesrobeanu, L.   Compt. rend. Soc. de biol., 113:490, 1933.
  c. Raistrick, H., and Topley, W. W. C.   Brit. J. Exper. Path., 15:113, 1934.
7. Olitsky, P. K., and Kligler, I. J.   J. Exper. Med., 31:19, 1920.
8. Okell, C. C., and Blake, A. V.   J. Path. & Bact., 33:57, 1930.
9. Dubos, R. J., and Geiger, J. W.   J. Exper. Med., 84:143, 1946.
10. Anderson, C. G., Brown, A. M., and Macsween, J. C.   Brit. J. Exper. Path., 26:197, 1945.
11. Olitzki, L., and Bichowsky, L.   J. Immunol., 52:293, 1946.
12. Farrell, L., Fraser, D. T., and Ferguson, H.   Canad. J. Pub. Health, 35:311, 1944.
13a. Steabben, D.   J. Hyg., 43:83, 1943.
  b. Branham, S. E., and Habel, K.   J. Immunol., 54:305, 1946.
  c. —— and Carlin, S. A.   J. Infect. Dis., 83:66, 1948.
  d. Morgan, W. T. J., and Schütze, H.   Lancet, 2:284, 1943.
14a. Boroff, D. A.   J. Bact., 57:617, 1949.
  b. —— and Macri, B. P.   J. Bact., 58:387, 1949.
15a. Boyd, J. S. K.   J. Hyg., 38:477, 1938.
  b. —— Tr. Roy. Soc. Trop. Med. & Hyg., 33:553, 1940.
  c. Madsen, S.   On the Classification of the Shigella Types, with Special Reference to the Flexner Group, Copenhagen, E. Munksgaards Forlag, 1949.
16. Weil, A. J., Black, J., and Farsetta, K.   J. Immunol., 49:321, 1944.
17. —— Black, J., and Farsetta, K.   J. Immunol., 49:341, 1944.
18a. Morgan, W. T. J.   Biochem, J., 30:909, 1936.
  b. —— Biochem. J., 31:2003, 1937.
  c. —— and Partridge, S. M.   Biochem. J., 34:169, 1940.
  d. —— and Partridge, S. M.   Biochem. J., 35:1140, 1941.
  e. Perlman, E., Binkley, F., and Goebel, W. F.   J. Exper. Med., 81:349, 1945.
  f. Goebel, W. F., Binkley, F., and Perlman, E.   J. Exper. Med., 81:315, 1945.
  g. Binkley, F., Goebel, W. F., and Perlman, E. J.   J. Exper. Med., 81:331, 1945.
  h. Boivin, A., and Mesrobeanu, L.   Rev. Immunol., 1:553, 1935.
  i. Freeman, G. G., Challinor, S. W., and Wilson, J.   Biochem. J., 34:307, 1940.

19. Tal, C., and Olitzki, L.   Immunol., 58:337, 1948.
20. Perlman, E., and Weil, A. J.   Proc. Soc. Exper. Biol. & Med., 60:58, 1945.
21a. Boivin, A., and Mesrobeanu, L.   Compt. rend. Soc. de biol., 125:796, 1937.
 b. —— and Mesrobeanu, L.   Compt. rend. Soc. de biol., 128:446, 1938.
22. Cooper, M. L., Tepper, J., and Keller, H. M.   J. Immunol., 60:189, 1948.
23. —— and Keller, H. M.   J. Immunol., 58:357, 1948.
24. Morgan, W. T. J., and Schütze, H.   Brit. J. Exper. Path., 27:286, 1946.
25. Branham, S. E., and Habel, K.   J. Bact., 54:57, 1947.
26. Boivin, A., and Delaunay, A.   Ann. Inst. Pasteur, 71:168, 1945.
27. —— Compt. rend. Soc. de biol., 133:252, 1940.
28. Watt, J., and De Capito, T. M.   U. S. Pub. Health Rep., 60:642, 1945.
29. Barksdale, W. L., and Ghoda, A.   J. Immunol., 66:395, 1951.
30. Davies, A.   Lancet, 2:1009, 1922.
31. Perlman, E., and Goebel, W. F.   J. Exper. Med. 84:223, 1946.
32a. Halbert, S. P., Smolens, J., and Mudd, S.   J. Immunol., 51:39, 1945.
 b. —— Mudd, S., and Smolens, J.   J. Immunol., 53:291, 1946.
33. Mudd, S., Halbert, S. P., and Smolens, J.   J. Immunol, 58:33, 1948.
34. Barnes, F. W., Dewey, M., Henry, S. S., and Lupfer, H.   J. Immunol., 56:255, 1947.
35a. Treffers, H. P.   Science, 103:387, 1946.
 b. —— Rubin, B. A., and Bell, C. A.   Federation Proc., 5:255, 1946.
36. Shaughnessy, H. J., Olsson, R. C., Bass, K., Frieiver, F., and Levinson, S. O.
      J.A.M.A., 132:362, 1946.

23

TUBERCULOSIS

Introduction: the Existence of Acquired Immunity to the Human Tubercle Bacillus. The literature dealing with the question of acquired resistance in man and animals to the tubercle bacillus is voluminous, but it is possible to sift certain fairly well-established concepts from the mass of controversial reports. The first important question which concerns us here is whether 'or not resistance to this organism can be acquired. Experimental work leaves no doubt on this score so far as animals are concerned. Koch (1) first demonstrated the ability of the infected guinea pig to resist superinfection, and thousands of observations have since supplemented his finding that infection with virulent or attenuated organisms is followed by a degree of acquired immunity.

For man the question has not been easily answered largely because of the widespread occurrence of symptomless infections and the chronic nature of the disease process. These factors make it difficult in the presence of clinical disease to know whether the patient is suffering from the result of his first exposure to the organisms or has had an antecedent potentially immunizing infection, and how long the process has been going on. Pathologists have had a better opportunity to formulate a retrospective conception of the disease and its modifications through acquired immunity, and the generally accepted viewpoint is formulated in these terms: When the **first infection** occurs via the respiratory tract a focus is established in the lung, frequently close to the pleura, and soon afterward the inflammatory process extends to the regional lymph nodes at the hilus. This line of tissue reaction can sometimes be seen in roentgenograms. Now if the process subsides these lesions eventually show varying degrees of fibrosis and calcification, and the bacilli in most instances disappear. Pathologic, and sometimes roentgenologic, evidence remains. The original focus together with the satellite involved node is termed the **primary complex.** The primary lesion may of course become progressive, but for the most part it does not. This form of tuberculous involvement is called the childhood type of disease because it occurs chiefly in the lower age groups; it is in the early years that initial infections are (or were in past years) most apt to develop. However, the childhood type of disease can also occur in adults previously unexposed to the disease.

If some time later a second infection happens either from without or through reactivation of bacilli implanted in the initial infection (it is very difficult to know which has taken place), then a lesion usually develops in a lung apex, but unlike the original focus this one shows no tendency to produce lymphangitis and lymphadenitis. This lesion is localized although it may, because of the nature of the tissue changes which occur in this disease, become progressively larger, and from it bacteria and contents may later be mechanically discharged into eroded bronchi or blood vessels. But if the pulmonary architecture is not too disrupted this secondary lesion remains a localized one, and this is considered an indication that the body has gained some property by virtue of which the bacteria are now confined to the area where they have set up, and through which they may eventually be again suppressed. This ability of the body with acquired resistance may account also for the relative infrequency of involvement of extrapulmonary sites such as the intestines, despite the persistence in many instances of bacilli in the sputum for long periods of time. It is in primary tuberculosis that extrapulmonary complications are most apt to occur (2). In addition, the lesions in the individual with reinfection tuberculosis show pathologic evidence of retarded development with a tendency to fibrosis which is not seen in primary progressive lesions in previously unexposed individuals. There is then pathologic evidence of localization of bacilli and of their inhibition or destruction in the individual who has previously experienced a primary infection. This process is referred to as the adult type of tuberculosis, and by inference it signifies the development of disease in the presence of immunity acquired from an antecedent exposure (3).

The qualifications which this brief synopsis requires are discussed thoroughly and clearly by Rich (4). For present purposes it is necessary to deal with one complication which has a profound bearing upon the question of the existence of acquired immunity in man. This is the fact of widespread occurrence of clinically apparent tuberculosis of reinfection type in persons over 40 years of age. Before this time the majority of active cases of pulmonary tuberculosis are of primary type (2, 5). But after 40 most cases are found, increasingly with age, to be of the reinfection type, occurring in persons who have already had a primary infection as determined by pathologic examination (2). Thus, most instances of clinically manifest pulmonary tuberculosis in the older age groups of the population are concentrated in a smaller segment of the population in which old primary lesions are demonstrable; those very people who, as the result of previous infection, should have acquired resistance are in fact most frequently ill of the disease. This is disconcerting if one thinks of the primary infection as conferring immunity, and at the present time there is no certain explanation for this observation. Two main possibilities, however, are discussed below.

We might first ignore the pathologic evidence just described and consider whether individuals with healed primary lesions may be actually more susceptible to the tubercle bacillus than persons without evidence of previous infection. It may be that the individuals who develop tuberculous lesions are to begin with genetically more susceptible to the organism, and whatever immunizing the primary infection may accomplish does not alter this basic susceptibility sufficiently to ward off subsequent attack. This does not speak against the fact of acquisition of resistance; it merely suggests quantitative modifications. Or it may be that the primary lesion in some way increases the body's susceptibility. Myers (6) favors this viewpoint on the premise that the primary infection renders the tissues allergic to the bacillus, hence more readily injured by it in any future engagement. The soundness of this concept suffers from lack of evidence that hypersensitivity existing at the time of reinfection with the relatively few bacilli involved can result in tissue destruction and malignancy of the disease process. In our own experience with animals rendered allergic by the administration of isolated components of the bacillus and subsequently infected, we have found no alteration in the course of the disease from that seen in untreated controls simultaneously infected.

If we take the other side of the argument, that a primary infection does confer resistance, how can we reconcile this with the finding that progressive pulmonary disease strikes most often in those who have had such an infection? It seems likely that this may happen because the primary lesion itself provides the microbial seed for later reanimation (5c, 5d). Whether the seed is planted at the time of primary infection by way of the blood stream, or whether the healed primary lesion itself later becomes activated and permits a few bacilli to escape into the blood stream to be implanted in other areas of the lung, is not certain. But it seems that a small dormant focus may become active at a time when resistance is depressed, and that this circumstance happens most frequently after the age of 40, for Medlar's (2) figures show that reinfection lesions occur less frequently in age groups below this. It is noteworthy that these reinfection lesions occur chiefly in areas of the lungs (dorsally and cephalic, especially in the upper lobes) where local physiologic conditions are probably most favorable for the proliferation of the tubercle bacillus (7).

Our current information available from pathologic and clinical studies makes it appear then that the years from 15 to 40 constitute a period of especial susceptibility to the development of **primary** progressive tuberculosis, but of little tendency to the development of reinfection or reactivation tuberculosis in the presence of a healed primary infection which has provided acquired immunity. After 40, however, the situation changes so that the risk of primary infection is less (possibly because those who have evaded it through their earlier years owe their escape to a constitutional insusceptibility which continues to function), but reactivation of an old primary infection is now favored because various environmental and physiologic factors may depress the acquired resistance gained in the past, and the bacilli are already at hand to take advantage of such circumstances. This is not to say that fresh reinfections do not occur in individuals with healed primary lesions; the possibility of this event would vary with the degree of exposure, the level of acquired immunity, and other factors. But we can best account for the large incidence of clinical pulmonary disease in individuals with old primary complexes by considering exogenous reinfection a relatively infrequent occurrence.

The viewpoint favored here is by no means unanimously held. The pros and cons of this question are discussed in detail by Rich (4), and clinical studies bearing upon this point are described in the literature (8).

We should pause for a moment to consider the very pertinent question in this connection of the worth to an individual of a healed primary infection for subsequent protection from clinical tuberculous. This is impossible to answer succinctly; the same element carries with it protective potentialities as well as the germ of a possible future active lesion. Perhaps for those whose adult lives are to be spent in intimate exposure to cases of tuberculosis the protective aspect outweighs the potentially dangerous one, while for those individuals (comprising the great majority of the population) whose associations with sources of tubercle bacilli are only occasional and transient there would seem to be little profit in having had a primary lesion, for the disease might well be evaded entirely without need for the benefits of specific immunity.

Another route is open to us for deciding whether the human being is able to acquire resistance to the tubercle bacillus—by seeking information derived from controlled observations following the use of vaccines in previously uninfected subjects. The vaccine most widely employed in man is prepared from a living attenuated bovine bacillus called "Bacille Calmette-Guérin" or BCG. Although this vaccine has been used for almost 30 years, statistically significant results have begun to emerge only recently. These data are discussed more fully in the final section of this chapter dealing with vaccination; here it need only be said that there is at hand satisfactory evidence that the vaccination of normal individuals with viable attenuated bacilli results in a decrease in incidence of clinically apparent disease and in mortality, and that the course of the infection is modified in those who develop the disease in the face of the immunizing treatment.

It seems safe to conclude then that the human being is capable of acquiring a degree of resistance to the tubercle bacillus. The discussion which follows is, therefore, not limited to the guinea pigs, rabbits, and mice from which a good deal of basic immunologic information has been obtained.

Immunity-Inducing Factor in the Tubercle Bacillus. Like other microorganisms the tubercle bacillus possesses antigens to which immunologic responses, antibodies and hypersensitivity, appear. It has not been established, however, that any of these antigens is the factor responsible for inducing specific resistance.

How far the question of the identity of the immunizing factor is from resolution is revealed by the lack of agreement on so general an aspect as whether or not killed bacillary vaccines are effective immunizing agents. The immunizing capacity of attenuated living organisms is almost unanimously conceded on the other hand. Much has been written on both sides of this matter concerning the efficacy of killed bacillary vaccines, of which samples are given in references (9). These works include experiences with organisms killed by a variety of chemical and physical methods, and the interpretations of results are poles apart. There is no need to belabor the issue now; eventually a conviction will emerge from the mass of experimental data still being garnered. The author's own experiences with killed bacillary cells, as well as with various cellular constituents, have spoken against the viewpoint that killed bacilli call forth significant immunity in guinea pigs, and tentatively at least this opinion seems tacitly supported by the fact that for the essayed immunization of human beings attention has for years remained focused upon the use of viable vaccines (notably BCG) despite the troublesome question of safety which the employment of a living vaccine raises. This persistent preoccupation with a viable vaccine appears to imply a general opinion that, as immunizing agents, living bacilli are at least considerably superior to killed cells.

The question of the usefulness of killed bacilli for immunizing purposes is fundamental to the entire concept of what microbial factor may be involved in immunizing the body to tubercle bacilli, for if only living organisms are effective it may be by virtue of some cellular property of a nature still unfamiliar to us, and not necessarily a fixed cellular antigen. This might be, for example, a diffusible factor released by proliferating organisms into the medium (or tissues), a possibility made cogent by the findings with the anthrax bacillus (see Chapter 19). With this potentiality in view the author and Dr. J. E. Forney have repeatedly injected into animals filtrates of young cultures of human type tubercle bacilli grown in the presence of normal plasma or whole blood, without eliciting resistance to challenge infection. Fresh, cold saline extracts of heavily infected tissues have similarly failed to show the presence of an immunizing factor.

It may be that an antigen of the tubercle bacillus *is* concerned in inducing protection, but that in the process of killing the cells this substance becomes so altered as to be ineffective. Or there may be a quantitative difficulty involved, since living bacilli proliferate in vivo while in the case of dead organisms the quantity of any potentially immunizing substance is restricted to the amount injected. Finally, there may be an antigenic constituent of bacilli growing in the tissues which is absent from those cultivated in vitro. This would, of course, be lacking in a killed bacillary vaccine.

In the author's laboratory several experimental procedures have been employed to gain information about these possibilities that an antigen is masked in one of the ways mentioned. The first type of experiment has been based upon the use of an immunizing agent of established efficacy—BCG vaccine—in a manner calculated to exacerbate its antigenic efficiency, with subsequent testing to find whether its immunizing potency is simultaneously increased. For this purpose paired groups of animals were immunized with BCG vaccine, in one case incorporated in an immunologic adjuvant (water-in-oil emulsion) and in the second instance suspended in ordinary saline suspension. Immediately before challenge with virulent organisms, blood samples were taken to determine the relative antibody titers in the two groups. A readily measured antibody response, that to the protein of the bacillus, was utilized as the index of antigenic stimulation by the two vaccines. In one such experiment those animals vaccinated with bacilli in adjuvant showed an appreciably higher incidence of measurable antibody, and one must assume that other antigens of the cells incorporated in the adjuvant may similarly have provoked responses more effectively (see Chapter 6). Despite this intensification of antigenic stimulus by the adjuvant no difference could be detected in the degree of protective resistance between the two groups. Both revealed very significant immunity as compared with unvaccinated control animals. This experiment suggests that a factor of nonantigenic nature may be concerned in protection-induction, but it cannot be considered as conclusive because resistance to the tubercle bacillus may reach the maximum of which the animal is capable in response to bacilli without adjuvant, and causing an increased antibody formation through the use of adjuvant may not necessarily alter the quantitative aspects of immunity itself even if this were dependent upon antibodies.

Next, we have sought evidence of whether an antigen of the bacillary cell is related to resistance by trying to detect, in animals possessing resistance, the presence of a distinctive antibody which may be absent in animals vaccinated with nonimmunizing preparations (e.g. defatted bacillary cells). Workers who employed various conventional serologic procedures in the past were not able to establish a relationship between a visualizable antibody response and immunity (10, 70). An extensive trial of this kind carried out in the writer's laboratory has included a comparison of the sera of animals immunized with BCG with the sera of guinea pigs which were vaccinated with variously killed cells or with isolated constituents of the bacillus. The latter animals were proved by challenge inoculation to be lacking in resistance. Tests have included the usual ones of agglutination and complement-fixation with whole cells and cellular components, and in addition the Elek modification of the precipitation test (11), the Coombs procedure for detecting nonagglutinating antibody (12), and the Pfaundler method of cultivating organisms in medium containing the serum under test in order to bring out slight degrees of agglutination. With none of these procedures have we been able to establish a liaison between the possession of a particular antibody and the existence of immunity. In fact, the antibody contents of the sera of BCG vaccinated animals are generally poorer, qualitatively as well as quantitatively, than those of animals vaccinated with some of the preparations (e.g. defatted bacilli) which do not instigate resistance. These results are of course subject to the suspicion which must attach to any correlative studies of this kind, especially when the answer is a negative one. As was pointed out in Chapter 9 and in various chapters in this section dealing with other infectious diseases, complications arise in attempted demonstrations of this kind even when a good deal is known about the relationships of antigens to resistance. In the present instance the search is still perforce a blind one. The point which gives this evidence some weight is not that animals with immunity may have little or no demonstrable antibodies, but that those **without immunity** have every one of the antibodies found in the immune, and often in greater amounts and incidence.

Another approach which should be applied to this question would make use of bacilli obtained directly from infected tissues for vaccination; perhaps these may reveal the presence of an antigenic substance which is lost to the microbes growing outside the body. To the writer's knowledge, such experiments have not yet been reported.

There is thus as yet no satisfactory evidence concerning the nature of the immunizing factor of the tubercle bacillus, either as regards its general or its specific characteristics. The experiments described have by no means exhausted the possibilities lying within the area in which they have probed, for in every case the proper conditions for demonstrating the factor may have been missed. Whatever the resistance inducing factor may be, it seems either to be partially or wholly destroyed upon the death of the bacterial cell, or it can only be produced by viable bacilli metabolizing in the tissues. The evidence available so far provides little comfort for the concept that a bacillary antigen is involved in the induction of acquired immunity to tuberculosis, but this viewpoint is of course subject to revision. The question will be discussed further in the subsequent section of this chapter dealing with the mechanisms of acquired resistance.

Relation of Immunity-Inducing Factor to Virulence of the Tubercle Bacillus. * In the absence of definite knowledge of an immunizing factor it is manifestly difficult to discuss its possible relationship to the virulence mechanisms of the bacterium. The task is not an impossible one, however, for some deductions can be made from the immunizing behavior of avirulent strains; moreover, the study of virulence on its own account has contributed to our understanding of this disease-producing agent.

We should first inquire about the general basis upon which the virulence of the tubercle bacillus may be grounded. As discussed in Chapter 3, there are two general premises from which to begin the rationalization of the virulence processes of an infectious agent, and in this instance we must consider both of them.

There is first the possibility that the disease-producing microbe possesses no virulence factor in the sense of an aggressive property which can interfere

---

* The discussion of virulence of tubercle bacilli can become considerably complicated if we include the pathogenic capacities of different variants of the microbe in various species of animals; for example, the ability of the human bacillus to progress in the human being and the guinea pig, but not in the rabbit and cow; and the ability of the bovine bacillus to infect all four species. If we were more enlightened about the factors which account for these differences in pathogenic ranges it would be of utmost interest to include these examples in a discussion of virulence. But this kind of information is practically nonexistent. Consequently our discussion is limited with a few exceptions to the comparison of virulent and avirulent strains of a particular variant in a susceptible host. For example, we may compare two strains of the human type bacillus, H37R$_v$ (virulent) and H37R$_a$ (avirulent), or two analogous strains of bovine bacilli, Ravenel (virulent) and BCG (attenuated, almost completely avirulent). In these cases the avirulent microbes are without pathogenic significance for any species of animal.

with some native defensive force of the host. The capacity of a virulent organism to propagate and spread through the body may depend entirely upon its ability to take better advantage of the cultural milieu supplied by the host than can an avirulent strain; it may, for example, utilize available nutriments more efficiently, or take better advantage of the gaseous environment of the tissues, or metabolize at a higher or lower level under the influence of certain constituents of the tissues or body fluids. So far there has not been much evidence recorded of comparisons of virulent and avirulent strains of a single bacillary type for differences of this general kind, but there are some suggestive data. Strains $H37R_v$ and $H37R_a$, virulent and avirulent representatives respectively of the human variant of bacillus, are said not to do equally well in culture medium, the avirulent growing less rapidly and extensively than the virulent strain (13). It has recently been reported (14) that saprophytic mycobacteria and avirulent variants of pathogenic strains oxidize lactic acid more rapidly than do the virulent organisms. This may result in the accumulation of incompletely oxidized metabolic products which could reach concentrations lethal to those organisms (the avirulent strains) more active in the oxidation process. There is some indication also that the $H37R_v$ bacillus has the capacity to utilize phospholipids, an ability which has been lost by the avirulent mutant $H37R_a$, and differences in the effects of various metabolites upon oxygen utilization have also been observed (15). These observations cannot be considered as answering the question under discussion, but they intimate that further study of the relative growth propensities of virulent and avirulent bacilli in milieus supplying features of the normal host environment may be rewarding. In the author's laboratory a current study is concerned with the effect of low oxygen tension, comparable to that of the tissues, upon the respiration of virulent and avirulent strains of human and bovine bacillary types (16). Oxygen utilization by all strains is impeded at tensions of 1 and 3 per cent, but it cannot be said that the avirulent are more pronouncedly influenced than the virulent strains in this respect. The effects of these oxygen and carbon dioxide concentrations upon growth, on the other hand, seems to be very definite. The writer and Miss Ruth Guy have observed a marked inhibition of avirulent strains while virulent bacilli under identical conditions proliferate progressively.

A second potential basis for pathogenicity lies in the possible possession by the virulent organism of some mechanism or substance capable of actively interfering with native defense forces of the host, thus permitting the bacillus to proliferate and spread. Such a substance might function, for example, by interfering with the activities of phagocytes, or it might neutralize some normally present bactericidal or bacteriostatic substance of the tissues or body fluids.

What evidence can be mustered for this hypothesis? Let us consider first the proposition that the phagocyte represents a significant defense mechanism of the normal body and that its capacity to suppress growth or destroy bacilli is interfered with by virulent organisms whereas the avirulent are unsuccessful in this effort. To begin with we have to marshal evidence that phagocytes possess such a potential restrictive power upon tubercle bacilli. All tubercle bacilli, whether virulent or avirulent, are readily phagocytized by polymorphonuclear leukocytes and monocytic cells after entrance into the body. It is obvious from the course of events following injection of bacilli of both kinds that avirulent organisms ultimately disappear from such cells while virulent organisms continue to multiply, producing progressive infection. That the inhibition and destruction of avirulent organisms in phagocytic cells is not a striking event, however, is made clear by the inability of various investigators, working with cells in tissue culture, to see any marked difference in the fates of ingested bacilli of both kinds over periods of observation as long as two or three weeks (4, 17). Fell and Brieger (18) employed virulent and avirulent avian bacilli in cultures of embryonic and adult avian cells and adult rabbit cells, and during a period of three to six weeks found a symbiotic relationship established between both kinds of bacilli and the macrophages; both organisms were proved by culture to be viable at the end of this time, and the phagocytic cells remained uninjured also. Similarly, Maximow (19) could find no striking effect of rabbit phagocytes upon human type bacilli (organisms which are relatively avirulent for the rabbit); in some cells he observed destruction of bacilli, but in the same tissue explants organisms could be seen proliferating in other cells. In later work (20) with bovine bacilli this investigator encountered differences between virulent microbes and an attenuated strain (BCG). In some instances the BCG was destroyed within cells, but in many cases these bacilli proceeded to proliferate within epithelioid cells and eventually to take over the culture. It is entirely possible, of course, that the potential role of the phagocytes in the destruction of avirulent bacilli cannot be adequately studied by tissue explant methods, for the destructive process may be so lenient as to require a more prolonged interval of observation than is afforded by this experimental method. Some basis for this viewpoint is provided by Corper's recovery of viable avirulent bacilli from human skin four months after their intracutaneous injection (21), and similar experiences have been described by other workers with BCG in normal animals (22); these are certainly indications that attenuated or avirulent bacilli are not abruptly wiped out in the body. Yet the normal body apparently possesses better capacity to deal with bacilli than do cells growing in vitro; this is witnessed by Brieger's (18b) parallel observations of virulent bacilli injected into the spleens of paired normal rabbits and subsequently permitted to develop in vitro and in vivo. In one case splenic tissue was explanted; in the other the animal was allowed to survive. In the tissue culture after about two weeks the organisms had taken over completely. When at this time the other infected rabbit was killed very few bacilli were found in sections of the spleen. We have then a twofold indication that tissue explants may not provide a fair representation of what may happen to bacilli in vivo.

This difference may depend upon some inhibitory factor present in the body, but it could just as well be the result of environment as related to the metabolic abilities of the bacillus. Perhaps the gaseous milieu, or some other equally simple feature, distinguishes cells of the body from those growing outside the body as a culture medium for the tubercle bacillus.

In view of these conflicting observations it is impossible to formulate a conclusion as to whether the phagocytic cells of the normal body constitute a specific threat to tubercle bacilli. Unquestionably, avirulent bacilli eventually disappear from phagocytic cells in vivo, but they might disappear just as well if they were not ingested by these cells (23). In other words the factor which results in eventual disappearance of avirulent organisms could be entirely unrelated to the cells in which these bacilli take up residence. Available information does not favor one viewpoint to the exclusion of the other.

We might continue to examine this question from another standpoint. If we suppose that normal phagocytes can inhibit or destroy avirulent bacilli in the body, can we then find evidence that virulent organisms are able to overcome this defensive mechanism, and so account for their disease-producing potentiality?

It seems perfectly evident in the first place that virulent tubercle bacilli do not discourage phagocytosis. Whatever their effect upon these cells may be it is not the antiphagocytic one so evident in the case of the pneumococcus and certain other bacteria (see Chapter 3). If virulent bacilli have an antago-nistic influence upon phagocytes therefore, this must be effective upon some phase of the relationship of cell to microbe after ingestion has occurred. Several discordant observations have been recorded of the possible influence of virulent as contrasted with avirulent bacilli upon phagocytic cells. Maximow (20) surmised from his tissue culture studies that virulent bacilli may pro-duce a toxic substance which destroys histiocytes even at a distance, and Bloch (24) has arrived at a similar conclusion with regard to polymorpho-nuclear cells from studies in mice, though this was reached through deduction rather than by direct visualization of the destructive process. This viewpoint has been only partially confirmed by others. In Brieger's (18a) work, men-tioned before, the phagocytes in chick tissue explants remained undamaged for several weeks though harboring virulent avian bacilli; bovine bacilli in rabbit explants tended to rupture cells, but this seemed to be a mechanical result of exuberant growth, occurring after about two weeks. An attenuated strain of this bacillary type (BCG) can apparently also overgrow the tissue culture, but the destructive effect does not equal that of virulent bovine bacilli (20). Virulent human bacilli appear to be intermediate between avian and bovine organisms in their influence upon susceptible host tissues in vitro. They do not destroy the tissue culture, but they may disrupt macrophages by their unchecked proliferation (18c). Lurie (25) failed to remark upon any injurious influence of virulent bovine bacilli upon normal monocytes under observation in the anterior chambers of rabbits' eyes for periods up to two weeks. Gottlieb's (26) experience was similar in the case of virulent human type bacilli in guinea pigs through several days of observation. This is not to say that destruction of these cells does not occur in vivo, for once hypersensitivity has set in these cells are susceptible to damage. But hypersensitivity is induced by avirulent bacilli as well as virulent; this does not distinguish the two kinds of organisms.

Recent work has suggested that virulent organisms perhaps have an influence more subtle than outright destruction of polymorphonuclear leukocytes (27). This is described as an inhibition of migration of these cells by virulent organisms after ingestion has taken place; a lesser effect of the same kind is, however, caused by avirulent organisms. Bloch (28) has found the same activity exerted by a lipoidal substance extracted from virulent bacilli (the cording factor, described later). Aside from paralysis of movement, however, no toxic effect of virulent organisms upon the leukocytes was found, for these cells remained viable as judged by their utilization of oxygen, and though gorged with tubercle bacilli and hobbled in their movements, they were still very proficient in ingesting and destroying test bacteria of another species. In fact, our own observations make it seem likely that the paralysis of locomotion may be the result of a mechanical obstruction due to clumping of leukocytes after they have ingested bacilli rather than an intrinsic injury to the cells themselves.

The consensus of information at this time does not convincingly support the existence of a "virulence factor," active upon phagocytic cells, as the explanation for the ability of pathogenic microbes to proliferate in the body. This summarized viewpoint is, of course, merely an opinion based upon still meager information.

The next consideration in the quest for a virulence factor in the tubercle bacillus is concerned with the possible existence of some extracellular defense mechanism of the normal host which can be obstructed or neutralized by virulent bacilli. There is no specific evidence that the tissue fluids of the normal animal possess the property of inhibiting the growth of avirulent, as opposed to virulent, organisms. Both kinds of bacilli grow very well in vitro in normal serum as a medium. Yet Woodruff (23) has observed that the human type tubercle bacillus fails to proliferate outside cells in the peritoneal cavity of the rabbit (for which these bacilli are relatively avirulent) while they multiply in the peritoneal cavity of the guinea pig (for which they are virulent). More pertinent evidence might be provided by studies of virulent and avirulent strains of the same progenitor in a single host, but this does not seem to be available. So far then we have no grounds for believing that a specific humoral factor of the normal body inhibits avirulent bacilli and that this factor may be vitiated by some neutralizing mechanism of the virulent microbes. Extracellular deterioration of avirulent organisms in vivo may depend upon some metabolic characteristic of the organism, as discussed earlier.

In summary, we can presently find no satisfying indication that virulent tubercle bacilli owe their pathogenic powers to a specific ability to interfere with the functioning of phagocytes or of some extracellular defensive factor of the body fluids. In fact, there is so far little information to suggest that tubercle bacilli are disturbed by a specific antibacillary factor either of the phagocytes or of the body fluids of the host; in this view, there is nothing for the organism to oppose. This brings us once more to the concept that perhaps it is some metabolic ability which distinguishes the two organisms.

Before leaving these considerations of relationships of virulence to native defense, the possibility must be entertained that the destruction of avirulent organisms does not come within the compass of the normal body at all. Perhaps it is only after these organisms have persisted in the tissues for a sufficient period of time to induce a **specific acquired immunity** that their dissolution occurs. This specific resistance exerts some restrictive influence upon virulent bacilli; against avirulent cells it may be markedly destructive. Observations by Lurie (22c) with BCG in the rabbit favor such a concept, for it was found by cultural methods that these attenuated organisms multiply for a period of about four weeks especially in lymph tissue, but that after this time a rapid decrease in numbers occurs. This could represent the period of accession of acquired resistance (although other interpretations are applicable). This viewpoint could account for the several weeks of undisturbed residence of avirulent bacilli within cells in tissue cultures, for it has been demonstrated repeatedly that explanted cells are incapable of producing antibody (see Chapter 5) and they may be incapable as well of taking part in any other immunologic modification which might constitute acquired resistance to the tubercle bacillus.

Relation of Virulence to Other Factors. We turn now to a survey of more general data concerned with tubercle bacillary virulence. The several interesting possibilities which have engaged the attention of bacteriologists during the past quarter century are outlined in the following discussion.

1. COLONIAL MORPHOLOGY. The tubercle bacillus as well as many other species of pathogenic bacteria may spontaneously dissociate in culture to yield colonies of varying morphologic appearances and, concomitantly, of cells with different antigenic and pathogenic properties. Petroff and others (29) have described S and R colonies, as well as various intermediate forms, and have shown in some instances a relationship between S dissociants and virulence, and R dissociants and avirulence. This work has been carried out with human, bovine, and avian bacilli. Although there is no question but that variants of differing virulence may be obtained here as in the case of other microbes either as the result of spontaneous dissociation or by selection through variations in cultural conditions, it is not presently possible to establish a relationship between variations in pathogenicity and the morphologic characteristics of smoothness or roughness so clearly that one might investigate one character in terms of the other, as, for example, can be done in the case of the pneumococcus where roughness of colony means loss of the capsular antigen of the microbe, and both are related to loss of virulence. Seibert and co-workers (30) have reported chemical differences in lipoidal constituents between S and R variants of an avian bacillus, and in limited trials some differences in their pathogenicity for hens. At about the same time, Winn and Petroff (31) published similar observations with an avian bacillus.

These studies remain exceptional, however, and it seems dubious that a dependable relationship between these colonial properties and virulence will eventually be established for other variants of tubercle bacilli. Thus, the H37 bacillus, a virulent human type organism, looks the same colonially as R1, a stable avirulent variant of a human bacillus, and two commonly employed human variants, H37R$_v$ (virulent) and H37R$_a$ (avirulent) are both rough strains.

More recently another colonial characteristic has been suggested as possibly related to virulence. Many years ago it was observed by Miehe (32) and later by Gardner (33) that tubercle bacilli growing in colonies arrange themselves in parallel cords. No one noticed a suggestive relationship between this morphologic characteristic of the colony and its virulence until 1947, when Middlebrook (13) worked with strains of varying virulence and observed that virulent bacilli grew on the surface of liquid media as thin quickly spreading veils, and on solid Dubos medium as thin translucent colonies with spreading tendency (34). This contrasted with a heaped-up growth in colonies of avirulent organisms. In structure the virulent colonies were seen to be composed of serpentine cords of bacilli, while avirulent colonies were made up of a jumble of nonoriented organisms heaped about in masses. Two strains of intermediate virulence for mice (R$_1$R$_v$ and BCG) were found to form serpentine cords also, but this was more readily inhibited by the presence of detergent in the medium than was the case with the virulent organisms.

Bloch (28) has found that after extraction with petroleum ether virulent bacilli lose their corded arrangement, and that the extracted substance possesses the capacity to interfere with leukocytic migration as described previously for the virulent organisms themselves. The same effect, and in addition cellular damage, has been described by Choucroun and co-workers as brought about by a lipopolysaccharide component of the tubercle bacillus (35). Again the question arises of the validity of this antiphagocytic effect as an index of virulence in view of the ability of proper concentrations of avirulent bacilli to bring about the same result, and for the other reasons discussed earlier. Further work may clarify this point.

It is difficult to assess the relationship of this colonial characteristic to virulence with certainty for the following reasons. Bloch (36) has found that the addition of chick embryo extract to the medium causes the formation of serpentine cords by avirulent bacilli, yet these organisms remain entirely avirulent for mice even when the animals after infection are treated daily with the extract in an effort to provide this factor within the host. The BCG organism normally grows in serpentine strands, but perhaps it may be regarded as an attenuated rather than an avirulent organism. Various strains of this bacillus may show more or less cord formation, but the ability of these strains to persist in animals bears no relationship to the degree of their cording (37). Finally, some saprophytic mycobacteria may also show the serpentine pattern of growth (38).

It is entirely possible, of course, that the tendency to form serpentine formations reflects some important but not crucial property of virulence, and that this ability may be present also occasionally in strains which lack some other necessary characteristic, and consequently have no virulence. A similar statement was made in Chapter 3 concerning other bacterial factors which may be related to virulence. On the other hand, the alignment of growth may be an **effect** (of rapid proliferation, for example) which characterizes virulent strains, rather than the **cause** of virulence, i.e. a virulence factor. This issue remains to be determined more precisely.

2. CYTOCHEMICAL PROPERTIES OF THE TUBERCLE BACILLUS RELATED TO VIRULENCE. Dubos and Middlebrook (39) have made the interesting observation that virulent mammalian and avian tubercle bacilli when suspended in an alkaline solution containing neutral red (the neutral red is then yellow) adsorb this dye to their surfaces, and cause it to become red, while the dye remaining in solution retains its yellow color. Similar fixation of the dye is not seen with avirulent bacilli. This ability to bind the dye in the form of its anion is characteristic of those cultures which exhibit the serpentine pattern of growth and apparently depends upon the occurrence of surface acidic groups. This reaction correlates quite well with the ability of a strain to cause progressive disease. There are exceptions, however. Richmond and Cummings (38) have found a saprophytic organism to be positive to this test, and in the writer's laboratory a virulent human type bacillus, which has been maintained for a long time on medium, though it continues pathogenic for the guinea pig, responds negatively to this test, while an avirulent human type bacillus is positive. The parallelism of the results of this test with virulence is nevertheless generally striking, and it would be important to know whether this cytochemical property represents cause or effect, i.e. whether it itself represents a virulence factor of the bacillus or is simply a distinctive characteristic resulting perhaps from a metabolic pattern of the organism which in fact determines its pathogenic capacities.

Other chemical distinctions between virulent and avirulent bacilli have been described. A detergent, triton $A_{20}^{®}$, inhibits the growth of avirulent bacilli while permitting virulent strains to multiply (40), while on the other hand certain amino acids exert a bacteriostatic and bactericidal activity against virulent strains and have much less influence upon avirulent ones (41). Again the precise significance of these facts is not yet appreciated, but it is not difficult to imagine that some such factors may explain the inability of avirulent strains to progress in the body.

3. RELATIONSHIP OF CONSTITUENTS OF THE BACILLUS TO VIRULENCE. Several possible leads to an understanding of virulence have come from the study of isolated components of the tubercle bacillus. The cording factor and the lipopolysaccharide have been described in preceding paragraphs; these two substances are apparently not the same. Lipopolysaccharide has been found in greater abundance in virulent than in avirulent strains, and the fraction shows a strongly positive neutral red test in the former case and a weak test in the latter (42, 43). The lipopolysaccharides of virulent strains

differ further from those of the avirulent organisms so far examined in possessing charasteristic amino acids (glutamic acid, diaminopymelic acid and alanine), and in having higher melting points.

A further distinction in lipoidal constitution has been found with respect to the relative contents of free mycolic acid extractable by hot acetone from strains of differing pathogenicity. Much more total lipid is obtained from virulent strains, and the proportion of mycolic acid in these fractions is relatively much greater also in the case of the virulent organisms (42c).

In a study concerned with the possible presence in the tubercle bacillus of a complex antigen of the Boivin type, the author has obtained polysaccharide-containing substances by the application of several procedures which have been employed in the past for the extraction of the somatic antigens of enteric bacilli (see Chapter 4). In order to test these substances for their potential immunizing abilities, small quantities of the lyophilized materials were injected into groups of guinea pigs several times. It later eventuated that the filtration procedure employed to remove bacillary bodies had not been entirely effective, as is often the case with tubercle bacilli suspended in organic solvents, and that a few bacilli, still viable, remained in the filtered preparations. The progress of infection in the treated animals was so striking in comparison with a control group which had received at the same time large doses of the acetone-dried bacilli of the same batch employed for the preparation of the complexes as to suggest that these complexes might have some relationship to virulence of the tubercle bacillus. In subsequent experiments, however, it has not been possible to induce either the avirulent human type H37R$_a$ strain or the attenuated BCG bovine strain to cause progressive tuberculosis by simultaneous and repeated injections of this substance. Whether the first experiment was fortuitous or whether the proper conditions for demonstrating the activity of this material have not been found remains a moot question (44).

4. The Relationship of Antigenic Components to Virulence. The lipopolysaccharide previously described is stated by Choucroun to possess antigenic properties and is furthermore credited with immunizing powers (9w). If these claims are substantiated by further work, and if the effect of the substance upon phagocytes proves to be of significance to the virulence of the bacillus, as discussed in earlier paragraphs, we shall have an example in this organism of a relationship between the properties of immunity-induction and virulence analogous to that seen in the case of the pneumococcal capsular antigen (see Chapter 18).

Aside from this possibility there is presently no other indication of the implication of a tubercle bacillary antigen in the virulence of the organism. So far as we know antibody responses to avirulent bacilli are qualitatively the same as those to virulent organisms, a consideration which in itself speaks against the concept of an antigen-virulence relationship. However, as has been already pointed out, failure to demonstrate such a relationship may be due to a deficiency of the technical procedures so far applied to the question.

5. RELATIONSHIP OF ACID-FASTNESS TO VIRULENCE. Nègre (45) has observed a correlation between the age of bacillary cultures, their acid-fastness, and their virulence. Young cultures, up to the fifth or sixth day of their development in synthetic medium, show many nonacid-fast forms, and in this period Nègre believes that their ability to produce disseminated lesions in experimental animals is significantly less pronounced than at a later time, e.g. three weeks. Whatever the merits of this concept with regard to bacillary age, there have been other descriptions of the fact that avirulent variants of tubercle bacilli are not so acid-fast as virulent strains (13, 46). Bloch (47) reverses Nègre's opinion by finding that young cultures, containing greater amounts of cord factor, are also more virulent for animals than older organisms. Again, the suggested relationship of culture age to virulence requires further clarification.

In summary, it is apparent from this lengthy survey of possibilities that we cannot be certain whether any of the characteristics of the tubercle bacillus discussed in this section can be regarded as a factor determining its virulence. The correlation of certain properties of the cell with virulence is good, e.g. cording, cytochemical behavior, and content of certain lipoidal constituents. But whether these microbial properties represent specific factors of pathogenicity or are instead the effect of some metabolic characteristic of virulent cells is impossible to know at the present time.

Mechanisms of Acquired Resistance. Again our information is not clear enough to permit factual conclusions, and we must trace through various possibilities in attempting to account mechanistically for acquired resistance to tuberculosis. The animal or human being which has acquired immunity to this organism combats the virulent bacillus in two ways: first, it tends to localize bacilli of reinfection to their site of entry, and secondly, it can inhibit their multiplication and perhaps slowly destroy them. In consequence of these activities the microbes fail to progress as efficiently in the immune host as they do in the normal host. These effects will be discussed so far as possible from the mechanistic standpoint. For the sake of clarity the discussion will again be subdivided, first to consider the possibilities of a humoral mechanism, then of a cellular one, and finally to survey what contributions the inflammation consequent to the hypersensitive reaction may make to acquired immunity.

As a preface to this discussion it should be pointed out that in the case of acquired resistance to tuberculosis we are so far without any striking clue to the manner in which the immune body may handle the organism comparable to what may be seen, for example, in the instance of the host immunized to the pneumococcus. Here a plainly evident event in the immune animal is practically nonexistent in the normal, viz. the virulent parasites undergo extensive phagocytosis and intracellular destruction. In the host immune to the tubercle bacillus only the end result is apparent; obviously, bacilli of reinfection are reduced in numbers and restricted in their spread, but there are no apparent occurrences which might account for this. Phagocytosis is good in the normal host; it seems questionable that an improvement in this activity in the resistant host could account for the altered situation. Extracellular lysis of the kind seen when antibody and complement act upon certain of the gram-negative bacilli would not be expected to take place with this gram-positive organism, and though there have been some reports of bacillary lysis this remains still an ill-defined possibility. Upon what mechanistic basis then can we account for the localization and discouragement of multiplication or the destruction of virulent bacilli in the immune host? We shall have to consider the evidence stepwise in an effort to gain some insight into the answer to this question.

1. EVIDENCE FOR A HUMORAL MECHANISM. Despite the ease of demonstrating the presence of antibodies in animals and man harboring the tubercle bacillus, proof of their relationship to protection has not been uncovered after almost half a century of trials by a succession of investigators. This matter has been discussed in a preceding section of this chapter. The suggestion has been made (4) that the mere fact of existence of antibodies following exposure of the body to the microbe is in itself presumptive evidence of their relationship to resistance. The validity of this reasoning seems dubious when we consider that instances of proved relationship of antibody to acquired resistance in bacterial diseases are so far restricted to a few cases; not enough ·to permit generalization. Antibody production is a most general pathway of response to antigenic substances of whatever source and, in the case of an infectious agent, proof of its relationship to immunity necessitates the demonstration of at least one of the three following circumstances (see Chapter 9).

(a) That animals with resistance possess an antibody which is not present in subjects treated with a nonimmunizing form of the same organism. For example, animals immunized with encapsulated pneumococci develop anti-SSS antibodies which are not produced by animals treated with the rough form of this coccus; the former have immunity, the latter do not. Now it is true that by varying the route employed for immunization, resistance may be engendered in rabbits with a vaccine composed of smooth cocci without the development of serologically demonstrable antibodies against the capsular polysaccharide. But anticapsular activity in the sera of such animals can be revealed by more subtle methods, for example, by absorbing the sera with the appropriate capsular substance and demonstrating their subsequent inability to transfer immunity, or by cultivating encapsulated organisms in the presence of such sera and observing that the bacteria grow in a thread-like agglutinated form (48) because proliferating cocci are prevented from separating by the small amount of anticapsular antibody present.

No analogous demonstration has been made in the case of the tubercle bacillus. There is, of course, no bacterial form here comparable to the rough avirulent pneumococcus, for avirulent tubercle bacilli induce resistance as do virulent strains. But bacterial cells killed by various means (e.g. treatment with organic solvents) fail to induce immunity, yet they provoke the formation of antibodies. In the writer's experience animals with immunity resulting from

BCG vaccination possess no antibody response which may not also be found following vaccination with nonimmunizing bacterial preparations. The bacterial substances employed as antigens for such tests have included protein, polysaccharide, phosphatides, bacillary wax and the Boivin type of extract, as well as whole bacillary cells and culture filtrates. A variety of serologic methods have been applied to this quest with a view to exaggerating minimal reactions to the point of detection; these procedures have included the complement-fixation test, the agar plate precipitation test, agglutination and the Coombs indirect agglutination methods, and the Pfaundler method of cultivating organisms in the presence of antiserum for the detection of minimal degrees of agglutination. In every case where antibody reactions could be demonstrated, they were as frequent and as intense in the animals **lacking resistance** as in those with it; for the most part, better in the former. It appears then that no antibody against these factors at least is concerned with resistance (9v, 49). It is entirely possible, of course, that we and our predecessors have failed to employ the one antigen which may be crucial to such tests, because the methods of fractionation did not isolate it, because the chemical isolation procedures destroyed it, or because bacilli cultivated in vitro fail to form it. Little can be done about these possibilities until we know of better ways for isolating the bacillary antigens. The author and Miss Ruth Guy (49) have found some indication that bacilli isolated from human sputum are more effectively agglutinated than those from culture, but the antigenic factor responsible for this difference has not been determined. This may represent only a quantitative rather than a qualitative distinction. It is possible also that a protective antibody, even though the correct antigen were supplied, may not reveal itself through the serologic methods that have been employed. It can only be said that the latter have included the most delicate procedures presently available.

(b) That serum of the immune animal affects the organism in vitro in a manner which may be related to protection in vivo. We turn now to another viewpoint of the possibility of an antibody mechanism of resistance, i.e. whether the serum of the immune individual or animal exerts one of the influences of antibody which we know to be related to acquired immunity in infections caused by other microbes.

First, we might consider the possibility that agglutination by antibody may play a part in acquired resistance. This seems especially suggestive in view of the fact that bacilli deposited in the tissues of the immunized animal remain better localized than they do in the normal host. Lurie (50) has found that when bacilli suspended in an agar menstruum are injected into immune animals, the microbes grow in clumps, while in normal animals they disperse through the agar. It has been recognized for many years that mammalian tubercle bacilli are agglutinated by serum only grudgingly in vitro, so much so that various artifices, such as the use of substitute strains, have been employed for such studies (51). Mudd devised a centrifugation—resuspension reaction to overcome this difficulty and found that rabbits immunized with living virulent bacilli form agglutinins measurable by this technic, with an especially good rise in agglutinating activity about six days following reinfection with bovine bacilli (52, 53). The response to secondary antigenic stimulation may be important, of course, in determining the efficacy of acquired resistance to various infections (see Chapter 6), and it could be of significance in tuberculosis. Guinea pigs, as is well known, are not as good antibody producers as rabbits, but the sera of immune (BCG vaccinated) animals also agglutinate tubercle bacilli, sometimes directly, in other cases only when the Coombs antiglobulin procedure is applied (49). More striking is the fact that when bacilli obtained directly from tuberculous sputum are employed for the test much better agglutination is seen than with cultured virulent organisms (49). One might infer from this that an antigen is present in bacilli of infection which is not formed (or produced only in small amounts) by organisms growing in vitro, and if so this would be even more suggestive of the efficacy of agglutination in the body.

It is difficult to make any important inference about acquired resistance from these observations because variously vaccinated animals lacking resistance reveal the same kind of agglutinative prowess. For example, the sera of animals treated with tuberculoprotein and fractions of bacillary wax have shown most striking agglutinative capacities against sputum bacilli, but these animals have no concomitant resistance to challenge infection. One is left then with the tentative impression that the agglutinating capacity of serum per se does not suffice as an explanation of acquired immunity to tuberculosis. It could perhaps constitute a subsidiary property which might contribute to resistance provided that other essential endowments of the immunized body were simultaneously at work.

If we turn now to the potential usefulness of an opsonizing effect of serum to acquired resistance, we derive little satisfaction from this premise also. In view of the pronounced tendency for phagocytic cells of the normal as well as the immunized animal to ingest virulent or avirulent bacilli, it is difficult to conceive how specific opsonization could improve the status of the host. An opsonizing activity upon bovine bacilli of the sera of rabbits vaccinated with heat-killed organisms has been described (53, 54), but on the other hand normal rabbit serum has a similar property (55). The serum of tuberculous (presumably immune) human beings does not opsonize bacilli for ingestion by rabbit leukocytes, while it is known that human antipneumococcus serum opsonizes these organisms for rabbit leukocytes very effectively (56). This finding implies an absence of opsonizing activity of the sera of immune human beings. It is difficult to assess these data as favoring the view that opsonization is a mechanism useful to the determination of resistance.

What likelihood is there that the sera of immune individuals may kill bacilli directly? It has already been remarked that the classic antibody-complement form of lysis would hardly be looked for in the case of a gram-positive bacterium. Some other kind of extracellular destruction of bacteria may occur, however, for acquired resistance to anthrax seems to function in this way (see Chapter 19). A number of investigators have looked for a bactericidal effect of immune body fluids upon tubercle bacilli in vitro, for the most part without success (17, 57). Some workers, however, have described either destruction of bacilli or inhibition of their growth under certain circumstances. Thus Kallós (58) states that the sera of patients with tuberculosis of the skin may inhibit bacillary growth, while the sera of individuals with pulmonary tuberculosis fail to do so. Pagel (59) has found similarly that the sera of victims of pulmonary disease do not adversely affect the organism in vitro but that about 70 per cent of sera from patients with disseminated disease suppress growth. In this case a study was made of the nature of the suppressive property. This capacity was nonspecifically removed from sera by various bacteria, including *E. coli,* and could not, therefore, be regarded as an expression of antibody activity. Strangely enough the sera of immune animals did not reveal a comparable suppressive property. The writer and Dr. John Forney have had occasion to affirm the latter finding by the use of Dubos liquid medium containing 15 per cent immune serum. Nor were we able to reveal that the sera of immune animals or human beings affect the respiration of tubercle bacilli in the Warburg apparatus (60). Myrvik and Weiser (61) have described a suppressive activity in the sera of rabbits vaccinated with heat killed bacilli in water-in-oil emulsion which appears to be related to lysozyme content (see Chapter 3).

Rich (4) has pointed out that bacilli die in considerable numbers extracellularly in the body, as when they disappear from caseous areas in which phagocytes are not present. He believes, however, that this may be the result of a lack of nutriment and oxygen rather than of an acquired property of the body; he has observed similar lysis of pneumococci in devitalized areas. Thinking along the same line, Dubos (62) suggests that the release of long-chain fatty acids from necrotic material by the action of tissue lipase may explain the disappearance of bacilli, for various organic acids have been shown to be inhibitory to the microbes in vitro. Lurie (50), however, has provided evidence that extracellular bacterial suppression may occur in vivo in the absence of tissue necrosis. By incorporating virulent bacilli in agar and injecting such material subcutaneously, he established "agar islands" containing bacilli in normal and BCG immunized rabbits. These islands were examined by bacteriologic and histologic methods at varying intervals. Although one may question the use of quantitative bacteriologic methods for the study of the tubercle bacillus, the histologic examinations showed very definite inhibition of growth (or destruction) of virulent bacilli; by two weeks many organisms could be seen in the islands from normal animals, and virtually none from the immunized. Similar observations were made in guinea pigs in which a more refined technic was employed (63). Here the bacillary-agar suspensions were enclosed in silk bags permeated with collodion of a porosity sufficiently great to admit the proteinaceous body fluids while phagocytic cells were excluded. Lurie concluded, therefore, that the tissue fluids of the immune animal tend to inhibit multiplication and to enhance destruction of virulent tubercle bacilli. Dubos (62) explains these observations on the basis of an accumulation of organic acids, inhibitory to the tubercle bacillus, in the immune and hypersensitive animals in which an intense allergic inflammation occurs about the implanted sacs. This is similar to his viewpoint expressed earlier with regard to the cause of bacterial inhibition in caseous foci. More will be said about this point in the later discussion of the relationship of the hypersensitive state to acquired resistance. Woodruff (23) has also recorded evidence of extracellular lysis of virulent human type bacilli inoculated into the peritoneal cavities of immune guinea pigs.

In this discussion of a possible bactericidal activity of immune body fluids little effort has been made to distinguish between a destructive versus a growth-inhibitory effect. It is difficult, of course, to make such a distinction in dealing with bacteria; with more highly organized protozoa where morphologic differentiation occurs, the task is more amenable to analysis, and there is evidence of an acquired humoral property which can interfere with reproduction (see Chapter 9). An attempt to influence the propagation of tubercle bacilli was made many years ago by Römer (64) who exposed minimal infectious doses of bacilli to the action of immune serum for 24 hours. This treatment failed to alter the infectivity of the organisms for guinea pigs. Yet as Rich (4) points out, in lesions in which bacilli may apparently lie dormant for many years it is difficult to conceive of how this can be due to any effect other than a bacteriostatic one. The only alternative to this would be a process of continuous multiplication finely balanced against microbial destruction, a state of affairs which seems very unlikely.

We must again summarize with the inconclusive statement that it is not now possible to arrive at any settled conviction upon the question being discussed. If there is a bacteriocidal or bacteriostatic effect of the body fluids of immune man or animals, it is not a striking one, for if it were one would expect more unanimity of experience among those who have sought for it.

What other activity may antibodies bring to bear upon a bacterium? It has been suggested (4) that they may render bacilli more liable to destruction by phagocytes once engulfment has taken place. Some intimation of this kind of antibody function has been described with respect to other microbes, but there is as yet no evidence to support this viewpoint in the case of the tubercle bacillus, and Lurie (25, 65) has devised experiments which speak against it. Phagocytic cells obtained from immune animals were permitted to engulf bacilli in vitro in the presence of normal or immune plasma and the cells were subsequently transferred to the anterior chambers of normal rabbits' eyes. After an appropriate interval the contents of the chambers were examined to determine the fates of the ingested organisms. Bacillary inhibition (presumably destruction) occurred equally well in both cases; there was no indication that the immune plasma had in any way outdone the normal in preparing bacilli for destruction by the macrophages.

(c) That the body fluids of immune animals may transfer resistance passively to normal animals. Evidence of passive transfer might not only affirm the possibility that a humoral immune mechanism exists, but could provide a basis for more specific data by permitting such an approach as the absorption of effective sera with antigens of the bacillus in order to find which bacillary component might account for the humoral protective factor. There have been only a limited number of trials of passive transfer of immunity to tuberculosis recorded in the literature, doubtlessly because of the technical difficulties involved in applying this experimental procedure to a chronic infection.

Rich's (4) analysis of existing experiments reveals that in most cases these are vitiated by the methods employed. In some studies serum was provided only once, at the outset of infection; in others where it was injected repeatedly, it derived from heterologous animal sources and was thus unsatisfactory for long-term administration because of the development of antibodies against the administered serum itself, and in other cases the number of animals dealt with was too small. In several of these last experiments, where one or two sheep were used as test subjects, positive results have been described (66). Much more information will be required before this facet of the question of humoral immunity can be properly evaluated. It may be said that this kind of experiment is one in which a negative result will always be open to doubt, since it is impossible to decide whether sufficient serum has been administered (or indeed, can be administered) under the proper circumstances. In unpublished work, Efford and the author have made a careful effort to fulfill the essential conditions for such experiments without finding any indication that the acquired immunity of guinea pigs is transmissible by serum or whole blood.

2. EVIDENCE FOR A CELLULAR MECHANISM. Whether there exists an acquired cellular resistance to any infectious agent is not definitely known (see Chapter 10). It is chiefly by inference that we suppose that an alteration of this kind may occur, and the inferences come mainly from our information about the obligatory intracellular parasites, viruses and rickettsias. Although the tubercle bacillus is by no means a parasite of this kind, it elects to reside within phagocytic cells, and it is conceivable that some intrinsic alteration in these could be involved in the acquisition of resistance for the body as a whole.

There is undoubtedly a greater destruction of tubercle bacilli within the phagocytes of the immune than of the normal host. Experiments directed at an explanation of this fact have been carried out by Lurie (25, 65) with the intent of determining whether the mononuclear cells per se may acquire an increased bacteriostatic or bactericidal property for tubercle bacilli. In a first study (65) it was found that mononuclear cells derived from tuberculous rabbits and guinea pigs were usually more actively phagocytic in vitro for various particles (India ink and staphylococci as well as tubercle bacilli) than cells from normal animals. This, however, does not answer the essential question, for phagocytosis is good even in the normal animal. The point is whether the phagocytes of the immunized host are able to destroy the organism more effectively once it has been ingested. In subsequent work Lurie employed a procedure which permitted the observation of bacilli in vivo (25).

Normal and immune rabbits and guinea pigs received injections of tubercle bacilli, and after two days washed fragments of lymph node or bone marrow were removed from these animals. These bits of tissue were transplanted to the anterior chambers of the eyes of normal rabbits. Quantitative cultural and histologic studies were carried out 11 to 14 days later. Small numbers of bacilli, faintly stained and beaded, were seen in the cells derived from immune donors, whereas sheafs of multiplying bacilli were found in the cells from the normal donors. In order to eliminate a possible influence of immune body fluids upon the bacilli in the two-day period permitted for phagocytosis to occur in vivo, similar experiments were carried out in which phagocytosis was permitted to occur in vitro in the presence of normal or immune plasma, the cells again being transferred to the anterior chambers of normal rabbit eyes. The results of these experiments were the same; there was no indication that a humoral factor partook in any way in the increased ability of the immune cells to inhibit growth.

There seems to be no reasonable basis for rejecting the results of these carefully carried out experiments. If their validity can be affirmed, they constitute evidence of a mechanism of cellular adaptation through which acquired immunity may be effected against the tubercle bacillus. In a more general sense also these observations may open a path of study of acquired immunity in other infectious diseases for which antibody responses do not supply a satisfactory explanation.

One obstacle to a ready acceptance of this viewpoint is the fact that destruction of tubercle bacilli by the cells of immune animals has not been uniformly amenable to demonstration in vitro (4, 17, 67). This situation is analogous to that discussed earlier in respect to the relationship of the phagocytes of the normal animal to avirulent bacilli in vitro. Here again destruction appears to be a slow and often incomplete process, and it may not be subject to study outside the body.

3. EVIDENCE FOR THE HYPERSENSITIVE STATE. The relationship of hypersensitivity to resistance has been discussed in a general vein in Chapters 10 and 15. In respect to tuberculosis the nature of the problem may be outlined as follows: in the course of tuberculous infection there develops a state of cellular hypersensitivity of the delayed or infectious type directed against the protein antigens of the bacillus. About 10 days to 2 weeks after infection this reactivity may be revealed by injection into the skin of either the entire organism or its protein constituent (purified protein derivative or old tuberculin). In both cases one finds after several hours a developing area of indurated inflammation; this reaches its peak ordinarily at about 48 hours, and may be accompanied by necrosis. Delayed systemic reactions, even fatal ones, may result from intravenous or intraperitoneal injections of these substances, or may follow intracutaneous administration if sufficient antigen is absorbed in the subject with a high level of sensitivity.

Coincidentally with this development it can be shown that the animal has gained the ability to resist superinfection. In view of the accelerated and intensified inflammatory response which accompanies this hypersensitive reaction, and because certain attributes of the inflammatory reaction are well known to serve the body in a protective capacity, the conception naturally developed that the two phenomena—resistance and the hypersensitive state —are synonymous. The writer will not attempt to refer to the individual contributions to the study; the work and opinions of Krause (68), Willis (69), and others supporting this concept, and that of Calmette (9k), Rich, and others denying its validity are fully discussed in Rich's volume, *The Pathogenesis of Tuberculosis* (4) and in Pinner's *Pulmonary Tuberculosis in the Adult* (70). The viewpoints of these two authors are opposed, and both can be read with profit. In the present discussion attention will be directed toward certain considerations which are amenable to direct experimental test and which the author believes provide a basis for the viewpoint that the development of hypersensitivity is independent of the acquisition of resistance; that the temporal relationship is a fortuitous one representing separate immunologic reactions of the tissues to different stimuli supplied concurrently by the etiologic bacillus.

Animals which have been rendered immune and hypersensitive to the tubercle bacillus through vaccination with an attenuated strain (BCG) may then be desensitized by the daily administration of old tuberculin so that they no longer respond to either intracutaneous or systemic injection of this substance. When such animals are challenged with virulent bacilli (the desensitizing treatment being continued throughout), they are found to retain their acquired resistance. This experiment has been performed by Rothschild and his associates (71) and has been affirmed by others, the writer among them. On the other hand, Willis and Woodruff (72) were able to establish these results in a restricted fashion only. They found that in many animals treated in this manner there was a period of perhaps two months during which the challenge infection was restrained, but if the experiments were continued for a longer time many of the subjects developed extensive pulmonary disease, much more pronounced than was seen in immune nondesensitized animals. This was put forward as evidence of a loss of resistance along with hypersensitivity. It is difficult to see, however, how one can ignore the protracted period during which the infection was held at bay in these experiments. Furthermore, not all desensitized animals developed the pulmonary spread, and overwhelming pulmonary infection may occur even in hypersensitive animals. This becomes especially frequent if animals are subjected to daily injections of control solutions employed to mimic the traumatic effects of daily tuberculin injections (73). The gist of evidence derived from this type of experiment seems very decidedly to favor the viewpoint that acquired immunity is a phenomenon distinct from the hypersensitive state. Ellison (74) has written an interesting discussion of this problem from the standpoint of the spontaneous loss of hypersensitivity which sometimes occurs in tuberculous patients.

If we approach the question from an immuno-mechanistic standpoint and inquire what basic features of the hypersensitive state could be responsible for acquired resistance, we arrive at two possibilities. The first is a specific one: that the immunologic response of the body which results in allergic reactivity (i.e. the response to proteins of the tubercle bacillus) is also the immunologic response which constitutes resistance. The second is nonspecific: that the **consequence** of the allergic reaction, the accelerated and intensified inflammation, constitutes an effective barrier to the bacillus.

As regards the first possibility, there is no serious evidence to indicate that the antiprotein response to the tubercle bacillus is in any way related to immunity. Repeated attempts to induce resistance in animals by vaccinating with protein have failed. Since, however, the injection of tuberculoprotein alone does not induce tuberculous hypersensitivity (see Chapter 14), it might be objected that the absence of this phase of the response may be the reason for failure of resistance. The writer and his associates have been successful in inducing the development of delayed hypersensitivity by the use of tuberculoprotein along with a lipoidal component of the bacillus (9v, 75), and in this case also, where the treated animals have developed tuberculin hypersensitivity as well as humoral antibody and anaphylactic reactivity to the protein, there is no concomitant resistance to challenge with the tubercle bacillus. In experiments in which animals vaccinated with BCG and others simultaneously treated with protein and lipid have attained the same levels of delayed hypersensitivity as measured by dermal tuberculin tests as well as by local reactivity to the injection of living virulent bacilli (the Koch phenomenon), it is found that while the first animals possess very definite resistance to challenge infection the latter are without it, and go through the same progression of infection as do control unvaccinated guinea pigs.

The second possibility infers that the accentuated inflammation which accompanies the hypersensitive response may localize bacilli mechanically. Localization of particles, including bacteria, is known to be a function of the inflammatory reaction. Since a mild inflammatory response follows the introduction of tubercle bacilli into normal tissues, the inference is that the more intense inflammation caused by the contact of bacilli with allergic tissues brings with it more of the protective aspects of this response—sufficient to account for acquired immunity (76). The fallacy in this viewpoint lies in the fact that there is no quantitative parallelism between the degree of inflammation and its protective attributes; an intense inflammatory reaction does not necessarily localize bacteria more effectively than does a mild or moderate one. It has been demonstrated by various experimenters that microbes injected into previously prepared areas of intense allergic inflammation are **more rapidly** swept to the draining lymph nodes by the increased fluid wave than is the case in the normal animal (77).

In this connection it is of interest to consider again the suggestion made by Dubos (62) concerning Lurie's (50, 63) experiments with tubercle bacilli in collodionized sacs implanted in normal and immune animals. It will be recalled that the inhibition of bacillary proliferation occurring in immunized animals was attributed by Lurie to a factor in the host fluids. Dubos on the other hand suggests that there may be a greater local accumulation of inhibitory organic acids in immune animals resulting from the more intense inflammation about the collodion sacs, this in turn a consequence of the hypersensitive response to bacillary protein. Presumably this rationale could be applied to any focus of bacilli in an immune hypersensitive host. This tentative explanation is a provocative one, but it is not sustained by the evidence cited earlier that immunity persists in the absence of hypersensitive reactivity, and may be lacking in its presence. Dubos pointed out that his proposal is not intended as a complete explanation of acquired resistance, but that it may constitute one factor in the total mechanism.

In résumé, there seems to be scant basis for the viewpoint that tuberculous hypersensitivity is significantly concerned in acquired resistance to the tubercle bacillus. From the immunologic standpoint the two responses of the body, immunity and hypersensitivity, appear to be mutually independent. Nor does available evidence support the proposition that the intensified inflammation resulting from the allergic reaction of the tissues may interfere with bacillary spread or proliferation.

SUMMARY

We are left then with a good deal of imaginative experimentation and interesting speculation, but little in the way of settled factual information upon which to ground an explanation of acquired resistance to the tubercle bacillus. There is some intimation of the existence of a humoral bactericidal or bacteriostatic property, but the nature of this is cryptic. It is not readily or regularly demonstrable in vitro; there is strong evidence that serum or blood do not transmit resistance passively, and it has so far not been identifiable with any of the serologic activities of the antibodies formed against the tubercle bacillus. Every antibody effect so far demonstrated in the sera of animals with proved resistance to infection can be revealed also in the sera of animals vaccinated with bacillary substances devoid of resistance-inducing properties.

When we consider the possibility of alteration in phagocytic cells themselves to account for acquired resistance, we find that bacilli deteriorate within these cells in the immune animal body, and Lurie's experiments suggest that mononuclear cells of the immune host may themselves acquire some property unfavorable to the organism. Of the nature of this alteration, however, nothing is known, and there is some difficulty in demonstrating this effect in tests carried out in vitro.

For the possibility that the hypersensitive reactivity per se of the vaccinated animal may be the instrument of protection, the evidence appears to be unfavorable for reasons detailed in preceding paragraphs.

Upon what basis are we then to account for acquired immunity to this infectious agent? A bactericidal or bacteriostatic mechanism alone could account for restriction of bacillary spread as well as the check upon bacillary proliferation. In view of the lack of clear evidence for either antibody or phagocytes as specific agents of resistance, the simplest tentative explanation might propose that the immune subject develops an inhibitory power which can affect bacilli by depressing their metabolic functions. In this view the essential event would be the development by the immune body of a factor deleterious over a period of time to the assimilative capacities of the parasite, regardless of whether it is intra- or extracellularly located. This postulation obviates the requirement of a specific humoral as opposed to a cellular mechanism. It leaves us, of course, with the necessity of defining the kind of bodily change that might alter the assimilative propensities of the bacterium, and virtually nothing is known about such possibilities. Yet in the case of acquired resistance to another organism, the anthrax bacillus, there exists a humoral antibacterial mechanism which does not seem to be antibody. A study of the metabolic abilities of virulent tubercle bacilli in the presence of the body fluids of immune animals under conditions (e.g. of gaseous environment) simulating those of the body might prove enlightening.

Practical Vaccination Procedures. 1. KILLED VACCINES. As discussed earlier in this chapter there is some difference of opinion about the ability of killed tubercle bacilli to induce immunity in experimental animals. Such vaccines have not been much employed in human beings. One of the more complete trials was carried out in Jamaica, B.W.I., by Opie, Flahiff and their co-workers, in patients upon admission to a mental hospital where the tuberculosis morbidity and mortality rates among the resident inmates were extremely high (78). After a period of 10 years there was evidence of protection among the vaccinated patients (9s). In the general population of Jamaica, where controlled vaccination had also been practiced, the observations were inconclusive (79).

2. ATTENUATED VIABLE BACILLARY VACCINES. Most prophylactic efforts in human beings have involved the use of attenuated living bacilli. Trudeau early reported studies with such organisms in animals with favorable results (80a, 80b), and subsequent experimental experiences have also been favorable almost without exception (80c, 80d). The attenuated variants which have been given most attention are listed in the following discussion.

Vole Bacillus. In recent years in Great Britain there has been considerable interest in an acid-fast bacillus, *Mycobacterium muris,* isolated from a field mouse, the vole (81). This microbe is a distinct variant of the mammalian tubercle bacilli; it has certain morphologic characteristics different from those of the human and bovine types, and it appears to be pathogenic not only for the vole, but in larger doses also for guinea pigs and rabbits (82). This organism has revealed good immunizing capacities under experimental conditions; vaccinated animals are protected against human and bovine types of bacilli as well as against the homologous organism. Interest in its protective potential for human beings centers in the fact that it is not an attenuated strain of one of the variants known to be pathogenic for man and hence could not revert to a phase virulent for human beings. Studies in man have so far been very limited, but this bacillus provides one obvious potential for human vaccination (83).

Bacille Calmette Guérin (BCG). For almost half a century the major interest of those concerned with the vaccination of human beings against tuberculosis has been concentrated upon a bacillus of bovine type which, in 1908, was first cultivated upon a medium of potato impregnated with glycerolated bile for the purpose of improving its dispersibility in aqueous suspensions (84). After 15 transfers the organism was found to have lost its lethality for guinea pigs when injected in amounts up to 1 mg., and from this time forward interest was diverted to its possible usefulness as a vaccinating agent. A report of its administration to infants was first made in 1925 (85a), and in the years since then the vaccine has been applied to millions of individuals in many parts of the world. Unfortunately, the inflexible criteria essential for an interpretation of experiments of this kind in human beings have not often been observed. Lately, interest in the vaccine has quickened in the United States and simultaneously more meaningful reports have appeared from other lands; some of these are described as follows (85b).

In Oslo, Heimbeck (5a) in 1927 instituted a program of vaccination in student nurses, and Birkhaug (86) subsequently summarized the results of this and other human experiments carried out in the Scandinavian countries. The morbidity and mortality rates were significantly decreased in those individuals who received vaccine over those who were not vaccinated, or who failed to respond with a positive tuberculin reaction to the vaccination. As an example of the results seen, among 287 vaccinated nurses the incidence of disease per 1,000 observation years was 8.0, and of deaths, 1.1. The comparable figures for an unvaccinated group of 280 nurses were 171.0 and 17.8. The number of subjects in these trials was not large, and the controls did not consist of alternate cases. In the same city Scheel (87) made similar observations among medical students. As a consequence of these and other favorable statistics the Norwegian government has proposed laws compelling the vaccination of children in certain age groups.

From Denmark, Holm (56) has reported experiences with the use of BCG over a period of almost 20 years. The tentative conclusions at the time of this accounting indicated that, as the Norwegian investigators had also observed, vaccination protects against the complications of the primary tuberculous infection. This was especially well illustrated by the occurrence of an explosive epidemic of tuberculosis in a school in which the students were exposed to a teacher with active disease. This institution had been part of a control program for some years so that radiologic and tuberculin-test information was available for each pupil. Of 133 who had received BCG vaccination, 1.5 per cent developed pulmonary disease, while among 105 tuberculin negative unvaccinated students 6.7 per cent developed pulmonary disease. Other interesting Danish experiences from which similar conclusions were derived have been recounted by Jensen and Ørskov (88).

In Sweden, Wallgren (89) initiated the systematic vaccination of infants of tuberculous families, keeping the subjects isolated from their families until tuberculin sensitiveness had appeared as a result of the vaccination. The children were then returned to their families; in over one third of instances this meant exposure to open cases of tuberculosis. In over 1,000 infants so treated between 1927 and 1937, only two instances of benign tuberculosis were found in a follow-up study carried up to 1939. Only a few children were left unvaccinated, and in these morbidity and mortality was high. More extensive studies have since been carried out by others (5c), with analogous results. The most recent of these clinical studies, by Dahlström and Difs (90), warrants a brief summary. This work was undertaken in army conscripts in whom the factors of age, sex, environment, numbers employed and follow-up study could be especially well controlled. Over 36,000 soldiers were vaccinated and more than 25,000 served as controls. The ratio of morbidity of unvaccinated to vaccinated in the period between six months and one year after vaccination was 4.3 to 1. The mortality ratio was 3 to 1, and it seemed probable that most of the fatal cases among the vaccinated had their incipience before there was opportunity for the development of resistance from the prophylactic procedure.

In the United States, Rosenthal and his associates (91) carried out an experiment in newborn infants somewhat similar to that of Wallgren, and concluded that the vaccine was of definite value in preventing the disease; there were 4.56 times as many cases in the unvaccinated, and four deaths in this group as compared to none in the vaccinated. In larger groups of infants without household contacts the results were similarly favorable; 3.31 times as great a morbidity rate in the unvaccinated, and 6.8 times the mortality.

Aronson and Palmer (92) set up a study in American Indians living in several widely scattered reservations, and have described the results of a six-year study. Of a group of 3,007 individuals between 0 and 19 years of age, about half were vaccinated by the intracutaneous method. The remainder, kept as controls, received injections of placebo. Environmental conditions and other factors were controlled. Of the vaccinated, 6 died of tuberculosis; of the controls, 52. Incidence of progressive disease was 8 among the vaccinated and 49 in the controls. Ferguson (93) has recounted a successful five years' experience in Canada with the use of the vaccine in student nurses and sanatorium personnel.

Although elements of doubt are inherent in the methods employed in many of these studies, some appear to be as blameless as can be expected of experiments involving groups of human beings. The results are almost unanimous in favoring the usefulness of the BCG vaccine for human immunization. An extensive controlled application of BCG vaccination in Europe, Africa, Asia, the Middle East and Latin America was undertaken, beginning in 1947, by the Joint Enterprise, a cooperative effort between the United Nations International Children's Emergency Fund (UNICEF), the Scandinavian Red Cross organizations, the World Health Organization, and the governments of the countries in which the vaccinations are carried out. The primary purpose of this campaign has been the introduction of BCG vaccination as one phase of tuberculosis control. The reports so far published provide a good deal of information about the methods of vaccine production, distribution, dosage, and administration, the range of postvaccination reactions and other points of interest. Eventually, it is to be hoped, there will emerge additional concrete knowledge about the central issue—the influence of this treatment upon the existence of the disease in the populations under study (94).

In such countries as the United States where the over-all tuberculosis morbidity and mortality rates are relatively low and continually declining, the mass application of vaccination is unnecessary and indeed undesirable, for it obviates the usefulness of the tuberculin test as a diagnostic procedure. In local areas of high exposure, however, or in such selected groups as students of medicine and nursing, sanatorium personnel and children in tuberculous households it is worth serious consideration. In one specific class of individuals, on the other hand, the use of BCG should be most assiduously avoided. It has been known for some years that silicosis predisposes to the ravages of the virulent tubercle bacillus, and that in experimental animals rendered silicotic through the inhalation of quartz particles even ordinarily avirulent variants of the bacillus may set up a progressive disease process. Vorwald and his associates (95) have found BCG also to induce progressive disease in such animals, and there is no reason to doubt that it may do the same thing in silicotic human beings.

BIBLIOGRAPHY

1. Koch, R.   Deutsche med. Wchnschr., 17:101, 1891.
2. Medlar, E. M.   Am. Rev. Tuberc., 58:583, 1948.
3. Baldwin, E. R., and Gardner, L. U.   Am. Rev. Tuberc., 5:429, 1921.
4. Rich, A. R.   The Pathogenesis of Tuberculosis, 2nd ed., Springfield, Ill., Charles C Thomas Co., 1951.
5a. Heimbeck, J.   Tubercle, 18:97, 1936.
 b. Holm, J.   Pub. Health Rep., 61:1298, 1946.
 c. Malmros, H.   Am. Rev. Tuberc., 56:267, 1947.
 d. Pinner, M.   Am. Rev. Tuberc., 56:368, 1947.
6a. Myers, J. A.   Tuberculosis Among Children and Young Adults, Springfield, Ill., Charles C Thomas Co., 1946.
 b. ——— J.A.M.A., 146:1492, 1951.
7. Dock, W.   Am. Rev. Tuberc., 53:297, 1946.
8a. Geer, E. K.   Arch. Int. Med., 49:77, 1932.
 b. Shipman, S. J., and Davis, E. A.   Am. Rev. Tuberc., 27:474, 1933.
 c. Amberson, J. B., and Riggins, H.   Ann. Int. Med., 10:156, 1936.
 d. Heimbeck, J.   Brit. J. Tuberc., 32:154, 1938.
 e. Rist, M. E.   Bull. Acad. de méd., Paris, 122:18, 1939.
 f. Israel, H. L., and Long, E. R.   Am. Rev. Tuberc., 43:12, 1941.
 g. Pollack, B. S., and Cohen, S.   J. Lancet, 61:111, 1946.
 h. Badger, T. L., and Ayvazion, L. F.   Am. Rev. Tuberc., 60:305, 1949.
9a. Calmette, A., Guérin, C., and Breton, M.   Ann. Inst. Pasteur, 21:401, 1907.
 b. Smith, T.   J.A.M.A., 68:764, 1917.
 c. Dienes, L., and Schoenheit, E. W.   Am. Rev. Tuberc., 13:379, 1926.
 d. Long, E. R.   Arch. Path., 1:918, 1926.
 e. Petroff, S. A.   J.A.M.A., 89:285, 1927.
 f. ——— and Steenken, W. J.   J. Immunol., 19:79, 1930.

g. Branch, A., and Enders, J. F. Am. Rev. Tuberc., 32:595, 1935.

h. Bogen, E., and Loomis, R. N. Trans. 31st Ann. Meeting Natl. Tuberc. Assoc., p. 1, 1935.

i. Coulaud, E. Compt. rend. Soc. de biol., 119:463, 1935.

j. ———— Rev. de la tuberc., 1:1181, 1935.

k. Calmette, A. L'Infection Bacillaire et la Tuberculose, Paris, Masson et Cie, 1936.

l. Opie, E. L., and Freund, I. J. Exper. Med., 66:761, 1937.

m. Smithburn, K. C., and Lavin, G. I. Am. Rev. Tuberc., 39:782, 1939.

n. Griffith, A. S., and Glover, R. E. J. Comp. Path. & Therap., 52:57, 1939.

o. Nagel, A. Ztschr. f. Immunitätsforsch. u. exper. Therap., 100:58, 1941.

p. Liebow, A. A., Burn, C. G., and Soper, W. B. Am. Rev. Tuberc., 41:592, 1940.

q. Damerow, A. P. Am. Rev. Tuberc., 41:512, 1940.

r. Potter, T. S. Proc. Soc. Exper. Biol. & Med., 54:143, 1943.

s. Wells, C. W., Flahiff, E. W., and Smith, H. H. Am. J. Hyg., 40:116, 1944.

t. Olson, B. J., Habel, K., and Piggott, W. R. Pub. Health Rep., 62:293, 1947.

u. Raffel, S. Am. Rev. Tuberc., 54:564, 1946.

v. ———— J. Infect. Dis., 82:267, 1948.

w. Choucroun, N. Am. Rev. Tuberc., 56:203, 1947.

x. Sarber, R. W., Nungester, W. J., and Stimpert, F. D. Am. Rev. Tuberc., 62:418, 1950.

y. Rist, N. Advances in Tuberculosis Research, 5:91, 1951.

10a. Pinner, M. Die Serodiagnose der Tuberkulose, Tuberkulose-Bibliothek, #28, Leipzig, J. A. Barth, 1927.

b. ———— Am. Rev. Tuberc., 18:497, 1928.

11. Elek, S. D. Brit. J. Exper. Path., 30:484, 1949.

12. Coombs, R. R. R., Mourant, R. E., and Race, R. R. Brit. J. Exper. Path., 26:255, 1945.

13. Middlebrook, G., Dubos, R. J., and Pierce, C. J. Exper. Med., 86:175, 1947.

14. Geronimus, L. P., and Birkeland, J. M. Am. Rev. Tuberc., 64:520, 1951.

15a. Marshak, A. J. Bact., 61:1, 1951.

b. Fitzgerald, R. J., and Bernheim, F. J. Bact., 54:671, 1947.

c. Lehmann, J. Lancet, 1:14, 1946.

16. Raffel, S., Heplar, J. Q., and Clifton, C. E., unpublished observations.

17. Hanks, J. H., and Evans, B. Am. Rev. Tuberc., 41:604, 1940.

18a. Fell, H. B., and Brieger, E. M. J. Hyg., 45:359, 1947.

b. Brieger, E. M. Tubercle, 30:227, 242, 1949.

c. ———— Advances in Tuberculosis Research, 4:236, 1951.

19. Maximow, A. A. J. Infect. Dis., 34:549, 1924.

20. ———— Ann. Inst. Pasteur, 42:225, 1928.

21. Corper, H. J., Damerow, A. P., Cohn, M. L., and Vidal, C. B. J. Infect. Dis., 58:158, 1936.

22a. Griffith, A. S. Med. Res. Council (Great Britain), Spec. Rept. Ser., No. 152, London, His Majesty's Stationery Office, 1931.

b. Birkhaug, K. E. Am. Rev. Tuberc., 26:6, 1933.

c. Lurie, M. B. J. Exper. Med., 60:163, 1934.

23. Woodruff, C. E. Am. J. Path., 10:739, 1934.

24. Bloch, H. Am. Rev. Tuberc., 58:662, 1948.

25. Lurie, M. B. J. Exper. Med., 75:247, 1942.

26. Gottlieb, R. Am. Rev. Tuberc., 25:172, 1932.

27a. Allgöwer, M., and Bloch, H. Am. Rev. Tuberc., 59:562, 1949.

b. Martin, S. P., Pierce, C. H., Middlebrook, G., and Dubos, R. J. J. Exper. Med., 91:381, 1950.

28. Bloch, H. J. Exper. Med., 91:197, 1950.

29a. Petroff, S. A. Proc. Soc. Exper. Biol. & Med., 24:634, 956, 1927.

b. ———— and Steenken, W., Jr. J. Exper. Med., 51:831, 1930.

c. Steenken, W., Jr., Oatway, W. H., Jr., and Petroff, S. A. J. Exper. Med., 60:515, 1934.

30. Seibert, F. B., Long, E. R., and Morley, N. J. Infect. Dis., 53:175, 1933.

31. Winn, W. A., and Petroff, S. A. J. Exper. Med., 57:239, 1933.

32. Miehe, H. Ztschr. f. Hyg. u. Infektionskr., 62:131, 1909.

33. Gardner, A. D. J. Path. & Bact., 32:715, 1929.
34. Steenken, W., Jr., and Gardner, L. U. Am. Rev. Tuberc., 54:62, 1946.
35. Choucroun, N., Delaunay, A., Bazin, S., and Robineaux, R. Ann. Inst. Pasteur, 80:619, 1951.
36. Bloch, H. J. Exper. Med., 88:355, 1948.
37. Suter, W. E., and Dubos, R. J. J. Exper. Med., 93:559, 1951.
38. Richmond, L., and Cummings, M. M. Am. Rev. Tuberc., 62:632, 1950.
39. Dubos, R. J., and Middlebrook, G. Am. Rev. Tuberc., 58:698, 1948.
40. ———— and Middlebrook, G. J. Exper. Med., 88:81, 1948.
41. ———— Am. Rev. Tuberc., 60:385, 1949.
42a. Asselineau, J., and Lederer, E. Bull. soc. chim. biol., 31:492, 1949.
  b. ———— and Lederer, E. Compt. rend. Acad. d. sc., 230:142, 1950.
  c. ———— and Lederer, E. Experientia, 7:281, 1951.
43. ———— Thèses Présentèes à la Faculté des Sciences de l'Université de Paris. Paris, Librairie Arnette, 1951.
44. Raffel, S. Proc. Soc. Exper. Biol. & Med., 64:507, 1947.
45a. Nègre, L., Boquet, A., and Valtis, J. Ann. Inst. Pasteur, 44:247, 1930.
  b. ———— Ann. Inst. Pasteur, 73:713, 1947.
46. Vaudremer, A. Compt. rend. Soc. de biol., 84:259, 1921; 85:1055, 1921.
47. Bloch, H. J. Exper. Med., 92:507, 1950.
48. Bailey, G. H., in The Newer Knowledge of Bacteriology and Immunology, ed. by E. O. Jordan and I. S. Falk, Chicago, University of Chicago Press, 1928, Chapter 59.
49. Raffel, S., Hanns, W., Guy, R., and Umbreit, L. Unpublished observations.
50. Lurie, M. B. J. Exper. Med., 63:923, 1936.
51. Mudd, S., Lucké, B., McCutcheon, M., and Strumia, M. J. Exper. Med., 49:779, 1929.
52. ———— J. Immunol., 13:113, 1927.
53. McCutcheon, M., Strumia, M., Mudd, S., Mudd, E. B. H., and Lucké B. J. Exper. Med., 49:815, 1929.
54. Hughes, J. J. Immunol., 25:103, 1933.
55. Lucké, B., McCutcheon, M., Strumia, M., and Mudd, S. J. Exper. Med., 49:797, 1929.
56. Sia, R. H. P., Robertson, O. H., and Woo, S. T. J. Exper. Med., 48:513, 1928.
57. Baldwin, E. R. J. Med. Research, 12:215, 1904.
58. Kallós, P., and Nathan, E. Ztschr. f. Immunitätsforsch. u. exper. Therap., 76:343, 1932.
59. Pagel, W. J. Path. & Bact., 50:111, 1940.
60. Heplar, J. Q., Futrelle, C., Raffel, S., and Clifton, C. E. Unpublished observations.
61. Myrvik, Q., and Weiser, R. S. Am. Rev. Tuberc., 64:669, 1951.
62. Dubos, R. Am. J. Med., 9:573, 1950.
63. Lurie, M. B. J. Exper. Med., 69:555, 1939.
64. Römer, P. H., and Joseph, K. Beitr. z. Klin. Tuberk., 17:365, 1910.
65. Lurie, M. B. J. Exper. Med., 69:579, 1939.
66a. Römer, P. H. Deutsche med. Wchnschr., 40:533, 1914.
  b. Mayer, E., and Hurley, D. J. Am. Rev. Tuberc., 2:604, 1918-19.
67. Kallós, P. Beiträge zur Immunobiologie der Tuberkulosa, Stockholm, H. W. Tulbergs Förlag, 1941.
68. Krause, A. K. Am. Rev. Tuberc., 14:211, 1926.
69. Willis, H. S. Am. Rev. Tuberc., 11:439, 1925
70. Pinner, M. Pulmonary Tuberculosis in the Adult, Springfield, Ill., Charles C Thomas Co., 1945.
71. Rothschild, H., Friedenwalk, J. S., and Bernstein, C. Bull. Johns Hopkins Hosp., 54:232, 1934.
72a. Willis, H. S., and Woodruff, C. E. Am. J. Path., 14:337, 1938.
  b. ———— Woodruff, C. E., Kelly, R. G., and Voldrich, M. Am. Rev. Tuberc., 38:10, 1938.
  c. Woodruff, C. E., and Kelly, R. G. J. Immunol., 45:79, 1942.
73a. Follis, R. H., Jr. Bull. Johns Hopkins Hosp., 63:283, 1938.

b. Birkhaug, K.   Acta tuberc. Scandinav., 13:221, 1939.
74. Ellison, R. T.   Am. Rev. Tuberc., 58:463, 1948.
75. Raffel, S.   Experientia, 6:410, 1950.
76. Menkin, V.   Physiol. Rev., 18:366, 1938.
77a. Rich, A. R.   Bull. Johns Hopkins Hosp., 47:189, 1930.
b. Cannon, P. R., and Hartley, G., Jr.   Am. J. Path., 14:87, 1938.
c. Klopstock, A., Pagel, W., and Guggenheim, A.   Klin. Wchnschr., 11:1826, 1932.
78. Opie, E. L., Flahiff, E. W., and Smith, H. H.   Am. J. Hyg., Sect. B., 29:155, 1939.
79. Wells, C. W., and Flahiff, E. W.   Am. J. Hyg., 40:109, 1944.
80a. Trudeau, E. L.   New York State J. Med., 58:97, 1893.
b. ——— Tr. A. Am. Physicians, 18:97, 1903.
c. Steenken, W., Jr., and Gardner, L. U.   Yale J. Biol. & Med., 15:393, 1943.
d. Zugar, B., and Steiner, M.   J. Immunol., 46:83, 1943.
81a. Wells, A. Q.   Lancet, 1:1221, 1937.
b. ——— and Robb-Smith, A. H. T.   Med. Res. Council (Great Britain), Spec. Rept. Ser. No. 259, 1946.
82. Griffith, A. S.   J. Hyg., 42:527, 1942.
83. Wells, A. Q.   Lancet, 1:53, 1949.
84. Calmette, A., and Guérin, C.   Compt. rend. Acad. d. sc., 147:1456, 1908.
85a. Weill-Hallé, B., and Turpin, R.   Soc. méd. hôp. de Paris, 49:1589, 1925.
b. Fenner, F.   Bibliotheca Tuberculosea, 5:112, 1951.
86. Birkhaug, K.   Am. Rev. Tuberc., 55:234, 1947.
87. Scheel, O.   J.A.M.A., 105:1925, 1933.
88. Jensen, K. A., and Ørskov, J.   Ztschr. f. Immunitätsforsch. u. exper. Therap., 70:155, 1931.
89. Wallgren, A.   J.A.M.A., 103:1341, 1934.
90. Dahlström, G., and Difs, H.   Acta tuberc. Scandinav., 25:Suppl. 27, 1951.
91a. Rosenthal, S. R., Blahd, M., and Leslie, E. I.   J. Pediat., 26:470, 1945.
b. ——— J.A.M.A., 136:73, 1948.
92. Aronson, J. D., and Palmer, C. E.   Pub. Health Rep., 61:802, 1946.
93. Ferguson, R. G.   Am. Rev. Tuberc., 54:325, 1946.
94a. The Conference on European BCG Programmes, issued by the Internat. Tuberculosis Campaign, Copenhagen, 1949.
b. Second Annual Report of the International Tuberculosis Campaign, issued by the Internat. Tuberculosis Campaign, Copenhagen, 1950.
c. Mass BCG Vaccination in Poland, 1948-49, issued by the Internat. Tuberculosis Campaign, Copenhagen, 1950.
d. Mass BCG Vaccination in Czechoslovakia, 1948-49, issued by the Internat. Tuberculosis Campaign, Copenhagen, 1950.
95. Vorwald, A. J., Dworski, M., Pratt, P. C., and Delahant, A. B.   Am. Rev. Tuberc., 62:455, 1950.

24

BOTULISM

The disease caused by the toxin of *Clostridium botulinum* represents the extreme in remoteness of relationship of etiologic parasite to host. The diffusible toxin produced by this bacillus in an anaerobic environment is extremely poisonous to human beings following ingestion, but there is little indication that contamination of a food by the bacterium or its spores alone makes it dangerous for the consumer because these organisms do not germinate in the intestinal tract or manufacture their toxin in that locale. A more intimate association of this bacillus to the affected host may be established artificially by injecting spores into animals along with necrotizing substances such as calcium chloride; the organisms may then proliferate sufficiently to produce intoxication (1). Rarely an analogous situation can come about in man. Hampson and others (2) have described cases of fatal intoxication in patients who had incurred deep wounds. The signs and symptoms were those of botulism, and type A bacilli were cultured from the wounds.

Immunity-Inducing Factor. *C. botulinum* provides one of two uncomplicated examples of the induction of immunity by a single factor of the bacterium, the soluble exotoxin. The other instance is that of *C. tetani*. In other cases where exotoxins are concerned in the pathogenic activities of a microbe the possibility that bacterial factors may also have a part in instigating resistance cannot be so readily excluded. This is illustrated by the discussions of diphtheria and gas gangrene in the two succeeding chapters.

Five distinct antigenic types of toxin, all with the same effects upon the body, are produced by various strains of the botulinus bacillus. These are designated as A, B, C, D, and E. C is not entirely homogeneous; two varieties, $C\alpha$ and $C\beta$, are distinguished, with some cross reactivity in neutralization by antitoxin (3). Human botulism is caused by types A, B and E toxins only. The first two are responsible for most cases in the United States and England, while the last is prevalent in Russia.

Type A toxin has been crystallized (4) and characterized chemically as a globulin-like protein composed of 19 constituent amino acids. This protein migrates as a single entity in electrophoresis and sediments with a single boundary in the ultracentrifuge (5). The type B toxin has been highly purified but not crystallized; it differs in chemical and serologic properties from the A toxin (6a).

Botulinus toxin is the most potent of any poison known. One mg. of

354

nitrogen of A toxin represents 220×10^6 mouse LD_{50}; or in other words 1 mg. of the toxin is sufficient to kill about 20,000,000 mice, and guinea pigs are about twice as susceptible (6b). The B toxin is not as potent molecule for molecule but it is only slightly less toxic than A in terms of comparable weights.

Botulinus toxin has been satisfactorily converted to toxoid by means of heat and formalin (7, 8). These preparations have negligible toxicity and induce satisfactory levels of antitoxin.

Relationships of Immunity-Inducing Factor to Virulence. As was noted before there is no difficulty in evaluating the relationship of the substance which incites acquired immunity to that which is responsible for the indirect pathogenic activity of the botulinus bacillus. The diffusible toxin is responsible for both these events. In the animal it appears to act upon the cholinergic motor nerve endings, interfering with the release of acetylcholine.

Mechanism of Acquired Immunity. Antitoxin can neutralize the poisonous properties of toxin as effectively as acid neutralizes a base. If the toxin can be influenced before it is taken up by the cells which it affects, disease can be obviated entirely.

Vaccination Procedures. Botulism has become an infrequent disease in the United States as in other countries where attention is given to the preparation of preserved foods. Outbreaks still occur however. Even in past years the number of individuals victimized by this food intoxication has never been sufficient to warrant the use of active vaccination procedures. It is conceivable however that information about immunization could become useful in time of war, for contamination of water supplies with highly purified toxins seems to be perfectly feasible. Such information is available. Alum-precipitated toxoids have been tested in man as well as animals. In human beings, two injections at two-month intervals result in the appearance of 0.02 unit of antitoxin per milliliter of serum; this presumably represents a protective level (9).

Passive protection with antitoxin administered as early as possible after the ingestion of contaminated food may be effective, but as in other bacterial intoxications the value of passive therapy declines precipitously once symptoms have set in. Unfortunately the incubation period may be short—sometimes only a few hours, most often one or two days—and there may be no warning of anything amiss during this interval. Successful treatment has been exceptional if one judges this by the paucity of reported cures.

BIBLIOGRAPHY

1. Keppie, J.   J. Hyg., 49:36, 1951.
2a. Hampson, C. R.   J. Bact., 61:647, 1951.
  b. Thomas, C. G., Jr., Keleher, M. F., and McKee, A. T.   Arch. Path., 51:623, 1951.
3. Pfenninger, W.   J. Infect. Dis., 35:347, 1924.
4a. Lamanna, C., McElroy, O. E., and Eklund, H. W.   Science, 103:613, 1946.
  b. Abrams, A., Kegeles, G., and Hottle, G. A.   J. Biol. Chem., 164:63, 1946.

5a. Putnam, F. W.   Federation Proc., 6:284, 1947.
 b. Buehel, H. J., Schantz, E. J., and Lamanna, C.   J. Biol. Chem., 169:295, 1947.
6a. Lamanna, C., and Glassman, H. N.   J. Bact., 54:575, 1947.
 b. van Heyningen, W. E.   Bacterial Toxins, Oxford, Blackwell Scientific Publications, 1950.
7. Forssman, J., and Lundstrom, E.   Ann. Inst. Pasteur, 16:294, 1902.
8. Weinberg, M., and Goy, P.   Compt. rend. Soc. de biol., 90:269, 1924.
9a. Nigg, C., Hottle, G. A., Coriell, L. L., Rosenwald, A. S., and Beveridge, G. W.   J. Immunol., 55:245, 1947.
 b. Hottle, G. A., Nigg, C., and Lichty, J. A.   J. Immunol., 55:255, 1947.
 c. Reames, H. R., Kadull, P. J., Housewright, R. D., and Wilson, J. B.   J. Immunol., 55:309, 1947.
 d. Bennetts, N. W., and Hall, H. T. B.   Australian Vet. J., 14:105, 1938.

25

DIPHTHERIA

Diphtheria like botulism is primarily a toxic disease, but it differs in the fundamental respect that the diphtheria bacillus manufactures its poison as a parasite upon host tissues. The situation of the bacterium is a superficial one, usually in the pharynx or less often in the nose, or both. Local damage is relatively mild; even in severe disease, tissue injury is limited to the affected mucosa. These alterations are serious only insofar as they may mechanically impede respiration, as when the diphtheritic membrane extends into the larynx or the bronchi. The disease proper, however, is essentially a systemic one affecting heart, kidneys, spleen, adrenals and sometimes peripheral nerves, and these effects are all mediated through the soluble exotoxin produced by the locally proliferating bacilli.

The fact that toxigenic organisms must flourish in intimate contact with the host's living tissues in order to produce generalized disease changes the complexion of the immunologic discussion to follow from the simple treatment accorded botulism, for in this case we must account for the microbe's ability to utilize the host as a medium for the manufacture of the toxin which brings about changes in distant tissues.

Protection-Inducing Factor. Whatever other factors may be concerned in inducing acquired resistance to diphtheria, the most important one is certainly the exotoxin of the organism. This was isolated in fairly purified form some years ago and given some chemical characterization (1), but recent studies employing newer serologic procedures have revealed in one such purified preparation 14 distinct antigens. Additional purification has reduced the antigenic components to three, hardly yet subject to precise chemical description (2). There is some evidence that the toxin of the bacillus represents the protein moiety of a respiratory enzyme, cytochrome b (3). This viewpoint supposes that when the protein combines with iron and porphyrin to complete the synthesis of the enzyme, its poisonous property disappears. In culture medium the iron concentration can be altered to control toxin production. If no iron is present the organism fails to grow at all; if a certain small quantity (about 100 micrograms per liter) is added, growth proceeds and toxin is produced, for under these conditions some enzyme synthesis occurs but there is insufficient iron to combine with all the toxic protein. When greater quantities of iron are added, to the level of about 500 grams per liter, growth is improved but toxin no longer appears in the medium because now

357

all the protein is combined to form enzyme (4). The concentration of iron which is optimal for toxin production in vitro is far lower than that which exists in the tissues of human beings, a fact which will be of considerable interest to the subsequent discussion of virulence.

Diphtheria toxin is a good antigen, and fortunately for prophylaxis it lends itself readily to detoxification and concentration. Purified toxoids contain only about 10 gammas of nitrogen per immunizing dose, and remain stable for long periods in the cold (5). Fortunately also the toxin appears to be antigenically homogeneous no matter what the bacillary strain of origin so that there need be no concern with differences in type or strain in applying prophylaxis (6).

The evidence that toxin constitutes the major immunizing factor of the bacillus is embodied in the simple fact that vaccination with this substance generally induces resistance to the disease (7). There are two reasons why we should bother to question whether this may not be the sole immunizing factor. One is the fact that antitoxin immunity is not always a sufficient guarantee of escape from the disease (8) and conversely some individuals with very low concentrations of circulating antitoxin may nevertheless be resistant to it (9). A second reason is the consideration that since toxin production depends upon proliferation of the bacilli in close association with the host's tissues, possibly some factor of the bacterial body itself may instigate an antagonism of the host to this, separate from the antitoxic response.

With respect to the **first** point, there may be several reasons for failure or apparent failure of toxoid to provide immunity to the disease, including variations in the immunizing efficacy of different toxoid preparations (10), differences in the abilities of individuals to respond to the antigenic stimulus (11), failure of antitoxin to neutralize toxin in vivo because of a disparity in the proper combining properties of antigen and antibody (12), the presumption that vaccinated individuals have responded with antitoxin formation without evidence from a Schick test (13), and, finally, the meaning of a negative Schick test as an index of immunity. Failure to react to the intradermal injection of an arbitrarily chosen dose of toxin can signify a wide range of antitoxin levels in the circulating blood, and at the lower levels consistent with a negative test it is possible for clinical disease sometimes to occur (9, 11b, 12, 14, 15). To explain on the other hand the existence of immunity when circulating antitoxin is scanty one might invoke the anamnestic response (see Chapter 6). Individuals with small amounts of antitoxin could respond to the first minute quantities of toxin liberated by infecting bacilli with a hurried addition to their protective substance.

There are some however who think that toxoid immunization may fail to correlate with resistance not for any of these reasons, but because immunity against the exotoxin alone of the diphtheria bacillus is only part of the story; that there are bacterial substances also of importance to the total protective response of the body, and these bacterial substances are not represented in the culture filtrates from which toxoids are prepared.

This brings us to the **second** point mentioned before; namely, that since toxin production depends upon proliferation of the bacilli in close association with the host's tissues, possibly some factor of the bacterial body itself may instigate an antagonism of the host to this, separate from the antitoxic response. With this thesis as a basis, Frobisher and his co-workers have vaccinated rabbits with nontoxigenic strains of bacilli and found that such animals develop the ability to localize virulent bacilli and also exotoxin at the initial focus of challenge infection (16). An unclarified feature of these observations is the peculiar ability of animals vaccinated with a vaccine in which toxin is not a component to act upon this heterologous substance. Rosenau and Bailey (17) failed some years earlier to induce resistance to toxin in guinea pigs vaccinated with nontoxigenic bacilli or with diphtheroids. Frobisher's data however are forthright, and have been underscored by later studies in which guinea pigs were immunized with virulent bacilli extracted with alcohol and ether and then disrupted by violent shaking with glass beads (18). It is apparent from the results of these experiments that such vaccines induce appreciable resistance to diphtheria in the complete absence of an antitoxic response by the treated animals. There seems no basis for doubting the validity of these findings, but further understanding of two points in particular would be desirable. The first point is why animals vaccinated with a nontoxin-containing preparation should be able to localize the toxin. The second point is how one can explain, if antibacterial immunity is important, the ability of animals passively immunized with antitoxin alone to inhibit the development of bacilli subsequently injected into the tissues, as is commonly seen in the ordinary virulence test with diphtheria bacilli.

What the immunizing factor in the bacillus may be is not known. Hewitt (19) has segregated about 50 serologic types within the groups *gravis, mitis* and *intermedius* by means of the agglutination reaction. Common antigens are shared by a number of types in all groups. These antigens may perhaps be the same as the type-specific heat-labile surface antigens and heat-stable group antigen described by Lautrop (20) and Oeding (21). Although the immunization study of Frobisher and Parsons (18) did not deal directly with the question of the specific factor inducing antibacterial immunity, it is apparent from the cross-protection tests that there is not a high degree of specificity involved. On the other hand Orr-Ewing (22) in a study of the effect of leukocytes upon diphtheria bacilli observed that the phagocytes of an individual infected with one type of organism were more active against it than against heterologous types. This implicates a type specific antibody in resistance, and by extension, a type specific antigen for the induction of this.

It is clear that further study of the possibility that acquired resistance to diphtheria may depend upon other factors in addition to toxin, and of the nature of these factors, is of practical as well as of scientific interest.

Relationship between Protection-Inducing and Virulence Factors. As it is the major immunizing factor, so the exotoxin of the diphtheria bacillus is also unquestionably the main expression of its pathogenicity. Diphtheria toxin causes widespread changes in the body including marked alterations in such vital tissues as the heart muscle, the central nervous system, the kidneys and the adrenals. The basic nature of this damaging activity is not known, but Pappenheimer (3) has made the interesting suggestion that since the toxin is a moiety of a respiratory enzyme of the bacillus, it may interfere with the synthesis of cytochrome b in the host by competitive inhibition.

Whether the bacillus possesses pathogenic activities aside from that inherent in its exotoxin is an open question. The fact that only toxigenic bacilli cause disease does not exclude the possibility that some other preliminary ability of the microbe is necessary to permit its establishment upon host tissues.

Not all strains of diphtheria bacilli are equally able to produce disease. Nontoxigenic strains are entirely devoid of this capacity, but among the toxin producers there are marked variations in pathogenicity and these have been found to correlate interestingly with certain colonial and morphologic characteristics of the organisms. Some years ago Anderson and his colleagues (7a, 23) subdivided diphtheria bacilli into groups on cultural grounds, and observed a decided parallelism of these characteristics with the severity of the disease caused by the organisms studied. One group grew upon tellurite-containing medium as blackish-grey, daisy head colonies, and this kind of bacillus was frequently associated with epidemic, rapidly progressive and malignant disease; to this organism the name *gravis* was applied. Another colony type on the same medium was black, shiny and convex; this type of bacillus was most often isolated from cases of less severity, and was named *mitis*. A third colonial form consisted of minute, flat grey colonies with raised centers; these organisms were called *intermedius*. These produce severe diphtheria but they are less frequent agents of disease and not so likely to cause epidemic outbreaks. These various organisms are differentiable through other growth characteristics as well. Other strains of toxigenic bacilli which do not fit this classification also occur (24).

Although European and British investigators have generally found an over-all correlation between these bacillary types and severity of disease (7a), this has not been the experience of workers in various areas of the United States (7a, 25). Nonetheless outbreaks of malignant diphtheria occur in this country, marked by more pronounced local damage, rapid progression, severe systemic changes and stubbornness to antitoxin therapy. Whatever the cultural characteristics of the strains isolated the essential fact remains that some diphtheria bacilli may cause exceptionally severe disease, and these differences in virulence require explanation.

There may be several possible reasons for such differences: (1) the highly virulent organisms may elaborate a toxin with more pronounced poisonous effects, (2) this toxin may be antigenically different from that produced by strains of ordinary pathogenicity to account for its refractoriness to neutralization by antitoxin in vivo, (3) there may be simply a greater production of toxin by the highly virulent bacilli, or (4) these organisms possess some special factor of virulence in addition to their toxigenicity.

For the first and second points there is no reasonable factual basis; practically all evidence points to the identity of diphtheria toxins manufactured by various strains (6), nor does there seem to be any additional toxic substance which might account for the increased virulence of some bacillary strains (26).

With regard to the third possibility, that highly virulent bacilli may produce more toxin than less virulent ones, Hewitt (6d) has assessed a large number of *gravis, mitis* and *intermedius* strains for their toxigenicity in culture and their virulence in guinea pigs. There was a good parallelism between these two characteristics, but there was no indication that *gravis* strains (generally of high virulence) could on the average produce more toxin in culture than *mitis* strains (generally of lower virulence). But that the situation in culture medium may be a poor reflection of what occurs in an animal host has been strongly suggested by Mueller's (4b) previously described experiments on toxin production in the presence of various concentrations of iron. The iron content of diphtheritic membrane was found to be many times that optimal for toxin production in vitro. When Mueller tested four strains of bacilli for their ability to produce toxin in media containing large amounts of iron, only one, a *gravis* strain isolated from a case of malignant diphtheria, elaborated a considerable quantity in the highest iron-containing medium employed. This surpassed by almost fifteen fold the toxin production of the other three strains, and this despite the fact that at **optimal** iron concentrations an *intermedius* organism (Park 8) was far superior to the *gravis* strain in toxin production. Zinnemann (27) has extended the significance of these observations in a medium more closely approximating the composition of animal tissues, but he found exceptions also; some *gravis* strains were no more toxigenic than *mitis* organisms in the presence of higher concentrations of iron. Most evidence implies so far, however, that the bacilli generally causing more serious diphtheria may do so because they alone are able to elaborate toxin even in the presence of the high concentrations of iron found in human tissues.

The fourth possibility to account for differences in virulence predicates that some factor other than toxigenicity may be concerned. This possibility does not necessarily relate only to the highly pathogenic strains since some special ability may be essential for any virulent diphtheria bacillus to proliferate on mucosal surfaces to the point of elaborating sufficient toxin for systemic effects. It could be then that the highly virulent strains have a more pronounced ability of this hypothetical kind, that they therefore multiply more effectively, and as a consequence of larger numbers produce more toxin.

When we seek the nature of this proposed ability, we must consider first that it may be exotoxin itself; this brings us back to our starting point. Perhaps minute quantities of toxin elaborated by the few bacilli of incipient infection can injure leukocytes locally, or otherwise derange the integrity of the surface epithelium. The fact that this small amount of toxin might be produced even in the presence of the high iron level of the tissues could then give the *gravis* type of bacillus an advantage in getting under way. Experimentally,

Ørskov and his co-workers have made observations which favor this reasoning (28). They examined the subcutaneous lesions induced in guinea pigs by *gravis, mitis* and *intermedius* bacilli, and found in the case of the *gravis* organism a paucity of leukocytes and scant phagocytosis. In contrast, sites of infection with *intermedius* bacilli revealed many polymorphonuclear cells and considerable phagocytosis of the organisms. This difference was not seen if the two organisms were injected intraperitoneally; phagocytosis occurred then equally well in both cases, possibly because in this cavity there was not the local concentration of toxin which might accumulate in the subcutaneous tissues. Further, if antitoxin were administered to the guinea pigs, the difference in phagocytosis did not show up even in subcutaneous lesions, suggesting again that the *gravis* organism damages leukocytes and escapes phagocytosis through its early formation of exotoxin. However, this does not explain the observation that toxoid-immunized human beings with measurable antitoxin levels in the blood stream may nevertheless proceed to develop diphtheria caused by bacteria of the malignant type, and this occurs much less frequently with the milder strains (7a).

A second possibility to account for differences in ability to establish infection is suggested by the studies of Orr-Ewing (22) of the comparative susceptibilities of various strains of diphtheria bacilli to phagocytosis. In her experience, most *gravis* strains resisted ingestion more successfully than did *mitis* strains. We might deduce from this that highly virulent strains possess a specific virulence factor in the nature of a leukocyte repellent. In the same vein, Lautrop (29) believes that more virulent bacilli possess more of the type-specific surface antigen which he has described (20), and that this endows such bacteria with resistance to phagocytosis as do the surface antigens of certain other bacteria.

Finally, the possibility exists that extraneous factors coinciding with the presence of bacilli upon tissue surfaces may decide their disease producing abilities. Thus, some other infectious agent may act synergistically with *C. diphtheriae* to produce malignant disease. Updyke and Frobisher (30) have investigated this possibility in animals. Since streptococci of group B had been isolated from several cases of malignant diphtheria caused by the *mitis* type of the diphtheria bacillus, this as well as bacteria of 32 other species was employed in rabbits and mice in combination with diphtheria bacilli. Although enhanced reactions were seen in some instances these were not judged to be comparable to malignant diphtheria in human beings.

In summary, the exotoxin of the diphtheria bacillus itself is the primary factor in its virulence, and variations in virulence may be due to the capacity of highly virulent strains of the bacillus to manufacture toxin in the presence of concentrations of iron in the tissues which are excessive for strains of ordinary virulence. In addition, there may be some bacillary factor which accounts for the ability of the organism to establish itself upon host tissues. There are various intimations of the nature of this factor including the suggestion that it may be a surface antigen with leukocyte repellent properties, but the evidence for this is still very sketchy.

Mechanisms of Acquired Resistance. The major immunity to diphtheria is embodied in the antitoxin response. Antitoxin neutralizes the baneful properties of the toxin without actually destroying it, for the combination is reversible and the liberated toxin is again poisonous. The mechanics of this neutralization by antibody are not known.

It is generally considered that once toxin has combined with susceptible tissues—and we are again ignorant of the nature of this combination—it is no longer amenable to the activity of antitoxin. This may be so, or it may be that toxin quickly sets in motion adverse changes which progress even though the toxin be subsequently neutralized. The net effect in either case is a precipitous decline with time in the effectiveness of administered antitoxin when an infection or an experimental intoxication has become established.

As was mentioned before, antibacterial resistance may be of importance to total immunity against diphtheria. The possible bacterial components which may instigate this have been discussed. The manner in which the body might put such an immunity into action is not clear, but again certain possibilities derive from several reported observations (31). Orr-Ewing (22) states that as the result of an infection with *gravis* organisms the body becomes better able to kill these bacteria through phagocytosis. One might infer that this is mediated by an antibody with opsonizing activity, and Lautrop (29) has found that antiserum developed against the surface antigens of diphtheria bacilli have some protective effect in vivo. Huang (32) has reported similar findings with horse sera containing antibacterial antibodies; he believes that these accounted for the rapid disappearance of serologically homologous organisms from the throats of convalescent patients. In contrast such sera failed to influence the carrier state in patients with bacilli of various heterologous serologic types. Frobisher and Parsons (18) as a result of their work with bacillary antigens as immunizing agents came to the conclusion that the body gains an ability for localizing the organism by the development of a hypersensitivity of the Koch (i.e. delayed) type. The possible significance of the allergic state in acquired resistance has been discussed in previous connotations (see Chapters 10, 15 and 23). Judging from the information available to us now, it would seem desirable to exclude all other possible grounds for antibacterial resistance (such as an antibody-leukocyte relationship) before considering this particular response of the body as an acquired resistance.

On the other side of the question of the possible importance of antibacterial immunity to diphtheria one must weigh the observations of Ipsen (12) of patients vaccinated with toxoid as compared with those who had acquired immunity as the result of natural exposure to toxigenic bacilli. Judging two such groups of individuals with equivalent blood antitoxin titers who had nevertheless developed diphtheria, he found that the toxoid vaccinated patients fared better in their illnesses than did the spontaneously immunized. This is a conclusion contrary to what might be expected if the latter group, through contact with bacilli as well as their toxin, had gained antibacterial resistance as well as antitoxic. Insofar as statistical information of this kind has validity, it speaks against a significant beneficial effect of an antibacterial resistance mechanism.

GENERAL COMMENT

Bringing together these discussions of immunity-inducing factors, the relationship of these to the virulence of the diphtheria bacillus, and the mechanisms of acquired resistance, we find that the dominant system concerned in diphtheria is one in which the chief protection-inducing factor is the same as the virulence factor of the organism, i.e. exotoxin, and acquired resistance consists of a direct attack by the host upon this. The elaboration of toxin could explain the entire picture of diphtheria bacillary virulence, including the primary ability of organisms to establish themselves in the tissues through local cell injury. There are, however, undertones of evidence suggesting that another system of parasite-host interplay may exist; that some component of the bacterial body itself may incite an antibacterial resistance and that a factor of the bacterial cell may account also for its capacity to become established in the host. The evidence for these occurrences needs amplification and, if this can be obtained, then we require more specific data about the nature of the bacterial components implicated. Possibly a surface antigen may be the immunity-inducing factor; type specific surface antigens have been described (20). Such antigens may discourage leukocytic action; an antagonism to phagocytosis by highly virulent strains has been described (22). Finally, to complete this conjectural picture, acquired antibacterial resistance may depend upon an opsonizing antibody (22, 29) or it may, as Frobisher (18) suggests, depend upon an allergic tuberculin-type of reactivity of the tissues to the diphtheria bacillus.

Practical Procedures for Vaccination. Because immunization of children against diphtheria constitutes one of the outstanding applications of biologic prophylaxis, the literature on this subject is voluminous. This will only be sampled here with a view to providing a concise reflection of current thought on the matter.

Toxoid is employed both in fluid form and precipitated on alum. Edsall (15) expresses the generally held viewpoint that the latter type of preparation is probably slightly superior, but alum-precipitated toxoid has the disadvantages of provoking enhanced reactions in those who are hypersensitive to the toxoid, and it also produces more frequent primary local reactions. It appears however that most hypersensitive reactions are caused by bacillary protein present in toxoid preparations; this allergic state presumably exists as the result of spontaneous exposures to the bacilli (5d, 33, 34). In such instances the use of purified toxoid should decrease the incidence of reactions. In those in whom the allergic reactivity is to the toxoid itself the occurrence of reactions cannot be avoided, but since very small doses of toxoid can reanimate antitoxin levels through the anamnestic response the severity of reactions may be

minimized in these cases also (15, 33, 35). Purified toxoid possesses a high
level of antigenicity (5c) so that the Schick test dose of toxin alone may serve
as an adequate booster stimulus.

A minimum of two doses of alum precipitated or three doses of fluid
toxoid are necessary to produce an adequate and sustained immunity. Injections with either agent should be at least three weeks apart, and preferably
longer. (This corresponds to the experience with botulinus and gas gangrene
toxoids in human beings). Most evidence indicates that the subcutaneous
route of administration is best, but the intramuscular route has also been
advised (36).

The duration of antitoxic immunity resulting from vaccination is variable.
Five years after immunization one group of workers found that 34 per cent
of children had reverted to Schick positivity (37). The need for reimmuniza-
tion is thus obvious, and the greater the efficacy of immunization programs in
causing a decrease in carriers of toxigenic bacilli, the less the occurrence of
spontaneous immunization and the larger the need for adequate artificial
restimulation.

The possible merits of employing bacterial as well as toxoid vaccination
suggested by the studies of Frobisher and Parsons (16, 18) in animals deserve serious consideration. It would seem wise however to harvest more
information from the laboratory before even experimental application is
considered in human beings.

It is a widespread practice among pediatricians to employ combined
vaccines consisting of diphtheria and tetanus toxoids and *H. pertussis*. This procedure possesses the obvious advantage of simplifying the immunization schedule and cutting down the number of injections required. Vaccines of this and
other kinds are discussed by Miller (36).

BIBLIOGRAPHY

1a. Eaton, M. D.   J. Bact., 31:347, 367, 1936.
  b. Pappenheimer, A. M., Jr.   J. Biol. Chem., 120:543, 1937.
2. Pope, C. G., Stevens, M. F., Caspary, E. A., and Fenton, E. L.   Brit. J. Exper. Path.,
       32:246, 1951.
3. Pappenheimer, A. M., Jr.   Federation Proc., 6:479, 1947.
4a. ——— and Johnson, S. J.   Brit. J. Exper. Path., 17:335, 342, 1936; 18:239, 1937.
  b. Mueller, J. H.   J. Immunol., 42:353, 1941.
5a. Pillemer, L., and Toll, D.   Science, 105:102, 1947.
  b. ——— Toll, D., and Badger, S. J.   J. Biol. Chem., 170:571, 1947.
  c. ——— Wittler, R. G., Clapp, F. L., and Adam, J. N., Jr.   J. Immunol., 58:223,
       1948.
  d. Lawrence, H. S., and Pappenheimer, A. M., Jr.   Am. J. Hyg., 47:226, 1948.
6a. Parish, H. J., Whatley, E. E., and O'Brien, R. A.   Brit. M. J., 2:915, 1932.
  b. Povitsky, O. R., Eisner, N., and Jackson, E.   J. Infect. Dis., 52:246, 1933.
  c. Zinnemann, K.   J. Path. & Bact., 58:43, 1946.
  d. Hewitt, L. F.   Brit. J. Exper. Path., 29:181, 1948.
7a. McLeod, J. W.   Bact. Rev., 7:1, 1943.
  b. Anderson, G. W.   Am. J. Pub. Health, 37:1, 1947.
  c. Langmuir, A. D.   In Rosenau's Preventive Medicine and Hygiene, ed. by K. Maxcy,
       7th ed., New York, Appleton-Century-Crofts, Inc., 1951.

8a. Eller, C. H., and Frobisher, M., Jr.   Am. J. Hyg., 42:179, 1945.
  b. Fanning, J.   Brit. M. J., 1:371, 1947.
9. Phair, J. J.   Am. J. Hyg., 36:283, 1942.
10. Bousfield, G.   Pub. Health Rep., 60:121, 1947.
11a. O'Brien, R. A., Okell, C. C., and Parish, H. J.   Lancet, 1:149, 1929.
  b. Parish, H. J., and Wright, J.   Lancet, 1:600, 1935.
  c. ——— and Wright, J.   Lancet, 2:882, 1938.
  d. Neill, J. M., Sugg, J. Y., and Richardson, L. V.   J. Immunol., 28:363, 1935.
  e. Steavart, D. J., and Jones, F. G.   Canad. Pub. Health J., 33:565, 1942.
12. Ipsen, J.   J. Immunol., 54:325, 1946.
13. Bullowa, J. G. M., and Scannel, M.   J.A.M.A., 122:595, 1943.
14. Gibbard, J., Bynoe, E. T., and Gibbons, R. J.   Canad. Pub. Health J., 36:188, 1945.
15. Edsall, G.   New England J. Med., 235:256, 1946.
16a. Frobisher, M., Jr., and Parsons, E. I.   Am. J. Hyg., 37:53, 1943.
  b. ——— and Updyke, E. L.   J. Bact., 54:609, 1947.
17. Rosenau, M. J., and Bailey, G. H.   J. Infect. Dis., 37:97, 1925.
18. Frobisher, M., Jr., and Parsons, E. I.   Am. J. Hyg., 52:239, 1950.
19. Hewitt, L. F.   Brit. J. Exper. Path., 28:338, 1947.
20. Lautrop, H.   Acta path. et microbiol. Scandinav., 27:443, 1950.
21. Oeding, P.   Acta path. et microbiol. Scandinav., 27:427, 1950.
22. Orr-Ewing, J.   J. Path. & Bact., 58:167, 1946.
23. Anderson, J. S., Happold, F. C., McLeod, J. W., and Thomson, J. G.   J. Path. & Bact., 34:667, 1931.
24. Morton, H. E.   Bact. Rev., 4:177, 1940.
25. Frobisher, M., Jr.   Am. J. Pub. Health, 33:1244, 1943.
26a. McClean, D.   Lancet, 1:595, 1941.
  b. Frobisher, M., Jr., and Mauss, E. A.   Am. J. Hyg., 37:225, 1943.
27. Zinnemann, K.   J. Path. & Bact., 55:275, 1943.
28. Ørskov, J., Andersen, E. K., and Poulsen, J. V.   Acta path. et microbiol, Scandinav., 21:181, 1944.
29. Lautrop, H.   Personal communication.
30. Updyke, E. L., and Frobisher, M., Jr.   J. Bact., 54:619, 1947.
31. Sordelli, A., Navarro, V., and Ferrari, R.   Rev. d. Inst. bact., Buenos Aires, 12:494, 1944.
32. Huang, C. H.   Am. J. Hyg., 35:317, 325, 1942.
33. Pappenheimer, A. M., Jr., and Lawrence, H. S.   Am. J. Hyg., 47:233, 241, 1948.
34. Ross, V., Clapp, F. L., and Schimpf, B. W.   J. Bact., 51:408, 1946.
35. Barr, M., and Glenny, A. T.   J. Hyg., 44:135, 1945.
36. Miller, J. J., Jr.   J.A.M.A., 134:1064, 1947.
37. Fraser, B. T., and Halpern, K. C.   Canad. Pub. Health J., 26:476, 1935.

26

GAS GANGRENE

Gas gangrene is caused usually by one or a combination of the predominantly saccharolytic and toxigenic species of *Clostridium*. The majority of cases are caused by *Cl. perfringens* (type A), *Cl. septicum, Cl. novyi,* and to some extent by *Cl. bifermentans* and the proteolytic *Cl. histolyticum.* Other proteolytic species of this genus often take part in the disease without, however, being able to initiate it. In addition other microbes such as the pyogenic cocci may by their presence in the tissues greatly facilitate the progress of the clostridia themselves. These complications will not be dealt with here, for gas gangrene can exist as an infection of single etiologic genesis, and it is from this that we may most profitably learn something of the interplay of parasite and host.

This disease stems from the contamination of traumatized tissues with soil. The relationship of the spore-forming gas gangrene bacilli to the tissues differs from that described for botulism or diphtheria, for in this case the organism is neither remote from the body which its toxin injures as is the case with *Cl. botulinum,* nor in contiguity with viable cells as is the case with *C. diphtheriae.* The gangrene microbes carry on their activities, which include toxin formation, in an environment between these extremes; they proliferate in nonviable tissues of the host whence their toxins diffuse to surrounding healthy areas.

Protection-Inducing Factors. It seems clear that the toxins of these bacilli are the substances of importance in accounting for acquired resistance to the disease. The toxins of the clostridia are now fairly well documented; 15 substances are listed as products of *Cl. perfringens* alone (1). Not all of these are produced by the organism associated with gas gangrene in man, however. There are six bacterial types in this species of which only type A is pathogenic for man, and we will limit discussion to it. This particular bacillus probably elaborates eight toxins of which the most important member is a phosphatide-splitting enzyme, lecithinase, referred to as alpha toxin (2). This hemolyzes erythrocytes, kills other kinds of cells, and is lethal to animals following intravenous injection. A second substance, again identified as an enzyme, is collagenase or kappa toxin (3). This is proteolytic and, as its name implies, it can destroy collagen. A third substance, theta toxin, is an oxygen labile hemolysin, chemically and antigenically related to similar labile hemolysins of other genera of bacteria (4). Hyaluronidase (mu toxin) is produced by type A *perfringens* as well as by other species of clostridia (5), and fibrino-lysin may also be formed by various strains of these organisms (6). Other substances with activities of restricted interest are also found in the filtrates of *Cl. perfringens* type A cultures, including a factor active upon human blood group substances, another active upon the virus receptors of erythrocytes, and a third which may not be a distinct entity (1). At the moment these have not been established as having a relationship to the interaction of organism and host.

All the primarily pathogenic clostridia listed earlier produce diffusible toxins with more or less analogous effects. Thus, *Cl. septicum* toxin causes hemolysis and cellular necrosis, and is lethal upon intravenous injection (7). This organism produces also collagenase, hyaluronidase, and a desoxyribo-nuclease which damages the nuclei of leukocytes and other cells (8). The total toxic filtrate is relatively weak in concentration, but potent in end results (9). *Cl. novyi* elaborates a toxin with similar activities but quantitatively more potent than that of *Cl. septicum;* here there are multiple toxic factors including two or possibly three lecithinases with necrotizing and lethal properties, and an hemolysin (10). *Cl. bifermentans* produces a lecithinase antigenically re-lated to that of *Cl. perfringens* but with relatively slight toxicity to the tissues of mice and guinea pigs (11). *Cl. histolyticum* is a member of the primarily proteolytic group of bacilli not usually accused of initiating gas gangrene, but British reports from the Middle East during World War II indicate that it may have some importance in this regard (12). Lecithinase and collagenase are produced by this organism, the latter in high concentration and probably iden-tical with that of *Cl. perfringens* (10b, 13).

With respect to immunity induction, these toxic substances are all anti-genic and the antitoxins incited by some of them serve to protect experimental animals against the bacteria themselves (12); this has been demonstrated in the cases of *Cl. perfringens* (14) and *Cl. novyi* (14b, 14d) and in more lim-ited fashion with *Cl. septicum* also (9).

In the case of *Cl. perfringens* the toxic components are sufficiently well known so that it has been possible to assess the capacities of individual toxic factors to induce resistance. Such studies have been carried out chiefly by Evans through the use of passive protection tests (15). Antitoxic sera pre-pared in horses, and containing individual antitoxins almost exclusively, were tested for their abilities to protect guinea pigs against virulent bacilli injected intramuscularly. Whereas antibodies induced by the theta toxin (15a), hy-aluronidase (15b), and collagenase (15c) were devoid of protective ability in these experiments, the antilecithinase (alpha antitoxin) proved highly ef-fective (15).

As for the possibility that a bacterial component may also be concerned in protective immunization, there is little evidence to support this. The antigens of the bacilli are sufficiently complex as to subdivide *perfringens* and *sep-ticum,* and perhaps others of the species, into types (16). But it seems un-likely that these antigens take part in the induction of resistance despite the antibodies which they provoke (17), though affirmative claims have been made in the case of *Cl. septicum* (18). A possible reason for the inefficacy of antibacterial factors in resistance lies in the fact that the tissue in which these organisms usually initiate infection is damaged or dead, and consequently blood-borne substances of potential protective value may not reach them, or viable leukocytes may not be present to destroy the microbes (19).

Relation between Protection-Inducing Factors and Virulence. The pathogenic capacities of the gas gangrene clostridia appear to depend upon their diffusible toxins. These probably explain the ability of the microbe to become established in the host as well as the subsequent local and systemic damage which characterizes the disease process (17a, 20). The systemic activities of various of these toxins have been described for *Cl. perfringens* (21), for *Cl. novyi* (20a) and for *Cl. septicum* (20b). In addition to the necrotizing propensities already mentioned as being common to all of them, *perfringens* toxin causes gross intravascular hemolysis and fall in blood pressure, *novyi* toxin acts principally upon the peripheral vascular system, and the *septicum* filtrate produces cardiac and renal damage.

The virulence function of the toxins of *Cl. perfringens* was well demonstrated in 1917 by DeKruif and Bollman (17a). Large numbers of washed bacilli were found necessary to initiate infection in guinea pigs, while much smaller numbers sufficed when injected along with toxic filtrate; the infectiousness of washed organisms was thereby increased 10,000-fold. This information has since then been made more specific with regard to the individual toxic components most concerned in the total effect. The lecithinase or alpha toxin of *Cl. perfringens* seems to be of most importance to its pathogenicity. In one study 94 strains isolated from human and animal feces and soil were tested for lecithinase production and virulence in mice. Of those strains virulent for mice, Kass found that 83 per cent produced the enzyme in culture (22). Evans (23) similarly found good correlation of lecithinase production with virulence in guinea pigs. However, in both studies many lecithinase-producing strains were revealed to be nonpathogenic for animals; in the first work half the lecithinase positive strains failed to harm mice, and in the second experiment two of 21 strains producing high concentrations of the enzyme proved impotent in animals. The failure of some virulent strains to produce the enzyme, and the inability of many enzyme producers to cause disease, make it seem likely that other factors in addition to lecithinase take part in the pathogenic activities of these organisms. Yet it is a peculiar fact that antilecithinase serum may apparently protect animals even against those strains which do not produce the enzyme in culture (23). Perhaps the tissues of the host may provide a better milieu for the manufacture of this factor than do the culture media employed to test for its presence in vitro. A limiting effect of iron upon toxin production suggests such a possibility (24).

The collagen-destroying enzyme (kappa toxin) might be imagined to be of some importance to the progress of gas gangrene (13c). The question of its importance to the disease has not been put to direct test so far as the writer is aware, but Macfarlane and MacLennan (3b) have observed disintegration of the supporting collagen in human and rabbit muscle following gangrene. If collagenase is injected intramuscularly into animals it causes local swelling; if administered intracutaneously there results local hemorrhage and necrosis, and if it is given intravenously it produces massive pulmonary hemorrhages (3d).

Although these observations are certainly suggestive of a role of collagenase in the pathogenic activities of the clostridia, antibodies against this enzyme have not been found to influence the initiation or progression of experimental gas gangrene (15c). This constitutes indirect evidence that the factor may not contribute to virulence, to an important extent at least.

The role of hyaluronidase in the virulence of clostridia has been investigated by several workers, one of whom (5) concluded that although no striking correlation exists between hyaluronidase elaboration and virulence among individual strains, nevertheless the majority of strains isolated from clinical cases of gas gangrene produce it. From a general standpoint, therefore, it appeared to this investigator that those organisms capable of pronounced tissue invasion are those which are apt to elaborate this particular factor. In the correlative studies of Kass (22) 54 per cent of bacilli virulent for mice produced hyaluronidase, but most of these elaborated lecithinase also. Only one fourth of the strains producing hyaluronidase alone were virulent, but the same number of strains producing neither hyaluronidase nor lecithinase could also produce disease. A third study (23) showed no coincidence of virulence with the production of this enzyme. It appears then that hyaluronidase, if it has significance in the disease producing capacities of *Cl. perfringens,* is quite limited in its influence.

Most of the species pathogenic for men, as well as some of the non-pathogenic clostridia, produce a fibrinolysin similar in its activities to the streptokinase of streptococci (page 33). This enzyme or enzyme-activator has been identified in the tissues of experimentally infected animals, and it may conceivably be related, through its ability to dissolve fibrin, to the spread of clostridia through the tissues (6, 25).

Finally, the theta hemolysin has been studied by the correlative method described for lecithinase and hyaluronidase. In guinea pigs the ability of strains of *Cl. perfringens* to cause disease has no relationship to their formation of this enzyme (23).

It might be revealing to carry out experiments with individual toxic components of *Cl. perfringens* of the kind performed by DeKruif and Bollman (17a) with the whole toxic filtrate. From the information presently available, however, it appears that the lecithinase of this bacillus is the single factor of most importance to pathogenicity, though it is certainly not the only one. As indicated in the preceding section, this substance is most effective also in immunizing against the disease. This identity of virulence factor with immunizing agent leads to the conclusion that acquired resistance functions through a direct suppression by the body of the virulence potentiality of the parasite.

Whether other factors than toxins may be involved in the infectious abilities of the gas gangrene bacilli is not known. Yet we have seen that the toxins about which we have information do not entirely answer the question of disease-producing ability. There may be other diffusible substances as yet unrecognized, for it is known that the production of toxins by clostridia may be limited by the iron content of the medium (24) and it is possible that this substance, or perhaps some other environmental ingredient, may mask the toxigenicity of some strains when attempts are made to determine this in culture. The culture test could thus fail to reflect the ability of an organism to produce a particular toxin in vivo.

The possibility that properties of the bacterial cells themselves may be concerned in virulence has never received clear support.

We can envision a qualified picture of the mechanism of gas gangrene infection upon the basis of the information we have, and this is essentially the same as that proposed by DeKruif and Bollman over 35 years ago (17a). Since these anaerobic bacilli cannot maintain themselves in living tissues, it is essential that they be presented with a locus of nonliving substrate in the body. An area devitalized by injury provides this condition, and the introduction of soil supplies the bacillary spores themselves as well as, perhaps, such substances as calcium salts which may establish more reducing conditions in the area. In this environment the spores germinate and the bacilli propagate and produce their various enzymes. These diffuse into neighboring viable tissues to injure or destroy cells thus creating the essential condition which permits the anaerobic bacilli to follow in their wake. In this way extension of infection takes place, abetted perhaps by hyaluronidase and fibrinolysin, and as the bacilli multiply they ferment tissue carbohydrate with the production of gas. Collagenase may add its characteristic activity to create the pulped muscle appearance generally seen in gas gangrene. These changes often become evident beyond the area of bacillary growth. Meanwhile, general intoxication occurs as well (20, 21); one evidence of this may be an intense intravascular destruction of erythrocytes with consequent bronzing of the skin.

The evidence for this portrayal is most complete for *Cl. perfringens* but presumably it applies to the other clostridia which are able to initiate gas gangrene infection. It should be reiterated that this picture is still tentative since unknown factors in addition to those described appear to determine the ability of the gas gangrene bacilli to establish disease.

Mechanism of Acquired Resistance. In the case of *Cl. perfringens,* and presumably also of the other clostridia under consideration, the fact that the toxins chiefly responsible for virulence also induce protective resistance to the organisms permits the formulation of a simple concept of the mechanism through which acquired resistance may be effective. In fact, experimental findings exceed the expectations deriving from studies such as those just described, for even with those virulent strains of bacilli which do not appear to elaborate lecithinase as determined by the in vitro methods employed, antitoxin against this factor protects animals against intramuscularly injected bacteria (23). Analogously, *Cl. septicum* antitoxin protects animals against infection with this organism (9), and the same is true for *Cl. novyi* (14d).

The mechanics of acquired immunity appear then to be straightforward. In the presence of a sufficient level of humoral antitoxin the necrotizing activity of toxin is neutralized, the bacteria cannot spread from the point of entry because surrounding tissue does not become devitalized, and the infection terminates. A recent inquiry into the possible presence of antilecithinase in myosin and other muscle proteins of animals immunized with *Cl. perfringens* toxoid turned up no evidence of muscle immunity (26).

Practical Vaccination Procedures. Gas gangrene is primarily a disease of battle casualties and although its incidence in World War II was far below that of World War I, the statistics still establish a need for an adequate prophylactic vaccine. The disease occurred in 1.2 per cent of several reported groups of wounded soldiers during World War II, and average mortality ranged between 22 and 70 per cent (12). Therapy, which has depended chiefly upon surgical intervention and the administration of antitoxin, has limitations, especially with regard to time, because the toxins become quickly fixed to tissues (9, 27). Since established gas gangrene may involve infection with other organisms such as pyogenic cocci, effective treatment is further complicated.

Reports on vaccination which have appeared since 1945 indicate that the efforts instigated by World War II have brought forth a multiple vaccine composed of the toxoids of *Cl. perfringens, Cl. septicum,* and *Cl. novyi* which, there is reason to expect, will provide satisfactory resistance to gas gangrene in human beings. A previous obstacle has been the lack of antigenic potency of toxoid preparations, and this has been overcome by newer cultural methods which furnish higher yields of toxin, and by chemical procedures for concentration (24, 28). But even without these advantages it appears that the proper number and spacing of injections of alum-precipitated toxoids can engender levels of antitoxin in human beings which have been found to protect animals from experimental infection. Thus, an antilecithinase activity of 0.10 unit or more per milliliter of serum protects guinea pigs and dogs against living clostridia (12, 14d). Three injections of toxoid, the last dose administered as long as 4 to 10 months after the first two, stimulate antitoxin titers of this magnitude in almost 100 per cent of treated subjects, and these concentrations persist up to 10 months (12, 14d, 29). Even when relatively weak toxoid preparations are employed a long interval between the second and last injection results in satisfactory responses in about 90 per cent of vaccinated individuals (29c).

The common experience with respect to local and systemic reactions to these toxoids has not been unusual. These do not exceed the reactions commonly seen to follow the administration of tetanus and diphtheria toxoids.

Passive therapy with multivalent antitoxic sera has been used for some years in conjunction with surgical treatment and antibiotic agents.

BIBLIOGRAPHY

1. van Heyningen, W. E.   Bacterial Toxins, Oxford, Blackwell Scientific Publications, 1950.
2. Macfarlane, M. G., and Knight, B. C. J. G.   Biochem. J., 35:882, 1941.
3a. Maschmann, E.   Biochem. Ztschr., 295:1, 351-391, 1937; 297:284, 1938.
   b. Macfarlane, M. G., and MacLennan, J. D.   Lancet, 2:328, 1945.
   c. Oakley, C. L., Warrack, G. H., and van Heyningen, W. E.   J. Path. & Bact., 58:229, 1946.
   d. ———— Warrack, G. H., and Warren, M. E.   J. Path. & Bact., 60:495, 1948.
4. Todd, E. W.   Brit. J. Exper. Path., 22:172, 1941.
5. McClean, D.   J. Path. & Bact., 42:477, 1936.
6. Reed, G. B., Orr, J. H., and Brown, H. J.   J. Bact., 46:475, 1943.
7. Bernheimer, A. W.   J. Exper. Med., 80:309, 1944.
8. Warrack, G. H., Bidwell, E., and Oakley, C. L.   J. Path. & Bact., 63:293, 1951.
9. Craddock, S., and Parish, H. J.   Brit. J. Exper. Path., 12:389, 1931.
10a. Walbum, L. E., and Reymann, G. C.   J. Path. & Bact., 44:379, 1937.
   b. Oakley, C. L., Warrack, G. H., and Clarke, P. H.   J. Gen. Microbiol., 1:91, 1947.
   c. Macfarlane, M. G.   Biochem. J., 42:590, 1948.
11. Miles, E. M., and Miles, A. A.   J. Gen. Microbiol., 1:385, 1947; 4:22, 1950.
12. Danielson, I. S.   Tr. New York. Acad. Sc., 9:297, 1946-47.
13a. Pasternack, J. G., and Bengston, I. A.   Pub. Health Rep., 55:775, 1940.
   b. McClung, L. S., and Toabe, R.   J. Bact., 53:255, 1947.
   c. Evans, D. G.   J. Gen. Microbiol., 1:378, 1947.
14a. Stewart, S. E.   War Med., 2:87, 1942.
   b. Robertson, M., and Keppie, J.   Lancet, 2:311, 1943.
   c. Altemeier, W. A., Zurste, W. L., Culbertson, W. R., Wadsworth, C. L., Tytell, A. A., Logan, M. A., and Tytell, A. G.   Ann. Surg., 126:509, 1947.
   d. Tytell, A. A., Logan, M. A., Tytell, A. G., and Tepper, J.   J. Immunol., 55:233, 1947.
15a. Evans, D. G.   Brit. J. Exper. Path., 24:81, 1943.
   b. ———— J. Path. & Bact., 55:427, 1943.
   c. ———— Brit. J. Exper. Path., 28:24, 1947.
16a. McCoy, E., and McClung, L. S.   Bact. Rev., 2:47, 1938.
   b. Orr, J. H., and Reed, G. B.   J. Bact., 40:441, 1940.
   c. Svec, M. H., and McCoy, E.   J. Bact., 48:31, 1944.
17a. DeKruif, P. H., and Bollman, J. L.   J. Infect. Dis., 21:588, 1917.
   b. Weinberg, M., Davesne, J., and Haber, P.   Ann. Inst. Pasteur, 49:303, 1932.
   c. Fredette, V., and Frappier, A.   Rev. canad. de biol., 5:428, 1946.
18a. Robertson, M., and Felix, A.   Brit. J. Exper. Path., 11:14, 1930.
   b. Henderson, D. W.   Brit. J. Exper. Path., 15:166, 1934; 16:393, 1935; 18:224, 1937.
19. Miles, A. A., and Miles, E. M.   Brit. J. Exper. Path., 24:95, 1943.
20a. Aub, J. C., Zamecnik, P. C., and Nathanson, I. T.   J. Clin. Investigation, 26:404, 1947.
   b. Pasternack J. G., and Bengston, I. A.   Nat. Inst. Health Bull., No. 168, 1936.
21. Zamecnik, P. C., Nathanson, I. T., and Aub, J. C.   J. Clin. Investigation, 26:394, 1947.
22. Kass, E. H., Lichstein, H. C., and Waisbren, B. A.   Proc. Soc. Exper. Biol. & Med., 58:172, 1945.
23. Evans, D. G.   J. Path. & Bact., 57:75, 1945.
24. Pappenheimer, A. M., Jr., and Shaskan, E.   J. Biol. Chem., 155:265, 1944.
25. Reed, G. B., Orr, J. H., and Smith, D.   Proc. Soc. Exper. Biol. & Med., 47:228, 1941.
26. Keppie, J., and Macfarlane, M. G.   Brit. J. Exper. Path., 29:458, 1948.
27. Evans, D. G.   Brit. J. Exper. Path., 26:104, 1945.

28a. Walbum, L. E., and Reymann, C. G.   J. Path. & Bact., 44:379, 1937.
   b. Kolmer, J. A.   J. Immunol., 43:289, 1942.
   c. Adams, M. H., and Hendee, E. D.   J. Immunol., 51:249, 1945.
   d. Logan, M. A., Tytell, A. A., Danielson, I. S., and Griner, A. M.   J. Immunol., 51:317, 1945.
   e. van Heyningen, W. E., and Bidwell, E.   Biochem. J., 42:130, 1948.
29a. Penfold, W. J., and Tolhurst, J. C.   M. J. Australia, 1:604, 1938.
   b. Bernheimer, A. W.   J. Immunol., 56:317, 1947.
   c. Adams, M. H.   J. Immunol., 56:323, 1947.

27

SMALLPOX

The viral disease smallpox is best known immunologically through the related agent of vaccinia which has been employed for human immunization for more than a century and a half. There are in fact a variety of pox diseases caused by viruses of related antigenic and pathogenic characters. Concerning three of these a few words of description will be given here and subsequent discussions will turn from one to another depending upon which offers fullest evidence upon the point at issue.

Smallpox in its traditionally severe form is called also variola major. A milder variety of the disease which has been occurring in the United States during the past 40 years (1) and in Great Britain for almost as long (2) is known as alastrim or variola minor. The causative viruses are very closely related antigenically. Vaccinia virus has a somewhat obscure history. In Jenner's day and later this was the agent of cowpox employed for the protective inoculation of human beings, but presently there is on one hand a widespread opinion that the strains in use for this purpose actually derive from smallpox virus modified by passage in laboratory animals (3) while on the other hand some long-time students of these agents believe that this kind of transformation does not come about readily if at all, and that the supposed recovery of vaccinia virus subsequent to inoculation of animals with variola may be due in fact to the introduction of the vaccinia as a contaminant in laboratories dealing with both viruses (4). In any case, cowpox virus as well as the vaccinia strains in current use are both closely related to the variola and alastrim agents in antigenic makeup and in resistance-inducing property (5).

Acquired immunity to smallpox is classic for the patina of history which it bears and also because it represents an outstanding example of solid and durable resistance to an infectious agent. Second attacks of variola may rarely occur in a modified form, and the advent of disease subsequent to vaccination was seen in American troops during and after World War II in Japan and Korea. These incidents may, however, have been related to an inferior vaccine rather than to a fundamental failure of the biologic process itself (6). Ordinarily vaccination is an almost absolute guarantee of protection.

Resistance-Inducing Factor. Although the vaccinia virus is better known constitutionally than most members of this class of disease agents, the factor responsible for inciting acquired resistance remains as cryptic to us as it was

375

to Jenner and his contemporaries in the late eighteenth century. If a process of elimination is applicable to this problem, however, we are probably close to its solution, for chemical and antigenic analyses of the vaccinia and, to a more limited extent, of the variola virus have provided a sizable list of defined components which, although antigenic, do **not invoke** immunity.

In the infected cell there occurs a cytoplasmic inclusion, called the Guarnieri body, which consists of an aggregated mass of particles held together in a matrix. The individual particles were first successfully separated and isolated from the inclusion bodies by Ledingham (7) and Craigie (8) by means of differential centrifugation. These particles are called elementary bodies and are actually the individual virus units themselves (9).

The viral bodies are composed of protein, nucleic acid, desoxypentose, copper, biotin, flavin and lipid consisting of neutral fat, phospholipid and cholesterol; qualitatively and quantitatively these ingredients are analagous to those occurring in most bacteria. Equally specific information is at hand regarding the antigenic constitution of the elementary bodies (10). Vaccinia and variola viruses both possess a soluble complex protein antigen which is found free in infected tissues (11). This is a surface constituent of the elementary body which, though it is readily given up to aqueous media employed for washing the organisms, persists also as an integral part of the virus despite repeated washings. This protein antigen is peculiar in that it acts as a dual stimulant of antibodies. One portion of the protein is heat labile and is referred to as the L component; the other part is heat stable and is known as S. The entire antigen is termed LS. Both anti-L and anti-S antibodies are formed by the vaccinated subject. Either alone can flocculate the entire antigen, but if one or the other part of the protein is destroyed by appropriate procedures, the individual activities of the antibodies may be demonstrated (12). Despite this extraordinary capacity to invoke antibodies, this antigen has no influence whatsoever in the immunizing process which the virus sets in motion. The administration of isolated LS substance to animals fails to induce protection, and if the serum of an animal immunized with living virus be completely deprived of its LS antibody content by absorption, its capacity to neutralize the infectivity of virus remains unimpaired (10, 13).

A second well-documented antigen of the elementary body of vaccinia is a nucleoprotein substance termed NP (13b). (This has not as yet been sought for in the variola virus.) It accounts apparently for about half the mass of the viral particle, and like LS antigen it too incites the formation of antibody without concomitant resistance to viral infection. The serum of an immune animal suffers no loss in its virus neutralizing power through absorption with this antigen (10).

A third antigen of the virus is known only in a fragmentary way and is referred to as X (14). This cannot be characterized as a positive entity; it is recognized only by the fact that after the serum of an animal immunized with virus has been thoroughly exhausted of the L, S, and NP antibodies by absorption it continues to agglutinate viral particles. Since viral inhibiting antibody also remains intact in such absorbed sera it is possible that the X antigen represents the immunizing substance of the virus. In any event, we have no clue as to the nature of this factor.

Finally, mention should be made of an antigenic hemagglutinating factor produced by vaccinia virus growing on the chick chorio-allantoic membrane (15) or in the skin of certain animals such as the rabbit and buffalo (16). This is not found in infected skin of the calf where, it is thought, an inhibiting substance may mask its activity. This factor causes agglutination of chicken and other erythrocytes. There is some uncertainty as to its nature, but the consensus of opinion holds it to be a soluble substance, made up probably of phospholipid in complex with a protein which may be the S antigen (5b, 16, 17). There is some indication that a second distinct hemagglutinating factor may be retained in the elementary body itself (18) but this possibility has yet to be clarified. The soluble hemagglutinating factor, though it possibly induces hemagglutination-inhibiting antibodies (19), shares with the LS and NP antigens a complete dissociation from the process of inducing protective immunity (17, 20).

This roster of the recognized pox virus antigens plainly leaves us with no intimation of the possible nature of an immunity-inducing substance which might account either for the viral inhibiting antibodies elaborated by infected or vaccinated animals or for any other kind of alteration in the host which may account for acquired immunity. Further discussion of this factor must be confined to very limited speculation grounded upon empirical observations of the circumstances in which most effective immunization occurs. The main fact of this kind which may eventually contribute to identification of the immunizing substance is the inadequacy of killed virus as an immunizing agent. There seems to be general agreement that a relatively enormous quantity of killed vaccinia virus confers at best only slight benefits (2, 5b, 6, 21). As in any instance of this kind, it is impossible to know here to which one of several possibilities this is due. Thus, there may be a destruction of the immunizing substance by the procedure employed for killing the virus; there may be a quantitative advantage in supplying living virus which can multiply in the tissues to provide more of the immunizing substance than could be furnished by a reasonable dose of killed organisms; or it may be that only the living virus can produce the factor which sets up the immune response in the host. There is at present no basis for a choice between these alternatives.

Relation of Virulence to Resistance-Induction. Since we are ignorant of the identities of the immunizing factors of variola and vaccinia viruses, there can be no discussion of their relation to the virulence of these viruses. This inability is compounded by the fact that we know nothing either about the mechanisms which determine the virulence of these agents. Certain interesting general facts have accumulated concerning their ability to cause disease in human and animal hosts which warrant description, however.

It is apparent from the difference between the diseases smallpox and alastrim that striking variations in pathogenicity exist between viruses which are otherwise very similar. Smallpox runs a much more severe course and is fatal to 30 or 40 per cent of those infected; deaths from alastrim occur in perhaps 1 per cent of its victims. Vaccinia virus is much less pathogenic than either of these for man as judged by the severity of the disease it causes. It infects the human being readily but the expression of this is ordinarily restricted to a single pock localized at the point of introduction of the agent into the skin. Under some circumstances vaccinia virus may produce multiple lesions in the neighborhood of the site of application through lymphatic spread, or by accidental surface contamination. Children with skin disease such as eczema are much more liable to generalized vaccinal pox than are normal individuals (22). In certain animals, such as the calf and rabbit, vaccinia produces much more extensive disease than does variola virus, and in the latter animal there is good evidence that a single elementary body of a virulent strain can give rise to infection (23).

The cellular tropisms of strains of virus are of considerable interest to the question of pathogenicity. Some strains of vaccinia virus are strictly limited to propagation in epithelial cells while others show an affinity for mesodermal fibroblasts and capillary endothelium. These affinities may be altered experimentally. Thus, if virus from the calf, with mesodermal tropism, is passed repeatedly upon the chorioallantoic membrane of chick embryos it becomes completely epitheliotropic and subsequently induces much less severe infection in rabbit skin than does the original calf virus (4). These strains of variable cellular affinities remain indistinguishable by the antigenic criteria afforded by our current knowledge (6). Differences in virulence of various strains of vaccinia may thus be due to this variation in tropism, but we do not yet have an explanation of the intrinsic factors which govern either tropism or virulence.

Mechanisms of Immunity. As an aftermath of many years of experimentation with the pox viruses we are left with three possible explanations for acquired resistance to them. The first and most likely of these entails mediation by humoral antibody, the second supposes that susceptible cells may be modified in some way to resist viral propagation, and the third imputes to allergic reactivity a protective function. Experimental observations favor the first viewpoint, but the evidence so far compiled has not excluded the possibility that immunity may in part be explained by the second. For the third hypothesis the evidence is weakest. In succeeding paragraphs testimony in respect to all three possibilities will be discussed.

The evidence for the activity of virus inhibiting antibodies as instruments of immunity stems from several kinds of observations. First, the fact of occurrence of an antiviral factor in the serum of vaccinated or infected human beings and animals can be demonstrated by mixing serum with the virus in vitro before injection into test subjects, or by injecting the serum into such subjects in advance of a challenge inoculation of virus. In either case the infectivity of the virus for the test subject is more or less inhibited, sometimes completely, sometimes partially (24). In its nature this humoral inhibitory factor appears to be antibody, for it is part of the blood globulin and it can be removed from serum by absorption with virus infected tissue or with elementary bodies themselves (5a, 33b, 33c).

Complete inhibition of infectivity is not seen in all circumstances; in some cases in fact it is difficult to ascertain even a partial effect. For example, if immune serum is mixed with virus and after a short interval is injected into rabbits intracerebrally there may be only a slight protective effect, while if the same mixture is tested by intracutaneous injection it is found to be entirely noninfectious (25). Analogously, it has been found that if immune serum and vaccinia virus are added to cultures of normal rabbit leukocytes the presence of the antiserum does not prevent the virus from entering the explanted cells, though the same mixture is noninfectious for rabbit skin (26). These qualifications are impossible to interpret at the present time, but they do not vitiate the general conclusion that a viral-inhibiting antibody is present in the blood of immunized subjects and that this can protect normal tissues from infection provided it is administered prior to the virus, or is mixed with the virus before injection.

Evidence that an inhibiting antibody exists and that it is capable of conferring passive protection should ordinarily be considered sufficient to prove the case for the importance of this substance in acquired resistance. There are, however, some deficiencies in the evidence in the present case. Thus several investigators have found that though the injection of killed vaccinia virus into animals may give rise to neutralizing antibodies these animals show relatively slight and temporary resistance to subsequent infection, and the presence of even a considerable level of neutralizing antibody is not necessarily indicative of a state of protection against inoculated virus (27). As has been pointed out in other connections, although the absence of a demonstrable antibody in the presence of resistance may be laid to difficulties in demonstrating the antibody, it is more difficult to rationalize a lack of resistance when an antibody supposedly related to it is present in good concentration.

The question of the influence of antibody in immunity has been approached from another experimental aspect. A number of workers have studied the status of the tissues of immune animals when removed from the blood supply of the host. In general the procedure has been to explant tissues of immune and normal animals as cultures, some bathed by normal plasma and some by that from immune donors. In this way various combinations can be obtained of tissues from immune animals growing in the presence or absence of antibodies, and of tissues of normal donors under the same conditions. Several earlier experiments of this kind suggested that the tissue of immune animals might possess some inhibitory activity upon vaccinia virus (28). Later work has been carried out under more critical conditions, and two of the best examples of this will be cited here.

The most elaborate experiments of this kind were undertaken by Goodpasture and Anderson (29) who employed, however, the virus of fowlpox rather than one of the mammalian viruses which we have been considering.

However, the relationship of this virus to its host is analogous to that of the variola and vaccinia viruses to their hosts, so that it seems valid to apply basic information learned from one case to the others. These investigators removed patches of immune epidermis from vaccinated cocks and grafted these onto the chorio-allantoic membranes of chick embryos. In this location such epidermal patches became as susceptible to infection with virus as were patches from normal birds. If a graft from an immune bird was subsequently removed from the chorio-allantoic membrane and grafted back to its immune donor it resumed the ability to resist infection, but if it were grafted back to a normal fowl it remained susceptible to virus. A patch of normal epithelium transferred to an immune bird on the other hand became resistant to virus. It seems evident from these experiments that the epidermal cells of immune animals possess no intrinsic power to resist fowlpox virus, and it is logical to deduce from this that it is the blood of the resistant animal which provides protection to the tissue through its content of antibodies. However, when these workers tried to verify this deduction by experiment difficulties were encountered, for the injection of immune serum into the chorio-allantoic veins of embryos bearing epidermal grafts did not confer immunity upon these, nor did the intravenous injection of such serum into young chicks protect their skins from infection. On the other hand the intravenous administration of immune whole blood or of plasma-leukocyte mixtures exerted a moderately protective effect. But these same materials injected directly into the skin area to be tested with virus were without influence upon the subsequent challenge inoculation. It is not possible to provide a point by point interpretation of these confusing findings; it can only be said that the general tenor of these observations, and especially those in which the blood cells of the immune donor seem to be related to the transfer of resistance, leaves a question still open as to the possible contribution of factors other than antibodies to acquired immunity. It may be noted that others also have found whole blood to be superior to serum or plasma in passive transfer experiments (25, 30).

In the second series of experiments to be described there resulted more direct evidence for the possible influence of a cellular factor in resistance. Rivers and co-workers (31) employed the corneas of immune and normal rabbits in tissue culture. The corneas of immune animals washed free of aqueous humor were found to be partially resistant to infection with vaccinia virus. The fact that the cornea has no blood supply and consequently receives all the humoral factors which support it from the vessels at the limbus makes it seem likely that washing would rid the excised tissue of antibodies very effectively. These experiments then support the concept of some kind of altered receptivity of cells of the immune animal to vaccinia virus.

Finally, there are other kinds of less direct evidence upon the question of the role of cellular immunity in resistance to the pox viruses. Vaccinia virus has been recovered from the tissues of immune rabbits for periods up to 252 days after infection (32), and it has been recovered also from immune corneas in tissue cultures (28b, 31) and from the leukocytes of immune rabbits in tissue cultures (26). These findings would seem offhand to speak against a cellular factor in resistance; but in the case of cultures, as well as animals, the same findings are made even when immune plasma is present. There is in fact no evidence of any kind to suggest that antibodies can destroy these viruses, so that these observations of the failure of cells to do so provide no real objection to the possibility of the existence of cellular immunity. Perhaps neither antibodies nor cells can destroy the viruses outright; immunity on whatever basis may consist wholly of a capacity to hinder the propagation of these organisms.

In summary, we have incontrovertible testimony to the importance of antiviral antibodies in acquired resistance to the pox viruses. There are in addition a variety of findings which suggest that cellular factors should not for the present be ignored in the concept of resistance to these viruses either. The correctness of this supposition will require further work for its resolution.

The intrinsic nature of the functioning of acquired immunity remains a riddle. So far as inhibiting antibody is concerned, vaccinia virus combines with this and it may then be removed from serum by the centrifuge (5a, 33). But if this combined antibody exerts a direct virucidal action this remains to be discovered. The presence of complement adds nothing to the process (26). It has been suggested that the inhibiting antibody may prevent virus from entering cells. One basis for this viewpoint is exemplified by Andrews' (24c) finding that if vaccinia virus is injected into the skin of a rabbit a few minutes before the introduction of an overneutralizing dose of antiserum into and around the site of inoculation, the virus is not completely suppressed, whereas if serum is injected in advance of the virus or mixed with it, no lesions develop. One might object that the preliminary injection of virus permits its entry into cells so that it is no longer exposed to the full effect of the later injected antibody. In any case, it appears from other work more directly applied to the clarification of the main point that antibody does not prevent the entry of virus into cells, for Florman and Enders (26) added virus and antibodies to cultures of rabbit leukocytes and found the virus inside these cells despite the fact that the same mixtures were noninfectious when tested in rabbit skin.

It was recounted earlier that several observers have found in passive immunity experiments that whole blood or plasma—leukocyte mixtures are more effective than serum or plasma alone in neutralizing viral infectivity (25, 29, 30). This leads to the suggestion that phagocytosis may play a part in the process of viral inhibition. Since, however, the recipient animal in such experiments can supply its own phagocytes it does not seem reasonable to suppose that the leukocytes of immune blood contribute simply a phagocytizing element; it would seem more likely that their contribution must be related to their derivation from an immune host and that they may on this account possess some special property concerned with resistance. This brings us again to the possibility that a cellular modification may be implicated in resistance to the pox viruses. This is a speculative viewpoint, however; the nature of the function of the phagocytes of the immune animal is still entirely obscure. Sabin (34) and Florman and Enders (26) have found in tissue cultures of immune rabbit leukocytes growing in the presence of immune serum that vaccinia virus enters the cells despite the antibodies and is able to persist for some time. Perhaps, as was suggested before, the hypothetical potentiality of these cells in resistance is limited to a virustatic activity.

It was mentioned earlier, as a third possibility to account for acquired immunity, that the allergic reactivity which develops against vaccinia and variola viruses as the result of vaccination or infection may be of some importance. The possible role of the delayed hypersensitive state in resistance to other infectious agents has been discussed in preceding chapters (Chapters 10, 15), and the conclusion was reached that on the basis of current evidence it appears in general to have no part in the resistance process. In the case of an obligate intracellular parasite such as a virus one might more easily imagine that hypersensitivity may have a protective role than in the case of the bacterial agents, for if cells should die of the allergic reaction when virus enters them the organism would be deprived of the habitat which is absolutely essential to survival and propagation.

Dienes (35) believes that in guinea pigs allergic reactivity to vaccine virus does account for acquired immunity. This conclusion is based chiefly upon the chronologic coincidence of resistance with the appearance of allergic responsiveness, about a week after vaccination. Humoral neutralizing antibodies, on the other hand, were not apparent in these experiments until 12 days after vaccination. This conclusion has not received general support, for it is known that immunity may be transferred passively by serum (within the limitations described before) while hypersensitivity is not, and that while vaccination with killed virus induces relatively slight immunity it causes the development of a good level of hypersensitivity (36). It seems probable from such facts that the allergic state does not constitute resistance to vaccinia virus.

SUMMARY

At the present time we have no lead to the identity of the immunizing factor in variola or vaccinia virus, nor do we know the properties to which the pathogenic activities of these agents may be ascribed. Acquired immunity to both viruses is of a high order of effectiveness, and experimental evidence points to an antiviral antibody as the major factor responsible for this. There exist sufficient lacunae in this evidence, however, to intimate that the antibody mechanism may not comprise the entire story of immunity. There is, in addition, some experimental basis for the tentative viewpoint that a form of cellular modification may contribute to the sum of protection against these viruses. The functioning of neither antibodies nor cells in their protective capacities is as yet understood.

Practical Vaccination Procedures. The classic Jennerian prophylaxis for smallpox consists of the superficial introduction of vaccinia virus into the epidermis. This represents one of the outstanding examples of effective protective vaccination, and after more than 150 years there has been no change in the essence of this practice. Originally the vaccine was cowpox virus, but it is possible that many of the current strains have been derived from variola virus by passage through animals. However, as described in the early part of this chapter, some experts doubt that variola can readily be converted to vaccinia by such passage; if this is so then the vaccinia strains in use are probably still cowpox (4). Whatever the case, a close immunologic relationship is known to exist between variola, alastrim and vaccinia viruses, as determined by cross neutralization tests with the sera of immunized subjects as well as by direct application of viruses to vaccinated subjects (5).

The vaccine preparation which is almost universally employed is derived from the skin of infected calves, and is called calf lymph virus. In bygone years there were often difficulties occasioned by bacterial contaminants in this vaccine, but attention to asepsis in harvesting the pulp and the addition of disinfectants to the finished material have almost eliminated this objectionable occurrence. Improvements in the routine of preparation are still being devised (37).

Two interesting changes in the basic procedure for preparing vaccine have been proposed in the past two decades. Neither of these has found acceptance as yet, partly because tradition is on the side of the calf lymph preparation, but both merit attention for their possible future usefulness. Rivers and co-workers (38) have described the use of minced chick embryo tissue in Tyrode's solution as a medium for cultivation of the virus, while Goodpasture and associates (39) demonstrated the usefulness of the chorio-allantoic membranes of chick embryos for this purpose. At the present time this last method would be a more practical one because the propagation of other infectious agents in chick embryos for vaccine production has become an established large scale commercial procedure.

The efficacies of these two vaccine preparations have been assessed by their devisers as well as by others. Rivers (38) believes from studies of vaccinated children that the tissue culture vaccine is not as potent as the calf lymph virus. About 25 per cent of the subjects vaccinated with culture virus showed reactions to a subsequent application of calf lymph virus indicative of solid immunity; the other three-quarters developed reactions suggesting partial immunity (vaccinoid). He suggests, therefore, that for practical purposes the culture virus might be employed for primary vaccination, to be followed in about six months by revaccination with calf virus. The advantage of primary vaccination with the culture virus lies in its complete freedom from bacterial contaminants and in the milder local and general responses which it induces. The subsequent application of the calf lymph virus in a partially or completely immune subject would then induce only a mild lesion while building up immunity to a maximum.

The chorio-allantoic-propagated virus possesses also the advantages of freedom from bacteria and the induction of a milder primary vaccination reaction. Vaccinia virus which has been adapted to growth in embryonated eggs becomes highly epitheliotropic and consequently less virulent for the skin of test animals (4). Assays of the allantoic virus in rabbits, monkeys and man in direct comparison with calf virus have indicated that the former immunizes as well as the latter when judged by revaccination tests as well as by the production of virus inhibiting antibodies (39, 40). Because some question arose concerning the immunizing potency of this virus after prolonged embryo passage (41), Buddingh (42) has suggested using the first egg passage virus as vaccine, reserving calf lymph for seed virus only.

The duration of the immunity induced by vaccination is a subject for recurrent experimentation and discussion. A typical evaluation states that this may last for 5 to 20 years, but that relative susceptibility often occurs after 5 years (43). Opinions of this kind have been almost entirely based upon the response of vaccinated subjects to revaccination, a criterion which goes back to the time of Jenner. According to this measure, the nonimmune individual receiving his first vaccination responds with the development of a vesicle beginning on about the fourth or fifth day; this becomes a pustule on about the eighth day and a scab by about the eleventh. A response of this kind is termed the primary take. A second kind of response is thought to reflect partial immunity. In this case the reaction begins with a papule on the second day (indicative of hypersensitivity to the virus) and the vesicle appears on the third and may form a scab by the fifth or six day. This is a milder as well as a more rapid process than that following a primary vaccination. Finally, complete immunity is inferred from the development of a papule alone on the second day without the appearance of any vesicle at all. The papule is again a hypersensitive manifestation, but the failure of pock formation is considered to be a token of immunity.

We cannot be certain that these interpretations are correct ones. Perhaps the virus-inhibiting antibody response might provide a closer approximation to the state of immunity (4). These are questions which pose obvious difficulties of solution, but correlative studies in man and animals might add enlightening information even to this venerable subject.

BIBLIOGRAPHY

1. Chapin, C. V., and Smith, J.   J. Preventive Med., 6:273, 1932.
2. Ledingham, J. C. G.   Proc. Roy. Soc. Med., 27:35, 1934.
3. ———— J. State Med., 34:1, 1925.
4. Buddingh, C. J.   Ann. Rev. Microbiol., 3:331, 1949.
5a. Downie, A. W.   Brit. J. Exper. Path., 20:158, 1939.
  b. van Rooyen, C. E., and Rhodes, A. J.   Virus Diseases of Man, New York, Thomas Nelson and Sons, 1948.
  c. Horgan, E. S., Haseeb, M. A., and Satti, M. H.   Brit. J. Exper. Path., 29:347, 1948.
  d. Downie, A. W., and MacDonald, A.   J. Path. & Bact., 42:389, 1950.
  e. ———— and McCarthy, K.   Brit. J. Exper. Path., 31:789, 1950.
6. Smadel, J. E.   Viral and Rickettsial Infections of Man, ed. by T. R. Rivers, Philadelphia, J. B. Lippincott Co., 1948, Chapter 15.

7. Ledingham, J. C. G. Lancet, 2:525, 1931.
8. Craigie, J. Brit. J. Exper. Path., 13:259, 1932.
9a. Hughes, T. B., Parker, R. F., and Rivers, T. M. J. Exper. Med., 62:349, 1935.
 b. Hoagland, C. L. Ann. Rev. Biochem., 12:615, 1943.
10. Smadel, J. E., and Shedlovsky, T. Ann. New York Acad. Sc., 43:35, 1942.
11. Craigie, J., and Wishart, F. O. Brit. J. Exper. Path., 15:390, 1934.
12. Smadel, J. E., and Hoagland, C. L. Bact. Rev., 6:79, 1942.
13a. Parker, R. F. J. Exper. Med., 67:361, 1938.
 b. Smadel, J. E., Rivers, T. M., and Hoagland, C. L. Arch. Path., 34:275, 1942.
14. Craigie, J., and Wishart, F. O. J. Bact., 35:25, 1938.
15. Nagler, F. P. M. J. Australia, 1:281, 1942.
16. Collier, W. A. Documenta Neerland. et Indonesica Morbis Tropicis, 1:81, 1949.
17. Burnet, F. M., and Stone, J. D. Australian J. Exper. Biol. & M. Sc., 24:1, 1946.
18. Gillen, A. I., Burr, M. M., and Nagler, F. P. J. Immunol., 65:701, 1950.
19a. Collier, W. A. Documenta Neerland. et Indonesica Morbis Tropicis, 1:110, 1949.
 b. Chu, C. N. J. Hyg., 46:49, 1948.
20. Burnet, F. M., and Boake, W. C. J. Immunol., 53:1, 1946.
21. Rhodes, A. J., and van Rooyen, C. E. Textbook of Virology, New York, Thomas Nelson and Sons, 1949.
22. Dible, J. H., and Gleave, H. H. J. Path. & Bact., 38:29, 1934.
23a. Parker, R. F. J. Exper. Med., 67:725, 1938.
 b. Sprunt, D. H., and McDearman, S. J. Immunol., 38:81, 1940.
 c. Parker, R. F., Bronson, L. H., and Green, R. H. J. Exper. Med., 74:263, 1941.
24a. Raynaud, M. Compt. rend. Acad. d. sc., 84:453, 1877.
 b. Sternberg, G. M. Tr. A. Am. Physicians, 7:68, 1892.
 c. Andrewes, C. H. J. Path. & Bact., 32:265, 1929.
 d. Pandit, C. G., Menon, K. P., and Sahib, M. O. Indian J. M. Research, 19:1185, 1932.
25. Fairbrother, R. W. J. Path. & Bact., 36:55, 1933.
26. Florman, A. L., and Enders, J. F. J. Immunol., 43:159, 1942.
27a. Parker, R. F., and Rivers, T. M. J. Exper. Med., 63:69, 1936.
 b. Magrassi, F., and Muratori, F. Boll. d. Ist. sieroterap milanese, 16:505, 1937.
28a. Steinhardt, E., and Lambert, R. A. J. Infect. Dis., 14:87, 1914.
 b. Harde, E. S. Ann. Inst. Pasteur, 30:299, 1916.
29. Goodpasture, E. W., and Anderson, K. Arch. Path., 30:212, 1940.
30. Douglas, S. R., and Smith, W. Brit. J. Exper. Path., 11:96, 1930.
31. Rivers, T. M., Haagen, E., and Muckenfuss, R. S. J. Exper. Med., 50:673, 1929.
32a. Olitsky, P. K., and Long, P. H. J. Exper. Med., 50:263, 1929.
 b. Dresel, E. G. Ztschr. f. Immunitätsforsch. u. exper. Therap., 75:337, 1932.
 c. Pearce, J. M. J. Infect. Dis., 66:130, 1940.
33a. Andrewes, C. H. J. Path. & Bact., 33:265, 1930.
 b. Smith, W. J. Path. & Bact., 33:273, 1930.
 c. Salaman, M. H. Brit. J. Exper. Path., 18:245, 1937.
34. Sabin, A. B. Brit. J. Exper. Path., 16:158, 1935.
35a. Dienes, L. Arch. Path., 21:357, 1936.
 b.——— and Naterman, H. C. J. Infect. Dis., 60:279, 1937.
36. Gastinel, P., and Fasquelle, R. Ann. Inst. Pasteur, 69:319, 1943.
37a. Ducor, D. H. Pub. Health Rep., 62:565, 1947.
 b. Parrish, H. J. Bacterial and Virus Diseases, 2nd ed., Baltimore, Williams and Wilkins Co., 1951.
38. Rivers, T. M., Ward, S. M., and Baird, R. D. J. Exper. Med., 69:857, 1939.
39. Goodpasture, E. W., Buddingh, G. J., Richardson, L., and Anderson, K. Am. J. Hyg., 21:319, 1935.
40a. Buddingh, G. J. Am. J. Pub. Health, 27:1135, 1937.
 b. ——— Am. J. Hyg., 38:310, 1943.
41. Cook, E. B. M., Crain, P. N., and Irons, J. V. Bull. of the Conference of State and Provincial Pub. Health Lab. Directors, May, 1948.
42. Buddingh, G. J., and Randall, C. C. Am. J. Hyg., 53:152, 1951.
43. U.S.P.H.S. Rep. No. 1697. The Control of Communicable Diseases, Pub. Health Rep., 50:1017, 1935.

28

POLIOMYELITIS

Poliomyelitis is one of the virus diseases which is generally supposed to leave in its wake a permanent resistance to reinfection. The recorded instances of second attacks of paralysis have been regarded as exceptional, but acceptance of this traditional viewpoint is complicated by several considerations. First, it is known that the paralytic cases constitute only a minor fraction, variously estimated at 0.10 to 20 per cent, of the total instances of viral invasion in human beings. Most attacks are either symptomless (but virus can be found in the stool), or of a mild nonparalytic type, evidenced by fever and headache but often without any sign of nerve involvement even though lesions may occur in the spinal cord (1). Therefore, the probability of a recurrence of overt disease would be most unlikely simply on the basis of chance (2). However, resistance, in animals at least, may result from such attacks (3). Many such episodes are undoubtedly ignored or remain undiagnosed, and a later attack of paralytic disease may be mistakenly regarded as primary. It is evident that the durability, or even the existence, of acquired immunity in human beings is difficult to evaluate from clinical evidence because of this possibility. Secondly, the fact that there are immunologically diverse strains of virus (4) means that data concerning the reoccurrence of the disease must take into account the factor of possible specificity of immunity. A second attack caused by a strain differing from the first would not impugn the possibility that the first was nevertheless an immunizing infection. Finally, the fact that paralytic attacks occur mainly in children might be regarded as suggesting that most adults have an acquired immunity. This is not *ipso facto* a valid deduction, however, for in the absence of proof to the contrary it could as well be inferred that some kind of physiologic change accounts for increasing insusceptibility with age (see Chapter 11 for a general discussion of this point). For a long time the finding of neutralizing antibodies in the blood of most adults has been considered a significant index of acquired resistance subsequent to previous exposures (5), but this criterion has lost some of its meaning since neutralization has been found to occur with the sera of a variety of animals for which the virus has no apparent predilection (6) and may, as Schultz points out, depend upon nonspecific inactivating factors in the serum (7, 8). The presence of neutralizing substances in the blood in itself does not necessarily denote the existence of acquired resistance to infection either in monkeys or man (5, 9).

In spite of these qualifications the indications are rather good that the adult population does enjoy a widespread acquired immunity to the disease (10). Hammon's (11) analysis of epidemiologic and immunologic evidence suggests that immunity is eventually acquired by the majority of urban residents from repeated exposures to the virus, and that restimulation of resistance may take place periodically, following a pattern similar to that seen, for example, in the case of the formation of antistreptolysin in response to the diffusible hemolysin of the streptococcus. Periodic invasions by virus may be limited to the intestinal tract (12). Supporting this conclusion is the well known fact that in monkeys an experimentally induced attack of the disease leaves a solid resistance to reinfection with the homologous virus, and chimpanzees or monkeys given active virus orally often escape contracting overt disease, yet gain a measure of acquired resistance to subsequent challenge (12). The possible mechanism of the resistance so stimulated will be discussed in a succeeding section.

Resistance-Inducing Factor. We do not know specifically the nature of the factor in poliomyelitis virus which induces resistance. Whether an antigen is responsible for this, or whether the virus may in addition act in a manner unrelated to its antigenic properties to modify susceptible cells so that they will no longer support viral activity, is not entirely clear now. Under the condition of intensive experimental vaccination resistance does appear to depend upon an antibody-antigen relationship, but this may not be true of the immunity which follows infection itself, as will be discussed further on. First we shall assess the chemical and immunologic studies of the virus which may contribute to the clarification of this question.

Physicochemical studies have given some characterization to the virus. It appears to consist of protein of high molecular weight with relatively homogeneous sedimentation behavior in the ultracentrifuge (13). This information has not yet helped our understanding of the host-parasite relationship.

There have been immunologic researches in profusion, but the results relating to the present consideration can be summarized briefly. The virus induces humoral anti-substances capable of neutralizing its infectivity when mixed with it in vitro, and able also to confer passive resistance upon animals under certain experimental circumstances. The question is whether these antibodies constitute also the acquired resistance mechanism of the body to naturally occurring infection. One line of evidence related to antigenicity is of immediate interest here. As mentioned before, differences in viral strains exist (4), and recently Kessel and Pait and others (4c-4g) have established three antigenic groups among a large number of strains tested. These differentiations are based upon the challenge of convalescent and vaccinated monkeys with homologous and heterologous strains as well as upon cross-neutralization tests carried out with the sera of such animals. General agreement in the delineation of types is obtained by these several procedures. Offhand this fact might seem to equate antibodies with resistance, for if the acquired immunity of convalescent animals distinguishes viral strains as do the humoral antibodies, it seems a fair conclusion that the first depends upon the second. In fact, however, resistance to infection is found to be significantly **less specific** than is antibody in its reaction with heterologous strains in neutralization tests. Animals show considerable ability to ward off infection with viruses of antigenic types other than that to which they had become immune, but antibodies distinguish these types clearly by failure to neutralize them in vitro. This suggests that a factor other than, or in addition to, antibodies may be involved in acquired immunity to poliomyelitis (4e, 4g, 14) and, by inference, that this may be determined by a property of the virus other than an antigen.

For the present we can say only that poliomyelitis virus is partly or wholly composed of protein, that this is antigenic and induces viral inhibiting antibodies, and that such antibodies under certain experimental conditions may act as instruments of protection. Their effectiveness in acquired resistance to spontaneously occurring infection will be discussed in the subsequent consideration of mechanisms of resistance to this disease.

Relationship of Virulence to Protection-Inducing Factor. The pathogenic properties of poliomyelitis virus are not at all understood. This agent has usually been considered exclusively neuronotropic, but it exists in high concentrations in the intestinal content of paralyzed or convalescent patients as well as in apparently healthy contacts, and it seems possible that it may multiply in this locale, or perhaps in other areas of the body apart from the nervous system (16b). This is, however, still only a possibility against which good arguments can be mustered (7).

Variations in the virulence of different poliomyelitis viruses probably occur. It is, of course, difficult to determine this possibility from studies of the human disease, for the abortive or carrier infections so common in epidemic times may just as well reflect a widespread incidence of acquired immunity in the population as the existence of strains of mild virulence. Sabin and Steigman (15), however, have found strains isolated from the stools of children suffering a mild nonparalyzing disease to possess strikingly less capacity to cause paralysis in monkeys than did viruses obtained from simultaneously occurring paralytic cases. Findings open to similar interpretation have been made by others (16a), and it seems from current evidence that one type, the Lansing virus, may cause paralysis perhaps in only one in a thousand of the individuals in whom the virus may for a time reside. Antibodies against this virus are almost universally found in populations sampled in far-flung parts of the world, while the incidence of paralysis caused by the virus is extremely low (16b).

Mechanisms of Resistance. The voluminous observations compiled by investigators of this disease gives us a choice in accounting for immunity between humoral neutralizing antibody and some kind of specific alteration of the nerve cells themselves. There may, of course, be a combination of both these effects. A final opinion cannot yet be formulated, so that the interpretation which follows is a provisional one.

To consider first the possibility that humoral antibody may account for resistance, we have the basic fact that it can neutralize the infectivity of the virus in vitro and also in vivo, under certain conditions at least. The latter demonstration is exemplified by the experiments of Lennette and Hudson (17) who were able to infect monkeys by the intravenous injection of virus provided that starch were given intracerebrally to break the barrier between the blood stream and the central nervous system. Animals so treated routinely become infected. Now if circulating antibodies were first established in animals by vaccination, then the intravenously injected virus usually did not succeed in establishing infection; i.e. neutralization of infectivity took place in the blood stream before the virus reached the central nervous system. Other analogous experiments have provided the same results. The nature of the activity of antibody upon virus is no more known here than in the case of the pox viruses discussed in the preceding chapter. The virus does not seem to be destroyed in vitro, since active virus may be recovered from neutral mixtures with antibody.

If we accept this potential protective ability of antibody in vivo as demonstrated by an unnatural mode of producing infection, the next question concerns the likelihood that antibody can also act upon virus which gains access to the central nervous system by its natural pathways. If the spontaneous pathway of the virus is one which permits its exposure to antibodies, then presumably these may be as effective as in the experiments just described. The portal of infection in man is not clearly established, but current possibilities include the oropharyngeal membranes (18) and the small intestine (19). From these locations the progression of virus to the central nervous system may take place entirely within neurons, for virus which is experimentally implanted in nerve tissue spreads this way to the brain and spinal cord (20-23). If this is the case it is possible that the humoral antibody which is **potentially protective** may be in actuality impotent because it has no opportunity to attack the virus in its intracellular locale. This line of theorizing would lead to the conclusion that acquired resistance to poliomyelitis must depend upon some other factor than antibody, a property perhaps acquired by nerve cells themselves. Let us see how available epidemiologic and experimental observations contribute to the clarification of this issue.

Studies of the occurrence of poliomyelitis in man have revealed that occasionally the disease attacks persons in whom humoral antibodies are already present, and on the other hand convalescence is not always attended by the formation of humoral antibody (5, 8). This fact in itself does not necessarily disqualify the importance of antibodies to immunity; there are examples provided by other diseases in which antibodies are known to be of utmost importance to immunity where infections may nonetheless occur in their presence because of an overwhelming infective dose, or possibly because of a temporary depression of the physiologic state of the host. Also, the existence of immunologically diverse strains of virus may account for infection by a strain heterologous to the antibodies. Thus, not much can be learned about the antibody-immunity relationship from this kind of investigation. In monkeys, the experience derived from many studies of vaccination have indicated that humoral antibodies may be induced by the extraneural injection of living or inactivated virus without, in most cases, a concomitant development of ability to resist virus injected directly into the brain or applied to the nasal membranes. In instances where resistance does eventuate from such vaccination, it is not necessarily coincident with the presence of demonstrable antibodies (17, 24-28). In animals convalescent from the disease itself, furthermore, there is very generally a high level of resistance to homologous virus, yet these animals develop relatively small amounts of humoral antibodies and immunity is often demonstrable long before they appear in the blood (25, 29).

Taken all in all, this information does not entirely satisfy the viewpoint that antibody is the important element in resistance to poliomyelitis. Additional evidence along the same lines has been presented within the past several years, however, which calls for a re-evaluation of this estimate. As described before, older experiments with vaccines of living or inactivated virus unanimously emphasized the irregularity of protective effects in monkeys. In 1936 Olitsky and Cox (26) affirmed this observation but pointed out that a greater degree of success could be achieved if large doses of active virus were injected over long periods of time, and indeed earlier investigators had also been successful with this procedure (30). Affirmation of these results was made in rodents with virus vaccines inactivated by formaldehyde or ultraviolet light, but these animals appear to be more readily immunized than monkeys (31-33). Morgan and others, however, have since then been inducing protective immunity in monkeys with regularity by the use of large and repeated intramuscular doses of living (34) as well as inactivated virus (35). This procedure induces high levels of humoral antibody also (36, 37). These findings may be interpreted to mean that if the level of humoral antibody is high enough, experimental animals may be protected against significant neuronal invasion by intracerebrally injected virus. Interestingly enough, this coincides with experiences derived from passive transfer experiments. If sufficiently large quantities of antibody are administered to monkeys a proportion of them escape infection by virus administered intracerebrally, but this is not the case when smaller quantities of antibody are employed, enough to provide circulating levels perhaps in the range of those seen in convalescent monkeys (24, 38). Thus in both cases we are left with the irrefutable fact that convalescent subjects, whether man or monkey, possess resistance **without** necessarily possessing the levels of circulating antibody that adequately vaccinated subjects develop. How can we reconcile this difference within the bounds of the assumption that antibodies explain immunity? Morgan (39) has reported that paralyzed and convalescent monkeys do have antiviral substances in high concentration—not in the blood, but in the grey matter of the spinal cord, and in the spinal fluid. This is said to appear about two weeks after the inception of infection, at a time when antibodies are sparse or absent in the blood stream. In contrast, animals vaccinated by the intramuscular method and brought to a high level of humoral antibody content show no evidence of this in their nerve tissue. At the time of test injection of virus into the brains of such animals, however, antibodies are stated to appear throughout the central nervous system (39b).

Before discussing the possible significance of this evidence it must be pointed out that Sabin and Steigman (40a) have not been able to confirm the presence of antiviral substances in the central nervous systems of monkeys with paralysis, nor could previous workers demonstrate this convincingly in the cords of convalescent monkeys (40b, 40c). The strain of virus employed by Sabin and Steigman was not the same as that used by Morgan, and tests for viral inhibiting substances were made in monkeys rather than mice. Perhaps these factors account for the difference in findings; this remains for future work to decide. For the present, we can attempt to assess the meaning of Morgan's observation on the basis of other information at hand.

The presence of viral inhibiting antibodies in the nerve tissue of convalescent animals, and its entrance into this tissue from the blood once challenge infection has been made in vaccinated animals, could resolve all the apparent differences brought to light by earlier experimenters with respect to the relationship of antibody to immunity. If infection results in antibody in the central nervous system without relation to its humoral level, this could explain immunity on an antibody basis despite low levels in the blood. On the other hand, the failure of vaccination despite the presence of humoral antibody could be explained on the basis that an insufficient amount accumulates in the central nervous system unless an adequate level is present in the blood, and this is attained only through an intensive vaccinating procedure.

The difficulties in accepting this viewpoint without reservation are these. First of all, the antiviral substance appearing in the central nervous system as the result of infection must be assumed to be formed locally, for its concentration may far exceed that in the blood, and further, direct tests for such antibodies in the cerebrospinal fluid of convalescent children have revealed it only occasionally (41). If these antibodies are manufactured locally, however, it is difficult to account for the failure of Schultz and Gebhardt (24), who injected inactivated virus repeatedly into the brains of monkeys, to establish resistance to subsequent intracerebral challenge with living virus. If local antibody formation were important to resistance these experiments might have been expected to divulge the fact, since inactivated virus is known to be capable of stimulating systemic antiviral antibodies when administered by conventional routes. Perhaps the antiviral substance found in the central nervous system is not antibody; it may be an antiviral property which can be engendered in the cells themselves only through the presence of living virus; thus Gard (42) has described the existence of a virus inhibitor attached to the tissue component of ground brain suspensions of mice convalescent from murine encephalomyelitis (mouse poliomyelitis [43]). This factor did not behave like antibody; it remained attached to the tissues; it failed to combine with virus in vitro, and it showed peculiar quantitative relationships in its protective activity.

A second point opposed to the concept of an antibody response in the nervous system also is the highly localized nature of the neuronal resistance to poliomyelitis which has been demonstrated by Howe and Bodian (44). In monkeys in which virus had been injected into one portion of the nervous tissue, other uninvaded portions remained susceptible. For example, if the spinal cord were transected and virus injected below, paralysis of the legs eventuated. After recovery, intranasally instilled virus caused paralysis of the muscles innervated by the motor cells above the transection precisely as if the animal had never before had experience with the virus. In other experiments histologic studies showed that if virus were administered intraocularly, upon subsequent recovery the olfactory bulbs could still be invaded by virus, and conversely. Similar findings had been made by Toomey earlier (45). It seems highly improbable that a resistance dependent upon local antibody formation should be so highly localized within the nervous system. This evidence speaks rather for some kind of modification of neurons which have been exposed to the virus.

If we turn now to a consideration of the circumstances under which immunity is revealed by animals with high levels of humoral antibody resulting from intensive vaccination or from the passive transfer of large amounts of serum, we find that they resist virus inoculated intracerebrally, intramuscularly, or intravenously. These routes of infection are, of course, artificial ones, and the trauma attendant upon the inoculation itself might well result in the passage of antibodies from the blood into the area of injection; this is in fact what Morgan found to be the case in intracerebrally challenged animals (39b). The question is whether an analogous circumstance exists in spontaneous infection; whether the virus is ever similarly amenable to the activity of antibodies. The answer to this hinges upon an understanding of the pathway which the natural infection takes en route to the central nervous system, and this is not yet clear. We might, however, consider the three most likely possibilities and in each case inquire as to the probable influence which might be exerted by humoral antibody.

The first case considers the virus at the outermost portal—upon the surface of the oropharynx or the intestine. Antiviral substances have been found in the nasopharyngeal secretions of human beings (46) and perhaps also in the intestinal tract, though this is disputed (11, 36). But Schultz and Gebhardt (47) found protection in only a portion of monkeys given large quantities of antiserum and challenged by intranasal instillation of virus, and Howe and Bodian (48a) could not demonstrate in chimpanzees given large amounts of antiviral serum that the parasite subsequently administered orally was inhibited from setting up the intestinal carrier state, though this may be of shorter duration than in untreated animals (48b).

Next we might consider that virus enters the body through terminal nerve filaments and progresses centripetally to the central nervous system entirely within neurons. In this case it seems doubtful that virus would be exposed to the activity of humoral antibodies.

Finally, there is the possibility that virus invades the body through a less specialized pathway; it has been suggested that it may circulate in the blood before localizing in nerve tissue (16b, 16c). The virus could in this case be acted upon by blood antibody. But if this is the picture of infection and resistance, it omits from consideration the fact that convalescent animals with low levels of humoral antibody possess more dependable resistance than may vaccinated or passively immunized animals with equal or better levels of circulating antibody (17, 24-28, 38).

These various observations and experiments dealing with convalescent, vaccinated and transfused animals do not seem to satisfy entirely the concept that antibody represents the exclusive expression of the immune host's ability to avoid the naturally communicated disease. Another line of evidence bearing upon the question of immunity mechanism is open to study. This concerns the existence of different antigenic types of poliomyelitis virus. It was described earlier that the existence of diverse strains of virus (4) might be considered weighty evidence in favor of the importance of antibodies to resistance for this reason—that if convalescent immune animals can distinguish antigenic strains of virus in resistance tests then immunity follows a highly specific line which is characteristic of antibodies; ergo antibodies probably account for resistance. Actually, however, it is found in such comparative tests that strain differences are much less apparent in direct challenge than in neutralization tests with the sera of immune animals, i.e. the antibodies of immune animals are much more selective in distinguishing strain differences than are the nerve tissues called upon to resist infection by strains heterologous to that which induced immunity (4e, 4g, 15). Again then this type of evidence fails to supply definitive support for the indispensability of antiviral antibodies to resistance.

In summary, testimony for the possible activity of antibody as a resistance mechanism against spontaneously occurring poliomyelitis includes these facts: (a) that such antibody can neutralize the infectivity of virus when mixed with it in vitro before injection into test animals, (b) that antibody present in large quantity as the result of intensive vaccination or passive transfer may protect animals against virus conditional to a challenge test which probably exposes the parasite to antibody before the agent has invaded nerve cells, but opposed to this is the fact that convalescent animals may possess immunity in equal measure without high levels of circulating antibody, (c) that antiviral substance has been reported as present in the central nervous system of convalescent animals, but this finding has not been made by all who have sought it, and there is some suggestion that the inhibitor, if it is present, may not be of antibody nature, (d) that resistance follows the same channel of specificity against virus types as do antibodies produced against them, though actually resistance is considerably broader in its scope than are the neutralizing properties of antibodies. No one of these lines of evidence so far leads clearly to the conclusion that viral-inhibiting antibody can itself explain resistance to the disease; there exists in every case an intimation that additional factors must play a role also, and perhaps an important one. What such additional factors may be is obscure; we can only speculate that some modification of the cells actually affected by the virus may leave them with a subsequent changed reactivity to reentry of the parasite. Positive evidence for this possibility is given by the highly localized nature of resistance following infection of segregated portions of the nervous system.

For the present we might adopt the viewpoint that antiviral antibodies may endow man or animals with resistance in circumstances where a sufficient concentration of these can influence virus before it has attained its intracellular locale. In the case of spontaneous infection this may be upon the mucous membrane surfaces where the infection probably has its inception. Direct evidence that viral inhibition **by antibody** occurs here is not yet established. Resistance may possibly also depend upon a modification of the nervous system itself brought about by a primary infection which may be asymptomatic, so far as neurologic manifestations are concerned at least. The neural resistance is ascribed by Morgan to a concentration of antibody in the nervous tissues, presumably produced locally, but for the reasons detailed before it seems wise to entertain the possibility that the central nervous system endowment resides in some property of the cells themselves which can inhibit viral proliferation. Further studies will be required before this or any other viewpoint can be defended without reservations.

Practical Procedures for Vaccination. At this time there is no prophylactic measure available for poliomyelitis, but for obvious reasons interest in this goal is sustained at a high level. The studies discussed in preceding portions of this chapter seem to predicate two bases for its possible attainment. The first is the creation of a high level of humoral antibody with the hope that this might provide resistance to spontaneous infection similar to that achieved by vaccinated monkeys and rodents to experimentally induced infections. The second is the induction of some modification in neurons themselves, comparable to the presumptive alteration which may be a consequence of infection.

HUMORAL IMMUNITY. Despite the optimistic results observed in vaccinated animals (31-36) the promise inherent in this procedure seems to the writer to be very limited. For this dour view there are several reasons. First, it has yet to be demonstrated that high concentrations of antibody in the body fluids can protect the body against the naturally communicated disease. Secondly, even if this demonstration can be successfully made, there is a problem in attaining high levels of antibody against poliomyelitis virus; multiple large doses of infected nerve tissue have so far been required for this purpose. It is possible, of course, that some method will eventually be devised for cultivating the virus outside the body for large scale production and concentration. The use of adjuvant for intensifying antibody responses has already received some attention (49). Thirdly, in this same connection of intensive vaccination with a preparation containing nerve tissue, there is inherent in the procedure the danger of producing "isoallergic" encephalitis (see Chapter 31). Finally, the existence of viral types poses the usual problem encountered in dealing with prophylaxis to infectious agents of diverse antigenic specificities. This difficulty could be met in part by the employment of a vaccine composed of mixed known types, but there is, of course, no certainty that an entirely new antigenic strain might not appear as the causative agent of a subsequent epidemic.

CELLULAR MODIFICATION. Perhaps a more promising approach to the problem of establishing acquired resistance to poliomyelitis may be afforded by attempts to alter the responsiveness of nerve cells themselves to virus. Such an attempt might feasibly be directed toward nerve endings of the oropharynx and intestine which probably constitute the pathway of infection. A modification might be induced for example through the interference effect, as suggested by Jungeblut (50) and Evans and Green (51), employing strains incapable of invading the nervous system. Such strains are not yet available, but the observations of Sabin and Steigman and others (15, 16) suggest that relatively avirulent strains might eventually be singled out for this purpose. A related virus might accomplish the same end; for example, one of the murine poliomyelitis viruses which is not pathogenic for the human being, and from which the human virus has perhaps sprung (52).

This same application of a related living virus to nerve terminals may induce other modifications in neurons than the interference effect. A more durable alteration analogous to that which we assume may occur in the central nervous system of infected subjects could eventuate. In both cases it is conceivable that merely swallowing the appropriate virus preparation could lead to the desired goal. A beginning in this direction has been made (53).

These are, of course, hypothetical possibilities predicated upon an interpretation of acquired immunity mechanisms which may prove to be erroneous, but the present status of our knowledge suggests that they constitute a reasonable direction for inquiry.

BIBLIOGRAPHY

1a. Bodian, D., and Howe, H. A. J. Exper. Med., 81:255, 1945.
 b. Turner, T. B., Hollander, D. H., Buckley, S., Kokko, U. P., and Winsor, C. P. Am. J. Hyg., 51:323, 1951.
2a. Paul, J. R., and Trask, J. D. Tr. & Stud., Coll. Physicians, Philadelphia, 54:158, 1932.
 b. Casey, A. E., Fishbein, W. I., and Abrams, I., 1946, Am. J. Dis. Child., 72:661, 1946.
 c. Fischer, A. E., and Stillerman, M. J.A.M.A., 110:569, 1938.
 d. Bridge, E. M., Clarke, G. H., and Abbe, D. Am. J. Dis. Child., 72:501, 1946.
3a. Kessel, J. F., Stimpert, F. D., and Fisk, R. T. Am. J. Hyg., 27:519, 1938.
 b. Melnick, J. L., and Horstmann, D. M. J. Exper. Med., 85:287, 1947.
4a. Burnet, F., and MacNamara, J. Brit. J. Exper. Path., 12:57, 1931.
 b. Paul, J. P., and Trask, J. D. J. Exper. Med., 58:513, 1933.
 c. Kessel, J. F., and Pait, C. F. Am. J. Hyg., 51:76, 1950.
 d. Morgan, I. M. Am. J. Hyg., 49:225, 1949.
 e. Bodian, D. Am. J. Hyg., 49:200, 1949.

f. ——— Morgan, I. M., and Howe, H. A.   Am. J. Hyg., 49:234, 1949.
g. Various Members of the Committee on Typing of the National Foundation for Infantile Paralysis.   Am. J. Hyg., 54:191, 205, 211, 216, 230, 243, 251, 255, 268, 1951.
5. Harmon, P. H., and Harkins, H. N.   J.A.M.A., 107:552, 1936.
6. Hammon, W. McD., Mack, W. N., and Reeves, W. C.   J. Immunol., 57:285, 1947.
7a. Schultz, E. W.   Ann. Rev. Microbiol., 2:335, 1948.
b. Evans, C. A., and Green, R. G.   J.A.M.A., 134:1154, 1947.
c. Faber, H. K.   Science, 114:570, 1951.
8. Burnet, F. M., and Jackson, A. V.   Australian J. Exper. Biol. & M. Sc., 17:261, 1939.
9. Flexner, S.   J. Exper. Med., 65:497, 1937.
10. Howe, H. A.   Viral and Rickettsial Infections in Man, ed. by T. M. Rivers, Philadelphia, J. B. Lippincott Co., 1948, Chapter 10.
11. Hammon, W. McD.   Bact. Rev., 13:135, 1949.
12a. Howe, H. A., Bodian, D., and Morgan, I. M.   Am. J. Hyg., 51:85, 1950.
b. Melnick, J. L., and Ledinko, N.   J. Immunol., 67:213, 1951.
13a. Loring, H. S., and Schwerdt, C. E.   J. Exper. Med., 75:395, 1942.
b. Beard, J. W.   J. Immunol., 58:49, 1948.
14. Kessel, J. F., and Pait, C. F.   Proc. Soc. Exper. Biol. & Med., 68:606, 1948.
15. Sabin, A. B., and Steigman, A. J.   Am. J. Hyg., 49:176, 1949.
16a. Brown, G. C., Ainslee, J. D., and Francis, T., Jr.   Am. J. Hyg., 49:194, 1949.
b. Paul, J. R.   The Merck Report, 61:3, 1952.
c. Horstmann, D. M.   Proc. Soc. Exper. Biol. & Med., 79:417, 1952.
17. Lennette, E. H., and Hudson, N. P.   J. Infect. Dis., 65:78, 1939
18. Anderson, J. A.   J. Pediat., 27:68, 1945.
19. Sabin, A. B., and Ward, R.   J. Exper. Med., 73:771, 1941.
20. van Riper, H. E.   J.A.M.A., 135:74, 1947.
21. Schultz, E. W., and Gebhardt, L. P.   J. Pediat., 6:615, 1935.
22. Faber, H. A.   Medicine, 12:83, 1933.
23. Howe, H. A., and Bodian, D.   Neural Mechanisms in Poliomyelitis, New York, The Commonwealth Fund, 1942.
24. Schulz, E. W., and Gebhardt, L. P.   California & West. Med., 43:111, 1935.
25. Sabin, A. B., and Olitsky, P. K.   J. Exper. Med., 64:739, 1936.
26. Olitsky, P. K., and Cox, H. R.   J. Exper. Med., 63:109, 1936.
27. Hudson, N. P., Lennette, E. H., and Gordon, F. B.   J. Bact., 31:32, 1936.
28a. Kramer, S. D.   J. Immunol., 31:167, 1936.
b. ——— and Grossman, L. H.   J. Immunol., 31:183, 191, 1936.
c. ——— Grossman, L. H., and Hoskwith, B.   J. Immunol., 31:199, 1936.
29. Jungeblut, C. W.   J. Infect. Dis., 58:150, 1936.
30. Aycock, W. L., and Kagan, J. R.   J. Immunol., 14:85, 1927.
31. Kramer, S. D., and Geer, H. A.   J. Immunol., 50:275, 1945.
32. Milzer, A., Oppenheimer, F., and Levinson, S. O.   J. Immunol., 50:331, 1945.
33. Loring, H. S., Schwerdt, C. E., Lawrence, N., and Anderson, J. C.   Science, 106:104, 1947.
34. Morgan, I. M., Howe, H. A., and Bodian, D.   Am. J. Hyg., 45:379, 1947.
35. ——— Am. J. Hyg., 48:394, 1948.
36. Ainslie, J. D., McCallum, J. L., and Francis, T., Jr.   Proc. Soc. Exper. Biol. & Med., 75:699, 1950.
37. Melnick, J. L.   Ann. Rev. Microbiol., 4:309, 1951.
38. Kramer, S. D.   Proc. Soc. Exper. Biol. & Med., 48:287, 1941.
39a. Morgan, I. M.   Am. J. Hyg., 45:390, 1947.
b. ——— Federation Proc., 8:618, 1949.
40a. Sabin, A. B., and Steigman, A. J.   J. Immunol., 63:211, 1949.
b. Landsteiner, K., Levaditi, C., and Pastia, C.   Ann. Inst. Pasteur, 25:805, 1911.
c. Jungeblut, C. W.   J. Immunol., 22:99, 1932.
41. Flexner, S., and Amoss, H. L.   J. Exper. Med., 25:499, 1917.
42. Gard, S.   Acta med. Scandinav., 119:27, 1944.
43. Committee on Nomenclature of the National Foundation for Infantile Paralysis.   Science, 108:701, 1948.

44a. Howe, H. A., and Bodian, D.   J. Exper. Med., 74:145, 1941.
   b. Bodian, D., and Howe, H. A.   J. Exper. Med., 81:255, 1945.
45. Toomey, J. A.   Am. J. Dis. Child., 52:802, 1936; J. Immunol., 35:1, 1938.
46a. Amoss, H. L., and Taylor, E.   J. Exper. Med., 25:507, 1917.
   b. Howitt, B. I.   J. Infect. Dis., 60:113, 1937.
   c. Bell, E. J.   Am. J. Hyg., 47:351, 1948.
47. Schultz, E. W., and Gebhardt, L. P.   J. Pediat., 7:332, 1935.
48a. Howe, H. A., and Bodian, D.   J. Exper. Med., 81:247, 1945.
   b. Howe, H. A.   Federation Proc., 10:410, 1951.
49. Salk, J. E., Youngner, J. S., Lewis, L. J., and Bennett, B. L.   Am. J. Hyg., 54:255, 1951.
50. Jungeblut, C. W.   J. Exper. Med., 81:275, 1945.
51. Evans, C. A., and Green, R. G.   J.A.M.A., 134:1154, 1947.
52a. Burnet, F. M.   Virus as Organism, Cambridge, Mass., Harvard University Press, 1945.
   b. Chang, T. W., and Wenner, H. A.   Proc. Soc. Exper. Biol. & Med., 78:659, 1951.
53. Koprowski, H., Jervis, G. A., and Norton, T. W.   Am. J. Hyg., 55:108, 1952.

GENERAL REFERENCES

Infantile Paralysis, New York, National Foundation for Infantile Paralysis, 1941.
Rhodes, A. J., and van Rooyen, C. E.   Textbook of Virology, New York, Thomas Nelson and Sons, 1949.

29

INFLUENZA

In the two decades that have elapsed since the first isolation of the viral agent of influenza (1) a prodigious amount of scientific energy has gone into the study of this parasite and the host's responses to it; indeed, this virus has become perhaps the most thoroughly investigated of all the filterable agents. Much of this interest has been due to the catastrophic pandemic of 1918 and the hope that any future occurrence of this kind might be met with some organized opposition. From that costly experience there was salvaged a certain amount of clinical, pathologic, and epidemiologic information without concurrent evidence of etiology; this leaves us in the peculiar situation of having many interesting observations to ruminate on with only surmise about the cause. There has not been a recurrence of a similar pandemic which might permit a retrospective approach to proof of etiology. Relatively mild epidemics have been occurring since then at short intervals, however, and these as well as interepidemic cases can now be diagnosed with certainty by the isolation of the etiologic agent in ferrets or chick embryos. From these sources the virus may be adapted to the mouse. This has permitted an experimental assessment of immunity, and some controlled measurements have also been carried out in human beings. From these it is evident that an immunity of rather good order but of limited endurance can be acquired. It is generally agreed that for the human being this may persist for perhaps six to eight months (2).

Immunity-Inducing Factors. Influenza virus contains nucleoprotein, neutral fats, phospholipid, cholesterol, nucleic acid and carbohydrate, a heterogeneous composition for a viral body only about 100mμ in diameter (3). Knight has made the interesting observation that virus may incorporate into its own substance constituents of the host in which it grows. Thus, strains obtained from allantoic fluid or mouse lung appeared to contain antigens characteristic of these sources. The validity of this finding stands or falls upon the question of the purity obtainable in viral preparations, and for this reason a final opinion cannot be reached yet (4).

Distinctive immunologic responses are induced by two or possibly three different known viral factors. A soluble antigen occurs free in infected tissues and is also a part of, or is adsorbed to, the viral particle itself. This is termed the S antigen; it has a particle size of about 10mμ; it is probably a protein and it invokes antibodies which react with it particularly well in the complement-fixation test. It is apparently not a homogeneous substance (5). Sec-

398

ondly, influenza viruses possess a factor which causes agglutination of human, chicken and other erythrocytes, and this seems to have the character of an enzyme (6). This factor is also antigenic and the antibodies produced by infected or vaccinated animals inhibit its hemagglutinative activity. Thirdly, the viral bodies induce antibodies which neutralize their infectivity upon mixture in vitro. This is the usual viral inhibiting effect directed against a factor or factors the nature of which is entirely unknown. This substance also functions as antigen in complement-fixation tests (7). There is some possibility that the hemagglutinating enzyme and this viral antigen are identical, and in fact many of the studies of strain differences carried out since 1941 have been based upon the relatively simple serologic procedure of hemagglutinin-inhibition rather than upon virus neutralization tests. It seems probable though that these factors are distinct, for recent observations indicate that the hemagglutinin-inhibiting and the viral neutralizing activities of an antiserum may diverge considerably (8), and furthermore these antibody effects may be separated by the absorption of a serum with proper viral preparations (9).

All influenza viruses are not the same antigenically. These factors which have been described occur in all of them but with different antigenic properties in two main types of virus. The first virus isolated from a human source in 1933 (1) is termed type A. A virus of entirely distinct antigenic character was found seven years later and is designated as type B (10). A third type is now recognized as C; this differs from A and B antigenically as well as in its behavior in chick embryos and mice, which it fails to infect (11). Relatively little is known so far about this virus. It has become amply apparent that strains of varying antigenic properties occur within each of these types, especially the A (12). In fact, more than one strain of A has been isolated during the same epidemic (13). It has been found that passage through mice is especially apt to result in the emergence of different antigenic strains (14), presumably through a process of selection of mutants. This process may be intensified in the presence of antibodies active upon the virus. Thus it may be that in a human population a mutant strain (or strains) least neutralizable by the antibodies current in the group as the result of past infections or immunization could emerge through selection. Archetti and Horsfall (15) have set up a test for this possibility in chick embryos and found that even an old passage strain of well known antigenic character could as readily become modified in its antigenic character by exposure to small amounts of antibody as could strains recently recovered from human beings. This may explain the recovery of more than one strain during the course of an epidemic, but it is quite possible also that the mutants might emerge during the passage in mice of a single recovered strain. Plainly, the antigenic lability of these viruses poses many problems which complicate epidemiologic and immunologic studies.

The antigenic variability of these viruses is reminiscent of the capacity of trypanosomes to cause relapsing infections through the emergence of anti-body-fast strains each time the host produces antibody against the current strain. This parasite can thus survive and usually destroy its host despite the repeated acquisition by the host of effective antibody responses (see Chapter 9). The relatively mild influenza virus does not persist in a single host in this fashion, but in an analogous sense Burnet (16) believes that the type A virus may survive in a population by "constantly building serological novelty on to its past antigenic structure. This in some way covers over but preserves what was past antigenic surfaces." (See also Hilleman and others [17].)

In this picture of antigenic variability the specific factors described earlier seem to have the following places. The soluble (S) antigen is the same in all strains of a type. The hemagglutinating factor on the other hand shows strain differences as does also the viral body antigen. This has both type and strain specificity, but the type specific component is distinct from the S antigen (18). An interesting tentative representation of the place of these factors in the structure of the virus has been suggested by Hoyle (19) who obtained evidence that the proliferating virus within allantoic sac cells during a single cycle of multiplication is neither infectious nor hemagglutinative; in fact, it seems to consist solely of the small particle S antigen. At the end of the six-hour multiplication cycle infective virus is liberated into the allantoic fluid; this proceeds to infect other cells and a new cycle of multiplication begins. Friedewald and Pickles (20) and Gard and von Magnus (21) had earlier reported evidence of the existence of two particles of different size in the allantoic fluid of infected embryos; a smaller hemagglutinative one, and a larger particle which was both hemagglutinative and infective. Putting together these bits of information Hoyle (19) suggests that the S antigen represents a core of virus in the stage of replication within the cell. This substance with only type antigenic character may then successively take on the strain specific hemagglutinative property and the infective capacity to become a complete virus body. These acquisitions endow the virus with strain specificity and perhaps also with the capacity, through the hemagglutinative enzyme, to attach to host cells. To this viewpoint there are exceptions; one of these to the effect that the failure to demonstrate hemagglutinating activity in the early stage of infection is due to the presence of inhibiting substances in the allantoic membrane suspensions themselves. Removal of this inhibitor frequently results in the simultaneous appearance of S antigen and hemagglutinin (18). Nevertheless Hoyle's representation provides a useful working diagram at least until these various intraviral relationships become clearer than they are now.

So far as the protection-inducing factor of the influenza virus is concerned this may reside in the viral particle as the unknown constituent which incites the production of neutralizing antibody, or it may be the hemagglutinin. (There is a lingering possibility that these two factors are synonymous, as noted before.) The evidence is strong, but not entirely conclusive, that one of these antibodies endows human beings as well as animals with the major part of their acquired resistance, as will be discussed further under mechanisms of immunity. The S antigen can be excluded from any relationship to immunity induction; antibodies against this factor have significance in a diagnostic sense only (5f, 18).

Relationship of Protection-Inducing Factor to Virulence. Influenza viruses reveal the same kind of fluctuations in virulence among strains as do other infectious agents. This may vary independently of antigenic differences (22). Variable pathogenicity for ferrets has been seen with two strains of type A isolated from the same epidemic (23).

The virus has tropism for cells of the respiratory epithelium, but neurotropic strains have been developed, and Burnet (24) suggests that the ability to invade cells other than those of the respiratory tract may be the feature of pandemic virus which could explain its vicious character.

The pathogenicity of type A virus is always greater for animals than that of type B; C is still very little known. The growth cycles of both viruses conform to the so-called one-step pattern seen with bacteriophages, i.e. viral particles invade a cell, multiplication ensues, and after an interval a burst of new virus is liberated to infect other cells. In the case of the A virus this period is 5 to 6 hours; for B, it is 9 to 10 hours (12a).

A final point of general interest concerning the virulence of these viruses has been described by Burnet and his co-workers in terms of the O (original) and D (derived) phases of an organism recovered from a human source (12a, 25, 26). The O phase during passage in the chick embryo soon mutates to the D phase. The differences between the two lie especially in the higher pathogenicity of O for ferrets, its greater resistance to the hemagglutinin-inhibitory action of human tears, and its ability to agglutinate human and guinea pig, but not chicken erythrocytes. Burnet believes that the O form has some special survival advantage as a human pathogen (5e, 26).

Turning now to specific virulence characteristics in an effort to relate these to the immunity-inducing factor we find that studies of pathogenicity have fallen into five main categories: (a) toxicity, (b) ability to infect cells (c) ability to multiply within cells, (d) ability to cause clinically or pathologically manifest disease, and (e) ability to communicate among hosts. These activities do not necessarily coincide, as will be pointed out.

(a) TOXICITY. It is well known that the onset of influenza in man is marked by general signs and symptoms of intoxication, including fever and malaise, before any respiratory involvement becomes evident. It has been proposed (24) that rapid virus multiplication may produce a gross disorganization of cellular metabolism with necrosis of cells and liberation of products. If this were the case, however, one should expect local effects of the virus to make themselves felt before the general intoxication, and this does not happen. Several years ago it was found that the systemic injection of virus into mice often killed them in one to three days, and this effect occurred even with heated or otherwise modified virus. This toxic activity depends solely upon the concentration of virus; if a sufficient amount is inoculated directly into the lungs, it kills without multiplying. The effect resides in the viral particle itself (22a, 27). Hepatic, splenic, cerebral and possibly cardiac damage has been described as resulting from this toxic action (28), and it may also account for a decrease in white blood cells, in animals at least (29). In fertile eggs the effect of large doses of virus is to depress oxygen consumption (30). The fever occasioned by these viruses could easily follow from this toxic activity, but Wagner and Bennett consider that it is instead related to the hemagglutinating capacity of the virus (31). Whether this is actually the case is not clear now; it has not so far been verified (32).

The final interpretation of the meaning of these findings in the understanding of the disease in human beings, and the characterization of the viral factor responsible for them, must await more information. The early febrile response in man is a definite enough occurrence. The question as to whether respiratory or systemic cellular damage may occur in man is difficult to answer because so few opportunities have arisen for the pathologic study of influenza uncomplicated by secondary bacterial infection. Parker and associates (33) have reported two post mortem examinations of cases of proven influenza infection without bacterial invasion in which destructive lesions were found nowhere, not even in the bronchiolar epithelium. On the other hand earlier autopsy reports describe alveolar and bronchiolar epithelial necrosis (34).

(b) ABILITY TO INFECT CELLS. One of the most stimulating aspects of the influenzal studies presently in progress is that dealing with the mechanism through which infection of susceptible cells may come about. The central lead in this direction has come from the studies of hemagglutination which began in 1941 with Hirst's (35) and McClelland and Hare's (36) descriptions of the ability of influenza virus to clump chicken erythrocytes. Since then a variety of viruses and rickettsias have been found to do this, but only in the cases of the agents of influenza, Newcastle disease of fowl, mumps and fowl plague, is this activity a property of the viral bodies themselves. In other cases the infectious agent produces a soluble agglutinating factor. The agglutinating activity of influenza virus is conceived by Hirst (6) to be enzymatic in nature. According to this generally accepted viewpoint, surface enzymes of the agent attach to a substrate (receptors) upon the surface of the red cell; they destroy this substrate and subsequently elute spontaneously, retaining the capacity to attack more cells. Erythrocytes which have been acted upon are not subject to re-agglutination, presumably because their receptors have been destroyed. Mild heating or other treatment of the virus designed to inactivate its infectivity also vitiates its enzyme activity, but its power to adsorb to erythrocytes remains intact if cations are present in the reaction medium (32, 37). The same general groups of receptors appear to function for the various influenza types and strains as well as for mumps, fowl plague and Newcastle disease viruses. Burnet (32, 38) has arranged a receptor gradient in which each virus in the series destroys receptors for itself and for those below it in the series, but not for those above. This suggests that there are a number of receptors on the cell and complementarily a number of specific viral enzymes of which each virus may have a set (37, 39).

A step toward the concept that hemagglutination may be related to infective ability came with the discovery that human erythrocytes may be agglutinated as well as those of the chicken and other animals, and this was followed by the even more pointed observations by Hirst (40) that the respiratory epithelium of ferret lung reacts to virus just as do erythrocytes. In excised lung preparations virus is adsorbed, then liberated, and the lung cells are incapable of taking up more virus. In the living lung adsorption similarly occurs, but **liberation** of virus does not take place. This implies that after adsorption to living cells the virus pursues a further course; one would logically expect this to be penetration of the cell and subsequent growth. A close correlation has been found to exist between the pathogenicity of viral strains and their abilities to agglutinate mammalian erythrocytes (41).

The next link in this chain of evidence is derived from studies of the natures of the substrate and the viral enzyme. The essence of these studies reveals that mucopolysaccharide substances obtained from various sources can, by themselves acting as substrate, inhibit the activity of viral hemagglutinin upon erythrocytes. These mucopolysaccharides have been found in human bronchial mucus, saliva, gastric mucus, purified blood group substance and in egg white and other extrahuman sources as well (32, 37, 42). Meanwhile there have been found also sources of enzymes other than the virus which are active upon the same substrates, either the isolated mucopolysaccharides or the erythrocyte surface itself. Thus, filtrates of cultures of *Vibrio comma* contain a receptor-destroying enzyme (RDE), and an enzyme with similar activity is present in *Cl. welchii* type A toxin (43). A chemical substance, periodate, also affects red cells so that they are no longer susceptible to the action of viral hemagglutinin (44).

These discoveries of extra-erythrocytic substrate and extraviral enzymes have supplied interesting grist for the inquiry into the role played by the hemagglutinating enzyme in the infectivity of influenza virus, and the findings so far have been rewarding. As mentioned before, mucopolysaccharide can divert the attachment of virus to cells. On the other hand, receptor-destroying enzymes can so change the cell surface that the virus can no longer attach to it; thus, Fazekas de St. Groth and Stone treated excised mouse lung with the *V. comma* enzyme and found that it could no longer adsorb virus, and this was followed by the demonstration that the same enzyme could protect chick embryos and mice from infection by the virus (45). Interestingly, recently isolated strains of virus are better dissuaded from infecting animals than are old laboratory adapted strains. Cellular receptors are quickly regenerated after their destruction by cholera vibrio RDE; this process begins after about a day and is complete at the end of six days (45a).

Burnet (16, 46) has recently summarized his view of the infective process in the following terms. The enzymatically active groups are incorporated in the virus surface. Once adsorbed, the virus sinks into the susceptible cell. The enzymatic function of the viral component is actually not necessary for adsorption to occur, since inactivated virus also attaches to receptor-containing surfaces, but it is possible that the enzyme may be useful in overcoming the thin film of mucus overlying the respiratory epithelium, for this mucus contains a potent inhibitor of hemagglutination (mucopolysaccharide). In line with this hypothesis, recent work indicates that the nasal secretions of patients in the acute stage of influenza are qualitatively changed in their ability to inhibit hemagglutinin, and this probably reflects the activity of the viral enzyme upon the mucus substrate (46).

Certain observations must be mentioned which hinder complete submission to this attractive viewpoint. One important obstacle of this kind is the finding of immature virus particles which possess hemagglutinative activity while lacking the ability to infect (20, 21, 47). However, this finding does not necessarily preclude an important role of hemagglutination in the infectious process, for in addition to the ability to adsorb to cell surfaces the virus must certainly possess other properties necessary for the initiation of proliferation at the expense of the cell, and these may be lacking in the immature virus. An analogy may be afforded by the case of the pneumococcus where the capsule so necessary for virulence does not in itself assure this property to an organism (see Chapters 3 and 18).

Perhaps more compromising to the viewpoint that the hemagglutinating enzyme is of importance to infectivity is a report which suggests the occurrence of virus particles which are infective without being hemagglutinative (48). It would be difficult or impossible to reconcile this with the concept just described, and it is of obvious importance to learn whether this finding can be verified more generally.

(c) ABILITY TO MULTIPLY WITHIN CELLS. The ability of influenza virus to infect cells is not necessarily followed by the capacity subsequently to multiply progressively in them. Schlesinger (47) has found that if a pneumotropic strain of virus is injected into the brain it invades cells and goes through a single cycle of multiplication to give rise to two immature virus products— a hemagglutinating particle and the S antigen—but no infective virus. The continuity of infection is thus interrupted, since the virus cannot parasitize fresh cells.

(d) ABILITY TO CAUSE DISEASE. It is surprising again that there is no ex post facto relationship between the disease-producing capacity of a virus and the foregoing properties. Virus obtained from human cases produces lesions primarily of the respiratory epithelium in ferrets and chick embryos. Such virus does not cause apparent disease in mice, hamsters or guinea pigs even though it may infect cells and multiply maximally in them. In mice, it is only after adaptation through several serial passages that the virus brings about signs of illness and anything more than trivial pneumonic lesions (14, 24).

The route by which virus reaches the respiratory epithelial cells is also related to the extent of disease production. In mice, intravenously injected virus reaches the respiratory epithelium to cause lung lesions, but these are minimal. On the other hand, the same virus brought to these cells by the airway causes typical full-blown disease (24, 49).

The respiratory tract lesions produced by influenza virus have usually been described in terms of necrosis of lining epithelium. In ferrets (50) complete destruction of the respiratory epithelium of the nasal mucosa occurs within 48 hours after intranasal instillation of the agent. This is followed by regeneration of cells from the basal layer beginning after about four days and reaching completion at three weeks. In the mouse the virus attacks mainly the lungs, epithelial lesions being especially pronounced in the bronchi and bronchioles. The fatal pneumonia which is seen in these animals is secondary to the blockage of bronchioles; consequently mice may die of pneumonia while the specific lesion of the respiratory epithelium itself is healing (24, 51). In monkeys the lesion is described as one of the bronchiolar epithelium, with adjacent areas of interstitial pneumonia (24).

In human beings, opportunities for pathologic study of uncomplicated influenza have been scarce, but what there is has not regularly disclosed evidence of epithelial destruction (33, 34, 53). In view further of a recent report by Harford and Hamlin (52) that they could find no evidence of destruction of bronchial epithelium in mice, though portions of the cytoplasm of nonciliated cells were seen to become detached, the entire question of respiratory tract lesions seems to deserve further consideration.

(e) ABILITY TO COMMUNICATE. Finally, an aspect of virulence which requires comment in respect to influenza viruses especially concerns the ability of the parasite to spread from one host to another. The point is a particularly cogent one in this case because of the mutability of strain characteristics which is so pronounced in these viruses. It is possible that members of a human population who, because of their backgrounds of past infection or immunization, may be resistant to a current epidemic strain of virus, could perhaps select from this an antigenic mutant capable of evading their resistance processes (15). Virus might in this way spread even through a partially immune population. This point is not directly related to the question of virulence mechanisms with which this discussion is most concerned, but its possible importance in explaining that aspect of pathogenicity which deals with the ability of the parasite to produce widespread infections is evident.

In summary of this discussion of virulence, we have a good deal of interesting information concerning such peculiar habits of influenza viruses as their infection of cells for the duration of one cycle of proliferation only, their multiplication within cells without producing gross signs or symptoms of infection, their production of minor disease when they have reached respiratory cells by one route (the hematogenous) and of major pathologic alterations if they have reached the same cells by another route (the respiratory passage). These observations are not yet assimilable into a comprehensible picture of the virulence mechanisms of the virus. What we are left with that makes sense at this time is one concept, founded upon rather good evidence, to explain the initial phase of pathogenicity of the influenza viruses—the ability to attach to susceptible host cells by means of the hemagglutinating enzyme. What the virus does as the next step, or how it does it, is not known except in broadest outline.

As to how this virulence factor, the hemagglutinin, may relate to the immunity-inducing element of the virus, some speculation can be made. Of the antibody responses which may be of importance to immunity, that against the viral antigen (virus neutralizing antibody) is possibly of most significance. The antibody directed against the hemagglutinating factor cannot, however, be discounted; as discussed in the succeeding section a peculiar set of experimental circumstances has left us without a secure basis for judgment of this question.

If the viral neutralizing antibody eventuates as the important element in immunity the situation may be analogous to that which obtains in anthrax infection (see Chapter 19), i.e. the protective response of the host is distinct from the response directed against an important virulence factor. This is of course an oversimplified statement, for we cannot be absolutely certain that the hemagglutinin is indeed a virulence factor or, if it is, that there are not other important virulence properties of the virus which the neutralizing antibody may affect.

If the hemagglutinin-inhibiting antibody should turn out to be of most significance to resistance we might then be dealing with an instance in which acquired immunity depends upon a host response which directly interferes with a virulence property of the infectious agent. This would constitute an analogue to the relationship which obtains between the immune host and the pneumococcus, for example (see Chapter 18).

Clouded as these issues are, this statement of possibilities represents lines along which useful information upon the question of relationship of virulence and immunizing factors might be pursued.

Mechanisms of Immunity. As in the case of other diseases caused by viruses, the question of mechanism of acquired resistance here resolves itself into two major possibilities: (a) that antibodies constitute the protective factor, or (b) that susceptible cells may in some way be so modified by an initial experience with virus as to deal with it differently in subsequent encounters.

(a) ANTIBODIES. It is generally thought that antibodies constitute the chief defense of the subject with acquired immunity to influenza. In support of this viewpoint it is known that the serum of convalescent ferrets administered intraperitoneally to mice protects them against small doses of nasally instilled virus (54). In human beings in whom antibody levels were determined prior to the occurrence of infection the attack rate was generally higher among those in the low antibody range (55). Subjects twice inoculated intranasally with viable virus at four-month intervals generally showed a higher incidence of refractoriness corresponding to higher antibody titers (56). Francis (57) inoculated 18 human beings intranasally with virus and only one, the lone subject without detectable antibody, developed a mild attack of influenza. Animal experiments also have suggested a fairly close relationship of antibody levels to resistance against intranasally implanted virus (58).

This general evidence for the bearing of antibody upon resistance has been based in part upon the measurement of antibodies by the virus neutralization test, in part upon the titration of hemagglutinin-inhibiting antibody. It is known now that the influenza virus incites the production of probably three distinct antibodies: the neutralizing antibody directed against a type and strain specific viral component of unknown nature, a hemagglutinin-inhibiting antibody which for some time was reckoned to be identical with the virus neutralizing substance but now appears to be a distinct response (8b, 9, 59), and the anti-S antibody which fixes complement in the presence of this soluble viral antigen, and which is type specific only.

Of these responses it is safe to say that the last named, the anti-S antibody, has no relationship to resistance, for whereas immunity follows strain-specific lines, the S factor is common to all strains within the type. Further, vaccination with this antigen stimulates no resistance (5f). This leaves as possibilities the viral neutralizing or the hemagglutinin-inhibiting antibodies to account for resistance. Walker and Horsfall (9b) have pointed out that many of the studies of antibodies in relation to immunity to influenza have been carried out by using the hemagglutinin-inhibition test, and if this antibody is distinct from the virus neutralizing one then the results of these experiments are invalid with respect to interpretation of the basis of immunity. At the present time we have the confusing situation in which evidence derived from two kinds of serologic tests—neutralization of infectivity and hemagglutinin inhibition—are put forth in support of the viewpoint that resistance is correlated with antibody level. So far as the writer is aware there have not yet been performed any experiments in human beings or animals in which the attempt has been made to dissociate the activities of these in relation to the immune state. It is only possible therefore to speak of antibody immunity without qualification as to the specific kind of antibody involved.

There have been a number of interesting speculations and some experimental observations concerning the manner in which antibodies may effect resistance. The intrinsic mode of action of antibodies upon the virus is not clear; if viral-neutralizing activity is the important effect, it is no more understood here than in the case of other viral agents (5f). If the hemagglutinin-inhibiting effect is more important to resistance, one can surmise that the antibody neutralizes the ability of the virus to become adsorbed to cell receptors. It seems probable that as with other viruses antibody is useful in this case only if it can make effective contact with the agent before cells become infected (16). Since the influenza virus probably spreads over the surface of the respiratory epithelium the significant antibodies may be those which are present in the thin surface film of fluid. In this connection Hare (54) some years ago made an interesting point; he found that immune serum passively administered intra-abdominally to mice protected them against nasally instilled virus even if the serum were given as late as 72 hours after the challenge inoculum. He commented that serum would ordinarily not be expected to have an effect when the disease is already under way, but in the case of influenza virus the release of fresh virus from the cells first attacked could probably be influenced by antibody, presumably during the surface film spread envisioned by Burnet (16). Recent evidence obtained from studies of mice directly relates immunity to the concentration of antibodies in bronchial washings more closely than to the concentration in the blood (60).

If antibodies upon the respiratory surface are of greatest importance to immunity the question of the effectiveness of local vaccination is of interest. Intranasal infection followed by recovery provides ferrets with solid immunity for about three months and with moderate resistance up to perhaps a year (24). In contrast, the subcutaneous inoculation of living virus provides good humoral antibody responses but the animals remain susceptible to nasal infection, though its severity is modified (61). Francis (62) found that one infective dose of virus given intranasally produced solid immunity in ferrets while 100 times this amount given subcutaneously provided only a partial resistance. In groups of mice immunized with living virus intranasally or inactivated virus intraperitoneally, the blood antibody levels are about the same, but the group immunized intranasally has considerably higher and more persistent immunity to challenge infection (58). The resistance of the intraperitoneally vaccinated mice is improved by the use of living virus (which produces small lung lesions), but even here immunity is not as good as that following intranasal virus installation (58). Since in these experiments antibodies were found in the lungs and nasal tissues more regularly than in the liver, spleen or brain, Burnet (16, 24) believes that intranasal vaccination with the production of respiratory tract lesions results in the temporary local holding of concentrations of antibody for dealing with subsequent exposures to virus. Yet these findings also provide some reason for thinking in terms of local cellular resistance, as will be discussed later. Attempts to protect ferrets by spraying immune serum into their noses have not given good results, though some modification of infection is thereby achieved (63). In human beings, Francis and his co-workers (64) have found that when the subcutaneous vaccination of subjects with either active or inactive virus induces a significant increase in the titer of neutralizing antibodies in the blood, the capacity of the nasal secretions to inactivate virus is also enhanced, and this is suggested as the important contribution of vaccination, by whatever route, to immunity.

Perhaps the difficulty in the ferret experiments (61) just mentioned, in which systemically vaccinated animals failed to resist nasally instilled virus despite good circulating antibody levels, lies in an incapacity of humoral antibodies to traverse the surface membranes of these animals and so to appear in the respiratory secretions. This effective accumulation of antibody in the respiratory tract surface film may be especially marked in human beings, for Henle and co-workers (65) found that people re-exposed to the inhalation of active virus four to nine months after a first inhalation handled the infections no better than did individuals who inhaled virus after being subcutaneously vaccinated to it.

There is thus fairly convincing evidence that the presence of antibodies in the respiratory tract is of especial importance to influenzal immunity. This viewpoint is bolstered by the fact that acquired immunity follows the lines of antigenic specificity, a suggestive indication that antibodies are implicated in the process. Yet, as intimated before, it seems premature to accept this as a fixed conclusion, for the writings on this subject are replete with qualifications which suggest that factors other than antibody may be concerned in resistance. Some of these qualifications will be sampled.

First, the various human studies previously described as establishing a relationship between antibody levels and immunity generally reveal that attacks occur even in individuals with higher antibody levels, though these are less frequent than in those with smaller amounts of antibody (24, 55, 56). This could mean that antibodies may not be as well concentrated in the nasal secretions of some individuals, but it could also reflect a necessity for something besides antibody (or in addition to it) for the determination of an adequate resistance. Furthermore, in a successful trial of vaccination in human beings carried out in 1943 and 1944 those who showed the most marked benefit from the procedure had received vaccine during a period of about six weeks prior to the occurrence of the epidemic. That segment of the subjects which received vaccine earlier benefited less from it, and this weakness of protection was not related to any obvious fall in antibody titer (66).

Second, there are the suggestions from animal experiments that something in addition to antibodies may be concerned in immunity. The work with ferrets previously described suggests this as a possibility, and mice (61) become much more resistant to reinfection if gross lung lesions have resulted from an initial infection than if only minor lesions have been produced as, for example, by strains of low virulence (24, 58).

One can philosophize about the significance of these observations endlessly without arriving at a conclusion. In extenuation of the irregularities of evidence in support of the role of antibody, it has been suggested previously that their mobilization in the respiratory epithelial film may differ in different species. Burnet (24) believes that perhaps the **quality** of antibody may be an important factor; this implies, for example, that systemically vaccinated ferrets possess neutralizing antibody which is not, however, effective in vivo. Though it is difficult to visualize how an antibody which is capable of neutralizing viral activity when mixed with it in the test tube should fail to do this upon encountering the virus in the body, there are indications that this point may be well taken. That differences in antibodies against these viruses may occur is suggested by the fact that the sera of young children are apt to show antibodies of stricter strain specificity than those of adults, and ferret sera similarly show very strict specificity in their neutralizing ability compared with the sera of other animals, including those of human adults (67). The specific characters of antibodies may indeed vary in different species against the same strain of virus (5e). A difference in performance in vivo of antibody was also shown by Hare's (54) experiments on the passive transfer of immunity to mice. Ferret serum injected intraperitoneally protected these animals against intranasal infection, but the serum of vaccinated horses, even when concentrated to contain the same neutralizing ability as that of the ferrets, was without protective value.

(b) ALTERED CELLULAR REACTIVITY. Aside from the hiatuses in work with antibodies, there are other grounds upon which cellular alteration or other nonantibody mechanisms have been implicated in influenzal immunity. One of these is the epithelial damage described as occurring in the ferret and mouse (50, 51, 68). During the stage of regeneration the temporary undifferentiated transitional epithelium is insusceptible to virus. At about three to four weeks, in the ferret, the normal ciliated columnar epithelium has been restored. Up to this time the healing membrane is resistant not only to virus but to chemical damage as well. Immunity to virus, however, persists for several months, while the nonspecific resistance to injury is lost at the time of epithelial restoration. Meanwhile, antibodies have, of course, appeared, and it becomes difficult to distinguish the relative importance of these two factors. Francis (68) says that antibodies persist in the ferret in good quantity beyond the time when immunity to reinfection has disappeared, and that even at this time the epithelium shows some signs of immunity (i.e. increased rapidity of repair). Whether the cellular changes are a significant factor in resistance is thus problematic; this is especially so since it has been demonstrated that the resistance of ferrets even during the stage of epithelial regeneration is directed chiefly against the homologous strain of virus, and this degree of specificity is hardly to be expected as a cellular attribute, though of course it is not an impossibility (69).

When we turn to the human being the evidence for cellular resistance on the basis of a hardy regenerating epithelium is difficult to evaluate, since there is considerable doubt that epithelial damage is part of the disease process (33, 53).

A second possible basis for the existence of cellular resistance is concerned with the hemagglutinin-receptor system. It is conceivable that the loss of receptors by susceptible cells as the result of an infection might make them indifferent to a succeeding exposure to virus. This is overruled, however, by the rapidity with which receptors regenerate; in animals this takes place within a matter of days (45a).

Another possibility might lie in the mobilization of the normal hemagglutinin-inhibitor of the respiratory tract mucus in greater than usual concentration, but if this can occur there is as yet no evidence for it. Finally, one might invoke the interference phenomenon as an explanation for immunity (see Chapter 10), but there is no more reason to do so in this instance than in any other virus-host relationship; the difficulty generally is that the interference effect is too short-lived to afford an explanation of the immune state.

SUMMARY

The evidence available favors the thesis that antibody is the important instrument of the host resistant to influenza virus. This tentative conclusion is based upon the capacity of the serum of an immune animal to transmit resistance to a normal animal, upon the general concurrence of blood antibody levels with resistance, upon the existence of some evidence that antibodies in the nasal secretions bear an even closer relationship to the immune state than do those in the blood, and upon the strain specificity of acquired immunity. Various gaps in this evidence have been pointed out; their existence as well as considerations of the cellular alterations which may occur during the course of the disease keep alive the possibility that altered cellular responsiveness to virus may also have some part in the immune process. This latter evidence is not sufficiently satisfying to establish a case for the cellular concept, but until the understanding of immunity is better secured than it presently is, it seems wise to keep this possibility under consideration.

The antibody which functions in protection may be the virus-neutralizer or the hemagglutinin-inhibitor. If it should be the latter then the picture of acquired resistance in this virus disease includes a direct defense by the host against a constituent of the virus which is probably a major factor in determining its virulence. In this view the host-parasite relationship would be in principle similar to that obtaining in pneumococcal disease (see Chapter 18). If on the other hand the viral inhibitor should prove to be the antibody important to resistance the situation might be more analogous to that discussed in respect to anthrax (see Chapter 19), in which the defensive response of the host strikes at some point in the parasite other than its known virulence property.

Practical Vaccination Procedures. The variety of prophylactic measures against influenza which have been investigated at various times are outlined separately in the following discussion.

VACCINATION. The vaccines which have been employed for human application have consisted of virus obtained from the extra-embryonic fluids of chick embryos and inactivated by formalin. The earliest virus preparations were permitted to react with chick red cells and were eluted for concentration (70). Subsequently, chick grown virus was centrifuged to give purer and more concentrated preparations (71). Virus has also been precipitated on calcium phosphate or protamine (72), and concentration by methyl alcohol combined with centrifugation has been recommended (73). The use of egg-cultured virus brings up the problem of hypersensitivity to egg proteins. Reactions, presumably to this constituent of the vaccine, have been reported, and tests for reactivity to egg are advised prior to the use of the vaccine (74).

The possibility of immunizing human beings with these inactivated virus preparations has been demonstrated, but its feasibility as a practical procedure has not. A successful trial was carried out in the United States in 1943-44 in 6,200 subjects. Attack rates during a subsequent epidemic were

3.2 among the unvaccinated as compared to 1.0 among the vaccinated. The durability of resistance was very mediocre, for those individuals vaccinated more than six weeks before the epidemic appeared showed progressively poorer effects with lengthening interval (66). During 1945 there was an epidemic of B type, and again vaccination proved itself, the attack ratio in this case being 12.4 to 1.0. It was not until 1947 that the procedure failed and this was due to the appearance of a new strain of type A which was not represented in the mixed virus preparation employed for vaccination. This event cast the procedure into a bog of doubt from which it has not yet emerged (75).

There are, as already mentioned, two basic faults inherent in the vaccinating procedure presently available. The more serious one concerns strain differences, but the impermanence of immunity is also a matter of importance. As regards strain variations, the readiness with which the virus mutates has been discussed in a preceding section; this carries such obvious implications with respect to immunity as to lead to doubt in some quarters that a dependable vaccine for influenza may ever be attained. On the brighter side, however, there are also some points. Salk and co-workers (75) believe that the number of strain variants must be finite since, after all, only two major types have been recovered during 20 years of experience with these viruses. (A third virus designated 1233 and referred to as type C was isolated in 1947 [76].) These investigators contend further that by isolating epidemic as well as interepidemic strains, a group of viruses may eventually be selected which will encompass the complete antigenic spectrum of A and B types. For this general purpose there has been organized a World Influenza Center at the National Institute for Medical Research in London to collect strains and information about them as promptly as possible. Burnet (16) makes an interesting suggestion which may prove of advantage to the devising of a reliable vaccinating procedure. He points out that the new A' strain which appeared in the United States in 1947 to unsettle the question of influenzal prophylaxis had already been isolated during the previous year in Australia. Since winter is the common season for influenza epidemics, it might be possible to synchronize vaccine production between the northern and southern hemispheres, the north providing strains for the next southern winter, and vice versa. It has been shown that the 1947 A' strain can immunize human beings; all that would have been required in 1947 was the presence of this strain in the vaccine (77).

With respect to the durability of immunity produced by vaccination (or infection) there are variable opinions, but generally speaking it seems that reliability does not stretch beyond one season (16, 65, 78). Efforts are being made to overcome this by the use of adjuvants (75, 79). Some success in this direction has been recorded, but whether adjuvants can make a sufficient difference to be worth while remains to be seen.

Despite these possibilities for betterment the viewpoints of some of the workers most acquainted with the problem of vaccination are not sanguine.

Francis and others (80) do not recommend widespread vaccination because of the short duration of the vaccination period and the general mildness of epidemics and their rapid dispersion. They do recommend it, however, for elderly and debilitated people, and for industrial, instiutional and essential public health personnel. Parish (81) has expressed himself in a similar vein.

MODIFICATION OF PHYSIOLOGIC BARRIERS. Aside from specific vaccination the facts at hand concerning the relationship of influenza viruses to host cells have permitted some experimentation and theorizing about the possibilities of interfering in some other way with the host-parasite relationship. If immunity is of brief duration then the use of some other protective method with short-lived effects is not beside the point, and especially so if such a method might sidestep the problem of antigenic variability of strains. Stokes and Henle (82) and Briody (12a) among others have discussed such methods. One concerns a modification of the mucopolysaccharides in the respiratory surface film and saliva to increase its hemagglutinin-inhibiting activity, and concomitantly its inhibition of viral infectivity. Treatment of mucopolysaccharide inhibitor with periodate changes it so that the viral enzyme is unable to split it; thus the treated inhibitor cannot be destroyed by virus and may serve as an anti-infectious agent (44, 83). Whether this substance could be used, or would be effective in vivo if it were employable, deserves consideration. It is interesting also to consider the use of substances which might by competitive inhibition divert the virus from cellular receptors. Thus, apple pectin inhibits hemagglutination, and it has been found to hinder the multiplication of A virus in the allantoic sacs of chick embryos (84). Another possibility is the application of the interference phenomenon (85). It seems questionable, however, whether this procedure could ever become feasible with influenza virus, since interference by inactive virus requires the administration of large amounts which are themselves toxic (86). Andrewes (87) has discussed this question.

Mention should be made of the use of immune serum by inhalation at the onset and during the course of an epidemic. This has been described as an effective procedure by Smorodintseff (88). In view of the relatively short periods over which epidemics spread, this may have some applicability.

The employment of physical methods such as ultraviolet irradiation or of chemicals such as propylene glycol and other substances vaporized in enclosed areas may also have some place in the protection of special groups, or in cutting down the wholesale dissemination of virus during epidemic periods (82).

BIBLIOGRAPHY

1. Smith, W., Andrewes, C. H., and Laidlaw, P. P. Lancet, 2:66, 1933.
2. Horsfall, F. L., Jr. Virus and Rickettsial Infections of Man, ed. by T. Rivers, Philadelphia, J. B. Lippincott Co., 1948, Chapter 14.
3a. Taylor, A. R. J. Biol. Chem., 153:675, 1944.
  b. Beard, J. W., Sharp, D. G., Taylor, A. R., McLean, I. W., Jr., Beard, D., Feller, A. E., and Dingle, J. H. South. M. J., 37:313, 1944.
  c. Knight, C. A. J. Exper. Med., 85:99, 1947.

4a. ———— J. Exper. Med., 83:281, 1946.

b. ———— Ann. Rev. Microbiol., 3:121, 1949.

c. Rivers, T. M. Virus and Rickettsial Infections of Man, ed. by T. Rivers, Philadelphia, J. B. Lippincott Co., 1948, Chapter 1.

5a. Hoyle, L., and Fairbrother, R. W. J. Hyg., 37:512, 1937.

b. Smith, W. Lancet, 2:1256, 1936.

c. Lennette, E. H., and Horsfall, F. L., Jr. J. Exper. Med., 72:233, 1940.

d. Henle, W., and Wiener, M. Proc. Soc. Exper. Biol. & Med., 57:176, 1944.

e. Francis, T., Jr. Ann. Rev. Microbiol., 1:351, 1947.

f. van Rooyen, C. E., and Rhodes, A. J. Virus Diseases of Man, New York, Thomas Nelson and Sons, 1948.

6. Hirst, G. K. J. Exper. Med., 76:83, 1942.

7a. Friedewald, W. F. J. Exper. Med., 78:347, 1943.

b. Henle, W., Henle, G., Groupé, V., and Chambers, L. A. J. Immunol., 48:163, 1944.

8a. Burnet, F. M., and Beveridge, W. I. B. Australian J. Exper. Biol. & M. Sc., 21:71, 1943.

b. Stuart-Harris, C. H., and Miller, M. H. Brit. J. Exper. Path., 28:394, 1947.

c. Meiklejohn, G., Weiss, D. L., Shragg, R. I., and Lennette, E. H. Am. J. Hyg., 55:1, 1952.

9a. Friedewald, W. F. J. Exper. Med., 79:633, 1944.

b. Walker, D. L., and Horsfall, F. L., Jr. J. Exper. Med., 91:65, 1949.

10a. Magill, T. P. Proc. Soc. Exper. Biol. & Med., 45:162, 1940.

b. Francis, T., Jr. Science, 92:405, 1940.

11. Taylor, R. M. Am. J. Pub. Health, 39:171, 1949.

12a. Briody, B. A. Bact. Rev., 14:65, 1950.

b. Hilleman, M. R. Proc. Soc. Exper. Biol. & Med., 78:208, 1951.

13a. Magill, T. P., and Francis, T., Jr. Proc. Soc. Exper. Biol. & Med., 35:463, 1936; Brit. J. Exper. Path., 19:273, 1938.

b. Smith, W., and Andrewes, C. H. Brit. J. Exper. Path., 19:293, 1938.

14. Hirst, G. K. J. Exper. Med., 86:357, 1947.

15. Archetti, I., and Horsfall, F. L., Jr. J. Exper. Med., 92:441, 1950.

16. Burnet, F. M. Bull. Johns Hopkins Hosp., 88:157, 1951.

17. Hilleman, M. R., Mason, R. P., and Rogers, N. G. Pub. Health Rep., 65:771, 1950.

18. Kirber, M. W., and Henle, W. J. Immunol., 65:229, 1950.

19. Hoyle, L. Brit. J. Exper. Path., 29:390, 1948.

20. Friedewald, W. F., and Pickles, E. G. J. Exper. Med., 79:301, 1944.

21. Gard, S., and von Magnus, P. Arkiv Kemi Mineral Geol., 24B:No. 8, 1946.

22a. Sugg, J. Y. J. Bact., 57:399, 1949.

b. Smith, W., Westwood, M. A., Westwood, J. C. N., and Belyovin, G. Brit. J. Exper. Path., 32:422, 1951.

23. Kalter, S. S., Chapman, O. D., Feeley, D. A., and MacDowell, S. L. J. Immunol., 59:147, 1948.

24. Burnet, F. M., and Clark, E. Influenza, London, Macmillan & Co., 1942.

25. ———— and Bull., D. R. Australian J. Exper. Biol. & M. Sc., 21:55, 1943.

26. ———— Bull. Johns Hopkins Hosp., 88:137, 1951.

27a. Henle, W., and Henle, G. Science, 100:410, 1944; Am. J. M. Sc., 210:362, 1945; J. Exper. Med., 84:623, 639, 1946; J. Immunol., 59:45, 1948.

b. Hale, W. M., and McKee, A. P. Proc. Soc. Exper. Biol. & Med., 59:81, 1945.

c. Sugg, J. Y. Proc. Soc. Exper. Biol. & Med., 77:728, 1951.

28. Chang, H. T., and Kempf, J. E. J. Immunol., 65:75, 1950.

29. Henle, W. Markle Found. Repts., 1946.

30. Greiff, D., Blumenthal, H. T., and Pinkerton, H. J. Exper. Med., 91:335, 1950.

31. Wagner, R. R., and Bennett, I. L., Jr. J. Exper. Med., 91:135, 1950.

32. Burnet, F. M. Ann. Rev. Microbiol., 6:229, 1952.

33. Parker, F., Jr., Joliffe, L. S., Barnes, M. W., and Finland, M. Am. J. Path., 22:797, 1946.

34a. McCordock, H. A., and Muckenfuss, R. S. Am. J. Path., 9:221, 1933.

b. Scadding, J. G. Quart. J. Med., 30:425, 1937.

35. Hirst, G. K. Science, 94:22, 1941.

36. McClelland, L., and Hare, R. Canad. J. Pub. Health, 32:530, 1941.

37. Hirst, G. K. Viruses 1950, ed. by M. Delbrück, Pasadena, Calif., California Institute of Technology, 1950.
38. Burnet, F. M. Australian J. Exper. Biol. & M. Cc., 8:81, 1945.
39. Hirst, G. K. J. Exper. Med., 91:161, 1950.
40. ──── J. Exper. Med., 78:99, 1943.
41. Friedewald, W. F., and Hook, E. W. J. J. Exper. Med., 88:343, 1948.
42. Hurst, E. W., and Stacey, M. Brit. J. Exper. Path., 31:410, 1950.
43a. Burnet, F. M., McCrae, J. F., and Stone, J. D. Brit. J. Exper. Path., 27:228, 1946.
  b. McCrae, J. F. Australian J. Exper. Biol. & M. Sc., 25:127, 1947.
44. Fazekas de St. Groth, S. Australian J. Exper. Biol. & M. Sc., 27:65, 1949.
45a. ──── Australian J. Exper. Biol. & M. Sc., 26:29, 271, 1948.
  b. Stone, J. D. Australian J. Exper. Biol. & M. Sc., 26:49, 287, 1948.
46. Fazekas de St. Groth, S. Nature, London, 167:43, 1951.
47. Schlesinger, R. W. Proc. Soc. Exper. Biol. & Med., 74:541, 1950.
48. Grieff, H. T., Pinkerton H., and DeWitt, R. J. Exper. Med., 91:321, 1950.
49. Rickard, E. R., and Francis, T., Jr. J. Exper. Med., 67:953, 1938.
50. Francis, T., Jr., and Stuart-Harris, C. H. J. Exper. Med., 68:789, 803 813, 1938.
51. Straub, M. J. Path. & Bact., 50:31, 1940.
52. Harford, C. G., and Hamlin, A. J. Exper. Med., 95:173, 1952.
53. Magill, T. P. The Pathogenesis and Pathology of Viral Diseases, ed. by J. G. Kidd, New York, Columbia University Press, 1950.
54. Hare, R. J. Path. & Bact., 49:411, 1939.
55a. Rickard, E. R., Lennette, E. H., and Horsfall, F. L., Jr. Pub. Health Rep., 55:2146, 1940.
  b. ──── Horsfall, F. L., Jr., Hirst, G. K., and Lennette, E. H. Pub. Health Rep. 56:1819, 1941.
56. Francis, T., Jr., Pearson, H. E., Salk, J. E., and Brown, P. N. Am. J. Pub. Health, 34:317, 1944.
57. ──── Proc. Soc. Exper. Biol. & Med., 43:337, 1940.
58. Oakley, C. L., and Warrack, G. H. J. Path. & Bact., 50:37, 1940.
59a. Burnet, F. M., and Beveridge, W. I. B. Australian J. Exper. Biol. & M. Sc., 21:71, 1943.
  b. Kilbourne, E. D., and Horsfall, F. L., Jr. J. Immunol., 67:431, 1951.
60. Fazekas de St. Groth, S., and Donnelley, M. Australian J. Exper. Biol. & M. Sc., 28:45, 61, 77, 1950.
61. Smith, W., Andrewes, C. H., and Laidlaw, P. Brit. J. Exper. Path., 16:291, 1935.
62. Francis, T., Jr. J. Exper. Med., 69:283, 1939.
63. Zellat, J., and Henle, W. J. Immunol., 42:239, 1941.
64. Francis, T., Jr., Pearson, H. E., Sullivan, E. R., and Brown, P. N. Am. J. Hyg., 37:294, 1943.
65. Henle, W., Henle, G., Stokes, J., Jr., and Maris, E. P. J. Immunol., 52:145, 1946.
66a. Burnet, F. M. Virus as Organism, Cambridge, Mass., Harvard University Press, 1945.
  b. ──── The Background of Infectious Diseases in Man, Melbourne, The Melbourne Permanent Postgraduate Committee, 1946.
67. Horsfall, F. L., Jr., and Rickard, E. R. J. Exper. Med., 74:433, 1941.
68. Francis, T., Jr. Problems and Trends in Virus Research, Philadelphia, University of Pennsylvania Press, 1941.
69. Sugg, J. Y., and Magill, T. P. Proc. Soc. Exper. Biol. & Med., 65:233, 1947.
70. Francis, T., Jr., and Salk, J. E. Science, 96:499, 1942.
71a. Taylor, A. R., Sharp, D. G., McLean, I. W., Jr., Beard, D., and Beard, J. W. J. Immunol., 50:291, 1945.
  b. Stanley, W. M. J. Exper. Med., 81:193, 1945.
72a. Salk, J. E. Science, 101:124, 1945.
  b. Chambers, L. A., and Henle, W. Proc. Soc. Exper. Biol. & Med., 48:481, 1941.
73. Cox, H. R., van der Scheer, J., Aiston, S., and Bohnel, E. J. Immunol., 56:149, 1947.
74. Curphey, T. J. J.A.M.A., 133:1062, 1947.
75. Salk, J. E., Laurent, A. M., and Bailey, M. L. Am. J. Pub. Health, 41:669, 1951.

76. Taylor, R. M.   Am. J. Pub. Health, 39:171, 1949.
77. Meiklejohn, G., Kempe, C. H., Thalman, W. G., and Lennette, E. H.   Am. J. Hyg., 55:12, 1952.
78a. Salk, J. E., Pearson, H. E., Brown, P. N., Smyth, C. J., and Francis, T., Jr.   Am. J. Hyg., 42:307, 1945.
   b. Francis, T., Jr., Magill, T. P., Rickard, E. R., and Beck, M. D.   Am. J. Pub. Health, 27:1141, 1937.
79a. Friedewald, W. F.   Science, 99:453, 1944; J. Exper. Med., 80:477, 1944.
   b. Henle, W., and Henle, G.   Proc. Soc. Exper. Biol. & Med., 59:179, 1945.
80. Francis, T., Jr., Getting, V. A., Hampil, B., Hirst, G. K., Leake, J. P., and Smillie, W. G.   Am. J. Pub. Health, 37:1109, 1947.
81. Parish, H. J.   Bacterial and Virus Diseases, Baltimore, Williams and Wilkins Co., 1951.
82. Stokes, J., Jr., and Henle, W.   J.A.M.A., 120:16, 1942.
83. Burnet, F. M.   Australian J. Exper. Biol. & M. Sc., 26:381, 1948.
84. Wooley, E. W., and Green, R. H.   J. Bact., 54:63, 1947.
85a. Henle, W.   J. Immunol., 64:203, 1950.
   b. Lennette, E. H.   Ann. Rev. Microbiol., 5:277, 1951.
86. Henle, W., Henle, G., and Kirber, M. W.   Am. J. M. Sc., 214:529, 1947.
87. Andrewes, C. H.   Brit. M. J., 2:1007, 1948.
88. Smorodintseff, A.   Proc. III Internat. Congress Microbiol., New York, 1940, p. 375.

30

MICROBIAL ANTIGENS AND TOXINS

A vast accumulation of lore concerned with the antigenic make-up of the cells and fluids of man and other animals, plants and microbes has been building up since the first discoveries of antigen and antibody activities in the 1880's. This knowledge, which has in many cases become exceedingly detailed, stands as an independent sector of immunology, best described perhaps by the term serology. Part of this study is, of course, directly related to immunity; e.g. the antigenic constitution of a bacterium, virus or toxin is obviously of immediate import to the proper evaluation of its relationship to the host and the host's method of dealing with it. Furthermore, such knowledge is of importance to diagnosis and to epidemiologic investigation. On the other hand, a great deal of the information falls within the purview of immunology largely because it deals with entities—antigens and antibodies—which are traditionally a part of the immunologist's domain. The antigens of red blood cells or egg white or horse plasma have immediate implications for the understanding of resistance to harmful agents only in so far as their study has helped to clarify general principles applicable to the understanding of antigens and antibodies of infectious and toxic agents also.

For the reason that so much of this serologic material is not directly concerned in the study of immunity, certain aspects of it are segregated here for special attention. Some of the information pertaining to infectious agents has been discussed in preceding chapters. The effort will be made in this and the two chapters which follow to bring together some of the main facets of this knowledge, by sampling some of the better known antigens of microbes and toxins and describing their variations; by discussing the cellular antigens of higher animals and indicating how these may relate to certain disease processes of noninfectious character; and by describing the ubiquity of certain antigenic factors among biologically unrelated plant and animal forms.

Antigens of Infectious Agents. Some of the antigens of bacteria, viruses and toxins have been described in previous connotations. The additional discussion provided here is intended to deal with certain special examples which have either not been mentioned or which warrant further detailing.

GRAM-NEGATIVE BACILLI. The **Boivin antigens** occur in various genera of gram-negative bacilli and cocci as the characteristic antigens of these organisms in their native state, before antigens have been lost through long continued cultivation or other circumstances. They are found in *Salmonella,*

Escherichia, Shigella, Pasteurella, Brucella and *Neisseria*. These are the substances which were earlier described as related to the virulence characteristics of the pathogenic species in the genera named, but they occur also in non-pathogenic species (Chapters 3 and 22). The Boivin antigens exist in the cell as complexes of polysaccharide, lipid (phosphatide) and protein. They are readily removed from bacteria by several simple procedures such as extraction with trichloracetic acid (1), or diethyleneglycol (2), or treatment with trypsin or urea (3).

The chemically isolated complexes are antigenic, inducing the formation of antibodies which agglutinate entire bacteria precisely as do antibodies formed in response to the bacterial cell itself (4). The complexes can be split stepwise to yield the three major components (2, 5). Of these, the polysaccharide is a nonantigenic hapten; it constitutes the specific determinant portion of the complex. The protein moiety is antigenic but less specifically so, i.e. the proteins of different complexes have the same antigenic characteristics. This substance apparently accounts for the marked endotoxicity of the Boivin antigens and in turn of the gram-negative organisms from which they are derived (6). The lipid does not seem to account for any known property of the complex as a whole.

An antigenic substance of chemically related kind which has been of particular interest in respect to the question of bacterial virulence is the Vi (virulence) antigen first described by Felix and Pitt (7) as a component of typhoid bacilli freshly isolated from cases of the disease. This is a surface antigen of the cell and is usually lost on cultivation. It is possibly superficial in location to the Boivin antigens, since antibodies produced against the smooth form of the bacterium from cultures (and possessing Boivin antigens only) are incapable of agglutinating organisms possessing the Vi factor. This accounts for the preoccupation of the older literature dealing with diagnostic procedures with the inagglutinability of strains of *S. typhosa* freshly isolated from cases of the disease. Since the Vi antigen is usually lost after several passages in culture media, the vaccines employed to prepare diagnostic antisera lacked this antigen, and of course the sera lacked antibody against it. It was known empirically that after fresh strains had been passed in culture for a period they could then be agglutinated with the testing serum. It is possible now of course to prepare antisera containing antibody against the Vi as well as the Boivin antigens, and with this to agglutinate strains fresh from the patient.

The Vi antigen occurs in several species of *Salmonella* in addition to the typhoid organism, and in another genus, *Escherichia,* as well (8). It is antigenically the same wherever found. The special relationship to virulence attributed to this antigen by Felix and others is not clearly established, since other investigators have failed to find a difference in pathogenicity between highly virulent paired strains of a particular *Salmonella,* one with and one without this substance (8). A good deal has been written also concerning the merits of this antigen in inducing immunity as compared with the Boivin substances. O (Boivin antigen-containing) strains without Vi can induce protection in mice (9c), but apparently Vi strains of *S. typhosa* devoid of O antigens can also immunize animals (10). It seems probable that both are of importance (11), and in fact the Vi should probably be considered simply as one of the Boivin antigens (12).

In addition to Boivin and Vi antigens the gram-negative bacilli possess "deeper-lying" substances which may function as surface constituents if the bacillus undergoes successive dissociations in culture medium. As described earlier, the Vi is most readily lost from the freshly isolated bacterial cell, leaving the Boivin antigens as dominant surface substances. These may be lost next; in the salmonellas the cell surface is then characterized by the presence of a polysaccharide of broad antigenic specificity common to all species of the genus. A further loss of antigen results in so-called P forms, in which proteins are the major surface components, while another proteinaceous (T) substance (or substances) comprises the core of the bacterial body (13). This antigenic "layering" will be discussed further in a subsequent section dealing with the methods employed in antigenic analysis. It is far from certain that antigens are actually stripped layer-wise from variant cells in which antigenic losses have occurred, but it is convenient to consider this to be the case for purposes of discussion.

In addition to these antigenic constituents of the bacterial bodies, the salmonellas possess antigens characteristic of their flagella. These are heat-labile substances, probably protein, and readily inactivated by alcohol. In some species, as in *S. typhosa,* the flagellar antigen is the same in all strains, but in most other species there occurs an extraordinary to and fro variation between two different sets of antigens, one set (phase 1) consisting of one or more substances more or less characteristic of the species, the second set (phase 2), of antigens which many other species may share. The flagellar antigens are not concerned in the virulence of bacilli or in their immunity-inducing capacities, but they permit a fine categorization of the genus into species, of which there are well over 150. The phase variation will be described further in later sections of this chapter.

The antigenic characterization of salmonellas has for some years been sufficiently precise to permit the description of species or types in terms of formulae consisting of symbols denoting the body antigens and the flagellar antigens in both phases. Roman numerals represent the Boivin antigens, the Vi is designated as such, small letters represent the phase 1 flagellar antigens, and arabic numerals denote the flagellar antigens of phase 2.

If the salmonellas are first tested for their contents of Boivin antigens they can be brought together into groups possessing certain of these substances in common. Thus, group A is typified by antigens I, II, and XII; group B by IV, V, and XII; group C by VI, VII, and VIII; group D by IX and XII; group E by III, X, and XV; group F by XI; group G by I, XIII, XXII, and XXIII; group H by I (partial antigen), VI, XIV, and XXV, and group I by XVI. Other groups not yet officially designated have been established, possessing antigens XVII, XVIII, XXI, XXVIII, XXX, XXXV, XXXVIII, and

XXXIX (14). If new additional information is obtained concerning flagellar composition the bacteria in these groups can be categorized into types. In this way a heterogeneous collection of enteric bacteria can be specifically identified in terms comprehensible to workers throughout the world. This mode of classification is designated as the Kauffmann-White schema. A few examples of *Salmonella* species described in terms of antigenic formulae are shown in Table 5. These formulations do not attempt to represent all the surface components of the organisms, but only those which have most significance in differentiation. Other qualifications as well as complete tabulations of types are discussed in various textbooks of medical bacteriology (14, 15).

Table 5. Kauffmann-White schema of serologic types of *Salmonella*

Group	Species	Somatic antigens (o) (Boivin and Vi)	Flagellar antigens (h) Phase 1	Phase 2
A	S. paratyphi	I, II, XII	a	—
B	S. schottmuelleri	I, IV, V, XII	b	1, 2
	S. typhimurium	I, IV, V, XII	i	1, 2, 3
C	S. hirschfeldii	VI, VII, Vi	c	1, 5
D	S. typhosa	IX, XII, Vi	d	—
	S. enteritidis	I, IX, XII	g, m	—

The examples provided in Table 5 illustrate several points of importance in regard to the antigenic properties of this genus. Two of the organisms shown possess Vi antigens (*S. hirschfeldii* and *S. typhosa*). Three species possess flagella which ordinarily exist in one phase only, i.e. they are **monophasic** (*S. paratyphi, S. typhosa* and *S. enteritidis*). A very close antigenic relationship is seen to exist between two important disease producing species, *S. schottmuelleri* and *S. typhimurium*. It is apparent from their formulae that precise information about their flagellar antigens would be required for their serologic distinction.

In view of the apparent complexities presented by the large number of *Salmonella* species presently identified, it is astonishing and gratifying to learn from a perusal of the work of those who have been most concerned with establishing this system that very few steps taken in logical fashion suffice for the recognition of many of these bacteria; certainly of the commoner ones (16). Some idea of the procedure for carrying out such antigenic analyses will be provided in the portion of this chapter dealing with the determination of antigenic constituents of cells and fluids.

STREPTOCOCCI. The antigens of the **streptococci** constitute a carefully and thoroughly studied system of which a brief description will be given here. The hemolytic organisms, which are of chief interest to students of infectious disease, have been categorized on the basis of their antigens into groups, and these in turn have been subdivided into specific types (17). Thirteen groups of streptococci are currently established on the basis of the presence in cells of antigenic polysaccharides, designated as C substances, which differ in their antigenic specificities in each of the groups. These appear to be subsurface antigens of the cell; hence serologic group determinations require that the antigen be extracted from the bacterial body and tested by the precipitation method (18).

Several of the groups are further divisible into clearly distinct types. In group A, which comprises the more important members of the beta hemolytic streptococci responsible for human infections, the type specific antigens are protein, and this is probably true also for members of group C. In groups B, D, E, F and G, however, the type substance is probably carbohydrate. The antigens of the human pathogens of group A have been most thoroughly studied. More than 40 types have been described. Unfortunately for ease of understanding, there can be two different kinds of type specific factors in these organisms. One is designated as M antigen and appears to be important in determining the virulence and the immunity-inducing properties of the organism. The second antigen, also a protein, is termed T. The antibodies which it invokes are apparently not protective, nor is this antigen concerned in the virulence of the organisms which possess it. It should be emphasized that M and T both represent chemical classes of antigens; each varies in its antigenic specificity to give type characteristics to a particular strain of organism. Some cocci possess M alone, some T alone, and some both. In some cases organisms with different M antigens may possess the same T, and vice versa. In contrast to the group antigen previously described, these antigens act as if they were predominantly surface constituents of the cocci, and in this case testing may be done by the direct agglutination procedure (19).

In addition to group and type specific antigens, streptococcal bodies contain nucleoproteins (P substance) common to all groups and related antigenically to the nucleoproteins of other gram-positive cocci. These proteins constitute a mixture which can be segregated by various chemical precipitation methods (20).

In summary, an antigenic map of the group A streptococcus would place the M substance at the cell surface, the T probably in the same region though perhaps not quite so superficial (since enzymic digestion first removes M, then T). In the body of the organism occur the less specific antigens including the group specific C carbohydrate and the nucleoproteins (21). As in the case of *Salmonella* and other bacteria the mapping of antigens here is provisional, for apparent differences in relative locations of antigens in the bacterial body may actually reflect merely a physical arrangement of molecules which permits access of antibody to only one of perhaps several antigens all present at the cell surface (22).

CAPSULAR ANTIGENS OF THE BACILLUS GROUP. It was described in Chapter 19 that the capsule of the anthrax bacillus is composed of d(−)glutamic acid polymer, a polypeptide, and in this organism this substance appears to have important properties with respect to virulence. Other species of the genus *Bacillus* share this capsular antigen. Recently, Tomcsik (23) has made unique observations upon two species of *Bacillus, B. megatherium* and a second organism resembling *B. anthracis* but without pathogenicity, and designated *Bacillus M.* Both bacilli have been shown to possess two capsular antigens which reveal themselves separately when they are acted upon by appropriate antisera. Addition of antipolypeptide serum produced by vaccination with *B. anthracis* causes swelling of the capsule of *Bacillus M* (Fig. 47A). Adding an antiserum produced against *Bacillus M* itself causes the appearance

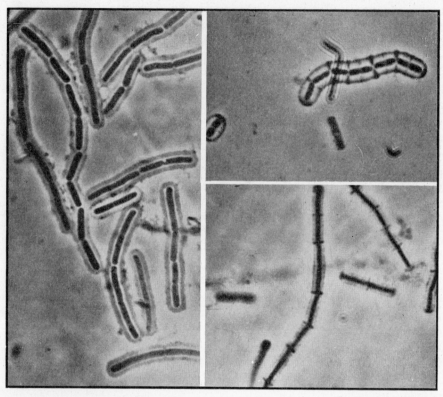

Courtesy of Dr. J. Tomcsik

A   B

Fig. 47. A, *Bacillus M* mixed with antipolypeptide serum, showing capsular swelling. B, *Bacillus M* after addition of homologous antiserum (antipolysaccharide antibodies), showing capsular striations and transverse septa. Phase contrast, 1,000 ✕.

of distinct striations and transverse septa in the capsule (Fig. 47B). These result from the reaction between a polysaccharide constituent of the capsule with its antibody. Tomcsik suggests that this may signify the existence of a capsular framework composed of antigenic polysaccharide, with polypeptide filling the interstices.

ANTIGENIC VARIATIONS. Repeated references have been made in preceding discussions in this volume to the variability of antigenic factors of bacteria and viruses in respect to their virulence, to their immunity-inducing properties, and to their constitution as biologic entities. Many kinds of variations may take place in microbes, including alterations in morphologic, metabolic, and pathogenic properties (24). Any transmissible change that may occur in such rapidly multiplying elements as bacteria or viruses can quickly manifest itself as a dominant character if the new trait is one which is better suited to the environment than that which it has replaced.

The present discussion will be concerned with variations in antigenic properties, but these are in some instances directly related to changes in morphology, as when flagella or capsules are lost and, in certain bacteria, to loss of pathogenicity, as when somatic or capsular antigens disappear (Chapter 3).

Two general kinds of antigenic variation may take place in a bacterial cell. In one case a factor may be either lost or gained, as exemplified by O antigens, capsules and flagella. (A temporary nongenetic loss of antigens may also be induced by certain environmental factors, e.g. a low concentration of phenol in an agar medium inhibits flagella formation; but when microbes are removed from this milieu they immediately acquire these appendages again.) In the second case the variation is a substitutive one. One or more antigens of a microbe vanish and are simultaneously replaced by antigenically distinct factors. The specific changes falling into these two categories of variation are described in the following discussion.

1. Loss or Gain Variations. (a) S-R variation; dissociation. Some years ago Arkwright (25) described the appearance of colonial variants in agar plate cultures of species of *Salmonella* and *Shigella*. The parent forms of these organisms were smooth in colonial appearance, grew differently in broth, and suspended evenly in saline. In contrast, some daughter colonies were rough in appearance, grew in broth in a granular form and, when placed in isotonic saline, tended to agglutinate spontaneously. It was soon apparent that the rough-appearing daughter colonies differed from the parent organisms in the loss of important antigenic factors; these have since been recognized as the O antigens or Boivin complexes described earlier in this chapter. This loss of antigens is often associated with a disappearance of the capacity of a bacterium to cause disease (Chapters 3 and 22). The phenomenon is termed dissociation and it reflects not just a separation of colonial types from a mixed bacterial population, but the development of variants from an initially antigenically complete single cell.

This same kind of change occurs among some species of bacteria to which the terms **smooth** and **rough** cannot be applied in the same descriptive sense as they are to the enteric bacteria studied by Arkwright, or to the pneumococcus, to take another example. As Topley and Wilson (15) state the case, "we have become entangled in the web of our words," for in some instances a bacterium in its entire antigenic form has a rough appearance, while it looks smooth when the surface antigens have been lost. This is true of the hemolytic streptococcus and the anthrax bacillus. Because usage has given the term "smooth" synonymity with completeness of antigenic structure and, in the cases of certain pathogenic bacteria, with virulence, while on the other hand the adjective "rough" has come to suggest an antigenically incomplete and avirulent variant, we have the paradoxical situation in which the smooth forms of the species just mentioned are actually rough in appearance, and vice versa. In the case of the hemolytic streptococcus the terms **matt** (for the complete organism) and **glossy** (for the dissociant) have been employed (26). These terms are helpful to the initiated but may perhaps confuse the issue further to those who have not been introduced to the semantics involved. Topley and Wilson (15) suggest that the letters S and R be retained as symbols for entire and incomplete antigenic variants whatever their appearance, and that the words, "smooth" and "rough" be employed for the literal description of colonies without regard to immunologic significance. This seems to be a logical solution; as these authors point out it permits one to speak, without implicit contradiction, of the **rough** colonial appearance of the **S form** of *B. anthracis*.

The S → R alteration may proceed further than the initial loss of dominant surface antigen. As was described earlier in discussing the antigens of salmonellas there may be progressive losses of bacterial components, a deeper lying substance each time appearing as the major surface antigen. Further, it appears that complete loss of any one component does not necessarily occur as a one-step process; there may be degrees of antigenic loss leaving both S and R antigenic factors as surface constituents.

The circumstance in which S → R dissociation may occur is often simply cultivation in laboratory medium. It is a common experience to find strains of bacteria which routinely, at each plating, give rise to a proportion of R colonies. If any single S colony is plated it will similarly give rise to some R forms. If one wants to force the issue—to set the stage for the development of R colonies only—this can be done by incorporating either antibodies or a bacteriophage active upon the S antigens in the culture medium. In neither case is there a literal induction of variation; one simply provides an environment which is hostile to the S forms and relatively favorable to the R and these consequently survive.

The reverse variation, R to S, occurs much less frequently than the S to R. Again favorable circumstances may be supplied for this change. Passage in animals is one such condition, for in the case of many bacteria it is only the S forms which can survive in host tissues (Chapter 3).

Antibodies (anti-R) can also be employed, and sometimes alterations in the composition of the culture medium may successfully select S variants for survival (27).

The S → R dissociation is a general phenomenon among bacteria, but its significance is not always clear. Loss of antigens and concurrent elimination of pathogenicity is seen in the gram-negative enteric bacilli, the gram-positive pyogenic cocci, in the anthrax bacillus and in species of *Hemophilus* and *Pasteurella* among others. In other cases it has not been possible up until now to assess the meaning of smooth and rough colonial forms from either the antigenic or the virulence standpoints. This is true, for example, of the tubercle bacillus (Chapter 23).

In some of the organisms just mentioned—the pneumococcus, the hemolytic streptococci, *H. influenzae* and species of *Pasteurella*—the change in antigenicity and pathogenicity is accompanied also by a morphologic alteration consequent to loss of the visible capsules at the surfaces of these organisms. In other instances, notably of the enteric bacilli, there is no visible capsular structure, but the O antigens, as surface components, are generally considered to represent this structure.

In the same system of variation as S → R may be mentioned the loss of Vi antigen. This is referred to as V → W variation, the W form lacking this component. The reverse change W → V may also occur (9b).

(b) H → O variation. The H → O change is again a variation which entails the loss or gain of antigens, and concurrently with this, of a morphologic unit, the flagellum. This variation was described in 1903, some years before the discovery of the S → R change, by Smith and Reagh (28). The significance of this information was not appreciated, however, until its rediscovery some years later by Weil and Felix (29) in *Proteus vulgaris*. Smith and Reagh found that an antiserum produced against a nonflagellated strain of the hog cholera bacillus lacked certain antibodies which were contained in antisera against motile strains of the same bacterium, and they determined that these antibodies were directed against the flagella. They described also the characteristic types of agglutination brought about by antibodies against the bacterial bodies and the flagella. Antisomatic antibodies acting upon either motile or nonmotile bacteria cause a tight granular aggregation in which the bacterial bodies are contiguous. In contrast, antiflagellar antibodies agglutinate motile organisms into fluffy cottonlike flocs; this is due to a clumping of the bacterial appendages while the bodies themselves remain separated (30). An antiserum produced against the motile bacillus contains of course both kinds of antibodies, but if this is mixed with a suspension of flagellated bacilli the fluffy type of agglutination occurs, presumably because the outermost structures of the bacterium, the flagella, take precedence in the clumping process.

The terms H and O derive from the writings of Weil and Felix (29). Since flagellated *Proteus* swarms across the surface of a solid medium to form a thin film of growth, they likened this to the mist produced by the breath upon a glass, and referred to the motile bacillus as of the mist or "hauch" type. The nonmotile form is without the breath mist, or "ohne hauch." Henceforth, all motile bacteria have been H forms, and the flagellar antigens H antigens, while the nonmotile forms and antigens are called O.

Flagella usually contain more than one antigen, and more perplexing, they often undergo variations in which they alternate between two distinct antigenic phases, as will be described in the next section. As a class these antigens are more susceptible to heat than those of bacterial bodies, but little has been learned so far about their chemical natures. Weibull's (31) recent physicochemical studies of the flagella of *P. vulgaris* and *B. subtilis* have revealed these to be protein in constitution, belonging to the group of elastic fibrous proteins designated as the keratin-myosin-epidermis-fibrinogen group. Weibull asserts that these appendages may be regarded as primitive hairs or muscle fibers.

There is no relationship between the occurrence of the H → O variation and the S → R change. A bacterium which has dissociated to the R form ordinarily retains its flagella. Loss of flagella can occur from either S or R organisms. The H → O change is an infrequent one, nor can it be so easily abetted experimentally as can the S → R variation. The addition of anti-H serum to culture medium may sometimes successfully select O forms for survival. Unlike the alteration from S to R which may be associated with loss of virulence, the H to O variation is not related to the parasitic activities of a microbe.

2. Substitutive Variations. (a) Phase flagellar variations. The variation of flagella between two antigenic phases is a **substitutive** one in which one set of antigenic components is lost but new antigens take their place. (Apparently, however, traces of the first antigens persist in the new offshoot [32].) This diphasic variation is remarkable in that the descendants of any single cell may possess either of two sets of flagellar antigens. Some cells have antigens more or less characteristic of them as a species, while others contain flagellar factors which are common to other species as well (33). Hence, the first antigens were originally designated as **specific phase** and the second as **nonspecific or group phase** antigens. Later it was found that the supposedly specific antigens may in fact occur in more than one type of bacillus, and that some salmonellas fluctuate between two sets of specific antigens rather than going over to the more limited variety of group antigens (34). These points are illustrated in Table 6, in which S. newport and S. nyborg are seen to possess the same "specific" phase antigens, and S. worthington possesses a factor in the nonspecific phase which is the same as the specific phase antigen of S. poona.

Table 6. Examples of phase 1 and phase 2 flagellar antigens of Salmonella

Type	O antigens	H antigens	
		Phase 1 (specific phase)	Phase 2 (nonspecific phase)
S. newport 563	VI, VIII	e, h	1, 2, 3
S. nyborg 1527	III, X, XXVI	e, h	1, 7
S. worthington 29	I, XIII, XXIII	l, w	z
S. poona	XIII, XXII	z	1, 6

For these reasons the original terms were abandoned and in their place were substituted the designations "phase 1" and "phase 2" to describe the H antigen variations within any single species (35).

The diphasic variation like the H → O variation is independent of the S → R change. Not all flagellated salmonellas undergo this alteration; as was shown in Table 5, *S. typhosa, S. paratyphi* and other species are so-called monophasic organisms. These organisms possess only a single phase 1 antigen. By incorporating antibody against this antigen in a liquid medium, however, Kauffmann was able to induce a conversion in *S. typhosa* to a new phase antigen (34a).

The usefulness of the phase antigens to diagnostic and epidemiologic work lies in the fact that it permits a finer serologic distinction among salmonellas which may be closely related in their somatic compositions and in their metabolic reactions. The use of antibodies against both flagellar phases as well as against the somatic factors is now routinely exploited for salmonella diagnosis in laboratories throughout the world.

(b) Other substitutive antigenic variations. An important kind of variation from the standpoint of resistance to infectious disease is one which occurs in certain parasites, sometimes spontaneously but more often under the influence of antibodies. Again, this consists of a substitution of one set of antigens for another, but unlike the fixed pattern of variation which is seen in the diphasic flagellar change, in this case the nature of the substituted antigens is unpredictable. The importance of this kind of change to the functioning of acquired immunity follows from the fact that the altered organisms maintain their virulence while becoming insensitive to the effects of the antibodies produced against them. The flexibility of this variation accounts for its usefulness as an evasive mechanism for the parasite, for presumably the variations in which it may take refuge are limitless. In the older literature such variants were described as serum fast.

Few bacterial species seem to be able to effect substitutive variations broader than the diphasic flagellar one, although under experimental prodding with proper antisera Bruner and Edwards (36) induced the development of four distinct phases in *S. paratyphi*, and other investigators have been able to induce analogous changes in monophasic flagellar strains as well as in somatic antigenic constitution (37).

The outstanding examples of lability in antigenic character are provided by the viruses of influenza, the protozoan parasites of the genus *Trypanosoma*, and the spirochetes of the genus *Borrelia*. The influenza virus may readily undergo antigenic changes during mouse passage, and this lability is accentuated in the presence of antibodies (Chapter 29). The trypanosomes developing from a single organism during the course of a relapsing infection in a single mouse have been found to undergo as many as seventeen distinct serial variations in antigenic character, the parasites of the last relapse residing in the body simultaneously with antibodies developed against 16 antigenically diverse forbears ([38], see also Chapter 9).

Similar findings have been made with *Borrelia*, and apparently the free-living *Paramecium* is similarly labile when subjected to the activity of antibody (38b, 39).

Presumably, antigenic types of bacteria in general have arisen through this same mutational process occurring spontaneously. Thus, there are 75 antigenically diverse types of pneumococci which have probably arisen from a common ancestor. But such variations have never occurred under observation in the laboratory; it has not yet been possible for example to derive from the type I pneumococcus some other type of the organism by cultivation in the presence of anti-I antibody in vivo or in vitro. If any change occurs under these conditions it is the $S \rightarrow R$ dissociation. Under special circumstances transformations of type can be effected experimentally, as will be described, but for this to take place it is necessary that an organism first lose its type specific antigen through the $S \rightarrow R$ change. The R form may then take on new S characteristics if certain specific conditions are provided.

GENETIC BASIS FOR ANTIGENIC VARIATIONS. The principles governing the variations which occur in bacteria and viruses are not yet known. Dubos (24) asserts that there can be little basis for the opinion that bacterial variation follows Mendelian laws so long as fusion and segregation cannot be shown to occur in these forms. Observations of this kind would permit interpretations in terms of combination and segregations of traits. (Recombination of characters has been found in one strain of *Escherichia coli* (40), but further search has so far failed to uncover another instance among the bacteria. Interestingly enough, however, Burnet (41) describes recombination of characters upon mixing strains of influenza viruses, a phenomenon which had already been reported for the viruses of bacteria (bacteriophages) (42).)

In view of the lack of sufficiently general evidence for application of Mendelian concepts to bacteria, geneticists for the most part seem to favor the viewpoint that the transmitted microbial variations are best interpreted in terms of the occurrence of mutations (43). Other possibilities are discussed by Lindegren (44).

In recent years there have appeared very interesting observations demonstrating that bacterial heredity in certain cases at least depends upon special chemical substances within the cell. This development was initiated by Griffith's (45) finding that if mice were injected with living R (unencapsulated avirulent) dissociants of type II pneumococci, together with heat-killed S (capsulated) type III microbes, the mice died of infection, and cultures from these animals yielded encapsulated pneumococci of type III. It was evident from these experiments that the R organism derived from the type II coccus had taken on the antigenically distinct capsule of the type III coccus and proceeded to proliferate as a type III organism. This transformation was later accomplished in vitro under analogous conditions (46). The type conversion plainly represented more than a simple assumption of capsular antigen supplied by the killed type III pneumococci included in the experimental environment, for the experiment failed if isolated capsular substance were added in place of the whole killed microbes.

The basic aspects of this transformation were later clarified by the work of Avery and his associates (47). A transforming principle was isolated from type III pneumococci; this consists of a polymerized form of desoxyribonucleic acid active in a dilution of $1:600,000,000$ in causing R cells derived from one pneumococcal type to form the capsule of the type supplying the transforming principle. Converted cells subsequently form more of the desoxyribonucleate as well as the new capsules. Not all noncapsulated strains are capable of responding to this stimulus. The factors determining successful or competent organisms are not clearly recognized, but one suggestive explanation is concerned with the varying capacities of strains to produce the enzyme desoxyribonuclease. These organisms manufacturing the enzyme in larger quantities might readily destroy the transforming principle and hence be incapable of undergoing transformation (48).

The mode of action of the nucleic acid upon the R cells may depend upon the stimulation of a series of enzyme reactions culminating in the synthesis of the new capsular polysaccharide. This effect may either reflect a direct action of a specific substance upon a gene, or the possibility that the transforming substance is itself gene material which substitutes for that lost by the cell in its mutation to the R form. There is not yet any direct evidence bearing upon these possibilities. In order for the transformation to occur in the pneumococcus it is necessary to provide, in addition to competent R cells and transforming principle, certain environmental factors including agglutinating antibody (or some other environmental condition which will bring cells together), the proper oxidation-reduction potential, pyrophosphate ions (present in serum and serous fluids) and another factor of unknown nature present in fraction V of bovine albumin. In other cases of transformation to be described these special environmental circumstances are not requisite (48).

Substances with analogous transforming properties have been isolated from types II and IV pneumococci (47b). In addition, transformations have been established for other antigens of the pneumococci, for the antigens of other bacterial species, and for genetic characters unrelated to antigenicity. In the first instance, a transforming nucleic acid has been reported as occurring in pneumococcus which causes the conversion of an extremely rough (ER) form of the organism to the ordinary R form and still another factor can reverse this (49). In the second case, Boivin (50) has demonstrated transformation in E. coli, the rough organism derived from a type possessing one polysaccharide somatic antigen changing to a type with another polysaccharide antigen. Again a desoxyribonucleic acid was the active agent. Analogous transformations have also been described for H. influenzae and Shigella paradysenteriae (51).

As for other transmissible characteristics of bacteria, a substance has been described which can endow them with resistance to an antibiotic, and others which alter enzymatic abilities (48).

A most interesting example of what appears to be the same effect has been observed in the case of a virus. A filterable agent which induces nonprogressive fibromas in cottontail rabbits is closely related antigenically to another virus which produces a malignant tumor growth, called myxomatosis, in rabbits. Berry and Dedrick (52) have reported the conversion of the fibroma into the myxoma virus by the same method originally employed by Griffith (45) for transformation of pneumococcal types, i.e. rabbits were injected with a mixture of active fibroma virus and heat inactivated myxoma virus. The possibility of the existence of a transforming factor in this case has apparently not been studied.

METHODS FOR ANTIGENIC ANALYSIS. There have been recurrent discussions in this volume of the antigenic structures of various infectious and toxic agents as related to some phase of the host-parasite relationship, and in other parts of this chapter certain bacteria and toxins have been chosen for amplified descriptions of antigenic composition. Information of this kind has often come from studies of a purely serologic nature in which the delineation of antigenic constitution of cells or fluids has been made without any knowledge whatever of the chemical natures of the substances being identified as antigens. In some cases chemical definition has come later, and this, of course, is of considerable importance to the understanding of the infectious agent or toxin and its activities in the body. But in the absence of chemical information a good deal can still be learned from serologic studies alone.

There are several general procedures that can be applied to such analyses. In addition to revealing the presence of distinct antigens, these methods often permit estimates of their relative quantities and, in the case of cells, of probable anatomic locations. The general methods employed for these purposes are outlined in the following discussion.

If, for example, we wish to learn something about the antigenic makeup of a single species or strain of bacterium, a vaccine of this organism in its entire form, e.g. smooth, flagellated, is used to produce an antiserum. This will probably contain antibodies against all the antigenic factors of the microbe. If this serum and the organism are mixed in a tube, agglutination will take place, but this provides no clue to the individuality of the antigen-antibody reactions concerned. In order to establish this information additional steps are required. For purposes of illustration, let us endow the flagella of the bacterium in question with two antigens, a and b, and the body with two antigens also, I and II. First a suspension of the organism is obtained from which the flagellar antigens have been eliminated, either by cultivation on a medium containing a small amount of phenol, in which case flagella formation will be inhibited, or by treating the flagellated organisms with hot alcohol to destroy the antigens. If such organisms are mixed and incubated with the antiserum and are subsequently removed by centrifugation, all antibodies against the body antigens of the bacteria will be removed from the serum, leaving only antibodies against the flagellar factors a and b. This absorbed antiserum will be active now only upon flagellated bacteria and so makes a first distinction between flagellar and somatic antigenic substances. It still fails, however, to distinguish the individual antigens which comprise these appendages. To proceed a step further in the analysis of the flagella, it may be necessary to find other strains or species of the bacterium, or perhaps a member of another genus, which reacts with this flagellar antiserum. If we assume that the common factor is the a flagellar antigen, then by absorbing the serum with this related microbe the anti-a antibody can be removed, leaving in the serum an antibody against the single antigenic factor b of the flagellum. The antiserum can now be employed to test other bacteria for the possible presence of this particular antigen.

Up to this point, the stepwise absorption procedure has demonstrated the presence of different antigens in the bacterium, the fact that some of these occur in the flagella and some in the body, and the existence of distinct flagellar substances.

The antigenic analysis of the body structure of this bacterium is undertaken in a similar way. In this case the same initial antiserum against the entire bacterial cell may be absorbed with the flagellated bacterium in the R phase of dissociation. This absorption will remove all flagellar and cellular antibodies except those against the S form, i.e. the O, antigens. These remaining antibodies can be further distinguished by treating the serum with other bacteria which may share one or another of the O antigens, again leaving an antibody against a single component in the serum. This serum will agglutinate S but not R bacteria, as shown in Table 7.

If this process is reversed by using isolated O antigens for absorption, then only antibodies against the R components would remain in the serum. If this absorbed serum is now mixed with S bacteria, agglutination would not take place despite the fact that S bacteria contain R antigens also (Table 7).

Table 7. Abilities of anti-O and anti-R antibodies to cause agglutination of S and R forms of a bacterium

Antibody		Bacterial antigens		Reaction
Anti-O	+	O R	$\longrightarrow$	Agglutination
Anti-O	+	R	$\longrightarrow$	No agglutination
Anti-R	+	O R	$\longrightarrow$	No agglutination
Anti-R	+	R	$\longrightarrow$	Agglutination

This procedure provides then not only a distinction between the various antigens of the bacterial body, but it gives also a tentative clue to their locations, for the failure of anti-R antibodies to agglutinate S cells suggests that the O antigens are surface components of the bacterium, effectively shielding the R factors from union with the antibodies directed against them. (This is the explanation which comes most readily to mind, but there are other possible interpretations which vitiate the concept of surface and deeper-lying antigens.

For example, it may be that S and R antigens are equally represented at the surface of the cell, but that steric hindrance may prevent antibodies from attaching to the R molecules. This question is clearly discussed by Spooner [22].)

Thus, by systematically taking advantage of the loss variations which may occur in a single bacterium, and in addition by employing related bacteria possessing one or more antigens in common with the cell under study, a complete diagram of the factors of this cell may frequently be obtained by the method of antibody absorption and cross agglutination.

The antibody absorption method, as indicated in the preceding discussion, also permits the detection of antigenic relationships between different cells and fluids. If two bacteria possess one or more common or closely related antigenic constituents, then a portion of the antibodies produced against one cell will act upon the other. If the **homologous** cell, the one employed for producing the antiserum, is permitted to react with it, all antibodies will be removed against itself as well as against the second (**heterologous**) bacterium. On the other hand, mixture of the heterologous bacterium with the serum will bind only the antibodies against the common components; the residual serum will then still act upon the homologous bacterium. This concept was expressed by Durham (53) over half a century ago by means of the following diagrammatic example in which Bacterium 1 represented the typhoid bacillus and Bacterium 2, *S. enteritidis:*

ANTIGENS	ANTIBODIES
Bacterium 1: a, b, c, d, e	Serum 1: A, B, C, D, E
Bacterium 2: c, d, e, f, g, h	Serum 2: C, D, E, F, G, H

Absorption of Serum 1 by Bacterium 2 removes antibodies C, D, E, but leaves antibodies A and B still active upon Bacterium 1. The reverse procedure results in the removal of antibodies C, D, E from Serum 2 by Bacterium 1, leaving F, G, H still active upon the homologous cell. It will be recognized that the principle involved here is the same as that expressed in the description of the removal of individual bacterial antigens in the preceding paragraphs.

It was pointed out in the discussion of antibody responses in Chapters 5 and 6 that antigen-antibody relationships are not usually, and perhaps never, so clearly defined as this diagram suggests. Against any one antigen a series of antibodies of somewhat differing activities may be produced. Thus, against antigen C of Bacterium 1 some of the antibodies, especially those produced early in the course of vaccination, may be highly specific because of a limited orientation to the pattern of the determinative group of this antigen. If the antigen C of Bacterium 2 is not chemically identical with that of Bacterium 1, these particular antibodies may not be absorbable by the heterologous antigen C at all. The same might hold true if antigen C of Bacterium 1 possesses a minor determinant group in the molecule which is lacking in that of Bacterium 2. Antibodies oriented toward this would not be absorbed by the heterologous antigen. But in either of these cases, some of the antibodies directed against the C of the first bacterium could fit the C of the second, and these would be cross-absorbed. The diagrams of antibody-antigen patterns illustrated in Chapter 5 may help to clarify this discussion.

At the risk of some repetition it may be worthwhile to provide a specific example of the uses of the absorption technic for purposes of antigenic analysis in the diagnostic laboratory. This example comes from a description provided by Edwards and Bruner (32) of the methods employed for the serologic differentiation of the salmonellas. For present purposes only a few of their main points will be considered.

The analysis of the O antigens is carried out first. For the preparation of anti-O sera a number of representative organisms are employed which as a whole include in their structures all the known O antigens. The flagellar antigens are destroyed by heat, and the vaccines are then injected into rabbits for antiserum production. One bacterium is chosen for its content of Vi antigen. Since this antigen is susceptible to heat, the H antigens in this case are destroyed by treatment of the suspension with absolute alcohol. An unknown organism to be analyzed is now mixed with each of the anti-O as well as the anti-Vi sera on slides; macroscopic agglutination reveals which groups of O antigens the bacillus under test may contain. If, for example, the bacterium possesses O antigens IV, V, XII, it will be agglutinated by a serum containing antibodies against antigens IV, XXVII, XII (*S. schleissheim*) because of the common occurrence of IV and XII. After this preliminary rough identification has been made it becomes necessary to narrow the analysis down to specific factors by the use of absorbed serums containing antibodies against single O factors. For this purpose, a pure anti-I serum may be obtained by absorbing *S. paratyphi A* antiserum (I, II, XII) with a subvariety of this organism containing only II and XII. Pure anti-II serum may be prepared by absorbing the same *S. paratyphi A* antiserum (I, II, XII) with *S. senftenberg* (I, III, XIX) and *S. typhosa* (IX, XII), and so on for the remaining somatic factors. Pure anti-Vi serum is prepared by absorbing *S. ballerup* antiserum with the W form of the same organism. By the use of these kinds of sera an organism may be placed in one of the *Salmonella* groups described earlier in this chapter.

To characterize the bacterium further, i.e. to delineate it as a type, it is necessary now to determine its flagellar antigenic structure. For the purpose of preparing H antisera fully motile cultures are employed. In order to obtain individual phase sera use is made of monophasic organisms wherever possible, but this possibility is, of course, very limited. Consequently, isolated colonies must be tested until the proper phases are obtained for the preparation of vaccines. Once an antiserum against the antigens of one phase has been prepared it becomes very useful to the subsequent preparation of a vaccine of the organism in its other flagellar phase. For example, to isolate phase 1 of *S. typhimurium* (flagellar formula i—1,2,3) a serum prepared against *S. newport* var. *puerto-rico* (1,2,3) is used. This antiserum against the phase 2 antigens 1, 2, 3 is incorporated in a semi-solid medium in a petri plate, and *S. typhimurium* is inoculated at one side of the dish. The organisms containing the phase 2 flagellar antigens, through their reaction with the antibodies in the medium, become immobilized to the area of inoculation, while those bacilli with the phase 1 (i) antigen swarm across the plate and may be easily picked for the inoculation of broth for preparation of the phase 1 vaccine.

Certain of the phase 1 factors (a, b, c, d, i, k, and others) occur as single antigens; the bacteria which contain these can therefore be employed as vaccines for the production of pure antibodies to these substances. In other instances, however, absorption must be employed in order to free antisera of antibodies against other antigenic constituents. The procedure is entirely analogous to that described for the procurement of single O antibodies. Thus, to obtain anti-f, an antiserum against *S. derby* (f, g) is absorbed with *S. essen* (g, m), and so forth. It is not necessary to test a culture to be examined with all the antiphase 1 sera, for after the O antigens have been identified one can refer to the proper group in the Kauffmann-White schema to find which flagellar factors occur in this particular group. These can then be tested for first.

In order to identify phase 2 antigens, the culture may be inoculated into medium to which antiphase 1 antibodies have been added, and the motile bacilli can then be isolated as described before.

The occurrence of hitherto unknown antigenic factors is brought to light by the failure of antisera against the known substances to agglutinate the organism. Isolated antibodies against the new antigen may be obtained by absorbing the serum with the recognized antigens contained in other bacteria which, however, lack the new factor.

Another serologic method applicable to antigenic analysis is the optimal proportions procedure described in Chapter 8. In dealing with a mixture of antigens in solution, as in a body fluid or a bacterial exotoxin, this precipitation method may show the presence of several zones of optimal flocculation, each dependent upon a separate antigen-antibody reaction. This principle is applicable also to the agglutination reaction with bacterial cells, as developed by Miles.

A more precise detection of an antigen in solution is afforded by the method of Heidelberger and Kendall for the quantitative determination of antibody. An antiserum prepared against a particular antigen is first calibrated by mixing it in measured quantity with various known amounts of the antigen. The several washed precipitates are analyzed by the Kjeldahl method for total contents of antibody and antigen nitrogen. From this information a calibration curve is prepared showing the quantities of antibody precipitated by various amounts of the antigen. This serum can now be employed for the quantitative determination of the same antigen in an unknown fluid. Following reaction the nitrogen content of the precipitate is determined, and the amount of antigen represented in the total precipitate can then be read off from the previously established curve (54).

ANTIGENIC DETERMINATION BY BACTERIOPHAGE. It has been established for some years that diagnostic use can be made of the specific affinity of bacteriophages for host bacteria. Craigie (55) established six bacteriophage-susceptible types among almost 600 strains of *S. typhosa*. These particular bacteriophages depend for their activities upon the presence of the Vi antigen in the bacillary strains, and while the Vi antigen of all six types appears to be identical as judged by serologic methods of study, the bacteriophage distinctions are clear enough so that the method can be applied to the routine investigation of outbreaks of typhoid fever. In other instances there is evidence of a direct relationship between lysability by phage and the presence in bacteria of serologically specific surface antigens. Burnet (56) found that various salmonellas possessing O antigen in common with *S. enteritidis* were susceptible to the same phages, and that this susceptibility was not present in R variants. With the polysaccharide-containing O substances of salmonellas and dysentery bacilli it was possible to block the lytic activities of bacteriophages specific for these organisms (57). Recently Miller and Goebel (58) have worked with *Shigella sonnei* phases I and II. When these two antigens were isolated and employed in bacteriophage blocking tests, it was found that the bacteriophages to which both bacterial types are susceptible could not be blocked by the specific antigens. On the other hand, the phages to which only the type II bacillus was susceptible could be blocked by this isolated antigen.

It seems evident from these varied experiences and other analogous ones (59) that in some instances specific antigenic components of the bacterial surface may function as the specific receptors for strains of bacteriophage, but that other surface components may also determine susceptibility. A single bacterial strain may possess multiple receptors for different strains of phage and one of these may or may not be a specific antigenic factor of the cell surface (22, 60).

Microbial and Animal Toxins. Some of the bacterial exotoxins have been described in preceding chapters (Chapters 3, 21, 22, 24, 25, 26, 29), and the nature of one of the important types of endotoxins, represented by the Boivin antigens of gram-negative bacilli, was dealt with in the discussion of bacillary dysentery (Chapter 22) and in an earlier portion of this chapter. As part of the general discussion of the antigens of infectious agents it remains to summarize information concerning others of the important antigenic substances which certain microbes secrete into the environments in which they grow, and which may have profound effects upon host tissues. The measurement of toxins in terms of standardized units, and the titration of antitoxic sera, are discussed in various textbooks dealing with medical bacteriology (14, 15).

TETANUS TOXIN. The toxins of *Cl. botulinum* have been described as the most potent poisons known. Close to these in lethality is the substance produced by another member of the same genus, *Cl. tetani*. Like botulinus toxin, this protein has been crystallized (61); each milligram is capable of killing about 10,000,000 mice.

Tetanus toxin or tetanospasmin acts powerfully upon the central nervous system without, however, causing any visible pathologic alterations (62). Its activity is exerted centrally as well as peripherally upon the neuromuscular junction. Whether it reaches the central nervous system by way of the nerves or through the blood stream has been a recurrent subject for experiment and debate for many years, but the issue is not yet settled (63).

The effect of tetanus toxin is to cause convulsive tonic contractions of the striated muscles. This often occurs first in the area where bacilli have become implanted, but characteristically it soon involves the muscles of the jaws and neck and the mouth may become firmly locked. Other muscle groups throughout the body may then undergo spasm, convulsive seizures being precipitated by various mild external stimuli such as noises or jarring of the bed.

The mechanism through which this simple protein substance may exert these devastating effects in man and animals has excited the curiosity of physiologists and biochemists, but studies of such basic activities as those of adenosinetriphosphatase of the tissues, or cholinesterase of the nerves, have so far provided no clues (61). Neither have any leads come from investigations in various animals (cold blooded species, the hen and the cat) which are relatively insusceptible to the toxin as to the basis for their imperviousness to a poison which is so strikingly active in other animals (64).

Tetanus toxin converts to toxoid spontaneously and rapidly; at 0° C., 75 per cent conversion occurs in the course of 10 days. The addition of a small amount of formalin brings about this change almost immediately. This toxoid has become established as one of the routine and dependable immunizing substances for man.

STREPTOCOCCAL TOXINS. Certain of the beta hemolytic streptococci produce a number of soluble poisons and enzymes, the most notorious of which is the erythrogenic toxin responsible for the rash of scarlet fever. This is formed mainly by some strains of group A organisms, but it may also be produced by group C and occasional group G streptococci. In any case it is not possible to predict which strains will produce the toxin, or in what quantities.

Erythrogenic toxin was discovered by the Dicks in 1924 (65). Interest in it has waned in recent years for several weighty practical reasons; because of a decrease in the incidence and severity of scarlet fever, because the antigenic heterogeneity of this toxin introduces difficulties into immunologic studies and practical applications, because of the inability of toxin to convert successfully to toxoid, and finally because immunity to the toxin fails to influence the occurrence of streptococcal disease itself, while chemotherapeutic and antibiotic agents can cut short the career of the microbe and its toxin.

Erythrogenic toxin is more heat stable than most other exotoxins, resisting 60° C. for several hours. It is antigenically heterogeneous, five substances with the same pharmacologic actions having distinctive antibody requirements for neutralization. This may explain the repeated attacks of scarlet fever which have been rather frequently observed in the same individual. Conversion to toxoid is unsatisfactory at best, so that for immunization the toxin itself must be employed.

The Dick test is a skin test for immunity to erythrogenic toxin analogous in principle to the Schick test for diphtheria. It is carried out by introducing a small amount of toxin into the skin. In subjects without antitoxin, this causes local erythema to appear after 6 to 24 hours. Another diagnostic test, the Shultz-Charlton reaction, may be employed to differentiate the rash of this disease from other possible causes. This consists of the injection of a small amount of antitoxin into an erythematous area. During the first few days of the disease local blanching may occur as a result of the neutralization of toxin in the restricted zone of the test injection. In view of the antigenic multiplicity of toxins it is obviously necessary to employ the proper substances for these tests, preferably polyvalent toxin for the Dick test, and polyvalent antitoxin for the Shultz-Charlton reaction.

The mechanism of action of erythrogenic toxin is not known (18, 21, 64).

Of the series of other factors elaborated by some strains of streptococci, several have been discussed in Chapter 3. These include leukocidin, hyaluronidase, streptokinase (fibrinolysin) and hemolysins. Of the hemolytic factors there are two, one referred to as streptolysin O, the other as streptolysin S. These seem to have no pathogenic significance in streptococcus infections, but the O lysin especially has proved useful in epidemiologic surveys, the occurrence of antibodies to it being used as an index of recent infection. Streptolysin O is elaborated by most strains of serologic group A, and by some of the group C and G streptococci, while the S lysin formation is limited to group A members. Individual organisms may produce one or both of these substances.

The O hemolysin is an easily oxidized substance (O = oxygen labile), while S is stable to oxidation but extremely labile to heat. The former is a protein, the latter probably a lipoprotein. The zone of hemolysis which surrounds beta hemolytic streptococci on blood agar plates depends upon the S substance, since O is inactivated under these aerobic circumstances.

A proteolytic enzyme is produced by some strains of hemolytic streptococci (66). This digests the M antigens of the organisms themselves, as well as other of its protein effluvia including streptokinase. The relationship of this substance to the course of the infection established by a streptococcus which produces it has not been clarified; so far no connection between virulence and proteinase production has been established (67). In fact, M antigen production and proteinase elaboration seem for the most part to be mutually exclusive, but in some strains proteinase may destroy M antigen as it is formed and this can, of course, seriously impede efforts to type such organisms serologically.

STAPHYLOCOCCAL TOXINS. Like the streptococci, staphylococci also elaborate a variety of biologically active substances into the environment in which they grow. These include a number of recognized antigenic poisons some of which have obvious potential relationships to disease production.

The alpha toxin of the hemolytic staphylococcus is probably a protein substance which has three known effects—lysis of erythrocytes, necrosis of skin, and a rapid lethal action following intravenous injection into rabbits and mice. It seems improbable that the hemolytic effect per se has any relationship to human or animal disease caused by these organisms (Chapter 3), but the destructiveness to cells implied by this activity as well as the dermonecrotic effect intimates the possible basis for the local tissue changes leading to abscess formation. The intravenous lethal activity of this toxin seen in experimental animals is not ordinarily considered to have a counterpart in the course of even widespread staphylococcal infection in the human being. Under certain circumstances, however, this activity may apparently be of great moment to man. Such lethal activity is probably illustrated by the tragic Bundeberg occurrence of 1929, in which a number of children who had been given injections of contaminated diphtheria prophylactic died within the subsequent 36 hours of acute staphylococcal toxemia (68). How this toxin may act is not yet known.

At least two other staphylococcal hemolysins have been described. One, termed beta toxin, lyses sheep but not rabbit cells, and acts only if the cells have been cooled after primary incubation with the toxin. This is called hot-cold lysis. The mechanisms of action which may be implied by this phenomenon are discussed by van Heyningen (64). Gamma toxin is apparently again a distinct antigenic lysin about which little is known (64). Neither of these substances seems to take part in the pathogenic activities of the staphylococci.

A diffusible staphylococcal substance important from the standpoint of human welfare is an enterotoxin which, though it is produced by a relatively small number of strains of this organism, accounts for most cases of food poisoning in human beings (69). This thermostable substance resists a half hour of boiling. Intoxication results from the ingestion of pre-formed toxin in foods in which the bacterium has grown rather than of the coccus itself. All kinds of foods have been implicated in this process, but creamy bakery products seem to be the chief offenders. Symptoms and signs include nausea, vomiting, abdominal cramps, diarrhea, and prostration; these begin within one to several hours after the contaminated food has been eaten, and last at longest for a day.

The collection of information about this toxin has been considerably handicapped by the paucity of susceptible animal species. Aside from human beings, only monkeys and young kittens are suitable subjects for study. Not all human beings are susceptible and those who are quickly gain immunity and so lose their usefulness as test subjects. The validity of the results obtained in kittens is in question because other factors of the staphylococcus can apparently induce vomiting in them (64).

The staphylococcal leukocidins, of which there are at least two, may of course have pathogenic significance as was discussed in Chapter 3. In addition, strains of this species may occasionally form fibrinolysin and spreading factor (Chapter 3), and practically all organisms isolated from human and animal infections elaborate a plasma-clotting factor designated as coagulase. Although the appearance of this substance most closely correlates with the virulence of strains as determined by their sources of isolation, it is difficult at present to see how this factor may contribute to the virulence of the organism ([64], see also Chapter 3).

ANTIGENIC TOXINS OF ANIMAL ORIGIN. The animal toxins include a number of poisons which are popularly known to be antigenic as well as dangerous; thus, it is generally appreciated that antitoxins may successfully counteract snake venoms. All snakes secrete a poisonous salivary juice, but only relatively few species meet the prerequisites which make them noxious to other animals, viz., the elaboration of a sufficient quantity of the poison and the possession of grooved teeth through which it can be injected into the tissues. According to Gay (70) there are over 150 varieties of poisonous snakes, i.e. effective injectors. Their toxins are all probably protein in nature. As mentioned before, they are antigenic, and in some cases readily convert to toxoids. The more dangerous snakes can inject a surprising quantity of poison in a single bite; Do Amaral's (71) data reveal that for the various North American rattlers this is between 60 and 350 mg. of dried material.

A variety of antigenic substances with biologic effects are listed among the constituents of snake venoms, including **proteolysins** and **histocytolysins** which cause local inflammatory reactions and necrosis, **cardiotoxin** which induces heart failure, **hematocytolysins** which may destroy erythrocytes or leukocytes or both, and which may in some cases be lecithinases, **hemorrhagin** which destroys the endothelium of capillaries and leads to hemorrhages into the mucous membranes, skin, and internal organs, **thrombinogens** and **anticytozymes** which respectively cause coagulation of and an anticoagulant effect upon blood, **neurocytolysins** which affect the voluntary and autonomic nervous system, **hemagglutinins**, and various other enzymes more recently discovered, of which **cholinesterase** is an important example. Some of these enzymes have been crystallized (64, 71).

The two main classes of venomous snakes are the *Colubridae,* of which the cobra is an outstanding example, and the *Viperidae,* which includes rattlesnakes, European vipers, and most poisonous snakes of North and South America. The venoms of the first group affect mainly the nervous system; that of the latter group acts chiefly upon other tissues to produce swelling, cellular necrosis, and hemorrhages. Githens (72) proposes the interesting thesis that the more primitive evolutionary forms secrete venoms toxic to the nervous system, and discusses various species of reptiles from this standpoint.

Many insects, as is commonly known, also secrete poisons which they can inject through biting. The toxin of ants is merely formic acid, while that of bees is antigenic and related in its effects to the venoms of the *Viperidae.* Practically all spiders, like snakes, have venom-producing organs, but only a few species attack man. In the main, the female is the biter, though there are exceptions. A notorious offender is *Latrodectus mactans,* the black widow spider. The venom of this beast is neurotoxic, producing intense pain, but in the case of other *Arachnida,* the poison may cause predominantly local damage. This subject is discussed in some detail by Hoffman and Culbertson (73).

BIBLIOGRAPHY

1a. Boivin, A., and Mesrobeanu, L.   Compt. rend. Soc. de biol., 113:490, 1933; 114:302, 307, 1933.
 b. ——— and Mesrobeanu, L.   Rev. d'immunol., 1:553, 1935, 2:113, 1936; 3:319, 1937; 4:40, 197, 1938.
 c. ——— and Mesrobeanu, L.   Ier Congrès des Microbiologistes de Langue francais, Paris, 1938, p. 1.
2. Morgan, W. T. J., and Partridge, S. M.   Biochem. J., 34:169, 1940; 35:1140, 1941.
3a. Raistrick, H., and Topley, W. W. C.   Brit. J. Exper. Path., 15:113, 1934.
 b. Walker, J.   Biochem. J., 34:325, 1940.
 c. Freeman, G. G., Challinor, S. W., and Wilson, J.   Biochem. J., 34:307, 1940.
4. Morgan, H. R., Favorite, G. O., and Horneff, J. A.   J. Immunol., 46:301, 1943.
5. Partridge, S. M., and Morgan, W. T. J.   Brit. J. Exper. Path., 21:180, 1940.
6a. Perlman, E., and Goebel, W. F.   J. Exper. Med., 84:223, 1946.
 b. Cundiff, R. J., and Morgan, H. R.   J. Immunol., 42:361, 1941.
7a. Felix, A., and Pitt, R. M.   J. Path. & Bact., 38:409, 1934.
 b. ——— Proc. 3rd Internat. Congr. Microbiol., New York, 1939, p. 798.
8. Kauffmann, F.   The Differentiation of *Escherichia* and *Klebsiella* Types, Springfield, Ill., Charles C Thomas Co., 1951.
9a. Ørskov, J., and Kauffmann, F.   J. Hyg., 36:514, 1936. Ztschr. f. Hyg. u. Infektionskr., 119:65, 1937.
 b. Kauffmann, F.   Ztschr. f. Hyg. u. Infektionskr., 117:778, 791, 1936.
 c. Batson, H. C., Landy, M., and Brown, M.   J. Exper. Med., 91:231, 1950.
10a. Felix, A., and Bhatnager, S. S.   Brit. J. Exper. Path., 16:422, 1935.
 b. ——— and Pitt, R. M.   J. Hyg., 35:428, 1935.
11. Carlinfanti, E.   Ann. Inst. Pasteur, 72:766, 1946.
12. Boivin, A., and Mesrobeanu, L.   Compt. rend. Soc. de biol., 128:835, 1938.
13. White, P. B.   J. Path. & Bact., 34:23, 325, 1931; 35:77, 1932; 36:65, 1933.
14. Smith, D. T., and Conant, N. F.   Zinsser's Textbook of Bacteriology, 10th ed., New York, Appleton-Century-Crofts, Inc., 1952.
15. Topley, W. W. C., and Wilson, G. S.   Principles of Bacteriology and Immunity, 3rd. ed., Baltimore, Williams and Wilkins Co., 1946.
16. Kauffmann, F., and Edwards, P. R.   J. Lab. & Clin. Med., 32:548, 1947.
17. Lancefield, R. C.   Harvey Lect., 36:251, 1940-41.
18. Swift, H. F.   Bacterial and Mycotic Infections of Man, ed. by R. Dubos, Philadelphia, J. B. Lippincott Co., 1948, Chap. 11.
19. Griffith, F.   J. Hyg., 34:542, 1934.
20. Heidelberger, M., and Kendall, F. C.   J. Exper. Med., 54:513, 1931.
21. Rammelkamp, C. H., and Dingle, J. H.   Ann. Rev. Microbiol., 2:279, 1948.
22. Spooner, E. T. C.   The Nature of the Bacterial Surface, ed. by A. A. Miles and N. W. Pirie, C. C. Thomas, Springfield, Ill., Charles C Thomas Co., 1949, Chap. 7.
23. Tomcsik, J.   Experientia, 7:459, 1951.
24. Dubos, R. J.   The Bacterial Cell, Cambridge, Mass., Harvard University Press, 1945.
25. Arkwright, J. A.   J. Path. & Bact., 23:358, 1920; 24:36, 1921.
26. Todd, E. W.   Brit. J. Exper. Path., 9:1, 1928. J. Exper. Med., 48:493, 1928.
27. Stryker, L. M.   J. Exper. Med., 24:49, 1916.
28. Smith, T., and Reagh, A. L.   J. Med. Research, 10:89, 1903.

29. Weil, E., and Felix, A. Wien. klin. Wchnschr., 30:1509, 1917.
30. Pijper, A. J. Path. & Bact., 47:1, 1938. J. Bact., 42:395, 1941.
31. Weibull, C. Acta Chem. Scandinav., 4:268, 1950.
32. Edwards, P. R., and Bruner, D. W. Station Circular #54, Univ. of Kentucky Agricultural Exper. Station, 1942.
33. Andrewes, F. W. J. Path. & Bact., 25:505, 1922; 28:345, 1925.
34a. Kauffmann, F. Ztschr. f. Hyg. u. Infektionskr., 118:540, 1936; 119:103, 1936.
   b. Edwards, P. R., and Bruner, D. W. J. Hyg., 38:716, 1938.
35. Salmonella Subcommittee. Proc. 3rd Internat. Congr. Microbiol., New York, 1940, p. 832.
36. Bruner, D. W., and Edwards, P. R. J. Bact., 42:467, 1941.
37. ——— and Edwards, P. R. J. Bact., 55:449, 1948.
38a. Taliaferro, W. H. The Immunology of Parasitic Infections, New York, The Century Co., 1929.
   b. Harrison, J. A. Ann. Rev. Microbiol., 1:19, 1947.
39. Sonneborn, T. Ann. Rev. Microbiol., 3:55, 1949.
40. Tatum, E. L., and Lederberg, J. J. Bact., 53:673, 1947.
41. Burnet, F. M. J. Gen. Microbiol., 5:46, 59, 67, 1951.
42a. Delbrück, M., and Bailey, W. T. Cold Spring Harbor Symposia Quant. Biol., 11:55, 1946.
   b. Hershey, A. D., and Rotman, R. Proc. Nat. Acad. Sc., 34:89, 1948.
43. Lederberg, J. Ann. Rev. Microbiol., 3:1, 1949.
44. Lindegren, C. C. Zentralbl. f. Bakt., 93:113, 1935.
45. Griffith, F. J. Hyg., 27:113, 1928.
46. Dawson, M. H., and Sia, R. H. P. J. Exper. Med., 54:681, 1931.
47a. Avery, O. T., MacLeod, C. M., and McCarty, M. J. Exper. Med., 79:137, 1944.
   b. McCarty, M., and Avery, O. T. J. Exper. Med., 83:89, 97, 1946.
48. Austrian, R. Bact. Rev., 16:31, 1952.
49a. Taylor, H. E. Compt. rend. Soc. de biol., 228:1258, 1949.
   b. ——— J. Exper. Med., 88:399, 1949.
   c. ——— The Nature of the Bacterial Surface, ed. by A. A. Miles and N. W. Pirie, Springfield, Ill., Charles C Thomas Co., 1949, Chap. 8.
   d. Austrian, R., and MacLeod, C. M. J. Exper. Med., 89:451, 1949.
50. Boivin, A. Cold Spring Harbor Symposia Quant. Biol., 12:7, 1947.
51a. Alexander, H. E., and Leidy, G. J. Exper. Med., 93:345, 1951.
   b. Weil, A. J., and Binder, M. Proc. Soc. Exper. Biol. & Med., 66:349, 1947.
52. Berry, G. P., and Dedrick, H. M. J. Bact., 31:50, 1936.
53. Durham, H. E. J. Exper. Med., 5:353, 1900-01.
54. Kabat, E. A., and Mayer, M. M. Experimental Immunochemistry, Springfield, Ill., Charles C Thomas Co., 1948.
55a. Craigie, J., and Brandon, K. F. J. Path. & Bact., 43:233, 249, 1936.
   b. ——— and Yen, C. H. Canad. Pub. Health J., 29:448, 484, 1938.
56. Burnet, F. M. Brit. J. Exper. Path., 8:121, 1927; 32:15, 349, 1929.
57. Gough, G. A. C., and Burnet, F. M. J. Path. & Bact., 38:301, 1934.
58. Miller, E. M., and Goebel, W. F. J. Exper. Med., 90:255, 1949.
59. Beumer, J. Rev. belge Path. Méd. exp., 18:244, 289, 1947.
60. Anderson, T. F. The Nature of the Bacterial Surface, ed. by A. A. Miles and N. W. Pirie, Springfield, Ill., Charles C Thomas Co., 1949, Chap. 5.
61. Pillemer, L., and Robbins, K. C. Ann. Rev. Microbiol., 3:265, 1949.
62. ——— and Wartman, W. B. J. Immunol., 55:277, 1947.
63. Friedemann, U., Zuger, B., and Hollander, A. J. Immunol., 36:485, 1939.
64. van Heyningen, W. E., 1950, Bacterial Toxins, Oxford, Blackwell Scientific Pub.
65. Dick, G. F., and Dick, G. H. J.A.M.A., 82:265, 1924.
66a. Frobisher, M., Jr. J. Exper. Med., 44:777, 1926.
   b. Elliott, S. D. J. Exper. Med., 81:573, 1945.
67. Rothbard, S., and Todd, E. W. J. Exper. Med., 87:283, 1948.
68. Burnet, F. M. J. Path. & Bact., 32:717, 1929; 33:1, 1930; 34:492, 1931.
69. Dack, G. M. Food Poisoning, Chicago, Univ. of Chicago Press, 1943.
70. Gay, F. P. Agents of Disease and Host Resistance, Springfield, Ill., Charles C Thomas Co., 1935, Chap. 4.

71. Do Amaral, A.   Newer Knowledge of Bacteriology and Immunology, ed. by E. O. Jordan and I. S. Falk, Chicago, Univ. of Chicago Press, 1929, Chap. 80.
72. Githens, T. S.   J. Immunol., 29:165, 1935.
73. Hoffman, W. A., and Culbertson, J. T.   Agents of Disease and Host Resistance, ed. by F. P. Gay, Springfield, Ill., Charles C Thomas Co., 1935, Chap. 60.

31

CELLULAR ANTIGENS

Aside from the general interest which attaches to the antigens of tissues and cells as serologically active substances, certain of these have particular significance for human welfare because of their relationship to immunologic diseases, pathologic states occasioned by the reactivity of an individual to antigenic factors present in other members of the same species (e.g. transfusion reactions, erythroblastosis fetalis), or possibly to antigens of his own tissues under special circumstances. The possibility of occurrences of this kind, proved or suspected, will serve as the focal point for the discussions in this chapter and the next.

The antigens of tissues and cells constitute a complex group, not yet well known despite the considerable volume of work since Nuttall's (1) first extensive survey of the antigenic relationships of the blood proteins of over 500 animal species. The best single source of information dealing with cellular antigen-antibody data presently available is Landsteiner's volume, *The Specificity of Serological Reactions* (2).

The antigens of animal tissues and cells may be serologically categorized in the following manner, ranging from the more generally distributed to the more restricted. This brings up certain cross qualifications, but no classification can avoid this.

1. Antigens occurring in more than one species of animal, and sometimes also in plants and microbes. These substances which exist in more than one biologic envelope are called **heterogenetic**.

2. Antigens occurring in all the members of a species, and restricted to this species, are termed **species specific**.

3. Antigens which occur in **some members** of a species only. Examples of these are the blood group antigens of man. These are referred to as **isoantigens**.

4. Antigens restricted to a particular organ or tissue of a species, and called **organ specific**.

The ways in which these categories overlap can best be illustrated by a few examples. Isoantigens may be heterogenetic as represented by the blood group A substance of man, which is found also in the horse, hog, rabbit and anthropoids (page 482). Organ-specific antigens may be restricted to one species or may be heterogenetic. Examples of the latter are the antigens of the ocular lens which seem to be the same in various animals, though different in each animal from any other bodily constituent. Certain antigens of the brain and spinal cord are also heterogenetic and organ specific.

These various possibilities permit, in certain circumstances, the occurrence of the previously mentioned immunologic diseases. For example, the isoantigenicity of blood cells can lead to the development of congenital hemolytic disease of the fetus, and of transfusion reactions. Isoantigenicity may also account for the failure of successful skin grafting between individuals in the same species. Organ specific and heterogenetic antigenicity may perhaps lead to the occurrence of certain forms of damage to the brain and spinal cord (demyelinating encephalomyelitis) in individuals who have received injections of viral vaccines containing nerve tissue derived from other species. It is even possible—in some instances highly probable—that under special conditions of injury or infection the antigenic structure of a tissue or organ of a single individual may serve as an antigenic stimulus to him. In this case the subject may destroy his own tissues through the action of **autoantibody.** Examples of all these possibilities will be considered in more detail later in this chapter.

Preliminary to the discussion of these various immunopathologic possibilities it is desirable to define the state of our information about the various categories of antigens as such.

1. Heterogenetic Antigens. There are many instances in which the same or closely related antigens occur in different biologic strata and species. In some cases these antigens may exist in the same organ or tissue of different animals (i.e. organ specific heterogenetic antigens), and in other cases they are found in different locales in different animals, sometimes indeed extending to lower plant and animal forms.

Considering first organ-specific heterogenetic antigens, one of the clearest examples is provided by the ocular lens (3). There seem to be two distinct proteins, alpha and beta crystallins, concerned in this antigenicity (4). These antigens exist in species ranging from fish to man, and, interestingly, they are capable under certain conditions of inducing antibodies in the subject from which they are obtained (5). Similar heterogenicity of organ-specific antigens is seen in the case of brain. This is true of constituents extractable with alcohol (6) as well as of more recently investigated heat-stable, water-soluble substances (7) and of saline extractable material which sediments in the high speed centrifuge as heavy particles (8). Not all brain antigens are completely organ specific; Lewis (9) has shown that this tissue shares antigenic material with testicle, which is similarly heterogenetic in its distribution, the same antigen occurring in the rabbit, guinea pig, rat and ox. Partial cross reactions with other organ antigens may also occur (7). On the other hand there appear to be some antigens in brain tissue which are more restricted in their organ specificity, and others are even more limited to the species as well as the organ (10).

An interesting group of heterogenetic antigens are those sedimentable from watery extracts of tissues by high speed centrifugation. Claude (11) found that normal chick embryo tissues contain such substances, and Kidd and Friedewald (12) obtained similar sediments from various organs, including liver, kidney, lung, brain, spleen and heart, of several animal species. These were found to be antigenically the same whatever the organ source, and furthermore to be closely related whether obtained from the mouse, rat, guinea pig or chicken. Against this antigen these workers found a normally occurring antibody in rabbits. This iso- and autoantibody should logically be expected to combine with the antigen in vivo; it does not do so presumably because the antigen is a cytoplasmic constituent shielded by its intracellular location from antibodies, just as viruses may be safe from the activity of antibodies once inside cells. It seems apparent from other work with sedimentable tissue constituents that these heterogenetic antigens are not the sole antigenic components of the sediment. Wassermann antigen has also been obtained from saline extracts of beef and human heart; this is again an example of a widely distributed antigen. In addition, organ- and species-specific antigens are also found (13).

By far the most thoroughly studied of the heterogenetic antigens has been the substance discovered by Forssman in 1911 (14) in the tissues of the guinea pig, cat and horse and in red cells of the sheep. Injections of emulsions of the tissues of the first three species into rabbits induced the formation of antibodies with marked hemolytic activity upon sheep erythrocytes. From this beginning there has evolved a large literature dealing with the distribution of the antigen, its nature, and its significance to interests ranging from the detection of adulterations in foodstuffs to its helpfulness in unraveling the lines of evolutionary development (2, 15).

The pivotal reaction employed to detect the distribution of Forssman antigen has been the ability of antibodies evoked by the material being tested to act upon sheep red cells. This method can lead to certain difficulties since the sheep erythrocyte stroma contains multiple antigens, and certain relationships of foreign cell substances have been shown to depend upon these rather than upon the Forssman antigen. An example of this will be discussed in later paragraphs dealing with the infectious mononucleosis antigen. It is however possible to prove the Forssman nature of an antigen under study by demonstrating the ability of known isolated Forssman antigen to combine with antibodies against the substance under test and thus to neutralize their activity upon sheep cells (i.e. by the absorption or neutralization procedure).

The distribution of this antigen is prodigal, extending from bacteria to man. Among animals it occurs in the *Carnivora* (dog, fox, cat, lion, and tiger); in the family *Cavidae* of the order *Rodentia* (guinea pig and agouti), and in species of *Muridae* in the same order (mouse and hamster, but not the rat); in the order *Artiodactyla* (sheep, goat and camel); in *Perissodactyla* (horse and togopony); in *Mystacoceti* (whale) and, among the primates, in the lemur and in man of blood groups A and AB. The substance occurs also in chickens and other birds, various fishes, and other animals (15c).

The occurrence of this antigen is sometimes limited to erythrocytes to the exclusion of other tissues, or vice versa. Thus, in the guinea pig it is present in all the tissues but not in the red cells, whereas in the sheep it exists only in erythrocytes. In other animals, however, including the dog, cat, tortoise and chicken, the antigen is found in both locations. One variety of corn, among the higher plants, appears to contain the antigen (16). It has been reported also as a constituent of ragweed pollen (17). Many species of bacteria contain the antigen but not all strains of a single species may have it. The pneumococcus and the dysentery bacillus have been most thoroughly studied in this respect (15a, 15b).

The nature of the Forssman antigen provides a challenge which has not yet been entirely met, but efforts to clarify this have left a deposit of useful serologic information. It was found some years ago that the antigen may be removed from tissues with any of a number of organic solvents—for example, alcohol or ether—but not acetone. The substance so removed, obviously not proteinaceous, was found to be reactive with anti-Forssman antibodies but not itself capable of stimulating antibody formation. This substance proved to be the first example obtained of a naturally occurring hapten (see page 45). Landsteiner then found that simple mixture with a protein (foreign serum) sufficed to render the hapten effective as an antigen in the animal body. Other tissue substances extractable with lipoidal solvents have since been found similarly to combine with protein carriers, simply on mixing, to become antigenic (2).

Landsteiner's (2) studies with the Forssman antigen isolated from horse kidney indicate that the moiety which provides specificity is a carbohydrate, and this is bound to lipoidal substances, perhaps fatty acids or lipid bases. In the cell the complete antigen is thought to exist as a carbohydrate-lipid-protein complex. The bacterial Forssman antigens are not always so clearly linked with lipoidal substances of the cell. In the Shiga dysentery bacillus there appears to be no relationship to lipid whatever (18), while in the pneumococcus a lipo-polysaccharide association seems to exist, the carbohydrate portion being the C substance (somatic carbohydrate) of the microbe (15a, 19). The outstanding physical property of the antigen obtained from bacteria or animal tissues is its remarkable heat stability, to the extent of withstanding autoclaving.

The Forssman antigen is clearly not a single entity in its various biologic associations. The heterogenetic relationship depends upon the existence of similar rather than identical chemical structures. These are in some cases sufficiently unlike so that reciprocal reactions do not occur, as illustrated in the following table taken from Landsteiner (2). These data reveal that although antibodies against human A cells act upon sheep erythrocyte antigen the reverse is not necessarily the case. Again, though antichicken cell antibodies fail to react with human A cell Forssman antigen, and antibodies against A cells do not act upon chicken cell antigen, both antibodies precipitate the antigen of sheep erythrocytes. A restricted range of relationship is also seen with some of the bacterial Forssman substances. Variations both in the central patterns of antigens and of responding antibodies probably determine the extent of heteroactivity in any particular test. It may be recalled from Chapters 5 and 6 that the antibodies produced in response to any single antigenic substance by an individual animal vary in their reactivities, both qualitatively and quantitatively, depending upon the degree of development of the combining groups of various globulin molecules for the determinative groups of the antigen. Such variability in antibody molecules may explain the failure of sheep erythrocyte serum 2 in Table 8 to react with human A substance while the serum 1 does so.

Table 8. Reciprocal reactions between Forssman antigens from various sources and different Forssman antibodies

ANTISERUM AGAINST	ANTIGENS (EMULSIONS OF ALCOHOLIC EXTRACTS)				
	HUMAN A ERYTHROCYTES	HORSE KIDNEY	SHEEP ERYTHROCYTES	CHICKEN ERYTHROCYTES	DOG ERYTHROCYTES
Human A erythrocytes	3+	0	2±	0	±
Horse kidney	0	3±	3+	2+	..
Sheep erythrocytes 1	3+	3+	3+	2+	..
Sheep erythrocytes 2	0	3±	3+	2±	2±
Chicken erythrocytes 1	0	±	3+	3±	2±
Chicken erythrocytes 2	0	±	3+	2±	±

Before leaving the discussion of Forssman antigen certain points of practical interest should be mentioned. One of these concerns the use of tissue extracts for the preparation of Wassermann antigen. In the Wassermann reaction the serum under test is permitted to react with an emulsion of alcoholic extract of normal animal tissue, and ox heart is generally employed for this purpose. The tissue of a Forssman-containing animal would be unsuitable for this preparation because many human sera contain appreciable amounts of Forssman antibody, and false positive fixation would occur.

A second potential source of difficulty in the Wassermann test exists if the serum of a syphilitic subject contains a high titer of Forssman antibodies. In the second step of the test sheep erythrocytes and rabbit antierythrocyte serum are added as indicator for the fixation of complement. If a part of the complement has been fixed in the primary reaction between the patient's serum and Wassermann antigen, the small amount of residual complement would ordinarily cause only incomplete lysis of the added sheep cells, and this would be interpreted as a moderately positive test. This result might be completely obscured by the presence of Forssman antibodies in the patient's serum, for the sum of these plus the antisheep erythrocyte antibody delib-

erately introduced into the test could bring the total concentration of hemolysin to the point where complete lysis might occur even with only a small
residue of complement. This follows from the quantitative interdependence of
complement and antibody in the lytic reaction; a small quantity of one may
be compensated by an excess of the other (see page 113). In this case the
patient with syphilis could show a falsely **negative** complement fixation test
(i.e. lysis of indicator cells). This situation can be circumvented by the routine absorption of sera with sheep cells prior to Wassermann testing.

Another interesting case of antigenic heterogenicity is that discovered by
Paul and Bunnell (20) in studies of patients with infectious mononucleosis.
Persons with this presumably infectious disease develop antibodies strongly
agglutinative for sheep erythrocytes. These were thought initially to be anti-
Forssman antibodies, but subsequent studies by Bailey and the writer and
others (21) have revealed that the antigen concerned in this reaction is a
distinct component of the sheep cell stroma which is shared also by the red
cells of the ox, a non-Forssman-containing species. This finding has proved
of diagnostic value because Forssman antibodies occur in many normal individuals in low titers, and even markedly increased amounts of a normally
occurring antibody fail to convey the diagnostic significance which the appearance of an entirely new antibody response implies. The fact that the
antibody of infectious mononucleosis only rarely appears in other circumstances is also a major point of diagnostic evidence. The determination of
the nature of sheep cell agglutinins appearing in a patient's serum—whether
they are directed against the Forssman or the infectious mononucleosis antigen of the erythrocyte—is provided by absorption tests. Thus, if the sheep cell
agglutinins are absorbed by a suspension of guinea pig tissue (Forssman
antigen) then the antibodies are of the Forssman type. On the other hand, if
this procedure fails while ox erythrocytes successfully remove the agglutinins,
then the indication is that the antibodies are directed against the infectious
mononucleosis antigen. There is, however, a third possibility which must be
considered. Information about another antigen of the sheep red cell has developed in respect to the serum sickness syndrome of human beings which may
follow injections of horse serum (see page 210). In this case again it was
noted some years ago that agglutinins for sheep erythrocytes are increased in
the sera of patients (22), and it was again found that these are not directed
against the Forssman antigen. Neither are they directed against the infectious
mononucleosis antigen (23). Instead these antibodies react with a third heterogenetic antigen of the sheep erythrocyte which occurs in rabbit cells also, as
well as in the tissues of other species.

Recent work by Tomcsik and Schwarzweiss has defined the chemical and
cellular relationships of these three heterogenetic antigens—Forssman, infectious mononucleosis, and serum sickness. Infectious mononucleosis antigen is extractable from ox cells by boiling 80 per cent alcohol (24). The
serum sickness antigen is also extractable from ox cells, but with boiling
absolute alcohol, and by this method small amounts are also obtainable from

guinea pig tissue and horse serum (25). The Forssman antigen, as has been described, is removed from sheep erythrocytes and various other tissues in which it occurs by simple extraction with alcohol at ordinary temperatures.

In addition to these three distinct thermostable heterogenetic antigens of the sheep erythrocyte, there have long been known to exist thermolabile antigens in these stromata also. One of these is a protein substance shared by ox and sheep erythrocytes as well as goat cells (26). The second is also a protein but it is species specific (27). It is this latter antigen against which the rabbit produces the major antibody response following injections of fresh sheep erythrocytes (28). The occurrences of these various antigens in five of the animal species which have been of most interest to serology and diagnosis are shown in Table 9.

Table 9. Occurrence of heterogenetic antigens of sheep erythrocytes in other species

ANTIGEN	OCCURRENCE OF ANTIGEN IN				
	SHEEP ERYTHROCYTES	OX ERYTHROCYTES	RABBIT ERYTHROCYTES	GUINEA PIG TISSUE	HORSE SERUM
Forssman	+	−	−	+	+
Infectious mononucleosis	+	+	−	−	−
Serum sickness	+	+	+	+	+
Protein antigen 1	+	+	..	..	..
Protein antigen 2	+	−	..	..	..
Protein antigen 3	−	+	..	..	..

Protein antigens 2 and 3 are the species-specific substances of sheep and ox erythrocytes respectively. It is to Antigen 2 that the rabbit vaccinated with sheep cells chiefly responds.

In addition to these examples of heterogenetic antigens, there are numerous other instances involving lower cellular forms as well as the tissues of animals. A common antigen occurs in the rickettsias of typhus and typhus-like fevers and certain strains of *Proteus vulgaris* in which they exist as O antigen (29). This forms the basis of a diagnostic reaction, the Weil-Felix test, for the rickettsial infections. The sera of suspected patients are tested for their ability to agglutinate the bacterium. These and other examples are discussed more fully in the general references cited earlier. Certain of the human blood cell antigens comprise important groups of heterogenetic substances which will be described in detail in the next chapter.

2. Species-Specific Antigens. Antigens characteristic of a species are by definition excluded from the class of heterogenetic substances. They may however show the more restricted characters described by the categories which

follow, i.e. they may be restricted to an **organ** of a species (organ specific) or they may be restricted to only certain individuals of a species (isoantigenic), or both concurrently.

Generally speaking, the species-specific antigens are proteinaceous, while the various substances extractable with organic solvents described before are usually heterogenetic. Landsteiner (2) suggests a logical explanation for this. He points out that proteins, being made up of many different amino acids, can have many more specific groupings than can the polysaccharides (or presumably, the lipids) which are composed of only a few different building stones. Protein antigens of tissues, however, may also be heterogenetic, as witnessed by thyroglobulin (30) and certain of the proteins of the optic lens (31), though species-specific constituents are also discernible in both cases (32).

Saline extracts of normal animal tissues contain substances sedimentable by the high speed ultracentrifuge. In addition to the heterogenetic Forssman and Wassermann antigens and the heterogenetic but organ-specific brain antigen found in the sediments of appropriate tissues, there occur also species-specific substances. In some cases these are common to various tissues of an animal, in others they are restricted to an organ (8b, 33).

Bailey and the writer some years ago made observations with heat-stable haptens of organs and tissues which again supply evidence for the existence of species-specific substances, though as yet there has been little correlative study of the natures of the antigens obtained by the various methods described in this section. It was observed that bacteria growing in ox muscle infusion broth adsorbed from it an antigenic constituent which engendered antibodies in rabbits vaccinated with these bacteria. Analogous heat-stable antigenic substances were eventually found to be present in broths made of many organs and tissues of a variety of animal species including, in addition to ox, the human being, dog, cat, rabbit, horse and rat. Studies of cross antigenicity were made by the precipitation and complement-fixation methods, but most extensively by the procedure of passive anaphylaxis in guinea pigs.

In cross tests with the precipitin and anaphylactic procedures, ox muscle was found to be closely related to muscle of the dog and horse, but distinct from the skeletal muscle of man, hog, sheep, cat, rabbit, guinea pig, rat, mouse, chicken, turtle or fish. The muscle antigens were for the most part organ as well as species specific. In chemical nature, these heat-stable antigens appeared to be proteoses (34).

Other examples of species specificity of antigens have been recorded for a variety of cells and tissues. Thus, the existence of such substances in erythrocytes is exemplified by the protein antigens of sheep and ox red cells noted in Table 9, and according to old work of Metchnikoff (35) species-specific antigens appear to characterize mammalian leukocytes also. The hemoglobins of various species can likewise be distinguished (36). In the spermatozoa of different animals, including the human being, heat-stable, species-specific antigens are found, as well as substances common to various species (37).

Although the blood sera of related species show cross-serologic activities it is well known that antibodies react most extensively with the homologous serum. According to Doerr and Berger (38) purified serum globulin and albumin are antigenically distinct, and each is characteristic of the species from which it is derived. Brain substance has been extensively studied as an example of heterogenetic organ-specific antigenicity, but apparently a species antigen, probably a protein, is also present in it (6c). Certain species-specific antigens have been described as occurring in multiple locales in the animal body. Examples include an antigen found in erythrocytes and tracheal epithelium, and another which has been detected in milk, erythrocytes and epithelium (39).

The existence of strictly species-specific tissue or body fluid antigens is probably very limited, perhaps because the homologous structures of related animals may be made up of chemically and hence serologically related molecules.

3. Isoantigens. Isoantigens are substances which are characteristic of certain members only of a single species, so that other individuals within the species can respond immunologically to them. The outstanding examples of such antigens are the blood group factors of man, including the ABO, the MN, and the various Rh and Hr antigens, as well as others which will be described in the next chapter. Despite the restriction of these antigens to only a segment of individuals within a species, and of certain ones to the red cells alone (i.e. organ specific) they are nonetheless heterogenetic in their distribution. Red cell isoantigens occur also in lower animal species.

Aside from the red cells it is difficult to find clearly defined examples of isoantigens. It seems very probable that the existence of such factors may account for the general failure of skin graft takes between members of a species, but it has not been possible so far to delineate this observation in precise serologic terms. This subject will be discussed later in this chapter in relation to the occurrence of immunopathologic states.

Certain reports suggest that individual human sera may possess distinctive antigens, demonstrable by precipitin reactions with absorbed rabbit antisera (40). The formation of isoprecipitins by a single rabbit against the sera of other rabbits has also been reported (41), as have rare occurrences of anaphylactic reactivity and the appearance of complement-fixing antibodies following plasma transfusion in man (42).

4. Organ-Specific Antigens. Antigenic constituents of animal tissues which are specific for a particular cell or organ have been mentioned in preceding paragraphs. Most of these are heterogenetic, occurring often in the homologous organs of various species of animals, but some have been described as species as well as organ specific. There are also organ-specific antigens which are isoantigens, as are for example certain of the human erythrocyte factors. All of these presently known are also heterogenetic.

The concept of organ specificity of antigens is closely allied to the question of immunologic disease brought about either through a response of one member of a species to substances present in another individual (e.g. iso-antibody formation against blood group antigens occurring during pregnancy, or following transfusions), or of an individual against organ-specific antigens of his own tissues. These two potential phenomena will be discussed more fully in succeeding sections. For the present, it is intended to establish the occurrence and nature of such substances.

It was mentioned earlier that antigenic substances can be sedimented from saline extracts of normal tissues by centrifugation at speeds of about 25,000 r.p.m. (11), and a variety of antigenic substances are present in such sediments. Some of these occur in various organs of an animal (12, 13), and some are organ specific. In the latter class, Henle and co-workers (8a, 8b) describe characteristic antigens of the brain, liver, kidney, lung, testicle and heart muscle of mouse and beef. Of these, the first two are heterogenetic with respect to species while the others appear to be species as well as organ specific. Similar organ antigens have been found by others (33).

Observations of the same kind have been made with sedimented particles of transplantable tumors of animals. Kidd (43) worked with two rabbit tumors, one the Brown-Pearce tumor, and the second a neoplasm sometimes resulting from infection with rabbit papilloma virus and referred to as V_2 carcinoma. In both cases rabbits develop specific antibodies against the sedimented cellular constituents. Landsteiner (2) points out that the antigens concerned may represent substances derived from the original rabbits in which the tumors arose, i.e. isoantigens. In this case they would not necessarily be specific substances of the tumor cells, for they could represent antigenic components characteristic of all the tissues of the parent rabbits. On the other hand, they could as well be organ-specific antigens in the parent rabbits or, interpreting Kidd's findings at face value, antigens of the tumors which have no other relationship to the rabbit at all. There has been no clear evidence as yet that a tumor arising *de novo* in an individual human being or animal possesses antigens characteristic of itself to the exclusion of other tissues of the host.

A good deal of work with organ antigens has been carried out with lipoidal extracts. Lipoidal extraction eliminates the entire range of species protein antigens which may obscure more specific factors, and thus permits the identification of specific substances by antibody activity. The substances extracted are not complete antigens; they are what Landsteiner (2) refers to as cell haptens, substances which in their natural state probably exist in complex with protein carrier and are removed from this by the action of lipid solvents. It seems dubious that the serologic activity of these haptens in general depends upon their lipoidal constituents; associated polysaccharides may, in many cases at least, be responsible for this. These haptens can frequently be made antigenic by simple mixture with foreign protein, such as serum, as Landsteiner first showed with Forssman antigen extract (2).

Characteristic of the work done with such extracts have been the studies of Witebsky and Steinfeld (6c), and of Lewis (44). Witebsky found that antibodies produced against whole brain react with alcohol extracted substance, while Lewis used the extract itself made antigenic by mixture with serum to vaccinate animals. In both cases a similarity or identity of specific brain antigen in various animals was noted. As mentioned in an earlier connotation, Lewis found that a similar antigen is extractable also from testes, but not from a variety of other organs studied, including liver, kidney, heart, lung and spleen. A specific extract from beef lung has also been described (45), and other examples are reviewed by Weil (46).

Another method of study has similarly resulted in the demonstration that various organs of a single animal may possess distinctive antigenic substances. It was related in the discussion of species antigens that heat-stable haptens occur in autoclaved infusion broths prepared from various tissues, and that bacteria grown in such broths adsorb these substances which can then induce antibodies in rabbits. By the use of in vitro and passive anaphylaxis tests it was found that antibodies developed against ox skeletal muscle reacted with various organs containing such muscle (e.g. tongue and esophagus) as well as with heart muscle, but failed to react with any of about 30 other tissues studied except lung. A common antigen was detected in lung and intestine which was also represented in heart and to some extent in skeletal muscle (34). In the dog, specific substances were also found in striated muscle, in smooth muscle, and in kidney, and similar specific factors were discovered in human organs and tissues where, however, an antigen common to lung and liver was detected (47). In an extension of this work Bailey and Gardner (7, 48) found an organ-specific heterogenetic antigen in the brains of rat, guinea pig, ox, hog and human being. This antigen appeared to be a component of myelin; it occurred in small amount if at all in gray matter, and the authors believe it to be neurokeratin.

Studies of organ specificity have been carried out with whole fresh tissue or cell emulsions also. Although many nonorgan-specific antibodies are engendered by vaccination with such preparations it has frequently been possible to isolate a specific organ reaction by absorbing the antiserum with blood and other tissues of the animal supplying the particular cells under study. This has been done for example by Fleisher and Arnstein (49) who found evidence of the formation of specific antibody to fresh guinea pig muscle, and by Cavelti (50) who induced the development of antibodies to various homologous tissues in rats by adding streptococci to the tissue emulsions, and found evidence of specific as well as cross reacting antibodies. In a more restricted sense such specificity was demonstrated by Hektoen and associates (51) who were able to establish the distinctiveness of muscle hemoglobin of the dog from blood hemoglobin and serum. Specific antigens in the heads and tails of spermatozoa have also been found (37b). It has been mentioned before that fresh lens proteins are organ specific (and heterogenetic), and that thyroglobulin has organ specificity, though in both cases species-specific factors are also apparent (30, 32a, 32b, 32c). Masugi (52) injected rabbits with rat liver emulsion; the rabbit sera were subsequently absorbed with rat blood after which they reacted most strongly with liver itself and only to a limited extent with serum. Mention should be made also of the important question of antigenicity of hormones. One of the most commonly used of these, insulin, is a protein which has been crystallized. It is identical or almost so in various animals and it shares no antigenic property with other proteins of the various animal species which have been studied (53). In a sense then it is an organ-specific antigen. It has a low degree of antigenicity for human beings; reactions to it have been reported, but these are infrequent considering its widespread parenteral application (54).

In addition to these serologic and anaphylactic methods, another procedure has been applied to the study of organ specificity. This consists of observing the cytotoxic effects of anti-organ sera in vivo. For this purpose antisera are produced to suspensions of an organ in animals of a heterologous species. These sera are then injected into individuals of the species under test and observations are made for the occurrence of specific effects upon the organ or cell in question. Examples of this procedure are provided by the observations (55) that antiplatelet serum induces hemorrhages simulating purpura hemorrhagica, that antisera against leukocytes or bone marrow cause leukopenia (56), and that antiliver serum produces hepatic damage (52, 57). In recent years studies with kidney tissue have received a good deal of attention. An injurious activity of antikidney serum was first observed by Lindemann in 1900 (58), but interest in the matter lagged until, over 30 years later, Masugi demonstrated the toxicity for the rat of an anti-rat-kidney serum produced in the rabbit (59). The induction of nephritis by antikidney sera has now been described in rats, rabbits, dogs and guinea pigs. The question of the mechanism by which antisera induce glomerulonephritis will be discussed later in relation to the general subject of iso- and autoimmunization; for the present we shall examine the evidence for organ-specific kidney antigens provided by this line of investigation.

Several workers have suggested that various organ-unspecific sera, such as those produced against liver, can also cause kidney damage (60). The lesion in this case however usually appears also to be unspecific; it is the kind of renal injury which may follow any of a variety of insults to the body, and as such it is generally distinguishable from the specific glomerular lesion induced by antikidney sera (61). That some cross reactivity does occur however is indicated by the following observations.

The specificity of the antibodies in antikidney sera has been revealed in several ways. If the serum is perfused through the kidneys of freshly killed animals, the nephrotoxic factor is absorbed (61c, 62); if the antiserum is absorbed in vitro with kidney tissue it loses its nephrotoxicity also (63); and if saline extracts of kidney are injected into rats immediately preceding the intravenous injection of antikidney serum the nephrotoxic effect is inhibited (64). As might be expected, the specificity of such sera is not absolute; in serologic tests Smadel (65) found antikidney serum reactive with liver, heart, erythrocytes and serum. This can be explained in part at least on the basis of multiplicity of antigens present in a suspension of whole kidney substance, some of which may be common to all tissues of the animal. However an antibrain serum was in one instance found to produce nephritic lesions, and antikidney sera after intensive absorption with liver may sometimes lose their nephrotoxic capacities (64). In addition, Seegal and her associates have shown that antiplacenta sera may cause nephritis in a large proportion of rats or dogs receiving it (66).

Recently two very interesting experimental approaches have been applied to the question of the specificity of antikidney antibody. In one case glomeruli were separated from perfused rat kidneys by the application of pressure and differential centrifugation of constituents. When anti-rat-kidney serum was absorbed with these glomeruli its ability to produce kidney damage was removed. In contrast tubular constituents failed to absorb the kidney-damaging factor (67). Complementing this work are the experiments of Heymann and associates (68) in which one series of rabbits was vaccinated with rat kidney cortex and a second series with medulla. Eight of nine sera produced against cortex caused nephritis in rats while only one of the seven sera directed against medulla did this, and the authors suggest that this may have been due to admixture of some cortical substance in the vaccinating preparation.

Finally, Pressman and co-workers have been attacking the same problem by the use of antikidney antibody labelled with radioactive iodine. Photographs reveal the localization of such antibody primarily in the glomeruli (69). The lack of strict organ specificity revealed by the less refined procedures just described has been affirmed by these experiments. Antibodies against kidney were permitted to react with this organ and were then eluted. When such antibody was injected into a fresh subject most of it went again to the kidney, but some (as in the original serum on first injection) localized in the liver and lung. Antibodies eluted from these organs upon second injection went either to kidney or back to these organs again. Similar cross reactivity of eluted antibody was seen in antisera prepared against lung. There exists then a preferential affinity of antibody for the organ against which it has been produced, but cross reactivity occurs also. Pressman believes that these anti-organ antibodies are produced against constituents of the vascular bed of the organ employed for vaccination (70).

Before leaving the subject of organ specificity it may be of interest to review briefly the studies which have been made of the development of organ-specific antigens during embryonic and early postnatal life. Bailey and Gardner (7) in their work with the heat-stable organ-specific antigens of brain found that in the rat, guinea pig and rabbit the substance was absent from embryonic nerve tissue. In the rat it appeared about 17 days postnatally, and in the guinea pig it was present at two days. These investigators correlated the absence of antigen with the absence of myelin in animals during embryonic or early postnatal life. In the human being, earlier work had shown that the antigenic specificity of nerve tissue appears in the third to fourth month of embryonic life (71). In chick embryos Burke and associates (72) have uncovered evidence of progressively changing antigenic specificity. The organ-specific embryo lens antigen is different from adult lens substance up to about the 300th hour developmental stage. The erythrocyte antigens before the 100th developmental hour also differ from those of the adult, and brain antigen shows analogous changes.

Iso- and Autoimmunization. The terms immunity and immunization have so far been employed in this book only in respect to resistance to infectious and toxic agents, and the matters which are about to be discussed do not fall into that category. There seem to be no adequate terms, however, to describe the process of the body's responses to noninfectious and nontoxic agents in which no question of resistance enters, but where the modes of response are analogous to those which may have a part in resistance. The words immunity and immunization will be used as expedients in the remainder of this chapter.

In preface to this discussion it should be explained that although iso-antigen was defined earlier as a substance which occurs in only a segment of the members of a species and which can serve as an antigenic stimulus to the remaining individuals, the term is also used in a broader sense to include certain organ-specific antigens which are found in all members of a species but which occur in other species as well. For example, certain antigens of brain are found in all rabbits, they are restricted in occurrence to nerve tissue, and they are closely related or identical to brain antigens of various other animals. If brain antigen from one species is injected into another the procedure is referred to as isoimmunization, for in a sense this is equivalent to the injection of brain substance from another individual of the same species and furthermore, as will be detailed, it is equivalent to autoimmunization, i.e. to the injection of brain substance from an individual into himself. This special case of equating immunization against the tissue of a heterologous species with iso- and autoimmunization exists because the antigen concerned is highly specific as regards organ and unspecific as regards species. Actually, such substances are generally without true iso- or autoantigenic properties unless some alteration is made in them, as will be described.

It has been established beyond doubt that both iso- and autoimmunization can occur, in some cases spontaneously, in many more through proper experimental manipulations. The isoantibodies of the various blood group factors represent of course entirely forthright responses by individuals to substances which are foreign to them. The concept is different when we deal with iso responses to tissue components which are apparently common to all members of a species, and this becomes even more striking when we deal with immunologic responses by an animal to its own tissues. In the latter case especially there is plainly implicit serious detriment to the individual's welfare, a situation to which Ehrlich applied the dramatic appellation "horror autotoxicus."

There are three main questions to be answered in a consideration of this subject:

1. What are the conditions under which the body can respond to antigenic substances of other individuals of its own species (excluding the blood group substances) or of its own tissues? Is it possible that an antigen restricted to a particular organ or tissue may be regarded as foreign by the cells which respond to antigens, or is there some signal by which these cells are apprised that the substance is native to the body? The observation of Kidd and Friedewald (12) of normal antibodies in rabbits against native cellular constituents suggest that tissue antigens may provide a stimulus for autoantibody production under ordinary physiologic circumstances. Burnet and Fenner (73) believe, on the other hand, that there is a warning signal which they term "self-marker components of the body cells," established during embryonic life.

2. When an immunologic response to iso- or autoantigens has occurred, is this capable of damaging the tissues in which the antigens exist? Kidd and Friedewald (12) explain the harmlessness of the normal antibodies against sedimentable cellular components as due to the cytoplasmic location of the latter. Like virus, such antigens may be protected by the cell wall from combination with antibodies. This may, however, be a special case.

3. If iso- and autoimmunologic responses can injure tissues, through what mechanism may this come about? Is there a destructive activity of antibodies upon cells, or can hypersensitization account for injury, or may both be invoked?

The best introduction to the evidence bearing upon these questions is a description of the various clinical and experimentally produced states in which iso- and autoimmunization are known or thought to be concerned.

TISSUE GRAFTING. One probable example of isoimmunization is provided by the events which occur in tissue grafting. It is well known that skin grafting between individuals of the same species, man or animal, is rarely successful. This problem has been studied extensively by Medawar in rabbits, and his as well as other findings strongly suggest that these failures are basically immunologic in origin. Thus, donor skin in a previously untreated recipient attaches and grows normally for perhaps 10 days, and then dies, following which the recipient becomes much more rapidly destructive to additional grafts from the same donor, but not from other donors. Further, rabbits can be put into this state of quickened response against grafts by preliminary treatment consisting of the intradermal injection of leukocytes from the donor (74). Dukes and Blocker (75) worked on the assumption that nuclear antigens may be involved in the immunizing process, and placed desoxyribonuclease under the graft in an attempt to modify these antigens before they could be absorbed by the recipients' lymphatic and vascular systems. Deterioration of grafts was significantly delayed by this procedure, intimating that part at least of a responsible antigen may have been inactivated. With all this evidence suggesting an immunologic basis for graft deterioration, no one has yet successfully demonstrated the presence of antibodies to donor skin, either by serologic test or by an effect of recipient serum upon donor tissue in culture. Yet it has been shown that in other special circumstances animals can develop antibodies against skin. Thus, Hecht and associates (76) prepared fine suspensions of rabbit skin mixed with alumina cream and injected these into rabbits along with staphylococcus toxin. Precipitating antibody for skin extracts resulted from this procedure, whereas rabbit skin suspensions injected alone failed to evoke the response. Addition of toxin is one of the procedures known to endow tissues with iso- and autoantigenicity, as will be described later.

The tissue transfer situation then is one which points convincingly to an isoimmunizing mechanism to account for tissue destruction, yet the final proof of this—the demonstration of a response by conventional serologic methods—has so far been elusive (77).

DEMYELINATING ENCEPHALOMYELITIS. An experimentally produced disease of much current interest is the striking brain damage which can be effected by the injection of heterologous, homologous or autologous brain substance into animals of various species. This line of investigation began with the observation that repeated injections of heterologous—or autolyzed or vaccinia-infected homologous—brain into rabbits causes paralysis without the concomitance of visible pathologic changes (78). Before long it became apparent that a certain proportion of animals treated with aqueous emulsions of heterologous brain develop clearly demonstrable encephalomyelitic lesions with myelin destruction (79), and that this may be brought about with great regularity by suspending homologous or even autologous brain in emulsions of water-in-oil to which killed tubercle bacilli have been added ([80], see also discussion of adjuvants, page 80).

Part of the interest which led to these findings arose from the infrequent but puzzling occurrence of disseminated demyelinating encephalomyelitis in people after vaccination against rabies, in which a vaccine made of nerve tissue is employed (81). A similar pathologic state may follow various virus diseases or vaccination against viruses (e.g. smallpox), or it may occur without known antecedent as a manifestation of multiple sclerosis, Schilder's disease and other encephalitides of unknown etiology (82). In the first instance one thinks of the possibility of isoimmunization, in the latter cases of autoimmunization.

There is no question in this case, as there is in that of skin grafting, that antibodies can be formed by an individual against brain substance of other members of his species or against his own brain tissues, provided that these are mixed with killed bacteria or permitted to autolyze, or are altered in other ways—some apparently very mild—from the native state. There is no evidence known to the writer bearing upon the ability of human beings to respond similarly to iso or auto brain substance, but observations are on record of antibody formation to rabbit brain rabies vaccine, and such antibodies react also with human brain substance (83). The question which so far remains moot is whether conversion to antigenicity can occur in vivo, under the influence of infection or in other abnormal circumstances, to induce an immunologic response analogous to that resulting from the injection of modified brain antigen. Some years ago a partial answer to this question was contained in a report by Weil and Liebert (84) that the serum of one of two patients with glioblastoma multiforme contained antibodies in low concentration against alcoholic extracts of human brain. The author is not aware of additional evidence of this kind. Such testimony would plainly be of great importance to the concept of autoimmunization.

HEMOLYSIS AND HEMAGGLUTINATION. Definite evidence exists in human beings and animals that antibodies can be formed against an individual's own red cells, and these are generally active against the erythrocytes of other members of the species as well. These are not produced against any of the known erythrocyte isoantigens; they appear rather to be directed against a species-specific and probably cell-specific antigen.

The first and clearest example of this occurrence was provided by Donath and Landsteiner's discovery of an hemolysin in the serum of occasional patients with syphilis and very rarely in individuals without this disease (85). This antibody unites with red cells at low temperature only, and causes hemolysis at body temperature only, in the presence of complement. A person so affected suffers intravascular hemolysis after the exposure of even a portion of his body to cold; the disease is called paroxysmal hemoglobinuria. There is no question here of the development of a destructive autoantibody. The antibody is unrelated to that which is responsible for the Wassermann reaction (86).

Autoantibodies against red cells are also produced in a variety of other circumstances. These are more restricted in their activity; they agglutinate but do not lyse the cells, and their agglutinative activity occurs only in the cold. Such antibodies are found in many patients with atypical pneumonia (87), but they occur less regularly also in other diseases including acute bacterial infections, trypanosomiasis, Raynaud's disease, cirrhosis of the liver and in lupus erythematosus (88). In fact many years ago Landsteiner (89) showed that such antibodies in low concentrations can be detected in normal plasmas at temperatures below 5° C.; when these are increased in amount by a pathologic process they usually function at temperatures ranging up to 25° C. A similar situation has been found in rabbits (90).

Although it seems improbable that the cold hemagglutinins ordinarily cause damage to the body, the possibility that this may happen is suggested by Stats' (91) finding that slight agitation of agglutinated cells suffices to break them down, if antibodies are present in high concentration. Also suggestive of an occasional damaging effect of such antibodies is the description by Stats and Bullowa (92) of a patient in whom gangrene of the tips of fingers and toes occurred after exposure to moderate cold, and who was found to have a high level of cold agglutinins, the basis for which could not be explained. Instances of acute hemolytic anemia have been seen to accompany atypical pneumonia (93) and it is recommended that chilling of patients with this disease be avoided in order to forestall the possibility of activation of the cold agglutinins (94). It has also been suggested that the physiologic jaundice of newborn infants may be caused by cold agglutinins, in this case transmitted from the mother (95); again avoidance of chilling is indicated.

The possible relationship of union between cold-activated antibodies and antigen to the occurrence of allergic reactions to cold was discussed in Chapter 16.

Another clinical condition in which an autoimmune mechanism seems to be implicated is acquired hemolytic anemia. It was believed for some time that the manifest destruction of erythrocytes in this disease might be caused by antibodies adsorbed to the cells, hence not demonstrable by serologic tests (96). With the introduction by Coombs of the antiglobulin test for demonstrating antibody attached to cells (see page 121) this hypothesis became amenable to proof which was supplied in 1946 (97). These antibodies act at body temperature, and can be eluted at 56° C. A degree of mystery still surrounds the question of mechanism of hemolysis, for this is unlike the rapid lytic effect seen in the usual antibody-complement system. Furthermore, not even agglutination of the patient's cells has been seen to occur in vivo; erythrocytes must be lightly centrifuged for the adherence tendency to become apparent. Evans and Duane (98) believe that slight agglutination in the blood stream may cause stasis with increased fragility of erythrocytes and possibly increased susceptibility to phagocytosis. Another uncertain point concerns the basis for the beneficial effect of splenectomy in the treatment of this disease. Usually this procedure is followed by clinical remission as well as a decrease in antibody upon the cells, suggesting that the spleen may be a principal site of autoantibody formation, but sometimes there is a recrudescence of antibody without a recurrence of the anemia (98).

Recent work indicates that autoantibodies may account for other kinds of anemia also, including the congenital type (99).

These hemolytic and hemoagglutinative antibodies then supply clear evidence that autoantibody formation can occur, though the serologic details of their activities are not yet altogether apparent.

GLOMERULONEPHRITIS. The kidney studies described earlier in this chapter make it evident that antibodies produced against renal tissue by an animal of a heterologous species can cause glomerular damage. From this fact it might appear that a direct cytotoxic activity of antibodies against kidney elements accounts for their injury. This may be so, but Kay (61c) has suggested an alternative mechanism for which there is also pertinent evidence. He believes that the damage is not inflicted directly by the antikidney antibody, but rather that the recipient of this antiserum in turn forms antibody against it, i.e. antiantibody. The injected antikidney antibodies become attached to renal tissue but are in themselves harmless to it. Now, however, the subject's antiantibody combines with the antikidney antibody in the kidney, and a hypersensitive reaction involving the glomerulus takes place. Kay presents the following observations to support this viewpoint: First, the period required for the development of nephritis following the injection of antirenal serum into rabbits corresponds to the interval necessary for the development of antiprotein precipitins. Secondly, this incubation period is reduced if the subject is pretreated with normal serum from the species supplying the kidney antibodies. This suggests that if the subject already has antiglobulin antibodies (equivalent to antiantibodies) at the time of injection of the antikidney serum, the kidney-damaging reaction can occur immediately. Thirdly, x-ray irradiation of rabbits to the point of interference with their antibody manufacturing ability makes them insusceptible to injury by subsequently injected antikidney serum. This indicates again that antiantibody production by the subject is necessary for the occurrence of renal damage.

Although these points seem to be well established and the interpretation appears clear, they fail to answer certain important questions relating to the mechanism of immunologic kidney damage. First of all, the simultaneous injection of antikidney serum and antiantibody against this (i.e. the injection of duck antirabbit kidney antibodies, and rabbit antiduck serum antibodies) does not reduce the lag time for the appearance of nephritis (100). Also the case dealt with by Kay is a restricted one, for while nephritis eventuates only several days after the injection of duck antirabbit kidney antibodies in the rabbit, and of chicken antidog kidney antibodies in dogs, antibodies which are not produced in fowl act more quickly. Thus, antibodies produced in the rabbit for the kidneys of the dog, the rat or the guinea pig, evoke nephritic lesions in these animals hours rather than days following injection. An interval of this brevity rules out any question of the necessity for antiantibodies.

We can only conclude tentatively that in some circumstances the production of kidney damage by antirenal serum may depend upon a hypersensitive response subsequent to the union of antibody with foreign globulin (the antikidney antibody) in the kidney substance. This viewpoint coincides with the concept that spontaneously occurring glomerulonephritis in the human being may depend upon a hypersensitive mechanism, as was discussed in Chapter 13. In certain instances, on the other hand, it may be that damage to glomeruli follows from a direct activity of antibody upon susceptible cells.

This discussion has so far dealt with renal injury occasioned by heterologous antibodies. This is an experimentally created situation; if we are to attempt to learn something from such experiences about the mechanism of occurrence of spontaneous nephritis, the next question concerns the possibility whether iso- or autoimmunization to kidney substances can take place. Several investigators have reported affirmative observations on this point in rabbits injected with rabbit kidney mixed with streptococcus or staphylococcus toxin (101) or with kidney which had undergone ischemic necrosis in vivo (102), and in rats injected with rat kidney mixed with streptococci (103) or adjuvant (104). Further, it has been reported that human beings with scarlet fever may develop antibodies reactive upon rabbit kidney antigen (101). But none of these findings have been unanimously confirmed (105). Consequently there is still some uncertainty as to whether antikidney antibodies can develop spontaneously in human beings, or even whether isoantibodies to kidney can be induced experimentally.

As to the possibility that an iso or auto antikidney response, if it should occur, could lead to the development of renal lesions in an immunized animal, opinions differ again. The most extensive work on this point has been carried out by the Caveltis. In rabbits infrequently, but in rats with regularity, they have found that glomerular lesions develop after repeated injections of homologous kidney substance mixed with killed hemolytic streptococci (106). The implication of this work for the explanation of spontaneous glomerulonephritis in man is evident. It is commonly agreed that the hemolytic streptococcus is concerned in the etiology of this disease. One viewpoint, expressed in Chapter 13, considers the renal lesion to be a consequence of hypersensitive reactivity to the streptococcus. Cavelti's findings, on the other hand, focus attention upon the activity of the streptococcus in so altering kidney tissue that it can function as an autoantigen. Subsequent pathologic alterations would then result from the immunologic response of the body to kidney itself rather than to the bacterium. If we apply to this problem the evidence available from studies with heterologous antibodies described earlier, there is reason to think that either mechanism could be at work. It is difficult to assess the final significance of Cavelti's findings at the present time. Confirmation has come from several sources (107), but failures have also been reported (108). This attractive possibility will require further work before final judgment of its validity can be made.

RHEUMATIC FEVER. The present status of our knowledge in respect to the etiology of rheumatic fever is analogous to that for glomerulonephritis. Here also, as described in Chapter 13, there is evidence to indicate that the development of the characteristic lesions of this disease may follow from a hypersensitivity developed to antigens of the streptococcus. The evidence in this case is stronger than that for glomerulonephritis, but not sufficiently tight as to preclude other explanations, and one among these is again the possibility of autoimmunization. Cavelti (106b) has found both in rabbits and rats that antibodies reactive with heart tissue extract can be induced by injections of homologous heart tissue mixed with streptococci. There has also been a degree of success in demonstrating antibodies against heart extract in patients with rheumatic fever (109). In rats, but not in rabbits, vaccination with homologous tissue has resulted also in the appearance of lesions in the endo- and myocardium, described by this investigator as grossly comparable to those which occur in rheumatic fever in the human being (110). The same lesions result from injections of connective tissue, but not of skeletal muscle, spleen or kidney. Confirmation of this observation has been described by Jaffe and Holz (111) and failure of repetition by Humphrey (108). Again, as in the case of glomerulonephritis, there is not yet available the conclusive evidence upon which one may predicate a final choice between the alternative hypotheses mentioned. In neither case do the lesions entirely satisfactorily mimic those of the disease in human beings, nor are other aspects of the testimony complete. Actually the two viewpoints are not necessarily incompatible in their broader outlines. Both subscribe to the requirement that infection with the hemolytic streptococcus sets in motion a chain of events leading to a pathologic state which is not a direct result of bacterial activity. In one case this sequence is regarded as based upon a state of hypersensitivity to streptococcal constituents or products; in the other, the streptococcus is thought to alter host tissue sufficiently so that it may become autoantigenic, and the antibody directed against this strikes back at normal tissue of the same kind.

WASSERMANN ANTIBODIES. For the past 50 years there has lingered a recurring belief that the peculiar antibodies which reflect the presence of syphilis may be respondent to the host's own tissue substance rather than to the etiologic agent of the disease itself. This conception was suggested by Weil and Braun (112) as a result of the finding that preparations of normal animal tissues serve as well as those of syphilitic organs as antigen in the Wassermann test, and the subsequent discovery that alcoholic extracts of normal tissues are equally suitable for this purpose. Landsteiner (2) remarks that these discoveries violated two contemporary immunologic tenets; first, that lipoidal substances (i.e. anything other than protein) could function in an antigenic capacity, and second, that the body could produce antibodies against an entity extractable from normal tissues.

There are compelling reasons for regarding the autoimmunization viewpoint as an attractive one. Aside from the main fact that luetic patients do possess antibodies which react in vitro with normal tissue substances (extractable from all tissues), Sachs and co-workers demonstrated some years ago (2) that the injection into rabbits of alcoholic extracts of normal rabbit organs mixed with heterologous protein sufficed to evoke antibodies active in the Wassermann test. These workers therefore concurred with Weil and Braun in the suggestion that the antibodies formed in the disease result from autoimmunization by haptens derived from pathologically altered tissues, aided in their antigenic capacities by the proteins of T. pallidum which act as carrier.

The opposite viewpoint holds that the Wassermann antibodies are a response to an antigen of the spirochete which is related to an antigenic factor of normal animal tissues. This has been championed especially by Beck (113) and Eagle (114). They have found that a cultured strain of spirochetes (not entirely identical with T. pallidum) serves as antigen in the complement fixation test with human sera, that it absorbs Wassermann reactivity from syphilitic sera, and that rabbits injected with ox heart lipids and suitable carrier develop antibody for the spirochetes. Since absorption of syphilitic sera with tissue lipids removes all Wassermann antibody while leaving behind antibody against the spirochetes, Eagle and Hogan (114a) suggest that the tissue antigen represents only a portion of the total antigen present in the spirochete.

An obstacle to the final clarification of this problem has been the lack of a method for the cultivation of T. pallidum itself. The findings just described would be more satisfying if the agent of the disease itself could have been employed for the serologic investigations. In later work, Eagle and Fleischman (114b) used heat-killed T. pallidum from rabbit tissues, and with these induced Wassermann antibodies. The difficulty here of course is the fact that tissue components were injected along with the spirochetes and these might account for the antibodies. Furthermore, the treated rabbits in these experiments did not produce antibodies reacting with the spirochetes themselves.

The question as to whether Wassermann antibody formation represents a response of the infected body to its own altered tissues, or to spirochetal antigen, is thus still open. Both Landsteiner (2) and Eagle (114a) propose that if the Wassermann response were an autoantibody phenomenon it should have less specificity than it shows, since many infectious diseases are destructive of tissues and hence should logically free autoantigens to stimulate the body's antibody forming apparatus. This is a two-edged argument, however; it is well known that though the Wassermann and related tests show a high degree of specificity, yet many positive reactions are seen also with the sera of nonluetic patients suffering from leprosy or malaria, and less frequently they may occur in infectious mononucleosis, after smallpox and other vaccinations, in measles and diphtheria, and in various states in which hyperproteinemia occurs (115).

Whether these antibodies in syphilis are evoked by spirochetal or tissue substances, in either case the question occurs as to why they do not attack cells of the body indiscriminately, for the Wassermann antigen is known to be isolatable from just about all organs and tissues of the normal body. Perhaps the best explanation for this failure of antibodies to damage cells is again Kidd and Friedewald's (12) suggestion based upon their work with sedimentable constituents of tissue substances, described earlier in this chapter. According to this view the Wassermann and other cellular antigens extractable with saline are cytoplasmic constituents which, like intracellular viruses, are sheltered from the action of humoral antibodies.

OCULAR DISEASE. Although the issues are not clear, other provocative possibilities of the occurrence of autoimmunization are met with in the cases of certain lesions of the eye. One of these is sympathetic ophthalmia, in which an injury to one eye involving the uveal tissue often results in a later granulomatous lesion in the uveal tract of the other eye. This sequel is thought to result from the patient's development of sensitivity to uveal pigment, since antibody and skin reactivity to this substance are detectable. It has not been finally established that either of these factors can result in the damage seen in these cases, however. Woods (116) believes that an accessory factor, such as the localization of bacteria in the eye, may be required in addition to the damaging effect of a hypersensitive reaction to establish the characteristic lesion of the disease.

A second situation for which an immunologic mechanism may be pertinent is one which follows damage to the ocular lens. As noted in an earlier section of this chapter, certain of the proteins of lens are organ specific and heterogenetic. Occasionally the extraction of a cataractous lens is succeeded by a postoperative intraocular inflammation. This has been thought to be due to a reaction between retained lens substance and ocular tissues sensitized to it. A hypersensitive state is indicated by the skin reactivity of many affected individuals to lens extract. This disease has been burdened with the appelation "endophthalmitis phacoanaphylactica" to suggest the possibility of a hypersensitive etiology. Attempts to reproduce this syndrome in experimental animals were fruitless until Burky in 1934 (117) added staphylococcus toxin to ox lens substance. The injection of this mixture into rabbits caused the development of antibodies and Arthus reactivity to lens antigen itself. When the animals were subjected to needling of the lens to simulate the operative procedure employed in cataract removal, they developed intraocular inflammation. This leaves still to be explained the manner in which, in patients, residual lens after removal becomes antigenic, for in these experiments injection of lens extract alone led to none of the consequences described above. Only the lens-toxin combination effected the immunologic response required for the later sequelae of lens needling.

In earlier work also Hektoen (4, 118) had found that while rabbits can respond to clear saline extracts of various mammalian lenses with antibody formation, and such antibodies reacted with rabbit as well as other lens extract, the animals failed to respond to their own lens substance. One wonders then how a cataractous patient may respond to his own lens substance. Hektoen's (118) experiments indicated little antigenic difference between cataractous and normal human lens so far as this could be determined by antibodies produced in rabbits. Yet slight changes may perhaps suffice to convert the substances to autoantigens, for Hektoen and Schulhof (4) found that the isolated proteins of rabbit lens were antigenic to rabbits while whole extracts were not, and they suggested that the chemical manipulations of isolation may have engendered this capacity to immunize.

YELLOW FEVER. Some years ago Hughes (119) noted that the sera of monkeys convalescent from yellow fever cause precipitation of a substance present in the blood of animals in the acute stage of the disease. The acute stage antigen varied roughly in amount with the severity of the illness, and did not parallel the virus content of the blood. Consequently, Hughes believed that this antigen might be a product of cellular injury produced by viral action, i.e. an autoantigen. Human convalescent sera showed in half of 10 trials similar reactivity with a monkey blood preparation, suggesting a lack of species specificity of the antigen. These results coincide with interpretations previously expressed by other investigators (120). Further work on this interesting question does not appear to have been done in more recent years.

1. ACTIVATION OF ISO- AND AUTOANTIGENS. We can return now to the questions posed earlier (see page 457) regarding the applicability of the concept of iso- and autoimmunization to the explanation of the occurrence of immunologic diseases. The first of these relates to the circumstances in which substances native to a species or an individual might take on the character of antigens for it. The ways in which this might come about spontaneously are discussed now on the basis of evidence supplied by the examples just considered.

First, it seems to be established that the fact of organ or tissue specificity in itself does not in general account for the capacity of a tissue constituent to function as an immunologic stimulus to the body in which it occurs, or to the body of another member of the species. Possible exceptions are the antigens of spermatozoa (121), the sedimentable tissue components described by Kidd and Friedewald (12), and insulin (54), but the usual experience has been that tissue substances can provoke iso and auto responses only when they have been modified in some way. A variety of experimental procedures have been found to effect the necessary modification. Tissue constituents soluble in organic solvents may become antigenic upon the addition of a foreign heterologous protein, for example, a serum. This has been demonstrated with Forssman, Wassermann and brain antigens (2, 44). Brain substance has been made iso- and autoantigenic also by allowing it to undergo aseptic autolysis, by infecting it in vivo with vaccinia virus (78c) or by emulsifying it with water and paraffin oil containing killed tubercle bacilli (80). Kidney, heart and other tissues have been made isoantigenic by the addition of killed streptococci (106b) or of streptococcus or staphylococcus toxins (76, 101, 117).

In clinical states, it has been observed that autoantibody formation may follow the use of a drug, such as a sulfa compound (122). The presumption is that the chemical may sometimes modify bodily constituents, and although deductive evidence of this kind is plainly insecure, there are direct indications that alterations of antigenicity can occur in vivo. Thus, the procedure of infecting rabbit brains with vaccinia virus and then employing the brain effectively to induce antibody formation in other rabbits is an indication of what could occur spontaneously in the body (78c).

What kind of intrinsic change in a tissue antigen might alter it sufficiently so that it could influence the immunologic mechanisms of the species or individual from which it was derived? There seem to be three possible pathways for such an occurrence:

(a) The tissue antigen is a hapten which is normally part of a complex with protein. If the hapten can be dissociated from this, and a new carrier of foreign origin substituted, iso- or autoantigenicity of the hapten might be established. The feasibility of this occurrence is suggested by the work of Landsteiner (2) and others (44) with tissue substances soluble in organic solvents. The question remains however, whether these tissue haptens can be moved from their natural moorings in the body, as for example under the influence of an infection, and whether some other carrier, perhaps supplied by the infecting parasite, can be substituted for the natural one. This is the hypothesis favored by Weil and Braun (112) and Sachs and co-workers (2) to explain Wassermann antibodies as a response to autoantigens, but there is not yet proof for it.

(b) There may be slight alterations in the antigens themselves, sufficient so that they present themselves to the antibody-manufacturing cells as foreign substances while yet remaining so closely related to the native antigen that the immune response (antibodies, hypersensitivity) may cross react with the native tissue component. The flexibility of cross reactivity between chemically related antigens and their antibodies could permit this kind of occurrence (see Chapter 5). In illustration of this the following example cited by Landsteiner (2) is pertinent. Antibodies were prepared in rabbits against horse serum denatured with acid as antigen. This antiserum reacted as follows:

With acid denatured horse serum   2+
With native horse serum   ±

If we consider the antibodies against the denatured serum to represent the response against an altered bodily constituent, it seems possible that even the subdued reactivity with the native substance could affect it in vivo.

Suggestive of this kind of possibility is the so-called Hübener-Thompsen phenomenon of panagglutination, in which the contamination of blood with certain bacteria brings out upon the erythrocyte surface antigens for which there are naturally occurring agglutinins in adult human sera. Cholera vibrio filtrate and the influenza virus hemagglutinin also change the antigenic complexion of the red cell surface (see page 402).

(c) A foreign factor, represented by a drug or infectious agent in the body, might serve simply as an **adjuvant,** causing a homologous or autologous substance which under ordinary circumstances has no capacities as an antigen to become an effective stimulus. From the viewpoint of basic immunologic considerations this thesis is perhaps least attractive of the three discussed, for if a substance possesses no apparent antigenic activity to begin with it seems improbable that an adjuvant should qualitatively alter its capacities. Yet in some instances in which iso- and autoantigenicity have been experimentally accomplished, it is difficult to see how the procedures employed can be looked upon as contributing more than an adjuvant activity. For example, Burky's (117) success in creating antibody responses to lens simply by admixture of staphylococcus toxin, and similar successes with uveal tissue (123), kidney (101) and skin (76) appear to fall into this category. On the other hand it may be that these toxins in some way alter antigenicity, as Schwentker and Comploier (101) believe. Burnet and Fenner (73) suggest that the inflammatory cells occasioned by the toxin may have an important part in the immunologic response. Other examples which may be conceived of as illustrations of an adjuvant effect are the repeatedly demonstrated antigenicity of homologous or autologous brain substance when mixed with water-in-oil emulsion and killed tubercle bacilli (80), and the effectiveness of simple mixture with killed streptococci in converting various rabbit and rat tissues to stimulators of antibodies in the respective homologous species (106b).

The fact is that we have no conclusive evidence that any one of these three possibilities accounts for the acquisition of antigenicity by homologous or autologous tissue substances treated in the manners described. We can be certain only that it has been established experimentally that antigens can be so affected as to function in the species or individual from which they stem.

Whether one or another or perhaps various combinations of the three pathways suggested is actually concerned in the acquisition of antigenicity under either spontaneous or experimental circumstances remains to be demonstrated.

2. OCCURRENCE OF TISSUE DAMAGE. The second question stated earlier in respect to iso- and autoimmunization concerns the possibility that an iso- or autoimmunologic response can cause injury to tissues against which it is directed. The answer to this is affirmative in both cases. Isoimmunization to nerve tissue has undoubted pathologic consequences, and it is probable that experiences with tissue grafting also supply testimony to the potential destructiveness of the isoimmunizing process. The hemolytic diseases described earlier provide clear-cut examples of the effects of autoantibody activity. In the other cases discussed the question must remain open as to whether the body can inflict injury upon itself as part of an immunologic sequence. The reasons for these persisting doubts have been discussed.

3. MECHANISM OF TISSUE DAMAGE. The third question concerns the possible mechanisms through which tissue injury could occur upon an immunologic basis. Several possibilities will be discussed in terms of evidence supplied by the clinically occurring and experimentally produced states described before.

Damage to tissues may conceivably be occasioned by: (a) antibodies acting directly upon cells, a cytotoxic effect; (b) an Arthus reaction in which anticellular antibodies react with antigen to produce vascular damage which in turn causes injury to an organ; (c) the development of delayed hypersensitive reactivity to a tissue antigen leading to injury or death of cells exposed to it; or (d) the direct toxicity of injected substances entirely apart from their antigenic characteristics. There is no reason to believe that any single one of these mechanisms need necessarily account for the sequence of events in every instance described earlier; it seems probable that one or another of these possibilities may be at work in different circumstances.

(a) Cytotoxicity of Antibodies. In one case at least it is apparent that autoantibodies act immediately upon the cells against which they are directed to produce damage. This is true of the autohemolysins concerned in the causation of paroxysmal hemoglobinuria, and it is very probably the case also in acquired hemolytic anemia and perhaps other anemias as well. As discussed before, the cold hemagglutinins are probably not ordinarily damaging, but in instances where exposure to the cold results in intravascular agglutination and interference with the circulation, we can attribute the eventual effect to a direct activity of antibodies upon cells (91-95).

In other instances no clear relationship of iso- or autoantibodies to tissue lesions is apparent. Thus, it has been found repeatedly in animals in which encephalomyelitis has resulted from injections of brain tissue with adjuvant that no correlation is demonstrable between antibody titers and the occurrence or extent of lesions (10, 80e, 124); in guinea pigs as a matter of fact circulating antibodies seem to be present rarely if at all (80d, 125). Although it is always precarious logic to base conclusions concerning the potential activities of antibodies in vivo upon serologically determined titers because of possible deficiencies in the methods employed for their measurement and for other reasons as well (see Chapter 9), it is a striking fact that in dogs, for example, high levels of circulating antibody may be demonstrable for weeks or months before paralysis begins, while in other instances encephalomyelitis may set in early after the provocative injections without antibody ever being detected (80d). One might question whether the accessibility of brain tissue to circulating antibodies in various subjects might influence the result, and on the other hand whether the tissue might absorb antibody from the circulation in large enough amounts as to make it undemonstrable by serologic tests in those cases where there is good access to nerve tissue. However, Plaut (126) could not produce lesions by the injection of antibodies directly into the brains of rabbits. There have been failures also with passive transfer by ordinary routes (80a, 80e), but of course the quantities transferred may have been insufficient, or again the antibodies may not have reached the brain substance effectively. In this connection it is interesting that Koprowski and Le Bell (83b) in testing the sera of three people in whom neurologic complications had occurred after injections of rabies vaccine found very high antibody titers in two, and a low titer in the third.

In the case of the nephritis caused by the administration of heterologous antibodies there has also been only a poor correlation of titers with nephrotoxicity of sera (61c, 65). In this case where the syndrome follows the passive transfer of serum, one might logically expect a direct activity of antibodies upon kidney substance, especially so since the removal of antibody by absorption eliminates its nephrotoxicity, and further, there is visual evidence of localization of antibody in glomerular tufts (70). That this expectation may not be fulfilled however is apparent from the work of Kay (61c, 100, 105a) discussed earlier. The possibility exists that the route through which damage occurs is more indirect, depending upon an Arthus type of reaction.

In Cavelti's work (106a) in which active vaccination with kidney tissue and streptococci was employed to initiate nephritic lesions, the correlation between the presence of antibodies and the occurrence of kidney damage was incomplete, and the suggestion was again made that absorption by tissues might account for this irregularity.

In the case of the ocular lens, antibodies per se do not appear to injure it, for Burky (117) found it necessary to damage the lens of animals possessing antibodies in order to bring about intraocular inflammation, and earlier Hektoen (118) injected potent antilens sera into the aqueous and vitreous humors of rabbits without causing injury to the lens.

(b) Arthus Reaction. It is conceivable that the tissue injury resulting from iso- or autoimmunization might in some instances reflect the vascular damaging effects of an antigen-antibody reaction, i.e. an Arthus reaction (see page 204). This would represent the indirect result of a serologic reaction in contrast to a direct deleterious activity of antibody upon the cells with which it unites. There are some suggestions that a mechanism of this kind

may explain certain of the lesions discussed earlier. In experimentally produced encephalomyelitis small lesions are described as occurring in relation
to blood vessels, but this relationship is not readily discernible when the damage becomes more extensive (79b, 127). The lesions have been described
(80a) as closely resembling those of the experimentally produced Arthus reaction resulting from the injection of antigens into the brains of sensitized rabbits
and monkeys (128). If an Arthus reaction does account for demyelinating
encephalomyelitis, however, it is difficult to know why this should be limited
to the brain, for under the experimental conditions employed for evoking
this syndrome the injected mass of antigen undoubtedly provides a sufficient
concentration in the circulation to combine with antibody and produce generalized Arthus lesions similar, for example, to those caused in rabbits by the
injection of large amounts of foreign serum (see periarteritis nodosa and
rheumatic fever, pages 225 and 226).

In respect to kidney lesions, Pressman's (69, 70) work reveals that antikidney antibody of heterologous origin localizes in the renal vascular bed,
and he suggests that various anti-organ antibodies are directed against the
cells of their vascular channels. It was mentioned earlier that Kay (61c, 100)
has recorded observations favoring the thesis that in the rabbit at least it
is not the localized antibody which causes damage, but the subject's counter-
response to the protein comprising this antibody, i.e. an antiantibody. The
reaction of antiantibody with antibody in immediate contiguity with renal
tissue is thought to result in damage to the organ. In effect, this could be an
Arthus mechanism, differing from that just discussed in the detail that the
organ antigen itself does not comprise a part of the deleterious antigen-
antibody union; its function is merely to localize the reaction to the specific
environment of the organ. A difficulty with Kay's proposal is its restricted
applicability, for the chronologic sequence necessary for the subject's response
to antirenal antibody is found only with antibodies produced in fowl. If rabbit
antikidney serum is injected into dogs, rats or guinea pigs, the nephrotoxic
effect becomes apparent within hours, an interval which is too short to permit
the counter-response on the part of the subject.

In the case of immunization against lens proteins there is an intimation
that the Arthus reaction may account for ocular inflammation following trauma
to the lens. As noted before, neither circulating antibody nor antibody injected
directly into the ocular humors affect the lens. Yet in patients, and also in
animals in which antibody has been induced, traumatization of the lens is
followed by acute inflammation of ocular structures (117). This suggests
that the setting free of lens antigen to unite with antibody may result in a local
Arthus reaction.

Experimental observations which have been made with tissue grafts are
also of interest to this discussion. In the transplantation of skin from one
rabbit to another, failure of the graft is the rule and the circumstances surrounding this strongly suggest the influence of an immunologic process. Antibodies, however, have never been demonstrated in skin recipients (73). The

absence of demonstrable antibodies would ordinarily be taken as prima facie evidence that an Arthus reaction could not be concerned in the destruction of the grafts. Nevertheless, one feature of the experiments carried out with tissue transplants suggests that the possibility of Arthus reactivity should still be reckoned with (75). It has been found that the anterior chamber of the eye is the single favorable location for the successful transplantation of tissues from one to another member of a species even after the recipient has been immunized by a previous transplant. Since no blood vessels are present here, the thought occurs that the capacity for tissue to survive may depend upon the absence of the vascular elements required for the development of an Arthus response. This thought is further bolstered by the demonstration that if the eye is first vascularized, it no longer serves as a proper locale for the survival of grafts (129). The analogy here to the conditions under which an Arthus reaction may be demonstrated in the cornea is evident (see Chapters 13 and 14), but the analogy does not constitute proof in view of such deficiencies in the chain of evidence as the lack of demonstrable antibodies just mentioned.

(c) Delayed Sensitivity. Evidence upon the question of delayed hypersensitive reactivity as an explanation for the lesions resulting from iso- or autoimmunologic processes is available only from experimental studies of encephalomyelitis and of tissue transplantation. The evidence in neither case is such as to permit conclusions, but in the current search for clarification of clinical and laboratory observations it is worthwhile to consider all possibilities.

In experimental encephalomyelitis two negative facts favor the possibility that delayed hypersensitive reactivity may constitute the basis for tissue destruction. These are first, the lack of correspondence between antibody titers and lesions, and second, the failure of passively transferred serum to cause lesions in a normal recipient (80a, 80e, 126, 130). As was pointed out before however, neither of these criteria is necessarily trustworthy, the first because antibody titers frequently fail to reflect the extent of their activity in vivo, the second because the transfer of Arthus reactivity requires a considerable concentration as well as quality of antibody which might not have been attained in the studies cited, as was indeed remarked by certain of the investigators themselves (80e). Furthermore, cellular exudates from affected animals also failed to convey to normal animals the encephalitic syndrome (80a), and the inability of both serum and cells to affect passive transfer casts some doubt upon the technical validity of these trials as a whole. Perhaps the requisite quantitative conditions have not yet been met.

More positive evidence for delayed hypersensitive reactivity as the basis for brain destruction is embodied in the work of Waksman and Morrison (80e) with rabbits. A correlative study was carried out of the occurrence of encephalomyelitis and skin and corneal reactions to nerve tissue. The parallelism of delayed type skin responses with the occurrence of the pathologic state was good but not complete, i.e. occasional animals with slight or no skin sensitivity had marked symptoms of brain damage, and vice versa. The corneal tests were positive in one third to one half of the animals developing encephalomyelitis, but more important than incidence is the fact of positivity of these tests, for this is generally accepted as evidence of delayed hypersensitive reactivity (see page 252).

Before commenting upon the qualifications which must be applied to these observations, it is desirable to formulate a picture of how delayed reactivity to a tissue constituent could mediate the destruction of that tissue in the animal's body. Ordinarily, when we consider delayed sensitivity we deal with an antigen entirely foreign to the sensitized subject. When this comes into contact with sensitized cells these respond to it with varying degrees of injury, or necrosis. In the present instance the antigen injected is a homologue of the subject's own bodily structure, and this structure undergoes injury. What cells become sensitized? The damage when it is severe, occurs in the antigen itself, i.e. in the myelin portions of the brain (79b, 80a). It does not seem reasonable that injections of myelin should result in sensitization of the same element in the treated subject. A more rational concept is that neighboring cells in the brain become sensitized (in common with other cells of the body, as indicated by positive skin and corneal reactions) and that these are damaged by the brain antigen in their vicinity. Then how account for the fact that the lesions extend to involve the myelin? Waksman and Morrison (80e) suggest that the cells damaged by the hypersensitive reaction are those which are responsible for the maintenance of myelin. This is purely a speculative resolution of the dilemma, but the only one so far available.

Finally, a consideration of the evidence for delayed reactivity encounters certain obstacles. The work with iso and auto brain immunization carried out in recent years has uniformly made use of the technical method of suspending brain substance in water-in-oil emulsion to which whole killed tubercle bacilli are added. It is known that this vehicle does more than act as an adjuvant, for in addition to increasing immunologic responses (131), the presence of tubercle bacilli also provokes a state of delayed allergic reactivity to antigens which may accompany them as part of the inoculum (see pages 254 and 255). On this basis Waksman and Morrison's success in demonstrating delayed reactivity to nerve tissue is not surprising. But in the earlier work of Schwentker and Rivers (78c) paralysis was induced in rabbits with autolyzed homologous brain substance without the use of the adjuvant mixture just described. Under such ordinary conditions of antigen administration there is no reason to believe that delayed hypersensitivity can be induced (see page 254), though the point was not specifically studied in this particular case. It seems then that encephalomyelitis may occur under circumstances which do not lead to the development of delayed reactivity. It is possible that the animals studied by Waksman and Morrison did indeed develop delayed sensitivity to brain substance, but that it was not this immunologic status which was responsible for their concurrent encephalomyelitis.

The case of tissue transplantation provides less pabulum for a discussion of the possibility that the recipient may develop delayed reactivity to homologous skin, but the fact that no demonstrable antibodies accompany the state of quickened rejection of tissue by an animal previously exposed to it suggests immediately that there may exist an immunologic state in which humoral antibodies have no part. The fact that rabbits can be put into this state by previous injection of leukocytes derived from the recipient but **only if these are injected intradermally** (74) is reminiscent of the requirement for the induction of delayed (contact) reactivity to plant and chemical substances (see page 250). For these reasons Burnet and Fenner (73) favor the thesis that delayed reactivity is concerned in this phenomenon. Opposed to this is the fact considered in the preceding section that the destruction of donor tissue does not occur in the anterior chamber of the eye unless this has been vascularized, and a blood supply is not necessary for the consummation of a delayed allergic reaction. Thus far there has apparently been no application of the procedures of skin and corneal testing to this problem. Such methods might prove of considerable aid to its resolution.

(d) Toxicity of Injected Substances. Practically all thought about these various conditions has revolved about immunologic mechanisms. It has occasionally been pointed out that some other process may account for these manifestations; for example, in the case of encephalomyelitis Alvord (125) suggests the possibility of a metabolic defect, occasioned presumably by the injections of brain substance to which the animal is subjected. Although it may be desirable to keep this avenue of explanation in mind, certainly there exist an array of observations which point convincingly to the likelihood that a response to antigen is involved. One may cite in this connection the effectiveness of heterologous brain in its native state as an inducer of encephalomyelitis, and the requirement that homologous and autologous tissue be altered in some way to serve the same purpose. This is typically antigen behavior; it would seem to be a superfluous condition for any direct effect of brain substance upon the tissues of a recipient.

SUMMARY

The antigens of cells and body fluids may possess specificity characteristic of an animal species (species specificity), of certain individual members only of the species (isoantigenicity), or of various organs of the animal (organ specificity). Iso and organ antigens are frequently heterogenetic, i.e. though they are restricted within a particular species to certain individuals or to certain organs, they may occur also in other species.

The true isoantigens are antigenic in their native state for those members of the species which do not possess them. The best examples of these are the blood group antigens, to be described in the next chapter. In addition, a variety of cellular antigens which are presumably common to all members of a species may nevertheless, under the proper circumstances, stimulate antibody responses in the species, and this is also referred to as isoantigenicity. Analogously, certain tissue antigens derived from an individual may, again with application of the proper conditions, be caused to evoke antibodies in that same individual. This is called autoantigenicity. There are exceptional instances, exemplified by spermatozoa and thyroglobulin, in which antigens common to all members of a species may nevertheless in their native state serve as an immunologic stimulus to the species. With these exceptions, some kind of modification of tissue seems to be necessary. The nature of the modification may vary considerably; it may be extremely mild, comprising simple mixture with foreign protein or bacterial toxin. Infection, as with a virus, aseptic autolysis, and other conditions may also serve the purpose.

Iso- and autoimmunization can be experimentally induced, and can lead to tissue damage (e.g. demyelinating encephalomyelitis).

The question as to whether iso- or autoimmunization can occur under spontaneous conditions or in such situations as following administration of vaccines containing tissue elements (e.g. rabies vaccine), and if so, whether tissue damage can result from this, has been discussed on the basis of information drawn from experimental and clinical studies of tissue grafting, demyelinating encephalomyelitis, hemolytic diseases, glomerulonephritis, rheumatic fever, the Wassermann antibody response, certain ocular diseases, and yellow fever. The conclusions which emerge from these considerations are the following:

1. Spontaneous autoimmunization occurs, as witnessed by the formation of autoantibodies against erythrocytes.

2. Isoimmunization is exemplified by serologic responses to spermatozoa, to brain tissue and probably to other structures and substances of the body.

3. The manner in which tissue antigens may spontaneously take on iso- or autoantigenic properties is not known with certainty, but several possibilities have been discussed.

4. The occurrence of spontaneous auto- and isoimmunization can result in the destruction of tissues (evidenced by hemolytic disease and the deterioration of skin homografts).

5. The mechanism through which such damage occurs may be by the direct action of antibody, as indicated by intravascular red cell lysis. The generality of this kind of mechanism however cannot yet be assessed. In some of the syndromes and conditions described, there is evidence to suggest the occurrence of Arthus reactions or of delayed hypersensitive reactions. It seems quite possible that different immunologic sequences may apply in different circumstances.

BIBLIOGRAPHY

1. Nuttall, G. H. F. Blood Immunity and Blood Relationships, Cambridge, Cambridge University Press, 1904.
2. Landsteiner, K. The Specificity of Serological Reactions, Cambridge, Mass., Harvard University Press, 1945.
3. Kodama, H. Arch. Hyg., 78:247, 1913.
4. Hektoen, L., and Schulhof, K. J. Infect. Dis., 34:433, 1924.
5. ――― J. Infect. Dis., 21:279, 1917.

6a. Landsteiner, K., and van der Scheer, J.   J. Exper. Med., 42:123, 1925.
  b. Witebsky, E.   Ztschr. f. Immunitätsforsch. u. exper. Therap., 51:161, 1927; 58:297, 1928.
  c. ———— and Steinfeld, J.   Ztschr. f. Immunitätsforsch. u. exper. Therap., 58:271, 1928.
7. Bailey, G. H., and Gardner, R. E.   J. Exper. Med., 72:499, 1940.
8a. Henle, W., and Chambers, L. A.   Science, 92:313, 1940.
  b. ———— Chambers, L. A., and Groupé, V.   J. Exper. Med., 74:495, 1941.
9. Lewis, J. H.   J. Immunol., 27:473, 1934.
10. Lumsden, C. E., Kabat, E. A., Wolf, A., and Bezer, A. E.   J. Exper. Med., 92:253, 1950.
11. Claude, A.   Proc. Soc. Exper. Biol. & Med., 39:398, 1938.
12. Kidd, J. G., and Friedewald, W. F.   J. Exper. Med., 76:543, 557, 1942.
13. Furth, J., and Kabat, E. A.   Science, 94:46, 1941.
14. Forssman, J.   Biochem. Ztschr., 37:78, 1911.
15a. Bailey, G. H., and Shorb, M. S.   Am. J. Hyg., 17:329, 358, 1933.
  b. Shorb, M. S., and Bailey, G. H.   Am. J. Hyg., 19:148, 1934.
  c. Buchbinder, L.   Arch. Path., 19:841, 1935.
  d. Brunius, F. E.   Chemical Studies on the True Forssman Hapten, the Corresponding Antibody, and their Interaction, Stockholm, Fahlcrantz, A. B., 1936.
16. Hyde, R. R., Chapman, J., and Kiesling, C.   Am. J. Hyg., 20:465, 1934.
17. Sammis, F. E.   J. Exper. Med., 71:591, 1940.
18. Fujita, K.   Ztschr. f. Immunitätsforsch. u. exper. Therap., 41:539, 1924.
19. Goebel, W. F., and Adams, M. H.   J. Exper. Med., 77:435, 1943.
20. Paul, J. R., and Bunnell, W. W.   Am. J. M. Sc., 183:90, 1932.
21a. Bailey, G. H., and Raffel, S.   J. Clin. Investigation, 14:228, 1935.
  b. Stuart, C. A., Griffin, A. M., Fulton, McD., and Anderson, E. G. E.   Proc. Soc. Exper. Biol. & Med., 34:209, 1936.
  c. Kemp, H. A., and Baker, B. O.   Am. J. Clin. Path., 6:560, 1936.
22a. Hanganutzui, M.   Compt. rend. soc. de biol., 91:1457, 1942.
  b. Davidsohn, I.   J. Immunol., 16:259, 1929; 18:31, 1930.
23a. Kagan, N. W.   Ztschr. f. Immunitätsforsch. u. exper. Therap., 72:20, 1931.
  b. Stuart, C. A., Tallman, J., and Brintzenhoff, E.   J. Immunol., 28:85, 1935.
  c. Schiff, F.   J. Immunol., 33:305, 1937.
24. Schwarzweiss, H., and Tomcsik, J.   Proc. Soc. Exper. Biol. & Med., 69:558, 1948.
25. ———— and Schwarzweiss, H.   Proc. Soc. Exper. Biol. & Med., 69:562, 1948.
26. Ehrlich, P., and Morganroth, J.   Berl. klin. Wchnschr., 38:569, 598, 1901.
27. Tomcsik, J., and Schwarzweiss, H.   Schweiz. Ztschr. f. allg. Path. u. Bakt., 13:447, 1950.
28. ———— and Schwarzweiss, H.   Schweiz. Ztschr. f. allg. Path. u. Bakt., 11:438, 1948.
29. Bendich, A., and Chargaff, E.   J. Biol. Chem., 166:283, 1946.
30. Hektoen, L., Fox, H., and Schulhof, K.   J. Infect. Dis., 40:641, 1927.
31. Uhlenhuth, P.   Festschrift f. R. Koch, Jena, G. Fischer, 1903.
32a. Stokinger, H., and Heidelberger, M.   J. Exper. Med., 66:251, 1937.
  b. Markin, L., and Kyes, P.   J. Infect. Dis., 65:156, 1939.
  c. Ecker, E. E., and Pillemer, L.   J. Exper. Med., 71:585, 1940.
33. Furth, J., and Kabat, E. A.   J. Exper. Med., 74:247, 1941.
34. Bailey, G. H., and Raffel, S.   Am. J. Hyg., 33:Sec. B., 86, 1941; 34:Sec. B., 8, 1941.
35. Metchnikoff, E.   Ann. Inst. Pasteur, 13:737, 1899.
36. Heidelberger, M., and Landsteiner, K.   J. Exper. Med., 38:561, 1923.
37a. Mudd, S., and Mudd, E. B. H.   J. Immunol., 17:39, 1929.
  b. Henle, W., Henle, G., and Chambers, L. A.   J. Exper. Med., 68:335, 1938.
38. Doerr, R., and Berger, W.   Ztschr. f. Hyg. u. Infektionskr., 96:258, 1922.
39. von Dungern, F.   München. med. Wchnschr., 46:1228, 1899; 47:962, 1900.
40. Cumley, R. W., and Irwin, M. R.   J. Immunol., 46:63, 1943.
41. Schütze, A.   Deutsche. med. Wchnschr., 28:804, 1902.
42. György, P., and Witebsky, E.   München. med. Wchnschr., 76:195, 1929.
43a. Kidd, J. G.   J. Exper. Med., 71:335, 351, 1940.
  b. ———— J. Bact., 39:349, 1940.

44. Lewis, J. H.   J. Immunol., 24:193, 1933; 41:397, 1941.
45. Salfeld, H., and Weichsel, M.   J. Immunol., 31:429, 1936.
46. Weil, A. J.   Bact. Rev., 5:293, 1941.
47. Bailey, G. H., and Raffel, S.   J. Exper. Med., 73:617, 1941.
48. ——— and Gardner, R. E.   Am. J. Hyg., 36:205, 1942.
49. Fleisher, M. S., and Arnstein, N.   J. Immunol., 6:223, 1921.
50. Cavelti, P. A.   Arch. Path., 44:1, 1947.
51. Hektoen, L., Robscheit-Robbins, F. S., and Whipple, G. H.   J. Infect. Dis., 42:31, 1928.
52. Masugi, M.   Beitr. z. path. Anat. u. z. allg. Path., 91:82, 1933.
53. Lewis, J. H.   J.A.M.A., 108:1336, 1937.
54. Harten, M., and Walzer, M.   J. Allergy, 12:72, 1940.
55a. Ledingham, J. C. G.   Lancet, 1:1673, 1914.
  b. Gottlieb, M. J.   J. Immunol., 4:309, 1919.
  c. Menne, F. R.   J. Infect. Dis., 31:455, 1922.
56a. Cruickshank, A. H.   Brit. J. Exper. Path., 22:126, 1941.
  b. Chew, W. B.   J. Immunol, 30:379, 1936.
  c. Nettleship, A.   Am. J. Path., 18:689, 1942.
57. Estes, H. R.   Arch. Path., 47:399, 1949.
58. Lindemann, W.   Ann. Inst. Pasteur, 14:49, 1900.
59. Masugi, M.   Beitr. z. path. Anat. u. z. allg. Path., 92:429, 1934.
60a. Pearce, R. M.   J. Med. Research, 12:1, 1904.
  b. Sata, A.   Beitr. z. path. Anat. u. z. allg. Path., 39:1, 1906.
61a. Smadel, J. E., and Farr, L. E.   J. Exper. Med., 65:527, 1937.
  b. ——— J. Exper. Med., 65:541, 1937.
  c. Kay, C. F.   J. Exper. Med., 72:559, 1940.
  d. Fouts, P. J., Corcoran, A. C., and Page, I. H.   Am. J. M. Sc., 201:313, 1941.
62. Sarre, H.   Deutsche med. Wchnschr., 65:1661, 1939.
63. Wilson, G. W., and Oliver, J.   J. Exper. Med., 32:83, 1920.
64. Swift, H. F., and Smadel, J. E.   J. Exper. Med., 65:557, 1937.
65. Smadel, J. E.   J. Exper. Med., 64:921, 1936.
66a. Seegal, B. C., and Loeb, E. N.   J. Exper. Med., 84:211, 1946.
  b. Loeb, E. N., Knowlton, A. I., Stoerk, H. C., and Seegal, B. C.   J. Exper. Med., 89:287, 1949.
  c. Seegal, B. C., Hasson, M. W., Loeb, E. N., and Knowlton, A. I.   Federation Proc., 10:418, 1951.
67. Solomon, D. H., Gardella, J. W., Fanger, H., Dethier, F. M., and Ferrebee, J. W.   J. Exper. Med., 90:267, 1949.
68. Heymann, W., Gilkey, C., and Salehar, M.   Proc. Soc. Exper. Biol. & Med., 73:385, 1950.
69a. Pressman, D., Hill, R. F., and Foote, F. W.   Science, 109:65, 1949.
  b. ——— Eisen, H. N., Siegel, M., Fitzgerald, P. J., Sherman, B., and Silverstein, A.   J. Immunol., 65:559, 1950.
70a. ——— and Sherman, B. Federation Proc., 10:416, 1951.
  b. ——— Federation Proc., 10:568, 1951.
71. Witebsky, E., and Sollazzo, G.   Ztschr. f. Immunitätsforsch. u. exper. Therap., 67:1, 1930.
72. Burke, V., Sullivan, N. P., Petersen, H., and Weed, R.   J. Infect. Dis., 74:225, 1944.
73. Burnet, F. M., and Fenner, F.   The Production of Antibodies, 2nd ed., Melbourne, Macmillan and Co., 1949.
74. Medawar, P. B.   J. Anat., 78:176, 1944; 79:157, 1945.
75. Dukes, C. D., and Blocker, T. G., Jr.   Personal communication.
76. Hecht, R., Sulzberger, M. B., and Weil, H.   J. Exper. Med., 78:59, 1943.
77. Medawar, P. B.   Nature, London, 157:161, 1946.
78a. Koritschoner, R., and Schweinburg, F.   Ztschr. f. Immunitätsforsch. u. exper. Therap., 42:217, 1925.
  b. Hurst, E. W.   J. Hyg., 32:33, 1932.
  c. Schwentker, F. F., and Rivers, T. M.   J. Exper. Med., 60:559, 1934.

79a. Rivers, T. M., Sprunt, D. H., and Berry, G. P.   J. Exper. Med., 58:39, 1933.
  b. —— and Schwentker, F. F.   J. Exper. Med., 61:689, 1935.
80a. Kabat, E. A., Wolf, A., and Bezer, A. E.   J. Exper. Med., 85:117, 1947; 88:417, 1948; 89:395, 1949.
  b. Morgan, I. M.   J. Exper. Med., 85:131, 1947.
  c. Freund, J., Stern, E. R., and Pisani, T. M.   J. Immunol., 57:179, 1947.
  d. Thomas, L., Paterson, P. Y., and Smithwick, B.   J. Exper. Med., 92:133, 1950.
  e. Waksman, B. H., and Morrison, L. R.   J. Immunol., 66:421, 1951.
81. Pait, C. F., and Pearson, H. E.   Am. J. Pub. Health, 39:875, 1949.
82. Olitsky, P. K., and Yager, R. H.   J. Exper. Med., 90:213, 1949.
83a. Kirk, R. C., and Ecker, E. E.   Proc. Soc. Exper. Biol. & Med., 70:734, 1949.
  b. Koprowski, H., and Le Bell, I.   Am. J. Hyg., 51:292, 1950.
84. Weil, A., and Liebert, E.   J. Immunol., 30:291, 1936.
85. Donath, G., and Landsteiner, K.   München. med. Wchnschr., 51:1590, 1904. Ergebn. Hyg. Bakt., 7:184, 1925.
86a. Smith, R. P.   J. Path. & Bact., 26:196, 1923.
  b. MacKenzie, G. M.   J. Clin. Investigation, 7:27, 1929.
87. Peterson, O. L., Hain, T. H., and Finland, M.   Science, 97:167, 1943.
88a. Fjelde, A.   Science, 113:750, 1951.
  b. Seale, R. A., and Mathieson, D. R.   Science, 115:528, 1952.
89. Landsteiner, K.   München. med. Wchnschr., 50:1812, 1903.
90a. Rous, P., and Robertson, O. H.   J. Exper. Med., 27:509, 1918.
  b. Robertson, O. H., and Rous, P.   J. Exper. Med., 27:563, 1918.
91. Stats, D.   J. Clin. Investigation, 24:33, 1945.
92. —— and Bullowa, J. G. M.   Arch. Int. Med., 72:506, 1943.
93. Battaglia, B.   Ann. Int. Med., 27:449, 1947.
94. Neely, F. L., Baria, W. H., Smith, C., and Stone, C. F.   J. Lab. & Clin. Med., 37:382, 1951.
95. Wexler, I. B., and Wiener, A. S.   Brit. M. J., 1:1228, 1951.
96. Dameshek, W., and Schwartz, S. O.   Med., 19:231, 1940.
97a. Boorman, K. E., Dodd, B. E., and Loutit, J. F.   Lancet, 1:812, 1946.
  b. Neber, J., and Dameshek, W.   Blood, 2:371, 1947.
  c. Sturgeon, P.   Science, 106:293, 1947.
98. Evans, R. S., and Duane, R. T.   Blood, 4:1196, 1949.
99a. Young, L. E., Christian, R. M., and Izzo, M. J.   M. Clin. North America, 35:571, 1951.
  b. —— Miller, G., and Christian, R. M.   Ann. Int. Med., 35:507, 1951.
  c. Wright, C., Dodd, M. C., Bouroncle, B. A., Doan, C. A., and Zollinger, R. M.   J. Lab. & Clin. Med., 37:165, 1951.
100. Kay, C. F.   Am. J. M. Sc., 204:483, 1942.
101. Schwentker, F. F., and Comploier, F. C.   J. Exper. Med., 70:223, 1939.
102. Parks, A. E., and Shanks, G.   J. Lab. & Clin. Med., 26:950, 1941.
103. Cavelti, P. A., and Cavelti, E. S.   Arch. Path., 39:148, 1945.
104. Frick, E.   Ztschr. f. Immunitätsforsch. u. exper. Therap., 107:411, 1950; 108:253, 1950.
105a. Kay, C. F., Lucchesi, P. F., and Rutherford, R. B.   J. Immunol., 42:369, 1941.
  b. Peck, J. L., and Thomas, L.   Proc. Soc. Exper. Biol. & Med., 69:451, 1948.
  c. Lange, K., Gold, M. M. A., Weiner, D., and Simon, V.   J. Clin. Investigation, 28:50, 1949.
  d. —— Weiner, D., Tchertkoff, V., and Simon, V.   Bull. New York Acad. Med., 25:447, 1949.
106a. Cavelti, P. A., and Cavelti, E. S.   Arch. Path., 40:158, 163, 1945.
  b. —— Méd. et Hyg., Sept. 23, 351, 1951.
107a. Sprunt, D., Rogers, W. R., and Dulaney, A. D.   Federation Proc., 9:344, 1950.
  b. Donoso, J., Rodriguez, H., and Steiner, A.   Rev. méd. de Chile, 77:498, 1949.
108. Humphrey, J. H.   J. Path. & Bact., 60:211, 1948.
109a. Cavelti, P. A.   Proc. Soc. Exper. Biol. & Med., 60:379, 1945.
  b. —— 7th Internat. Cong. Rheumat. Dis., New York, 1949.
110. —— Arch. Path., 44:13, 1947.
111. Jaffe, R., and Holz, E.   Exper. Med. & Surg., 6:189, 1948.

112. Weil, E., and Brown, H. Wien. klin. Wchnschr., 22:372, 1909.
113. Beck, A. J. Hyg., 39:298, 1939.
114a. Eagle, H., and Hogan, R. B. J. Exper. Med., 71:215, 1940.
   b. ———— and Fleischman, R. J. Exper. Med., 87:369, 1948.
115. Hecht, H. J. Lab. & Clin. Med., 30:992, 1945.
116. Woods, A. C. New York State J. Med., 36:67, 1936.
117. Burky, E. L. J. Allergy, 5:466, 1934.
118. Hektoen, L. J. Infect. Dis., 31:72, 1922.
119. Hughes, T. P. J. Immunol., 25:275, 1933.
120. Soper, F. L., Frobisher, M., Jr., Kerr, J. A., and Davis, N. C. J. Prev. Med., 6:341, 1932.
121. Henle, W. J. Immunol., 34:325, 1938.
122. Dameshek, W. J.A.M.A., 123:77, 1943.
123. Lucic, H. Proc. Soc. Exper. Biol. & Med., 40:273, 1939.
124a. Kopeloff, L. M., and Kopeloff, N. J. Immunol., 48:297, 1944.
   b. Koprowski, H., and Jervis, G. A. Proc. Soc. Exper. Biol. & Med., 69:472, 1948.
125. Alvord, C. E., Jr. J. Immunol., 61:355, 1949.
126. Plaut, F. Klin. Wchnschr., 8:1801, 1929.
127. Jervis, G. A., and Koprowski, H. J. Neuropath. & Exper. Neurol., 7:309, 1948.
128a. Davidoff, L. M., Seegal, B. C., and Seegal, D. J. Exper. Med., 55:163, 1932.
   b. Kopeloff, N., Davidoff, L. M., and Kopeloff, L. J. Immunol., 30:6, 1936.
129. Medawar, P. B. Brit. J. Exper. Path., 29:58, 1948.
130. Hill, K. R. Bull. Johns Hopkins Hosp., 84:302, 1949.
131a. Dienes, L. J. Immunol., 20:221, 1931.
   b. Hanks, J. H. J. Immunol., 28:105, 1935.
   c. Raffel, S. Experientia, 6:410, 1950.

32

BLOOD CELL ANTIGENS

The isoantigens of the erythrocyte stroma are accorded this separate chapter because of the volume of information about the red cell antigenic systems, especially those of the human being, and also because these substances constitute something of a special case among the cellular antigens of higher forms, for they represent the clearest examples of true isoantigens, i.e. antigens of distinct specificities occurring in different members of a single species. The isoimmune responses considered in the last chapter were dependent in practically every instance upon some modification of the antigen in question, for example, upon alteration by autolysis, or upon the admixture of various foreign substances. Isoantigenicity in this sense depends upon the same conditions as are required for **autoantigenicity** of tissues and cells. But in the case of the blood cell antigens serologic specificity is sharp. The individual who lacks a particular factor which fellow members of his species possess can respond to it immunologically in its unmodified form, precisely as to any entirely foreign substance. Some of these antigens are not confined to the erythrocytes, and many occur in more than one species (i.e. are heterogenetic), but it remains true that in any particular species in which these antigens are studied it is found that they are present only in a proportion of its members.

The most thoroughly known of the erythrocyte isoantigens are those of the human being, and considerable practical as well as academic interest attaches to them. Consequently the discussion which follows will be limited to human blood group factors; following this a brief description will be made of analogous substances in lower animals.

In man there are a number of antigenic systems known. The formulation of this knowledge encompasses only about a half century. With passing years the accretion of information continues, though it seems improbable that any major antigens still remain undetected. The latest important system uncovered however, the Rh, was appreciated as late as 1939. In the following discussion the human blood group systems will be considered in chronologic order. Some of the volumes devoted exclusively to this subject are listed in the bibliography (1).

ABO Factors. In 1900 Landsteiner (2) reported the basic observation of agglutination of the erythrocytes of some individuals by the sera of others, and he succeeded upon this basis in categorizing human erythrocytes into three groups. Shortly thereafter a fourth group was recognized by his associates

(3), and the essence of the major system of human erythrocyte isoantigens had been established.

In addition to delineating a system of antigens, Landsteiner's work uncovered the unique existence of naturally occurring reciprocal antibodies, every individual possessing antibodies against those factors not present in his own cells. The antigens and corresponding antibodies were mapped as shown in Table 10.

Table 10. The ABO system of antigens and antibodies

ANTIGEN IN ERYTHROCYTE, AND BLOOD TYPE	ISOANTIBODIES IN SERUM
O	anti-A (α) and anti-B (β)
A	anti-B (β)
B	anti-A (α)
A, B	none

The O antigen has no real part in this system because the human being does not ordinarily recognize it through the development of isoantibodies against it. In reality, however, the O substance is an antigen; it has been isolated from group O erythrocytes, and its antigenic character has revealed itself in the occasional occurrence in human beings of antibodies against it (4). But generally speaking only the A and B factors function as antigens. Consequently the occurrence of isoantibodies centers about these factors. If one or the other antigen exists in the red cells of an individual, he will possess antibody only against the factor which is absent; if neither factor is present (group O) he will have antibodies against both, and if both factors are present (group AB) he will have no isoantibodies. As noted in the table, the isoantibodies are referred to by Greek letters corresponding to the antigens upon which they act.

INHERITANCE. The fact of genetic transmission of the ABO substances was demonstrated in 1910 (5), and some years later Bernstein (6) proposed the accepted version of the workings of the Mendelian principles in this inheritance. The occurrence of the A, B and O antigens was shown to be controlled by three allelomorphic genes, to which a fourth was later added, A_2, a subgroup of A (7). This means that there is a locus available in each of two chromosomes for one of these four genes. The possible combinations of genes and the corresponding phenotypes are shown in Table 11.

As seen, the genes for antigens A_1, A_2 and B appear to be dominant to O, and A_1 is dominant to A_2. In all cases, however, the recessive gene is represented by the appropriate antigen in the erythrocytes. Thus occasional individuals have been found to possess anti-O agglutinins which act upon O cells and also upon the cells of individuals heterozygous with respect to O (i.e. AO, BO [8]).

Until a few years ago it was generally considered that the basic gene in this system might be that determining O antigen, and that the A and B variants represent mutations from this. Owing largely to Morgan's researches this viewpoint has changed (4, 9). It seems likely that the original antigen is a factor called H, common to all human beings, and lacking now only in those possessing completely mutated genes of O, A or B type (1a).

Table 11. Possible ABO genotypes and phenotypes

GENOTYPE	PHENOTYPE
OO	O
A_1A_1 A_1A_2 A_1O	A_1
A_2A_2 A_2O	A_2
B B B O	B
A_1B	A_1B
A_2B	A_2B

The application of blood grouping technic has turned up information of much interest to ethnologists and geneticists. A sampling of some of these findings will suggest to the general reader the fascinating implications of such studies. In Table 12 are shown the statistics in round figures for phenotypes observed in various nations and races of the world.

Table 12. Ethnic and geographic distribution of ABO factors

RACE OR NATION	O	PERCENT INCIDENCE OF GROUPS $A(A_1 \text{ AND } A_2)$	B	$AB(A_1B \text{ AND } A_2B)$
Great Britain	47	42	8	3
North America	45	42	10	3
France	43	43	11	3
Germany	40	43	12	5
India	31	19	41	9
Japan	27	41	18	14
China (Canton)	46	23	25	6
North American Indians	91	8	1	0
Eskimos	81	13	2	4

The presumptive mutation from basic H to O has been particularly striking among the so-called primitive races, while in Caucasians there has been a greater shift to gene A and in Orientals to B. An informative discussion of this aspect of blood group studies is provided by Boyd (10). This author has made a striking application of the grouping procedure to several hundred mummies, some more than 5,000 years old, in which A and B antigens could be detected in muscle by means of absorption tests (11).

NATURE AND TISSUE DISTRIBUTION OF ANTIGENS. The A, B and O factors are found in the human fetus as early as two to three months in its development. The alpha and beta antibodies on the other hand do not appear prior to the general initiation of antibody manufacture, i.e. several months postnatally (see Chapter 6).

The A and B substances as well as the H, are present in most tissues of the body, from which they can be extracted with alcohol. They may also occur in the body fluids except for cerebrospinal fluid, but they are not invariably present in this water-soluble form. Only certain individuals, referred to as secretors, have antigens in their fluids as well as in tissues, and this trait is inherited on a genetic basis distinct from that determining the blood group itself. Tests for the presence of A and B antigens in the salivas of persons throughout the world have revealed that about 80 per cent are secretors (1a). Oddly enough, the O substance is not found outside erythrocytes, according to Morgan and Watkins (4). This conclusion hinges upon their distinction of basic H antigen from O, as noted before. The secretion of O substance described by other investigators has been shown by Morgan to be in truth a secretion of the H factor, while the O antigen is apparently restricted to red cells.

In chemical nature, the A, B, O substances are structurally similar. The A factor may be obtained, aside from its human sources, from commercial peptone, hog gastric mucin, the stomachs of the cow and horse, from horse saliva, and from various anthropoids and the tissues of some rabbits. The hog mucin and horse saliva preparations have been identified as complexes of polysaccharide with amino acids of which the carbohydrate moiety is made up of N-acetylglucosamine and galactose residues. The amino acid portion is still unrecognized. A substance of similar composition and probable molecular weight of 260,000 has been obtained from human sources (12). The isolated antigen induces antibodies in human beings (13) but it requires conjugation with a carrier to provide a similar stimulus to the rabbit (14). The polysaccharide portion of the complex appears to be of importance to its serologic specificity as witnessed by the ability of antisera against antigenically related carbohydrates from an extraneous source (type XIV pneumococcus) to precipitate isolated A substance and to agglutinate A cells (12, 15).

The B substance is obtainable from human gastric juice (16) and it also runs through other families and genera of animals. H antigen occurs also in far-flung locales (17).

The A antigen, as mentioned earlier, is not serologically homogeneous. In 1911 von Dungern and Hirszfeld (18) found that when the sera of individuals of B type (containing alpha agglutinins) were absorbed with A cells, certain of these sera retained the ability to agglutinate some samples of A erythrocytes. Since then it has been established that there are two A factors, labelled A_1 and A_2. These have some antigenic relationship, since intensive treatment of a serum containing alpha 1 and alpha 2 antibodies with A_2 cells will eventually reduce the alpha 1 agglutinating activity (19). Nonetheless individuals of A_2 or A_2B type can be stimulated to produce antibodies against A_1, and more rarely the reverse may occur. A_1 is the more frequent antigen, so that about 80 per cent of persons of A or AB type possess this factor, while the remaining fifth are of A_2 or A_2B make-up.

Other subgroups of A have been described, including A_3 and A_4, but these are rare. The B substance appears to be homogeneous.

ISOANTIBODIES. Antibodies against the A and B factors occur in reciprocal relationship to the antigens, as has been stated. The existence of these iso-agglutinins is generally considered to provide the clearest available evidence for the concept of literally normal antibodies, determined by genetic factors rather than esoteric antigenic stimuli (see Chapter 6). Wiener (20) however has championed the viewpoint that the isoagglutinins may result from a process of spontaneous vaccination made possible by the wide distribution of the A and B antigens in nature.

For the heterogeneous A antigens there are corresponding antibodies. The usual alpha antibody agglutinates both A_1 and A_2 cells (and of course A_1B and A_2B also), while an alpha 1 antibody acts only upon A_1 and A_1B cells. Nearly all sera of group B individuals contain both antibodies, and in addition a small proportion of A_2 people (about one to two per cent) and about one quarter of A_2B individuals possess the alpha 1 agglutinin.

The normal isoagglutinins are of interest from a general serologic standpoint in that they are substances of high molecular weight and occur in an electrophoretic fraction of the serum, between gamma and beta, which is not the usual locale of antibodies (21). This is not a unique situation however (see Chapter 6).

MN Factors. The second system of human erythrocyte antigens to be uncovered was again revealed by Landsteiner and his associates (22). The antigens comprising this system are termed M and N. These antigens, unlike the ABO, are not accompanied by reciprocal isoagglutinins. Their demonstration consequently had to be made by the vaccination of animals (rabbits) with various samples of human red cells and the subsequent application of agglutination and absorption tests.

The inheritance of the MN antigens exemplifies the simplest of the Mendelian ratios. There are two allelomorphic genes either of which may occupy the locus available in the usual two chromosomes. Phenotypes correspond to genotypes, and the possibilities are restricted to the following:

GENOTYPE	PHENOTYPE
MM	M
MN	MN
NN	N

Cells of homozygous subjects seem to contain more of the antigen, whether M or N, than do mixed antigen erythrocytes, for in both cases stronger agglutination occurs in appropriate antisera (22).

Matings of individuals with these various genotypes result in offspring with antigen distributions just as predictable as the colors of the sweet peas with which Mendel illustrated his classic doctrine. These ratios are shown in Table 13.

Table 13. Distribution of M and N antigens in offspring of various matings

PARENTS	CHILDREN (PHENOTYPES)		
	100%	50%	25%
MM × MM	M	—	—
NN × NN	N	—	—
MN × MM	—	M, MN	—
MN × NN	—	N, MN	—
MN × MN	—	MN	N, M
MM × NN	MN	—	—

There are differences in distribution of these antigens in various races, though these are not so striking as in the case of the ABO substances. Thus, Germans, Negroes and Japanese all show about the same distribution; 30 per cent are of type M, 20 per cent are N, and the remaining 50 per cent are MN. In American Indians in contrast there is a marked emergence of the M substance, so that 60 per cent are of this type, only 5 per cent are of N type, and 35 per cent of MN (23).

NATURE AND TISSUE DISTRIBUTION OF ANTIGENS. Both M and N factors occur in various tissues outside the erythrocytes, but they are not present in body fluids in significant amounts (24). The chemical nature of these substances seems to be still entirely unknown.

The beautifully simple system of antigens illustrated in Table 13 has been marred somewhat by the demonstration of subfactors of both M and N, referred to as M_2 and N_2. In both cases these antigens are characterized as weak M and N substances, failing to agglutinate, or agglutinating only slightly, upon mixture with appropriate antisera. The occurrence of these variants seems to be rare (1a, 25). A more serious disturbance of the *status quo* has been introduced by Race and Sanger's (1a) finding of an antibody in certain human sera which reacts with some samples of all three types of MN cells. This antibody has been named anti-S. The corresponding antigen, S, is thought by these investigators either to represent a mutation of both M and N genes (to MS and NS) so that the original M and N characters remain but the additional S antigenic character is superimposed, or a separate additional gene, S, for which the presumptive allelomorph s has however not yet been found.

NATURE OF ANTIBODIES. Although, as was mentioned earlier, there are no naturally occurring isoantibodies for the M or N factors, agglutinins occasionally result from transfusion or from deliberate vaccination with small amounts of blood. In some instances these are active only at low temperatures. The anti-S antibody has been found only in human sera, again in very few instances. Attempts to produce antibodies against this substance in animals have so far been fruitless (1a).

Rh Factors. The most recently discovered major system of blood cell antigens again is due to the work of Landsteiner, this time with Wiener (26). These investigators found that red cells of the monkey (*Macacus rhesus*) evoked antibodies in rabbits and guinea pigs which agglutinated not only monkey cells, but also the cells of about 85 per cent of human beings. To this antigenic factor the name Rh (for rhesus) was given. This finding followed shortly after an interesting interpretation made by Levine and Stetson (27) of a case in which the antibodies produced by a pregnant woman of group O acted upon the transfused cells of her husband, also of group O. These workers postulated correctly that the mother had produced the antibodies in response to an unknown antigen of the fetal erythrocytes, an antigen inherited from the father.

Before long this postulated antibody was equated with the anti-Rh substance produced in rabbits, and it was shown in quick succession that such antibodies may follow from transfusions as well as from pregnancy, and that they can be the cause of transfusion reactions and of a hemolytic disease of the newborn called erythroblastosis fetalis (28). The brilliant sleuthing which resulted in this coherent picture was preceded by a fascinating series of deductions pointing to the same conclusions, especially well exemplified by the writings of Darrow (29).

With respect to Rh antigen, red cells were first simply designated by Landsteiner and Wiener as positive or negative. This classification expanded rapidly and confusingly as it became apparent that the antigen is not a homogeneous substance. All the complexities cannot be gone into here; a clear detailed discussion of them is provided by Race and Sanger (1a). To attack this problem in a relatively brief fashion, the first lucid basis for understanding by the nonspecialist was provided by Fisher's (30) characterization of six antigens represented by three pairs of allelomorphic genes designated as C,c, D,d and E,e. Three genes are carried in the same chromosome, closely linked, so that the chromosomal and antigenic make-up of an individual may be, for example, CDE/cde or CDe/cde, or some other combination. All the antigens represented by these gene notations are present in the erythrocyte of the individual, and all may be tested for, though it is difficult to find antibodies against some of the factors because of their weak antigenicity. This is especially true of anti-d. The most potent antigen on the other hand is D, and this was the original Rh positive factor demonstrated by Landsteiner and Wiener.

In addition to these antigens, subgroup factors have been found. Thus, a gene for C^w is allelomorphic to C and c, or more rarely factors designated as C^u and c^v may occur in the same chromosomal locus. D^u can take the place of D or d, and E^u is an alternative to E or e.

During the interval of several years before Fisher's genetic interpretation was published a continuing flood of work appeared in the American literature in which a different system of notation for antigens and genes was evolved, mostly by Wiener (31). This nomenclature designates genes as rh' (C), Rh_o (D), rh" (E), hr' (c), Hr_o (d) and hr" (e), all supposedly allelomorphic at a single chromosome locus. The symbols employed to identify cell types consist of the letters R and r as central characters embellished with various super-scripts (numbers or letters) and primes to the number of three. In some cases these letters symbolize single antigens (e.g. R_o=D) while in others a letter refers to a combination of antigens (e.g. r=cde). A complete list of these symbols for the various genotypes is provided in the tables in Race and Sanger's book (1a). A few samples of comparative designations in the two systems are shown in Table 14.

Table 14. Examples of Rh designations in the Fisher and Wiener classifications

FISHER SYSTEM (GENOTYPE AND ERYTHROCYTE TYPE)	WIENER SYSTEM (ERYTHROCYTE TYPE)
cde/cde	rr
cDe/cde	$R^o r$
cDe/cdE	$R^o r$
C^wde/cdE	$r'' \, ' \, r''$
C^wDe/cDE	$R^3 R^2$
CdE/C^wDe	$r^y R^3$

The advantage of the British (Fisher) system which designates simul-taneously genes and antigens over the use of complex symbols seems quite plain.

For general practical purposes the Rh factor is still referred to in terms of positivity or negativity, and "Rh positive" means the presence of at least one gene for factor D, which is the most commonly occurring and strongest anti-gen. Analyses of the cells have been made by the use of separate anti-D, d, C, c and E, e as well as subgroup sera, but the rarity of certain of these sera, especially pure anti-C^w, d and e, has hindered such studies. The rarity of oc-currence of these antibodies is due in part to weakness of antigenicity, and in some cases in addition to the paucity of individuals capable of responding to a factor because it is so widespread in the population. Thus, gene e occurs in about 96 per cent of individuals; consequently only four subjects in every hundred can respond to this antigen. The most comprehensive antigenic analy-sis so far recorded was carried out with pure sera against factors C, c, D, d, E, and e upon cells of a group of 100 subjects (32).

An examination of the results of tests carried out at the level of detecting the most frequent antigen only—the D or Rh_o factor—reveals the distribution in various nations and races shown in Table 15. This information is abstracted from the compilations of various investigators, and appears for the most part in Race and Sanger's book (1a).

It is apparent from these samples that the incidence of the major Rh antigen in Caucasians is in the neighborhood of 85 per cent. A low frequency of about 65 to 70 per cent is found in Basques, while at the other extreme are Chinese, Japanese, American Indians, and Negroes, in whom the D anti-gen is practically always present.

The commoner genotypes occurring in the white races are CDe/cDE,

Table 15. Distribution of D (Rh$_0$) antigen in various peoples

NATION OR RACE	Rh POSITIVE (PER CENT)
English (London)	84.09
Irish (Dublin)	83.76
Scottish	82.81
American (Negroes)	95.50
American (White)	85.77
American (Indians)	99.20
Australian (White)	82.29
Norwegian and Swedish	85.55
Argentine (White)	87.77
Argentine (Basques)	64.40
Canada (Jews)	91.83
Canada (English)	81.19
Spain (Basques)	69.46
Japanese	98.00
Chinese	99.30

10.5 per cent; CDe/cde, 33.5 per cent; CDe/CDe, 19 per cent; cDE/cde, 9.3 per cent; and cde/cde, 14.8 per cent. The last named combination comprises the large majority of Rh negative individuals. As noted above the D factor occurs in 85 per cent of whites. The C antigen occurs in 70 per cent and the E in 30 per cent.

NATURE OF ANTIGENS. The chemical nature of the Rh substances is not clearly established. There are reports of the isolation from erythrocytes of a heat-labile lipoprotein (33) of which an ether-soluble lipoidal portion may be the active hapten (34). A lecithin has also been reported as the bearer of Rh activity (35).

As in the case of the M and N factors, there is here also a dosage effect. That is, red cells homologous with respect to a particular factor such as cc, agglutinate to greater titer with an anti-c serum than do cells with only one dose of c antigen (Cc). This extends to other antigens also, especially e and C^w, but it is only occasionally seen in the case of antigens E, C and D. There seems to be some confusion as to whether the Rh antigen can occur in locales other than the erythrocyte stroma. Reports of their presence in saliva and in tissues (36) have not been confirmed (1c, 37). They may be present in amniotic fluid and gastric juice (38) but apparently there have been few efforts to extend this kind of inquiry.

NATURE OF ANTIBODIES. The antibodies formed against the Rh substances through transfusion or vaccination or as the result of pregnancy have, on the contrary, received a great deal of attention. In addition to providing specific information concerning the circumstances in which the antibodies against the various factors are produced, and the effect of these in causing transfusion reactions and disease in the fetus and newborn, these investigations have contributed generously to the store of information about the more general nature and activities of antibodies. It is with this latter aspect that the following discussion will be most concerned.

It may be recalled that in Chapter 6 a discussion was made of the varying serologic behaviors and physicochemical characteristics of antibodies produced under various circumstances. These conditions include the particular antigen in question, the animal species responding to it, the route of administration of the vaccinating substance, and the intensity and duration of application of the antigenic stimulus.

In the human being, as well as in experimental animals, we know that the antibody response may be variable in respect to its chemical character and its serologic activities. While most antibodies occur in the gamma globulin and are of ordinary globulin molecular weight of about 150,000, a portion of the Wassermann antibodies and some of the isoagglutinins directed against the erythrocyte factors A and B have much higher molecular weights and may be found in other electrophoretic portions of the serum. Again, the antibodies developed by atopic individuals against environmental antigens are different from most of those produced against injected antigens or the components of infectious agents, both in their physicochemical properties (such as heat stability) and in their very limited reactive capacities with the antigens which incite them (Chapter 13).

The antibody responses against the Rh antigens have provided more evidence of the same general kind with regard to physicochemical and serologic variability, and have in addition supplied information concerning an aspect of the reactions of antibodies with cellular components which, so far as the writer knows, has not previously been appreciated.

For several years following the discovery of this group of antigens the corresponding antibodies appeared to behave entirely conventionally. They were seen to agglutinate the proper red cells at body temperature, they were absorbable from sera, and could be eluted from erythrocytes. During this period however one especially puzzling occurrence was repeatedly encountered by students of this system, to wit, Rh negative mothers of erythroblastotic infants frequently seemed to lack the antibodies which should account for the destruction of fetal red cells. Only in 1944 was it discovered that such sera often do contain antibodies which are however incapable of causing agglutination of erythrocytes under the ordinary conditions of serologic titration. But these antibodies could reveal themselves by a blocking action. Thus, if the serum were mixed with appropriate erythrocytes no visible reaction resulted, but if a known agglutinating serum for the same cells were subsequently added to the mixture, these also failed to cause aggregation. This failure depends upon the fact that the combining sites upon the red cells have been preempted by the nonagglutinating antibody.

The blocking antibody was referred to also as incomplete (39) or univalent. Such antibody presumably possesses but one combining group in consequence of which it can unite with antigen but cannot bring together molecules or particles of this to form a lattice structure (Chapter 5).

The subsequent work of a number of investigators disclosed interesting physicochemical differences between incomplete and agglutinating antibody. Thus, the former is more stable to heat, pressure and chemicals than the latter, and appears to pass the placenta more readily (40). Further, a gradation of incompleteness was demonstrated by Hill and Haberman and Mohn and Witebsky (41) on the basis of various tests to be described later, and the three or four antibodies of graded activity were found to be distributed in various portions of serum globulin (41c, 42). This is all reminiscent of the kind of testimony to the variability of antibody responses in general which was presented in Chapters 5, 6 and 13, and so far requires no special comment.

Soon after the detection of the blocking antibodies other methods in addition to the blocking reaction itself began to be devised for their demonstration, and certain of these procedures are pertinent to the understanding of their serologic behaviors. It was first found that many samples of incomplete antibody would bring about agglutination if the test were carried out in serum or albumin rather than in saline (43) and this was soon proposed as an example of the old and almost forgotten conglutination reaction, in which the presence of normal bovine serum intensifies the agglutinating activity of antibody (44). As a matter of fact, as was discussed in Chapter 8, the conditions for this reaction with Rh antibodies do not coincide with those required for the demonstration of conglutination, for in the latter case the presence of complement is necessary (45).

A second method for the demonstration of the incomplete antibodies was proposed by Coombs, Mourant and Race (46). In this case an antibody against human globulin is added to red cells previously treated with blocking antibody. The multivalent antiglobulin attaches to the incomplete antibody upon the erythrocyte surface and serves thus to aggregate the cells. This procedure has other interesting applications and has been described in Chapter 8.

Finally, the most recent of the methods for the detection of incomplete antibody involves the pretreatment of erythrocytes with proteolytic enzymes. Following their exposure to a cholera vibrio culture filtrate or to trypsin, red cells become susceptible to agglutination by incomplete antibody without the requirement for albumin or for any other special condition (47). This finding turns attention from the concept of incompleteness of the antibody to the possibility that some feature of the antigen in the erythrocyte stroma may be basic to the type of activity displayed by such antibody, and to this point we shall revert shortly.

It is upon the basis of these various methods for demonstrating incomplete antibodies that the gradation of incompleteness referred to before was made. Thus, Hill, Haberman and Guy (42) referred to conventional agglutinating antibody as of the first order. Antibody which has blocking activity, which agglutinates in the presence of albumin or serum, and which can be demonstrated by the antiglobulin test is called agglutinoid, or antibody of the second order. Antibody of the third order is termed cryptagglutinoid. This does not have a blocking action, peculiarly enough, but it agglutinates in the presence of serum or albumin and is also detected by the Coombs antiglobulin procedure. The ordinary agglutinin is found in the gamma globulin, the agglutinoid in the euglobulin, and the cryptagglutinoid in beta and euglobulin, and as noted before these antibodies are also distinguishable by their susceptibilities to various physical and chemical influences. Witebsky's (41c) categories are in general similar, but he adds a fourth class of antibodies which show themselves in no test except the antiglobulin one.

As stated before, these various findings are entirely compatible in their general connotations with the store of information concerning other kinds of antibodies discussed in Chapters 5, 6 and 13. Incomplete antibodies have also been found against A antigen of the ABO system as well as against other group factors to be discussed later. The single disturbing feature of this information has been the consistent finding that the incomplete antibodies against the Rh factors represent the **matured response** of the vaccinated individual rather than the initial response to antigen. There has been considerable evidence adduced from various immunochemical studies that the earliest formed antibodies to an antigenic stimulus are univalent, and that as the antibody-producing apparatus warms to its task, a preponderance of multivalent antibody begins to appear (Chapter 5). But contrary to this, in the present case, individuals who have responded to the Rh substances either form no agglutinating antibody at any time, or if it does appear it is apt to be present only during the earlier phases of the response and is often succeeded by antibodies entirely of the incomplete kind (48). If we are to regard the agglutinating antibodies as multivalent and the incomplete as univalent, this departure from the rules which seem to prevail for other serologic systems requires explanation.

A final explanation cannot yet be provided, but a concatenation of certain recent observations certainly suggests one. In the first place, the finding (47) that trypsin treatment can cause erythrocytes to become agglutinable by incomplete antibody intimates that an alteration of the stromal surface may bring the Rh antigen into a more accessible relationship to antibodies. Consonant with this thought, Coombs and associates (49) have made the interesting observation with bovine erythrocytes that although different samples of cells appear to absorb equal quantities of antibodies (produced in rabbits, guinea pigs or patients with infectious mononucleosis), not all are equally well agglutinated by them. This led to the thought that some feature of the cell aside from its content of antigen may be responsible for its agglutinability; perhaps in the cells of some individuals the antigen might be deeply seated in the stroma so that after antibody has combined with it not enough of the molecule protrudes from the surface to permit attachment to other erythrocytes and subsequent aggregation. This picture was put to test by the ingenious device of "layering" antibody in the stroma until the last layer applied presumably sticks out from the surface sufficiently so that agglutination of cells can come about. This was done by first mixing erythrocytes with appropriate antierythrocyte antibodies, as shown diagrammatically in Figure 48A. No agglutination occurred. To this mixture there was now added an antiglobulin serum; this antibody now combined with the original antistromal antibody (Figure 48B). In a third step, globulin was added to the mixture; this combined, again presumably layer-wise, with the previously applied antibody (Figure 48C). Finally, when antiglobulin antibody was again applied in step 4, this molecule now protruded sufficiently from the stromal surface to combine with the antibody molecules protruding from neighboring erythrocytes, and agglutination occurred (Figure 48D).

If we apply these experiments to the interpretation of the effectiveness of proteolytic enzymes in making erythrocytes agglutinable by incomplete Rh antibodies, it seems possible that the antigen which is originally deeply situated in the stroma is put into a more accessible location by the removal of stromal constituents susceptible to proteolysis. In this case, so-called incomplete antibody can then agglutinate the cells because it possesses multiple combining groups which can now be put to effective use, i.e. the antibody protrudes from the cell surface sufficiently to attach to another cell.

A third piece of suggestive evidence lies in the report by Race, Sanger and Selwyn (50) of their discovery of an individual entirely lacking in any of the Rh factors except the D. This individual's genetic formula is represented as $-D-/-D-$. The cells of this donor were found to be especially rich in this factor, possibly as an expression of the dosage effect described earlier. The noteworthy point concerning these cells from the standpoint of the present discussion is their capacity to be agglutinated **in saline by incomplete** anti-D antibody, and the authors suggest that this makes it almost certain that the incomplete antibody is not univalent. Further studies of these cells have since been made with results which point in the same direction, though some qualifications are introduced (51).

On the basis of these important bits of information we might imagine that incomplete anti-Rh antibody differs from saline agglutinating antibody not in lacking multivalence, but in the configuration of the combining groups upon the antibody molecule. If the combining groups are close together and one of these must reach into the stroma for the antigen with which it combines, the other may then be rendered ineffective insofar as reaching into another cell stroma is concerned. When on the other hand the antigen is located upon the surface (as after treatment with trypsin or in the special instance of the individual described by Race and associates) then hindrance of the second combining group will not occur and the antibody molecule can attach to contiguous erythrocytes to bring them together. According to this image the combining group of saline agglutinating antibody may be so spaced (e.g. at opposite ends of the molecule) that the activity of one is not interfered with by the attachment of the other to a deep-lying antigen in the cell membrane. Theoretically, both antibodies should be equally proficient in precipitating antigen molecules from solution. A test of this assumption would be of much interest.

It appears to the writer then that the concept of univalence does not apply

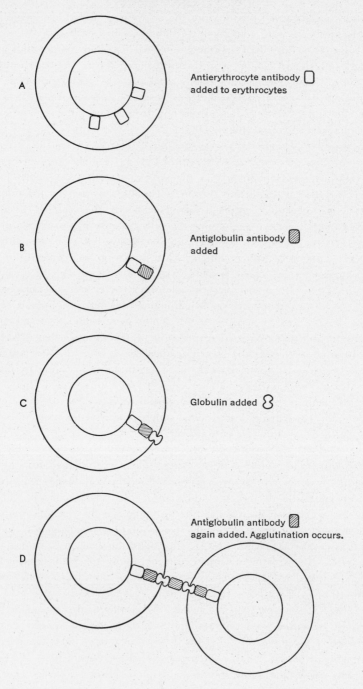

Fig. 48.   Agglutination of red cells through "layering" of antibody in the stroma.

to these incomplete Rh antibodies, and it seems quite possible that similar considerations may explain other instances in which blocking antibodies have been demonstrated (Chapter 8). In this view, there is no need to seek for a special exemption of Rh antibodies from the laws which appear to govern the development of combining power of antibodies generally.

Other Blood Group Systems. Other distinct systems of human blood cell antigens are briefly described in the following paragraphs.

The **P factor** is an antigen which was discovered by Landsteiner and Levine (22) in the same study which revealed the MN substances. The P factor is thought to represent a dominant Mendelian character, and occurs in about three quarters of Caucasians (1a). In Negroes the antigen appears in over 97 per cent of individuals (52). It probably does not occur in tissues or secretions, though sparse efforts have been made to ascertain this point. Antibodies acting upon this antigen may occur in the sera of some P negative individuals who have no history of either transfusion or pregnancy, and in the sera of untreated animals as well. This would appear, in the human being, to be a naturally occurring isoagglutinin, but if so it has not the regularity of occurrence of antibodies in the ABO system. Although an allelomorph p is postulated, no antibody has yet been found in experimentally produced sera to verify the prediction that such an antigen exists.

Other blood group factors, including Lutheran, Kell, Lewis, Duffy, Levay and Jobbins are discussed in some detail by Race and Sanger (1a). Race's laboratory has been responsible for much of the existing knowledge concerning these systems.

The **Lutheran factor** appears as a dominant character in about 8 per cent of individuals. Antibody against this has been found in several patients following transfusion.

The **Kell system** is better known because more instances have been found of antibody against it. In this case the two allelomorphic genes and the antigens which they determine have been almost certainly established as factors independent of other blood group substances. These are designated as K, present in about 10 per cent of the population, and k, found in almost 99 per cent. Heterozygous erythrocytes, as in other instances discussed, give reactions with both antibodies. These antibodies are usually of the incomplete type.

The **Lewis groups** (53) are governed by two genes designated as Le^a and Le^b. The frequency of the first is about 20 per cent in adults and of the second, about 75 per cent. In infants, however, the proportion of Le^a positives is much higher, in the neighborhood of three quarters of those tested (54). This curious phenomenon is explainable on the basis that the Le^a gene is dominant in infants so that the cells of heterozygotes react with antibody, while it is recessive in adults so that only the erythrocytes of homozygous individuals are agglutinated by anti-Le^a serum.

Both Le^a and Le^b antigens are secreted and can thus be found in the saliva of many, but not all, individuals possessing these factors (55). An

interesting observation of still unknown significance is the inverse relationship between the occurrence of Le^a antigen and secretion of the A, B, O
factors. Le^a positive subjects are uniformly nonsecretors of these antigens
(55).

The **Duffy group** substance (56) occurs in 65 per cent of English bloods.
The gene for this factor and its presumptive allelomorph are designated as
Fy^a and Fy^b. The antibodies uncovered in human beings as the result of
transfusions have all been of the incomplete variety.

Other factors mentioned before have been found in isolated instances
only. This is true of the **Levay factor,** found in 3 individuals (a father and
two sons) but absent from 350 others tested in England. An analogous
paucity of occurrence has been noted with antigens **Jobbins, Gr.,** and others
yet unnamed (1a).

Determination of Blood Groups. A number of books devoted entirely
to the subject of the blood groups deal in detail with the methods for determining the antigenic constitution of human erythrocytes (1). In all cases
these tests depend ultimately upon the reaction of agglutination. Sometimes
this is carried out on slides, sometimes in tubes; certain determinations are
better made at room temperature and others at 37° C.

ABO determinations are generally performed on slides with drops of the
subject's blood in saline suspension mixed with known anti-A and anti-B
sera. These sera are usually of human origin. The mixed drops are read for
agglutination after a few seconds to 5 or 10 minutes at room temperature.
The preliminary segregation into types is made on the basis of the following
combinations of reactions:

> Cells agglutinated by neither serum = O
> Cells agglutinated by anti-A   = A
> Cells agglutinated by anti-B   = B
> Cells agglutinated by both sera   = AB

Additional assurance of correctness in typing is provided by testing the
subject's serum for its content of antibodies against known cells. In this case
the following reactions may occur:

> Serum agglutinates A and B cells   = O type
> Serum agglutinates A cells only   = B type
> Serum agglutinates B cells only   = B type
> Serum fails to agglutinate both cells   = AB type

In such specialized institutions as blood banks a routine test is performed
also to distinguish the subgroups of A. For this purpose the serum of a group
B individual (who may possess antibody active against A$_1$ and A$_2$ cells) is
absorbed with A$_2$ erythrocytes. The absorbed serum then agglutinates A$_1$
cells while nonagglutinated cells of A character are assumed to be A$_2$.

The MN typing procedure is not a routine one since these factors have
virtually no significance for transfusion reactions or hemolytic disease of

the newborn. Studies of MN constitution are pertinent, however, to genetic and ethnologic researches, and their determination may be of practical aid in cases of disputed parentage. The sera employed for MN diagnosis are obtained from rabbits vaccinated with ON and OM cells. Prior to use these sera are absorbed with A_1 cells (i.e. A_1N or A_1M, whichever is appropriate) because rabbits may have a naturally occurring anti-A_1 antibody. Typing is carried out on a slide by admixture of a drop of each serum with the cell suspension to be tested. Simultaneously tests with known M, MN and N cells is recommended.

Determinations of Rh antigens are carried out by one of several standard methods. Generally speaking these antibodies are more reactive at 37° C. than at lower temperatures; consequently in two of the procedures sketched later incubation is performed at body temperature. For these tests antibodies supplied by human beings have been found most satisfactory; these are obtained from persons who have been stimulated to their manufacture as the result of incompatible transfusion or through pregnancy, and nowadays a good deal of use is made also of the deliberate vaccination of proper subjects. An improper subject for this purpose is any female who is a potential bearer of children, for reasons which will be made clear in a later portion of this chapter.

For the determination of cell types sera are employed from which anti-A and anti-B antibodies have been removed by absorption with A_1B cells of the appropriate Rh character. Thus, if the test serum is one in which the anti-D, anti-C or anti-E antibody is the important element, A_1B cells of type cde/cde are employed for absorption. Alternatively, purified A and B substances may be added to the serum to neutralize the alpha and beta agglutinins. Typing can then be carried out by one of the following methods:

1. A tube test, in which serum and cell suspension are mixed and incubated at 37° C. for one to two hours.

2. A slide test, in which drops of the serum diluted in albumin are mixed directly with drops of whole oxalated blood, and warmed over a lamp for several minutes before reading (43).

3. The Chown (57) test in which a small amount of the serum is drawn up into a capillary tube, and a small sample of whole blood is drawn up immediately afterward. This test may be incubated at room temperature or at 37° C. before reading.

When it is desired to determine the antibody content of a serum, as for example that of the mother of an erythroblastotic infant, or of a patient who has suffered a transfusion reaction, the same kinds of tests are performed except that in this case cells of known Rh composition are used. These should be of O type in order to avoid the complications introduced by the AB factors. In order to test for the presence of anti-D only, Race and Sanger (1a) suggest that at least four Rh positive (D) and three negative (d) cell samples be used, for with fewer specimens the probability of error may be quite high.

When it is desirable to extend these tests to account for the possibility of the presence of incomplete antibodies, one of the special technics previously described may be applied. The simplest satisfactory procedure is the slide test in which no saline diluent is employed. Under these circumstances both incomplete and agglutinating antibodies may be detected. Almost equally simple is the use of trypsin which, as described before, makes cells agglutinable by incomplete antibody at 37° C. The antiglobulin procedure constitutes the third and most sensitive detector of incomplete antibody. The principle involved here has been described earlier (Chapter 8). When this method is applied to the determination of humoral antibody the procedure is termed the **indirect test,** i.e. the test serum and erythrocytes are permitted to react, nonspecific serum proteins are removed by centrifugation, and the washed cell suspension is subjected to the activity of the antiglobulin antibody. The **direct test** consists of the addition of antiglobulin serum to washed cells suspected of being spontaneously sensitized by incomplete antibody, as in the case of babies with erythroblastosis or of individuals with acquired hemolytic anemia (see Chapter 31). Such spontaneously absorbed antibodies may also be revealed by eluting them at 56°C. and demonstrating their activity by any of the methods just described (58).

Grouping of cells for P factor is carried out usually with human and horse antisera at room temperature. Absorption of known positive human serum with the cells under examination adds to the precision of the determination (59). When antibodies are to be demonstrated the serum is first absorbed free of cold agglutinins of nonspecific significance with O, P— cells. The test with P cells can then be carried forward.

The Lutheran, Kell and other factors mentioned are tested for by the same general methods employed for the Rh system (1a).

Practical Implications of Blood Groups. Aside from their general immunologic and ethnologic interest, the blood cell isoantigens are of immediate practical concern to three aspects of human welfare: (1) the procedure of blood transfusion, (2) the occurrence of hemolytic disease of the fetus or newborn (erythroblastosis fetalis), and (3) the determination of parentage. Again the reader should be guided to the volumes mentioned before for detailed information about these problems, but the following discussions are intended to convey some sense of the central points involved in dealing with them.

1. TRANSFUSIONS. It is rather startling to realize that in all the long history of mankind only the past half-century has witnessed the development of a most elemental kind of mutual aid—the donation of blood by a healthy individual to an ill or injured confrere. This procedure which prior to 1900 was entirely unfeasible is presently a routine and indispensable support to the victims of all kinds of serious illnesses and surgical manipulations.

Preparatory to transfusion, routine examinations include tests for the ABO and Rh antigens of donor and recipient. Race and Sanger (1a) point out that with the antisera available to their laboratory and to similar institutions it is possible to identify a total of almost 30,000 phenotype combinations of all the blood antigens discussed in preceding paragraphs. Many of these however are rarely if ever involved in isoimmunization. Consequently, except in special cases of incompatibility, only a restricted identification of phenotypes is made.

In the case of the ABO system assurance of compatibility before a first transfusion is absolutely essential because of the existence of naturally occurring isoagglutinins. Since normal antibodies are not a consideration in dealing with the other systems of antigens a first transfusion could be given without the necessity of matching, provided however, that the recipient is not a female who has had a pregnancy at some time in the past, for in that case the possibility of isoimmunization to fetal red cells exists. But it is evident that if this easy course were to be followed, these recipients would be poor risks for subsequent transfusions, or if women, for subsequent pregnancies as well, for transfusion can immunize to the fetal cells as well as vice versa. From this viewpoint the importance of routinely matching all the stronger antigens of donor and recipient is plain, and the A and B and certain of the Rh factors fall into this category.

Identification of the ABO character of erythrocytes is carried out with known sera against A, A_1 and B factors as described before. In addition, a confirmation of these results is permitted by the naturally occurring reciprocal isoagglutinins. For this purpose, both donor and recipient sera are tested against known cells of types A_1, A_2, B and O. It is of some importance to include the subgroup of A for test, because 0.6 per cent of persons of group A_1 have antibodies for A_2, and 1.5 per cent of individuals of group A_2 have antibodies for A_1. Further, among AB individuals 3 per cent of A_1B can agglutinate A_2 cells, and 25 per cent of A_2B agglutinate A_1 cells. Transfusion incompatibilities do not often arise from these intragroup factors however, possibly because the antibodies concerned are generally weak in activity.

To complete the necessary pretransfusion information a third test, the **crossmatch**, is carried out. In this test the donor's serum is mixed with the recipient's cells, and vice versa. This should be performed without the use of saline as diluting fluid so that incomplete antibodies can make themselves known. This test will generally bring out intragroup incompatibilities due to the A subgroups already mentioned; it is then that a serious effort must be made by means of anti-A_1 and A_2 testing sera to find a proper donor.

Transfusion reactions usually result from the action of the recipient's antibodies upon the donor's cells. This is so because the donor's blood is diluted by the larger blood volume of the recipient to the point where transfused antibodies usually fall below the level of effectiveness, and furthermore about 85 per cent of individuals are secretors and so have A and/or B substance in solution in their plasma to neutralize injected antibodies. The recipient's antibodies on the other hand are not much diluted by the volume of blood which he receives, and only a limited quantity of erythrocytes is being supplied for these antibodies to act upon. In consequence of this state of affairs, subjects with type O cells are termed **universal donors,** i.e. their blood should be acceptable to any recipient because their cells contain no isoantigen for the recipient to act upon. Conversely, persons of AB type are referred to as **universal recipients** because such individuals have no antibodies against either A or B antigens and should therefore be able to accept any blood. There are however some obvious obstacles to the reliability of this rule.

(a) If the universal donor has high levels of antibodies and the recipient's blood volume is small, the transfused antibodies may not be diluted beyond the point of activity. Universal donor O blood contains both alpha and beta agglutinins potentially active upon the cells of recipients of types A, B or AB (60). It is possible to avoid reactions due to injected antibodies by adding purified A and B substances to the donor blood to neutralize them (61).

(b) The agglutinins for A_2 cells which some A_1 and A_1B individuals may possess have an unfortunate proclivity to agglutinate O cells also, hence such subjects are not suitable recipients of universal donor blood.

(c) The O donor blood may be unsuitable because the cells contain incompatible antigens of another system, such as the Rh, to which the recipient has previously responded with the formation of antibodies.

Identification of the Rh factors of donor and recipient cells is made also with known antisera. Unless the recipient has experienced some previous exposure to the cells of another individual (through transfusion or pregnancy) he will have no isoantibodies.

The major Rh antigen is the D (Rh_o) factor; this is responsible for about 95 per cent of instances of Rh isoimmunization. The following procedure is generally employed in testing recipient and donor for Rh compatibility. The recipient's cells are tested with anti-D serum only and is classified on this basis as positive or negative. The donor's cells are also tested with this serum. Let us assume first that the recipient is d (negative). If the donor is positive for this factor his blood is ruled out for transfusion to the negative recipient. If the donor's cells are d (negative), a second test is made with anti-C and anti-E sera; if either test is positive, indicating the presence of C or E antigen or both, the cells are excluded for transfusion to the d (negative) recipient. This is an entirely logical procedure in view of the fact that about 90 per cent of d individuals have also c and e factors, i.e. are of genotype cde/cde, and thus capable of responding to C and E antigens.

In the instance where the potential recipient is positive to test with anti-D serum, cells from the D positive donor are used without further testing. It is evident that theoretically at least a D (positive) recipient may be of a genotype which would permit him to respond to C or E or both, just as a person of d character might do. In fact, about 65 per cent of D positive individuals are of homozygous e character, hence theoretically responsive to E, and about 19 per cent are of homozygous c genotype and consequently potentially responsive to C antigen. It is therefore difficult to understand why the effort is made to determine the presence of C and E antigens in donor cells when these are to be given to a —d— recipient, while the same effort is not made when the recipient is —D—. Whatever the logic of the situation from the theoretical standpoint, however, it is known empirically that while cde/cde subjects can frequently form antibodies against C and E, individuals of D character, though they may be cDe/cDe, only rarely form such antibodies.

Antigens in some of the other systems described may also be responsible for transfusion incompatibility. This possibility should appear in the crossmatch test. In fact, it is through this occurrence that new antigenic systems are usually discovered. Transfusion reactions have been recorded as due to the Kell and Duffy antigens and the S antigen of the MN system. Rarely anti-M and anti-N have also apparently caused harmful reactions.

2. ERYTHROBLASTOSIS FETALIS (62). The demonstration that fetal erythrocyte antigens may stimulate the pregnant mother to form antibodies against them, and that such antibodies may subsequently traverse the placenta to destroy the developing infant's cells, was made by Levine and associates in 1941 (63). Subsequently antibodies were found also in the colostrum, and these may be absorbed by the suckling infant to maintain a high postnatal level in his blood stream (64). The contemporaneousness of these findings with the discovery by Landsteiner and Wiener (26) of the Rh antigen system, and the demonstration of the occurrence of transfusion reactions on the same basis (28) has already been noted.

About 90 per cent of instances of hemolytic disease in the fetus result from isoimmunization to Rh antigen, and in this antigenic system the D substance is by far the most dangerous. Hence a union in which the wife is d (negative) and the husband D (positive) comprises the combination most apt to result in fetal or infant mortalities. However, other Rh antigens including c, C, C^w and E can bring about the sequence of events leading to the disease.

The circumstances under which this may happen are those in which the mother has been sufficiently stimulated to produce antibodies against the fetal erythrocyte factor. If this has resulted from a previous transfusion, then the first pregnancy may yield an affected child. For this reason it is especially important to avoid transfusion to any Rh negative female, from infancy through the childbearing period, of Rh positive blood. If the initial antigenic stimulus is provided by the fetus itself then the first pregnancy generally proceeds without untoward occurrences; it is only in the second or subsequent pregnancies that the effect of the isoimmunization becomes apparent.

It is a fortunate fact that infants with erythroblastosis constitute only a fraction of the total number of children born to parents in whom the Rh incompatibility proper for the occurrence of the disease exist. In one study of this point (65) 3,940 pregnant women were found to be Rh negative (dd). Statistically, 3,309 of the husbands of these women should have been Rh positive (Dd or DD), and in all these instances the stage was set for the occurrence of erythroblastosis. Actually, however, only 175 of these women produced anti-D antibody with subsequent injury to the fetus, i.e. 1 in 19 of the possibilities. Part of this discrepancy can be accounted for by the fact that of the Rh positive husbands, something more than half were heterozygous (Dd). Half the offspring of these marriages would receive the d gene from both parents and would thus fail to immunize the mother. A second factor which accounts in part for the difference between expected and actual occurrence of hemolytic disease is that some of these were first pregnancies. Taking these points into account, Race and Sanger (1a) opine that even so not more than 1 in 10 of the pregnancies in which conditions are suitable actually result in injury to the fetus. The factors which may account for this residue of unexplained good fortune can only be guessed at. It seems likely that many individuals are not easily induced to form antibodies against an antigen which probably penetrates to the mother's circulation in only minute quantities. Differences in quantity of erythrocytes which may traverse the placenta as well as individual differences in the capacity to produce antibodies to any particular antigen are both factors here (see Chapter 6). In addition the kind of antibody response influences the result, for incomplete antibodies pass the placenta more readily than do the saline agglutinins.

The suggestion has been made that various kinds of mental deficiency may result from Rh isoimmunization. Snyder (66) for example has discussed the high incidence of Rh negative mothers and positive children found in studies of cases of undifferentiated mental inadequacy.

Although the Rh system of antigens is of most importance, other blood group factors may also be concerned in the occurrence of hemolytic disease. The Kell antigen (K) has been shown to be involved in a few instances, and k in another. One would expect however that the ABO factors might supply a major incidence of such occurrences, for here reciprocal antibodies may already be present before conception occurs, and further it has been known for some years that pregnant women respond to A and B antigens of the fetus when the child is a secretor, as is most often the case (67). Tovey (68) states that incompatibility of fetus with mother occurs twice as often on the basis of A and B antigens as on that of Rh positivity and negativity. Yet the occurrence of fetal disease due to anti-A or B antibodies has not definitely been established; if it happens it would seem to be a rare event (69). There is as yet no entirely adequate explanation for this. The suggestion (36) that antigens in solution in fetal plasma may neutralize maternal antibodies does not account for the absence of hemolytic disease in nonsecretors. Tovey (68) suggests that a combination of circumstances, no one regularly demonstrable, may in sum protect the fetus. These include the factor of neutralization just mentioned as well as relative impermeability of the placenta to alpha and beta agglutinins, a lack of sensitivity of some fetal erythrocytes to agglutination by these antibodies, and the fact that the anti-A and anti-B antibodies are not as active at body temperature as they are in vitro. None of these factors are applicable to the Rh antigen-antibody system.

On the other hand, we may simply be unaware of the harmful effects of incompatibility in the ABO system possibly because such effects may appear earlier in the prenatal sequence than does congenital hemolytic disease. There may, for example, be interference with conception when the sperm contains A or B substance and the vaginal secretions the appropriate antibodies, or miscarriages may occur early. A suggestion of such possibilities is embodied in limited studies which indicate that there are less A offspring of matings in which the mother is O (i.e. possesses anti-A antibodies) and the father is A, than in the reverse circumstance of group A mother (without antibodies against A) and O group father (70).

3. PARENTAGE DETERMINATIONS. There are occasions when it is desirable to determine the likelihood of parentage, as in questions of disputed paternity and in the occasional confusion of babies in obstetric nurseries. For this purpose the various blood group markers may be very helpful, but practically always upon the basis of exclusion rather than of affirmation. This is so because the determination that an infant has blood antigens which he could have inherited from a putative father or mother is not proof that another individual with the same antigenic constitution may not have been the parent in question. If on the other hand the antigens of the child could not have come from the mating in question then the disputed parent can with certainty be excluded from consideration.

The groups which can be used for such purposes are the ABO, MN, and Rh. The other factors described earlier can also be employed, but in some cases the antigen is weak (P) or antisera are still scarce. There are also certain qualifications which attach to the three systems named. In the ABO system there is some doubt about the usefulness of the subgroups of A, and in the MN system there is difficulty in procuring potent antisera and sometimes in reading the tests. Race and Sanger (1a) suggest that when anti-S sera become more generally available the subdivision of MN by anti-S will greatly increase the value of this group for identification purposes. In the Rh system some antisera are not easily come by. Using the four most common sera, anti-C, anti-c, anti-D and anti-E, however, 12 Rh groups may be defined, and 78 possible matings with a large variety of genotypes among the offspring. The chance of excluding an erroneously accused putative parent on the basis of these antisera is 25 per cent. If all possible blood systems are employed, including ABO, MNS, Rh, Kell, Lutheran, Duffy and the heritable trait of secretion or nonsecretion of AB factors as well, the chance of excluding a wrongfully accused putative parent rises to 62 per cent (1a).

There are other situations in which blood factor determinations may be of value to jurisprudence. Blood stains, saliva and seminal stains can all be tested for their content of antigens, for the A and B substances especially retain their antigenic characteristics in dried specimens (71).

Blood Group Factors of Lower Animals. Certain of the antigens of human erythrocytes occur also in lower animals. The presence of A and B factors, singly or in combination, in the saliva of the horse, and in the gastric mucosa of the swine has been mentioned. Anthropoid apes possess isoagglutinins as well as the ABO antigens in their erythrocytes, and M and Rh antigens exist in the cells of rhesus monkeys.

Aside from this heterogenetic distribution of the antigens which are found in man, the existence of intraspecies isoantigens is also observed in lower animals, including fish (72). Sometimes there is a coincident presence of reciprocal isoagglutinins (73). The discovery of animal isoantigens actually preceded by a short interval Landsteiner's findings with human blood cells, for Ehrlich and Morgenroth in 1900 described the formation of anti-red cell antibodies in goats injected with the laked blood of other goats (74). Although investigations of chickens (75) and cattle (76) has suggested a high degree of individuality of cell antigens, Landsteiner (17b) points out that even a moderate number of antigenic characters would furnish a large number of combinations, so that the situation in these animals may actually be very much like that which exists in the human being. If there are 20 independent blood factors characteristic of a species, there will be 2^{20} or over a million different possible combinations of these.

An analogy to the findings in man also appears in the occurrence of hemolytic disease in newborn animals. Foals may be so affected by antibodies produced in the pregnant mare and ingested via the colostrum (78), and there seems to be more than one antigen which may be concerned in this effect. Hemolytic disease has also been observed in newborn dogs. In this case, bitches negative for a factor (Do) present in blood with which they were transfused (Do positive) were mated with Do positive males. Do negative puppies were normal, while the Do positive offspring of such a union had hemolytic desease. The dam's milk carried the antibody responsible for this occurrence (79).

BIBLIOGRAPHY

1a. Race, R. R., and Sanger, R.   Blood Groups in Man, Oxford, Blackwell Scientific Pub., 1950.
 b. Keynes, G.   Blood Transfusion, Bristol, John Wright and Son, Ltd., 1949.
 c. Wiener, A. S.   Blood Groups and Transfusion, 3rd ed., Springfield, Ill., Charles C Thomas Co., 1943.
 d. DeGowin, E. L., Hardin, R. C., and Alsever, J. B.   Blood Transfusion, Philadelphia, W. B. Saunders Co., 1949.
2. Landsteiner, K.   Zentralbl. f. Bakt., 27:357, 1900. Wien. klin. Wchnschr., 4:1132, 1901.
3. von Decastello, A., and Sturli, A.   München. med. Wchnschr., 49:1090, 1902.
4. Morgan, W. T. J., and Watkins, W. M.   Brit. J. Exper. Path., 29:159, 1948.
5. von Dungern, E., and Hirszfeld, L.   Ztschr. f. Immunitätsforsch. u. exper. Therap., 6:284, 1910.
6. Bernstein, F.   Klin. Wchnschr., 3:1495, 1924.
7. Thomsen, O., Friedenreich, V., and Worsaae, E.   Acta. path. et microbiol. Scandinav., 7:157, 1930.
8a. Henry, N. R.   M. J. Australia, 1:395, 1946.
 b. Boorman, K. E., Dodd, B. E., and Gilbey, B. E.   Ann. Eugenics, 14:201, 1948.
9. Annison, E. F., and Morgan, W. T. J.   Nature, London, 165:884, 1950.
10. Boyd, W. C.   Genetics and the Races of Man, Boston, Little, Brown & Co., 1950.
11. ——— and Boyd, L. G.   J. Immunol., 32:318, 1937.
12. Aminoff, D., Morgan, W. T. J., and Watkins, W. M.   Biochem. J., 46:426, 1950.

13. Witebsky, E. Ann. New York Acad. Sc., 46:887, 1946.
14. Morgan, W. T. J., and Watkins, W. M. Brit. J. Exper. Path., 26:247, 1945.
15a. Beeson, P. B., and Goebel, W. F. J. Exper. Med., 70:239, 1939.
b. Kabat, E. A., Bendich, A., Bezer, A. E., and Knaub, V. J. Exper. Med., 87:295, 1948.
16. Witebsky, E., and Klendshoj., N. C. J. Exper. Med., 72:663, 1940.
17a. Morgan, W. T. J. Experientia, 3:257, 1947.
b. Landsteiner, K. The Specificity of Serological Reactions, Cambridge, Mass., Harvard University Press, 1945.
c. Kabat, E. A., and Mayer, M. M. Experimental Immunochemistry, Springfield, Ill., Charles C Thomas Co., 1948.
18. von Dungern, E., and Hirszfeld, L. Ztschr. f. Immunitätsforsch. u. exper. Therap., 8:526, 1911.
19a. Landsteiner, K., and Witt, D. H. J. Immunol., 11:221, 1926.
b. Wiener, A. S., and Kosofsky, I. J. Immunol., 42:381, 1941.
20. ———— J. Immunol., 66:287, 1951.
21a. Pedersen, K. O. Ultracentrifugal Studies on Serum and Serum Fractions, Uppsala, Almqvist and Wiksells Boktryckeri, A. B., 1945.
b. Deutsch, H. F., Alverdy, R. A., Gostling, L. J., and Williams, J. W. Federation Proc., 6:425, 1947.
22. Landsteiner, K., and Levine, P. Proc. Soc. Exper. Biol. & Med., 24:600, 941, 1927.
23. ———— and Levine, P. J. Immunol., 16:123, 1929.
24. Kosjakov, P. N., and Tribulev, G. P. J. Immunol., 37:283, 1939.
25. Jakobowicz, R., Bryce, L. M., and Simmons, R. T. Nature, London, 165:158, 1950.
26. Landsteiner, K., and Wiener, A. S. Proc. Soc. Exper. Biol. & Med., 43:223, 1940.
27. Levine, P., and Stetson, R. E. J.A.M.A., 113:126, 1939.
28a. Wiener, A. S., and Peters, H. R. Ann. Int. Med., 13:2306, 1940.
b. Levine, P., Vogel, P., Katzin, E. M., and Burnham, L. Science, 94:371, 1941.
29. Darrow, R. R. Arch. Path., 25:378, 1938.
30. Fisher, R. A. Am. Scientist, 35:95, 1947.
31. Wiener, A. S. Laboratory Digest, 1949.
32. Haberman, S., Hill, J. M., Everist, B. W., and Davenport, J. W. Blood, 3:682, 1948.
33a. Calvin, M., Evans, R. S., Behrendt, V., and Calvin, G. Proc. Soc. Exper. Biol. & Med., 61:416, 1946.
b. Lubinski, H. H., and Portnuff, J. C. J. Lab. & Clin. Med., 32:178, 1947.
34a. Carter, B. B. J. Immunol., 61:79, 1949.
b. Wolf, A. M., Schlutz, C., Freundlich, M., and Levinson, S. O. J.A.M.A., 144:88, 1950.
c. Evans, R. S., Moskowitz, M., and Calvin, M. J. Immunol., 65:383, 1950.
35. Spielmann, W. Ztschr. f. Naturforsch., 4:284, 1949.
36. Boorman, K. E., and Dodd, B. E. J. Path. & Bact., 55:329, 1943.
37. Levine, P., and Katzin, E. M. Proc. Soc. Exper. Biol. & Med., 48:126, 1941.
38a. Witebsky, E., and Mohn, J. F. J. Exper. Med., 82:143, 1945.
b. Mohn, J. F., and Witebsky, E. New York State J. Med., 48:287, 1948.
39a. Wiener, A. S. Proc. Soc. Exper. Biol. & Med., 56:173, 1944.
b. Race, R. R. Nature, London, 153:771, 1944.
c. Diamond, L. K. J. Clin. Investigation, 24:122, 1945.
40a. ———— and Abelson, N. M. J. Clin. Investigation, 24:122, 1945.
b. Boyd, W. C. J. Exper. Med., 83:221, 401, 1946.
c. Hill, J. M., Reid, A. F., and Haberman, S. Texas State J. Med., 45:477, 1949.
d. Baar, H. S. Nature, London, 155:789, 1945.
41a. Hill, J. M., and Haberman, S. J. Lab. & Clin. Med., 31:1053, 1946.
b. ———— Haberman, S., and Jones, F. Blood, 3 (Suppl. 2):80, 1948.
c. Mohn, J. F., and Witebsky, E. J. Lab. & Clin. Med., 33:1361, 1369, 1948.
42. Hill, J. M., Haberman, S., and Guy, R. Am. J. Clin. Path., 19:134, 1949.
43. Diamond, L. K., and Abelson, N. M. J. Lab. & Clin. Med., 30:204, 1945; 31:668, 1945.
44a. Wiener, A. S. J. Lab. & Clin. Med., 30:662, 1945.
b. ———— Hurst, J. G., and Sonn-Gordon, E. B. J. Exper. Med., 86:267, 1947.
45. Hole, N. H., and Coombs, R. R. A. J. Hyg., 45:480, 1947.

46. Coombs, R. R. A., Mourant, A. E., and Race, R. R.   Lancet, 2:15, 1945. Brit. J.
      Exper. Path., 26:255, 1945. Lancet, 1:264, 1946.
47a. Pickles, M.   Nature, London, 158:880, 1946.
  b. Morton, J. A., and Pickles, M.   Nature, London, 159:779, 1947.
48a. Diamond, L. K.   Proc. Soc. Exper. Biol. & Med., 40:546, 1947.
  b. —— and Denton, R. L.   J. Lab. & Clin. Med., 31:821, 1945.
49. Coombs, R. R. A., Gleeson-White, M. H., and Hall, J. G.   Brit. J. Exper. Path.,
      32:195, 1951.
50. Race, R. R., Sanger, R., and Selwyn, J. G.   Nature, London, 166:520, 1950.
51a. Sturgeon, P.   J. Immunol., 68:277, 1952.
  b. —— and Brown, R. A.   J. Immunol., 68:287, 1952.
52. Wiener, A. S., and Unger, L. J.   Am. J. Clin. Path., 14:616, 1944.
53. Mourant, A. S.   Nature, London, 158:237, 1946.
54. Andresen, P. H.   Acta path. et microbiol. Scandinav., 24:616, 1947.
55. Grubb, R., and Morgan, W. T. J.   Brit. J. Exper. Path., 30:198, 1949.
56. Cutbush, M., Mollison, P. L., and Parkins, D. M.   Nature, London, 165:188, 1950.
57. Chown, B.   Am. J. Clin. Path., 14:114, 1944.
58. Haberman, S., and Hill, J. M.   Texas State J. Med., 40:182, 1944.
59. Henningsen, K.   Acta path. et microbiol. Scandinav., 26:639, 1949.
60a. DeGowin, E. L.   J.A.M.A., 108:296, 1937.
  b. Malkiel, S., and Boyd, W. C.   J.A.M.A., 129:344, 1945.
61. Witebsky, E.   Ann. New York Acad. Sc., 46:887, 1946.
62a. Potter, E. L.   Rh, Its Relation to Congenital Hemolytic Disease and to Intragroup
      Transfusion Reactions, Chicago, Year Book Publishers, Inc., 1947.
  b. Pickles, M.   Hemolytic Disease of the Newborn, Springfield, Ill., Charles C Thomas
      Co., 1949.
63. Levine, P., Katzin, S. M., and Burnham, L.   J.A.M.A., 116:825, 1941.
64. Witebsky, E., Anderson, G. W., and Heide, A.   Proc. Soc. Exper. Biol. & Med.,
      49:179, 1942.
65. Hartmann, O.   In reference 1a, 1949.
66. Snyder, L. H.   Minnesota Med., 29:121, 1946.
67a. Edgecombe, K.   J. Path. & Bact., 33:963, 1930.
  b. Smith, G. H.   J. Path. & Bact., 57:113, 1945.
68. Tovey, J. H.   J. Path. & Bact., 57:295, 1945.
69a. Halbrecht, I.   Am. J. Dis. Child., 68:248, 1944.
  b. Polayes, S. H., and McNally, J., Jr.   Am. J. Clin. Path., 18:375, 1948.
70a. Hirszfeld, L., and Zborowski, H.   Klin. Wchnschr., 1:1152, 1925.
  b. Levine, P.   Ann. New York Acad. Sc., 46:939, 1946.
  c. Waterhouse, J. A. H., and Hogben, L.   Brit. J. Social Med., 1:1, 1947.
71. Boyd, W. C.   J. Crim. Law. Criminol., 36:455, 1946.
72. Cushing, J. E.   Science, 115:404, 1952.
73a. Fishbein, M.   J. Infect. Dis., 12:133, 1913.
  b. Little, R. B.   J. Immunol., 17:377, 1929.
74. Ehrlich, P., and Morgenroth, J.   Berl. klin. Wchnschr., 37:453, 1900.
75a. Landsteiner, K., and Miller, C. P., Jr.   Proc. Soc. Exper. Biol. & Med., 22:100,
      1924.
  b. Todd, C.   Proc. Roy. Soc., London, s. B., 106:20, 1930; 107:197, 1930.
76. Ferguson, L. C., Stormant, C., and Irwin, M. R.   J. Immunol., 44:147, 1942.
77. Levine, P.   Exper. Med. & Surg., 2:36, 1944.
78a. Bruner. D. W., Hull, F. E., Edward, P. R., and Doll, E. R.   Am. J. Vet. Research,
      9:237, 1948.
  b. Coombs, R. R. A., Crowhurst, R. C., Day, F. T., Heard, D. H., Hinde, I. T.,
      Hoogstraten, J., and Parry, H. B.   J. Hyg., 40:403, 1948.
79a. Young, L. E., Ervin, D. M., Christian, R. M., and Davis, R. W.   Science, 109:630,
      1949.
  b. —— O'Brien, W. A., Miller, G., Swisher, S. N., Ervin, D. M., Christian, R. M.,
      and Yuile, C. L.   Tr. New York Acad. Sc., 13:209, 1951.

INDEX

505

Beta lysin, bactericidal activity, 6
Beta toxin of staphlyococci, 438
Biochemical maturation in acquired resistance, 162
Biotin, influence upon resistance, 181
Blocking antibody, atopic sensitivity, 75, 222
  heat stability, 222
  serologic reactions, 120, 121
Blocking reaction, 120, 121
Blocking test, demonstrating relationship of antibody to acquired resistance, 136
  Rh antibodies, 121
Blood, bactericidal activity, 129
Blood group factors, lower animals, 501
  man, 479
  parentage determinations, 501
Blood groups, human, determination, 494
  significance in transfusions, 496
Blood leukocytes, fragility, 12
Blood platelets in anaphylaxis, 204
Boivin antigen, 48, 417
  chemical nature, 418
  components, 418
  methods of isolation, 418
  Shigella, 312
  species in which it occurs, 417, 418
  Vibrio comma, 306
Boivin complexes as antigens, 48
Bone marrow depressants, influence upon resistance, 188
Borrelia, antigenic variation, 427
Botulinus toxin, 354
Botulinus toxoid, 355
Botulism, 354
  acquired resistance, 355
  vaccination, 355
Brain, species-specific antigen, 451
Brucella, antisera, zone phenomenon with, 97
  native resistance, 7
Brucellosis, acquired immunity, 160
  infectious hypersensitivity, 249

Capsular antigen of anthrax bacillus, 289
Carbohydrates as antigens, 46
Cataract formation, autoimmunization, 465
d-Catechin, effect upon hypersensitivity, 234
Cattle, anaphylaxis, 211
CDE factors related to Rh system of antigens, 486
Cell haptens, 452
Cells, reactivity in delayed hypersensitivity, 251
Cellular antibody in delayed hypersensitivity, 251
Cellular antigens, 443
Cellular immunity, acquired, poliomyelitis, 395
  pox viruses, 380
  tuberculosis, 342
  viral diseases, 144, 145

Cellular and tissue mechanisms of acquired resistance, 143
Cellular transfer of delayed hypersensitivity, 251
Chemicals, influence upon resistance, 187
Chemotaxis, 12
  theories concerning, 13
Chickenpox, acquired resistance, 159, 160, 161
Cholera, 304
  acquired resistance in human being, 304
  mechanisms, 306
  antibodies in acquired resistance, 306, 307
  local intestinal antibody, 308
  vaccines, 167, 309
Chown test for determination of Rh factors, 495
Clostridia, antitoxin in protection, 372
  protection-inducing factors, 367
  spreading factor, 33
  toxins, 32, 367
  virulence, 368, 369, 370
Clostridial infections, native resistance, 19
Clostridium
  bifermentans, in gas gangrene, 367
  botulinum, 354
    immunity-inducing factors, 354
    toxins, 354
    toxoid, 355
    virulence, 355
  histolyticum, in gas gangrene, 367
  novyi, in gas gangrene, 367
  perfringens, in gas gangrene, 367
    hemolysins, 35
  septicum, in gas gangrene, 367
Coagulase of staphylococci, 35
Collagenase of clostridia, 32, 367
Collodion particle technic for demonstrating agglutination, 108
Colostrum, antibodies transmitted by, 168
  Rh antibodies in, 499
Commensalism, 1
Common cold, acquired resistance, 159
Complement, absorption, by various antigen-antibody systems, 111
    mechanism, 111
  test, 118
    conglutinating, 118
  activities, 109
    differences in various species, 110, 111
    in vivo, 109
  affinity for, antibody, 111
    antigen, 111
    antigen-antibody complex, 109, 111
  agglutination, affected by, 109
  antisera, destruction by, 114
  chemical characterization, 110
  components, 110
  concentration, serum, 110
    variations in infections, 110
  cow, 110
  deterioration, 111
  deviation, 113, 114
  fixation. See also Complement fixation
    irregularities, 115
    test, choice for, 115

INDEX

(1)

Al